An Atom-First Introduction to Chemistry
Version 2.0

David W. Ball

FlatWorld

978-1-4533-9565-3

An Atom-First Introduction to Chemistry
Version 2.0

David W. Ball

Published by:

FlatWorld
175 Portland Street
Boston, MA 02114

Gen: 20190129

Brief Contents

Contents

About the Author

David W. Ball

Dr. Ball is a professor of chemistry at Cleveland State University in Ohio. He earned his PhD from Rice University in Houston, Texas. His specialty is physical chemistry, which he teaches at the undergraduate and graduate levels. About 50 percent of his teaching is in general chemistry: chemistry for nonscience majors, GOB, and general chemistry for science and engineering majors. In addition to this text, he is the author of a math review book for general chemistry students, a physical chemistry textbook with accompanying student and instructor solutions manuals, and two books on spectroscopy (published by SPIE Press). He is coauthor of a general chemistry textbook (with Dan Reger and Scott Goode), whose third edition was published in January 2009. His publication list has over 220 items, roughly evenly distributed between research papers and articles of educational interest.

Acknowledgments

The decision to write a new textbook from scratch is not one to be taken lightly. The author becomes a saint to some and a sinner to others—and the feedback from the "others" is felt more acutely than the feedback from the "some"! Ultimately, the decision to write a new book comes from the deep feeling that an author can make a positive contribution to the field, and that it is ultimately time well invested.

It also helps that there are people supporting the author both personally and professionally. The first person to thank must be Jennifer Welchans of FlatWorld Knowledge. I have known Jen for years; indeed, she was instrumental in getting me to write my first academic book, a math review book that is still available through another publisher. We reconnected, and I learned that she was working for a new publisher with some interesting publishing ideas. With her urging, the editorial director and I got together, first by phone and then in person, to discuss this project. With all the enthusiasm and ideas that FlatWorld brought to the table, it was difficult *not* to sign on and write this book. So thanks, Jen—again. Hopefully this won't be the last book we do together.

Thanks also to Michael Boezi, editorial director at FlatWorld, for his enthusiastic support. Jenn Yee, project manager at FlatWorld, did a great job of managing the project and all of its pieces—manuscript, answers to exercises, art, reviews, revisions, and all the other things required to put a project like this together. Vanessa Gennarelli did a great job of filling in when necessary (although Jenn should know better than to take a vacation during a project). Kudos to the technology team at FlatWorld, who had the ultimate job of getting this book out: Brian Brennan, David Link, Christopher Loncar, Jessica Carey, Jon Gottfried, Jon Williams, Katie Damo, Keith Avery, Mike Shnaydman, Po Ki Chui, and Ryan Lowe. I would also like to thank the production team at Scribe Inc., including Stacy Claxton, Chrissy Chimi, Melissa Tarrao, and Kevin McDermott. This book would not exist without any of these people.

Thanks to Mary Grodek and Bill Reiter of Cleveland State University's Marketing Department for assistance in obtaining a needed photograph.

A project like this benefits from the expertise of external reviewers. I would like to thank the following people for their very thoughtful evaluation of the initial manuscript at several stages:

- Sam Abbas, Palomar College
- Bal Barot, Lake Michigan College
- Sherri Borowicz, Dakota College of Bottineau
- Ken Capps, Central Florida Community College
- Troy Cayou, Coconino Community College
- Robert Clark, Lourdes College
- Daniel Cole, Central Piedmont Community College
- Jo Conceicao, Metropolitan Community College
- Bernadette Corbett, Metropolitan Community College
- James Fisher, Imperial Valley College
- Julie Klare, Gwinnett Technical College
- Karen Marshall, Bridgewater College
- Tchao Podona, Miami-Dade College
- Kenneth Rodriguez, California State University–Dominguez Hills
- Mary Sohn, Florida Institute of Technology
- Angie Spencer, Greenville Technical College

- Charles Taylor, Pomona College
- Susan T. Thomas, The University of Texas at San Antonio
- Linda Waldman, Cerritos College

Thanks to ANSR Source, who performed accuracy checks on various parts of the first-edition text.

The idea for an "Atoms-First" approach to introductory chemistry was originally proposed to me by Sean Wakely, Product and Editorial Vice President of FlatWorld. I appreciate his attempts to expand the applicability of this book.

Special thanks to my colleague Alexis Felty for performing an accuracy check of the entire second edition. Her exquisite attention to detail helped make sure that this book is more error-free, and I greatly appreciate her efforts. Thanks also to my colleague Neda Hamed, who performed an accuracy check of the new content in this "Atoms-First" version of the text, saving me from some embarrassing typos and turns of phrase. Should any errors still exist, they are the responsibility of the author, who would appreciate learning of them.

Finally, much appreciation to FlatWorld's Vicki Brentnall, digital content manager, and Lindsey Kaetzel, associate digital editor, who shepherded the second edition through. The entire process was much less painful because of Vicki and Lindsey and their willingness to explore increasingly impossible requests from the author about increasingly minute issues.

David W. Ball

December 2018

Preface

In 1977, chemists Theodore L. Brown and H. Eugene LeMay (joined in subsequent editions by Bruce Bursten and Julia Burdge) published a general chemistry textbook titled *Chemistry: The Central Science*. Since that time, the label *the central science* has become more and more associated with chemistry above all other sciences.

Why? Follow along, if you will. Science is grounded, first and foremost, in mathematics. Math is the language of science. Any study of true science must use math as an inescapable tool. The most fundamental science is physics, the study of matter and energy. (For the sake of argument, I include astronomy as part of physics.) Then we progress to the study of the description of matter and how that description can change—that's chemistry.

At this point, however, several directions are possible. Do you want to study the chemistry of living things? That's biology. The chemistry of the earth? That's geology. The chemistry of how compounds work in our body? That's pharmacology. The application of chemistry to better our lives? That's engineering (chemical engineering, to be more specific, and we've just opened the door to the applied sciences). Granted, there are connections between more fundamental sciences and others—geophysics, astrobiology, and so forth—but a map of the sciences and their interconnections shows the most obvious branches after chemistry. This is why we consider chemistry the central science.

This concept is reinforced by the fact that many science majors require a course or two of chemistry as part of their curriculum (indeed, perhaps this is the reason you are using this textbook). Do you want to study biology? You'll need some chemistry courses. Are you a geology major? You'll need to know some chemistry. Many engineering disciplines, not just chemical engineering, require some background in chemistry as well. The reason that chemistry is required by so many other disciplines is that it is, to overuse the word, central.

Chemistry is not just central; it's all around you. You participate in chemistry every day. This idea is one of the major themes in this book. Chemistry is all around you, and you practice it every day whether you know it or not. Throughout these chapters, I will attempt to convince you that you play with chemicals every day, perform chemistry every day, and depend on chemistry every day. This is what makes chemistry an integral part, and what *should* make chemistry an integral part, of the modern literate adult.

The goal of this textbook is not to make you an expert. True expertise in any field is a years-long endeavor. Here I will survey some of the basic topics of chemistry. This survey should give you enough knowledge to appreciate the impact of chemistry in everyday life and, if necessary, prepare you for additional instruction in chemistry.

The text starts with an introduction to chemistry. Some users might find this a throwaway chapter, but I urge you to look it over. Many people—even scientists—do not know what science really is, and we all can benefit if we learn what science is and, importantly, what science is not. Chemistry, like all sciences, is inherently quantitative, so Chapter 2 discusses measurements and the conventions for expressing them. Yes, chemistry has conventions and arbitrarily adopted, agreed-on standards against which everything is expressed. Students are sometimes dismayed to learn that a hard science like chemistry has arbitrary standards. But then, all fields have their arbitrary standards that experts in that field must master if they are to be considered "experts." Chemistry, like other fields, is no different.

Chemistry is based on atoms, so that concept comes next—indeed, the goal of this book is to introduce "atoms first" because they are the primary building blocks of our universe, and one tactic in studying chemistry is to focus on atoms as soon as possible. The structure of atoms determines how they behave in chemistry, so the next chapter discusses the structure of atoms, especially their electrons. Atoms make molecules, another important topic in chemistry, and how atoms do that is the subject of the next chapter, chemical bonds. As it turns out, chemical bonds give molecules certain shapes, and because the shape of a molecule impacts its properties, there is a chapter that discusses molecular shapes.

Matter exists in three common phases, and those phases also have an impact on how atoms and molecules behave. Chapter 7 discusses the two condensed phases of matter, the solid and liquid phases. Then the text gets to an important part of chemistry, which is an introduction to how chemicals *change*—chemical reactions and how we depict them.

Quantities are important in chemistry, as in all sciences. Chapter 9 introduces how chemistry keeps track of amounts, a topic called stoichiometry. A very important unit, the mole, is also introduced here. With these last two important topics on the table, the book presents a bit more detail on how electrons are important in chemistry, using the concepts of oxidation and reduction and some of their more practical applications. A discussion of gases, the third common phase of matter, follows, and then there is a presentation of that combination of multiple substances that we call a solution.

Energy is also an important topic in chemistry, so now that atoms and molecules, chemical reactions, and stoichiometry have been introduced, there is a presentation of energy as a quantitative property. The remaining chapters discuss certain applied topics that are still fundamental to our understanding: acids and bases, chemical equilibrium, and nuclear chemistry. The text finishes with a quick introduction to organic chemistry, if only to whet the appetites of those who thirst to know more.

Throughout each chapter, I present two features that reinforce the theme of the textbook—that chemistry is all around you. The first is a feature titled, appropriately, "Chemistry Is Everywhere." These features examine a topic of the chapter and demonstrate how this topic shows up in everyday life. In Chapter 1, "Chemistry Is Everywhere: In the Morning" focuses on the personal hygiene products that you may use every morning: toothpaste, soap, and shampoo, among others. These products are chemicals, aren't they? Ever wonder about the chemical reactions that they undergo to give you clean and healthy teeth or shiny hair? I will explore some of these chemical reactions in future chapters. But this feature makes it clear that chemistry is, indeed, everywhere.

The other feature focuses on chemistry that you likely indulge in every day: eating and drinking. In the "Food and Drink App," I discuss how the chemistry of the chapter applies to things that you eat and drink every day. Carbonated beverages depend on the behavior of gases, foods contain acids and bases, and we actually eat certain rocks. (Can you guess which rocks without looking ahead?) Cooking, eating, drinking, and metabolism—we are involved with all these chemical processes all the time. These two features allow us to see the things we interact with every day in a new light—as chemistry.

Each section starts with one or more Learning Objectives, which are the main points of the section. Key Takeaways, which review the main points, end each section. Each chapter is full of examples to illustrate the key points, and each example is followed by a similar Test Yourself exercise to see if a student understands the concept. Each section ends with its own set of paired exercises to practice the material from that section, and each chapter ends with Additional Exercises that are more challenging or require multiple steps or skills to answer.

The mathematical problems in this text have been treated in one of two ways: either as a conversion-factor problem or as a formula problem. It is generally recognized that consistency in problem solving is a positive pedagogical tool. Students and instructors may have different ways to work problems mathematically, and if it is mathematically consistent, the same answer will result. However, I have found it better to approach mathematical exercises in a consistent fashion, without (horrors!) cutesy shortcuts. Such shortcuts may be useful for one type of problem, but if students do not do a problem correctly, they are clueless as to why they went wrong. Having two basic mathematical approaches (converting and formulas) allows the text to focus on the logic of the approach, not the tricks of a shortcut.

Tabulations of unnecessary data, such as the densities of materials, are minimized for two reasons. First, they contribute nothing to understanding the concepts. Second, as an introductory textbook, this book focuses on the concepts and does not serve as a reference of data. There are other well-known sources of endless data should students need them.

WHAT'S NEW in the second edition: The entire manuscript has been re-evaluated and updated as necessary. Typographical errors have been corrected, and in a few places answers to exercises were slightly modified to accommodate for proper significant figures. Most importantly, the periodic table has been updated to include the completed seventh period, complete with IUPAC names and symbols.

Good luck, and good chemistry, to you all!

David W. Ball

December 2018

CHAPTER 1
What Is Chemistry?

Opening Essay

If you are reading these words, you are likely starting a chemistry course. Get ready for a fantastic journey through a world of wonder, delight, and knowledge. One of the themes of this book is "chemistry is everywhere," and indeed it is; you would not be alive if t weren't for chemistry because your body is a big chemical machine. If you don't believe it, don't worry. Every chapter in this book contains examples that will show you how chemistry is, in fact, everywhere. So enjoy the ride—and enjoy chemistry.

Source: © Thinkstock

What is chemistry? Simply put, **chemistry** is the study of the interactions of matter with other matter and with energy. This seems straightforward enough. However, the definition of chemistry includes a wide range of topics that must be understood to gain a mastery of the topic or even take additional courses in chemistry. In this book, we will lay the foundations of chemistry in a topic-by-topic fashion to provide you with the background you need to successfully understand chemistry.

chemistry

The study of the interactions of matter with other matter and with energy.

1.1 Some Basic Definitions

Learning Objective

1. Learn the basic terms used to describe matter.

The definition of chemistry—the study of the interactions of matter with other matter and with energy—uses some terms that should also be defined. We start the study of chemistry by defining some basic terms.

matter

Anything that has mass and takes up space.

Matter is anything that has mass and takes up space. A book is matter, a computer is matter, food is matter, and dirt in the ground is matter. Sometimes matter may be difficult to identify. For example, air is matter, but because it is so thin compared to other matter (e.g., a book, a computer, food, and dirt), we sometimes forget that air has mass and takes up space. Things that are not matter include thoughts, ideas, emotions, and hopes.

Example 1

Which of the following is matter and not matter?

1. a hot dog
2. love
3. a tree

Solution

1. A hot dog has mass and takes up space, so it is matter.
2. Love is an emotion, and emotions are not matter.
3. A tree has mass and takes up space, so it is matter.

Test Yourself

Which of the following is matter and not matter?

1. the moon
2. an idea for a new invention

Answer

1. The moon is matter.
2. The invention itself may be matter, but the idea for it is not.

FIGURE 1.1 The Phases of Matter
Chemistry recognizes three fundamental phases of matter: solid (left), liquid (middle), and gas (right).

Source: © Thinkstock

To understand matter and how it changes, we need to be able to describe matter. There are two basic ways to describe matter: physical properties and chemical properties. **Physical properties** are characteristics that describe matter as it exists. Some of many physical characteristics of matter are shape, color, size, and temperature. An important physical property is the **phase** (or **state**) of matter. The three fundamental phases of matter are solid, liquid, and gas (see Figure 1.1).

FIGURE 1.2 Chemical Properties
The fact that this match burns is a chemical property of the match.

Source: © Thinkstock

Chemical properties are characteristics of matter that describe how matter changes form in the presence of other matter. Does a sample of matter burn? Burning is a chemical property. Does it behave violently when put in water? This reaction is a chemical property as well (Figure 1.2). In the following chapters, we will see how descriptions of physical and chemical properties are important aspects of chemistry.

FIGURE 1.3 Physical Changes
The solid ice melts into liquid water—a physical change.

Source: © Thinkstock

physical change

A change that occurs when a sample of matter changes one or more of its physical properties.

chemical change

The process of demonstrating a chemical property.

If matter always stayed the same, chemistry would be rather boring. Fortunately, a major part of chemistry involves change. A **physical change** occurs when a sample of matter changes one or more of its physical properties. For example, a solid may melt (Figure 1.3), or alcohol in a thermometer may change volume as the temperature changes. A physical change does not affect the chemical composition of matter.

A **chemical change** is the process of demonstrating a chemical property, such as the burning match in Figure 1.2. As the matter in the match burns, its chemical composition changes, and new forms of matter with new physical properties are created. Note that chemical changes are frequently accompanied by physical changes, because the new matter will likely have different physical properties from the original matter.

Example 2

Describe each process as a physical change or a chemical change.

1. Water in the air turns into snow.
2. A person's hair is cut.
3. Bread dough becomes fresh bread in an oven.

Solution

1. Because the water is going from a gas phase to a solid phase, this is a physical change.
2. Your long hair is being shortened. This is a physical change.
3. Because of the oven's temperature, chemical changes are occurring in the bread dough to make fresh bread. These are chemical changes. (In fact, a lot of cooking involves chemical changes.)

Test Yourself

Identify each process as a physical change or a chemical change.

1. A fire is raging in a fireplace.
2. Water is warmed to make a cup of coffee.

Answers

1. chemical change
2. physical change

A sample of matter that has the same physical and chemical properties throughout is called a **substance**. Sometimes the phrase *pure substance* is used, but the word *pure* isn't needed. The definition of the term *substance* is an example of how chemistry has a specific definition for a word that is used in everyday language with a different, vaguer definition. Here, we will use the term *substance* with its strict chemical definition.

Chemistry recognizes two different types of substances: elements and compounds. An **element** is the simplest type of chemical substance; it cannot be broken down into simpler chemical substances by ordinary chemical means. There are about 118 elements known to science, of which 80 are stable. (The other elements are radioactive, a property we will consider in Chapter 16.) Each element has its own unique set of physical and chemical properties. Examples of elements include iron, carbon, and gold.

A **compound** is a combination of more than one element. The physical and chemical properties of a compound are different from the physical and chemical properties of its constituent elements; that is, it behaves as a completely different substance. There are over 70 million compounds known, and more are being discovered daily. Examples of compounds include water, penicillin, and sodium chloride (the chemical name for common table salt).

Elements and compounds are not the only ways in which matter can be present. We frequently encounter objects that are physical combinations of more than one element or compound. Physical combinations of more than one substance are called **mixtures**. There are two types of mixtures. A **heterogeneous mixture** is a mixture composed of two or more substances. It is easy to tell, sometimes by the naked eye, that more than one substance is present. A **homogeneous mixture** is a combination of two or more substances that is so intimately mixed that the mixture behaves as a single substance. Another word for a homogeneous mixture is **solution**. Thus, a combination of salt and steel wool is a heterogeneous mixture because it is easy to see which particles of the matter are salt crystals and which are steel wool. On the other hand, if you take salt crystals and dissolve them in water, it is very difficult to tell that you have more than one substance present just by looking—even if you use a powerful microscope. The salt dissolved in water is a homogeneous mixture, or a solution (Figure 1.4).

substance

Matter that has the same physical and chemical properties throughout.

element

A substance that cannot be broken down into simpler chemical substances by ordinary chemical means.

compound

A combination of more than one element.

mixture

A physical combination of more than one substance.

heterogeneous mixture

A mixture composed of two or more substances.

homogeneous mixture

A combination of two or more substances that is so intimately mixed that the mixture behaves as a single substance.

solution

Another name for a homogeneous mixture.

FIGURE 1.4 Types of Mixtures

On the left, the combination of two substances is a heterogeneous mixture because the particles of the two components look different. On the right, the salt crystals have dissolved in the water so finely that you cannot tell that salt is present. The homogeneous mixture appears like a single substance.

Source: © Shutterstock, Inc.

Example 3

Identify the following combinations as heterogeneous mixtures or homogeneous mixtures.

1. soda water (Carbon dioxide is dissolved in water.)
2. a mixture of iron metal filings and sulfur powder (Both iron and sulfur are elements.)

Solution

1. Because carbon dioxide is dissolved in water, we can infer from the behavior of salt crystals dissolved in water that carbon dioxide dissolved in water is (also) a homogeneous mixture.
2. Assuming that the iron and sulfur are simply mixed together, it should be easy to see what is iron and what is sulfur, so this is a heterogeneous mixture.

Test Yourself

Are the following combinations homogeneous mixtures or heterogeneous mixtures?

1. the human body
2. an amalgam, a combination of some metals dissolved in a small amount of mercury

Answers

1. heterogeneous mixture
2. homogeneous mixture

There are other descriptors that we can use to describe matter, especially elements. We can usually divide elements into metals and nonmetals, and each set shares certain (but not always all) properties. A **metal** is an element that is solid at room temperature (although mercury is a well-known exception), is shiny and silvery, conducts electricity and heat well, can be pounded into thin sheets (a property called *malleability*), and can be drawn into thin wires (a property called *ductility*). A **nonmetal** is an element that is brittle when solid, does not conduct electricity or heat very well, and cannot be made into thin sheets or wires (Figure 1.5). Nonmetals also exist in a variety of phases and colors at room temperature. Some elements have properties of both metals and nonmetals and are called **semimetals (or metalloids)**. We will see later how these descriptions can be assigned rather easily to various elements.

metal

An element that conducts electricity and heat well and is shiny, silvery, solid, ductile, and malleable.

nonmetal

An element that exists in various colors and phases, is brittle, and does not conduct electricity or heat well.

semimetals (or metalloids)

An element that has properties of both metals and nonmetals.

FIGURE 1.5 Metals and Nonmetals

On the left is some elemental mercury, the only metal that exists as a liquid at room temperature. It has all the other expected properties of a metal. On the right, elemental sulfur is a yellow nonmetal that usually is found as a powder.

Source: © Thinkstock

Figure 1.6 is a flowchart of the relationships among the different ways of describing matter.

FIGURE 1.6 Describing Matter
This flowchart shows how matter can be described.

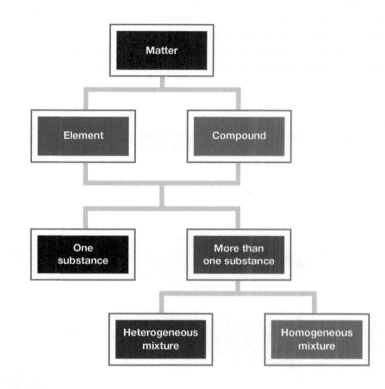

Chemistry Is Everywhere: In the Morning

Most people have a morning ritual, a process that they go through every morning to get ready for the day. Chemistry appears in many of these activities.

- If you take a shower or bath in the morning, you probably use soap, shampoo, or both. These items contain chemicals that interact with the oil and dirt on your body and hair to remove them and wash them away. Many of these products also contain chemicals that make you smell good; they are called *fragrances*.
- When you brush your teeth in the morning, you usually use toothpaste, a form of soap, to clean your teeth. Toothpastes typically contain tiny, hard particles called *abrasives* that physically scrub your teeth. Many toothpastes also contain fluoride, a substance that chemically interacts with the surface of the teeth to help prevent cavities.
- Perhaps you take vitamins, supplements, or medicines every morning. Vitamins and other supplements contain chemicals your body needs in small amounts to function properly. Medicines are chemicals that help combat diseases and promote health.
- Perhaps you make some fried eggs for breakfast. Frying eggs involves heating them enough so that a chemical reaction occurs to cook the eggs.
- After you eat, the food in your stomach is chemically reacted so that the body (mostly the intestines) can absorb food, water, and other nutrients.
- If you drive or take the bus to school or work, you are using a vehicle that probably burns gasoline, a material that burns fairly easily and provides energy to power the vehicle. Recall that burning is a chemical change.

These are just a few examples of how chemistry impacts your everyday life. And we haven't even made it to lunch yet!

FIGURE 1.7 Chemistry in Real Life
Examples of chemistry can be found everywhere—such as in personal hygiene products, food, and motor vehicles.

Source: © Thinkstock

Key Takeaways

- Chemistry is the study of matter and its interactions with other matter and energy.
- Matter is anything that has mass and takes up space.
- Matter can be described in terms of physical properties and chemical properties.
- Physical properties and chemical properties of matter can change.
- Matter is composed of elements and compounds.
- Combinations of different substances are called mixtures.
- Elements can be described as metals, nonmetals, and semimetals.

Exercises

1. Identify each as either matter or not matter.
    a. a book
    b. hate
    c. light
    d. a car
    e. a fried egg
2. Give an example of matter in each phase: solid, liquid, or gas.
3. Does each statement represent a physical property or a chemical property?
    a. Sulfur is yellow.
    b. Steel wool burns when ignited by a flame.
    c. A gallon of milk weighs over eight pounds.
4. Does each statement represent a physical property or a chemical property?
    a. A pile of leaves slowly rots in the backyard.

    b. In the presence of oxygen, hydrogen can interact to make water.

    c. Gold can be stretched into very thin wires.

5. Does each statement represent a physical change or a chemical change?

    a. Water boils and becomes steam.

    b. Food is converted into usable form by the digestive system.

    c. The alcohol in many thermometers freezes at about −40 degrees Fahrenheit.

6. Does each statement represent a physical change or a chemical change?

    a. Graphite, a form of elemental carbon, can be turned into diamond, another form of carbon, at very high temperatures and pressures.

    b. The house across the street has been painted a new color.

    c. The elements sodium and chlorine come together to make a new substance called sodium chloride.

7. Distinguish between an element and a compound. About how many of each are known?

8. What is the difference between a homogeneous mixture and a heterogeneous mixture?

9. Identify each as a heterogeneous mixture or a homogeneous mixture.

    a. Salt is mixed with pepper.

    b. Sugar is dissolved in water.

    c. Pasta is cooked in boiling water.

10. Identify each as a heterogeneous mixture or a homogeneous mixture.

    a. air

    b. dirt

    c. a television set

11. In Exercise 9, which choices are also solutions?

12. In Exercise 10, which choices are also solutions?

13. Why is iron considered a metal?

14. Why is oxygen considered a nonmetal?

15. Distinguish between a metal and a nonmetal.

16. What properties do semimetals have?

17. Elemental carbon is a black, dull-looking solid that conducts heat and electricity well. It is very brittle and cannot be made into thin sheets or long wires. Of these properties, how does carbon behave as a metal? How does carbon behave as a nonmetal?

18. Pure silicon is shiny and silvery but does not conduct electricity or heat well. Of these properties, how does silicon behave as a metal? How does silicon behave as a nonmetal?

Answers

1. a. matter
   b. not matter
   c. not matter
   d. matter
   e. matter

2. solid: wood; liquid: water in a pond; gas: air in the atmosphere (answers will vary)

3. a. physical property
   b. chemical property
   c. physical property

4. a. chemical property

   b. chemical property
   c. physical property
5. a. physical change
   b. chemical change
   c. physical change
6. a. physical property
   b. physical property
   c. chemical property
7. An element is a fundamental chemical part of a substance; there are about 115 known elements. A compound is a combination of elements that acts as a different substance; there are over 50 million known substances.
8. Homogeneous mixtures are the same throughout; heterogeneous mixtures are combinations of two or more substances.
9. a. heterogeneous
   b. homogeneous
   c. heterogeneous
10. a. homogeneous
    b. heterogeneous
    c. heterogeneous
11. Choice b is a solution.
12. Choice a is a solution.
13. Iron is a metal because it is solid, is shiny, and conducts electricity and heat well.
14. Oxygen is a nonmetal because it does not conduct heat or electricity well and is not shiny.
15. Metals are typically shiny, conduct electricity and heat well, and are malleable and ductile; nonmetals are a variety of colors and phases, are brittle in the solid phase, and do not conduct heat or electricity well.
16. Semimetals have properties of both metals and nonmetals.
17. Carbon behaves as a metal because it conducts heat and electricity well. It is a nonmetal because it is black and brittle and cannot be made into sheets or wires.
18. Silicon acts as a metal because it is shiny and silvery; it acts as a nonmetal because it does not conduct electricity or heat well.

1.2 Chemistry as a Science

Learning Objective

1. Learn what science is and how it works.

Chemistry is a branch of science. Although science itself is difficult to define exactly, the following definition can serve as a starting point. **Science** is the process of knowing about the natural universe through observation and experiment. Science is not the only process of knowing (e.g., the ancient Greeks simply sat and *thought*), but it has evolved over more than 350 years into the best process that humanity has devised to date to learn about the universe around us.

   The process of science is usually stated as the *scientific method*, which is rather naïvely described as follows: (1) state a hypothesis, (2) test the hypothesis, and (3) refine the hypothesis.

science

The process of knowing about the natural universe through observation and experiment.

Actually, however, the process is not that simple. (For example, I don't go into my lab every day and exclaim, "I am going to state a hypothesis today and spend the day testing it!") The process is not that simple because science and scientists have a body of knowledge that has already been identified as coming from the highest level of understanding, and most scientists build from that body of knowledge.

hypothesis

An educated guess about how the natural universe works.

An educated guess about how the natural universe works is called a **hypothesis**. A scientist who is familiar with how part of the natural universe works—say, a chemist—is interested in furthering that knowledge. That person makes a reasonable guess—a hypothesis—that is designed to see if the universe works in a new way as well. Here's an example of a hypothesis: "if I mix one part of hydrogen with one part of oxygen, I can make a substance that contains both elements."

experiment

A test of the natural universe to see if a guess (hypothesis) is correct.

Most good hypotheses are grounded in previously understood knowledge and represent a testable extension of that knowledge. The scientist then devises ways to test if that guess is or is not correct. That is, the scientist plans experiments. **Experiments** are tests of the natural universe to see if a guess (hypothesis) is correct. An experiment to test our previous hypothesis would be to actually mix hydrogen and oxygen and see what happens. Most experiments include observations of small, well-defined parts of the natural universe designed to see results of the experiments.

Why do we have to do experiments? Why do we have to test? Because the natural universe is not always so obvious, experiments are necessary. For example, it is fairly obvious that if you drop an object from a height, it will fall. Several hundred years ago (coincidentally, near the inception of modern science), the concept of gravity explained that test. However, is it obvious that the entire natural universe is composed of only about 118 fundamental chemical building blocks called elements? This wouldn't seem true if you looked at the world around you and saw all the different forms matter can take. In fact, the modern concept of *the element* is only about 200 years old, and the last naturally occurring element was identified about 80 years ago. It took decades of tests and millions of experiments to establish what the elements actually are. These are just two examples; a myriad of such examples exists in chemistry and science in general.

theory

A general statement that explains a large number of observations.

When enough evidence has been collected to establish a general principle of how the natural universe works, the evidence is summarized in a theory. A **theory** is a general statement that explains a large number of observations. "All matter is composed of atoms" is a general statement, a theory, that explains many observations in chemistry. A theory is a very powerful statement in science. There are many statements referred to as "the theory of _____" or the "_____ theory" in science (where the blanks represent a word or concept). When written in this way, theories indicate that science has an overwhelming amount of evidence of its correctness. We will see several theories in the course of this text.

law

A specific statement that is thought never to be violated by the entire natural universe.

A specific statement that is thought never to be violated by the entire natural universe is called a **law**. In science, a law is the highest understanding of the natural universe, and is thought to be inviolate. For example, the fact that all matter attracts all other matter—the law of gravitation—is one such law. Note that the terms *theory* and *law* used in science have slightly different meanings from those in common usage; theory is often used to mean hypothesis ("I have a theory…"), whereas a law is an arbitrary limitation that can be broken but with potential consequences (such as speed limits). Here again, science uses these terms differently, and it is important to apply their proper definitions when you use these words in science. (See Figure 1.8.)

There is an additional phrase in our definition of science: "the natural universe." Science is concerned *only* with the natural universe. What is the natural universe? Its anything that occurs around us, well, naturally. Stars; planets; the appearance of life on earth; and how animals, plants, and other matter function are all part of the natural universe. Science is concerned with that—and *only* that.

Of course, there are other things that concern us. For example, is the English language part of science? Most of us can easily answer no; English is not science. English is certainly worth knowing (at least for people in predominantly English-speaking countries), but why isn't it science? English, or any human language, isn't science because ultimately it is *contrived*; it is made up. Think of it: the word spelled b-l-u-e represents a certain color, and we all agree what color that is. But what if we used the word a-w-f-f-o-r-n to describe that color? (See Figure 1.9.) That would be fine—as long as everyone agreed. Anyone who has learned a second language must initially wonder why a certain word is used to describe a certain concept; ultimately, the speakers of that language agreed that a particular word would represent a particular concept. It was contrived.

That doesn't mean language isn't worth knowing. It is very important in society. But it's not *science*. Science deals only with what occurs naturally.

Example 4

Which of the following fields would be considered science?

1. geology, the study of the earth
2. ethics, the study of morality
3. political science, the study of governance
4. biology, the study of living organisms

Solution

1. Because the earth is a natural object, the study of it is indeed considered part of science.
2. Ethics is a branch of philosophy that deals with right and wrong. Although these are useful concepts, they are not science.
3. There are many forms of government, but all are created by humans. Despite the fact that the word *science* appears in its name, political science is not true science.
4. Living organisms are part of the natural universe, so the study of them is part of science.

Test Yourself

Which is part of science, and which is not?

1. dynamics, the study of systems that change over time
2. aesthetics, the concept of beauty

Answers

1. science
2. not science

The field of science has gotten so big that it is common to separate it into more specific fields. First, there is mathematics, the language of science. All scientific fields use mathematics to express themselves—some more than others. Physics and astronomy are scientific fields concerned with the fundamental interactions between matter and energy. Chemistry, as defined previously, is the study of the interactions of matter with other matter and with energy. Biology is the study of living organisms, while geology is the study of the earth. Other sciences can be named as well. Understand that these fields are not always completely separate; the boundaries between scientific fields are not always readily apparent. Therefore, a scientist may be labeled a biochemist if he or she studies the chemistry of biological organisms.

FIGURE 1.8
Defining a Law
Does this t-shirt mean "law" the way science defines "law"?

Source: © Thinkstock, with alterations

FIGURE 1.9
English Is Not Science
How would you describe this color? Blue or awfforn? Either way, you're not doing science.

qualitative

A description of the quality of an object.

quantitative

A description of a specific amount of something.

Finally, understand that science can be either qualitative or quantitative. **Qualitative** implies a description of the quality of an object. For example, physical properties are generally qualitative descriptions: sulfur is yellow, your math book is heavy, or that statue is pretty. A **quantitative** description represents the specific amount of something; it means knowing how much of something is present, usually by counting or measuring it. As such, some quantitative descriptions would include 25 students in a class, 650 pages in a book, or a velocity of 66 miles per hour. Quantitative expressions are very important in science; they are also very important in chemistry.

Example 5

Identify each statement as either a qualitative description or a quantitative description.

1. Gold metal is yellow.
2. A ream of paper has 500 sheets in it.
3. The weather outside is snowy.
4. The temperature outside is 24 degrees Fahrenheit.

Solution

1. Because we are describing a physical property of gold, this statement is qualitative.
2. This statement mentions a specific amount, so it is quantitative.
3. The word *snowy* is a description of how the day is; therefore, it is a qualitative statement.
4. In this case, the weather is described with a specific quantity—the temperature. Therefore, it is quantitative.

Test Yourself

Are these qualitative or quantitative statements?

1. Roses are red, and violets are blue.
2. Four score and seven years ago….

Answers

1. qualitative
2. quantitative

Food and Drink App: Carbonated Beverages

Some of the simple chemical principles discussed in this chapter can be illustrated with carbonated beverages: sodas, beer, and sparkling wines. Each product is produced in a different way, but they all have one thing in common. They are solutions of carbon dioxide dissolved in water.

Carbon dioxide is a compound composed of carbon and oxygen. Under normal conditions, it is a gas. If you cool it down enough, it becomes a solid known as dry ice. Carbon dioxide is an important compound in the cycle of life on earth.

Even though it is a gas, carbon dioxide can dissolve in water, just like sugar or salt can dissolve in water. When that occurs, we have a homogeneous mixture, or a solution, of carbon dioxide in water. However, very little carbon dioxide can dissolve in water. If the atmosphere were pure carbon dioxide, the solution would be only about 0.07% carbon dioxide. In reality, the air is only about 0.03% carbon dioxide, so the amount of carbon dioxide in water is reduced proportionally.

However, when soda and beer are made, manufacturers do two important things: they use pure carbon dioxide gas, and they use it at very high pressures. With higher pressures, more carbon dioxide can dissolve in the water. When the soda or beer container is sealed, the high pressure of carbon dioxide gas remains inside the package. (Of course, there are more ingredients in soda and beer besides carbon dioxide and water.)

When you open a container of soda or beer, you hear a distinctive *hiss* as the excess carbon dioxide gas escapes. But something else happens as well. The carbon dioxide in the solution comes out of solution as a bunch of tiny bubbles. These bubbles impart a pleasing sensation in the mouth, so much so that the soda industry sold over *200 billion* servings of soda in the United States alone in 2015.

Some sparkling wines are made in the same way—by forcing carbon dioxide into regular wine. Some sparkling wines (including champagne) are made by sealing a bottle of wine with some yeast in it. The yeast *ferments*, a process by which the yeast converts sugars into energy and excess carbon dioxide. The carbon dioxide produced by the yeast dissolves in the wine. Then, when the champagne bottle is opened, the increased pressure of carbon dioxide is released, and the drink bubbles just like an expensive glass of soda.

Soda, beer, and sparkling wine take advantage of the properties of a solution of carbon dioxide in water.

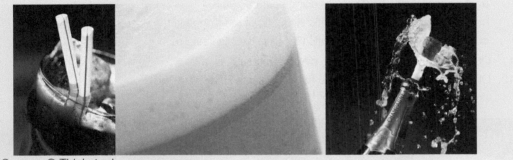

Source: © Thinkstock

Key Takeaways

- Science is a process of knowing about the natural universe through observation and experiment.
- Scientists go through a rigorous process to determine new knowledge about the universe; this process is generally referred to as the scientific method.
- Science is broken down into various fields, of which chemistry is one.
- Science, including chemistry, is both qualitative and quantitative.

Exercises

1. Describe the scientific method.
2. What is the scientific definition of a hypothesis? Why is the phrase *a hypothesis is just a guess* an inadequate definition?
3. Why do scientists need to perform experiments?
4. What is the scientific definition of a theory? How is this word misused in general conversation?
5. What is the scientific definition of a law? How does it differ from the everyday definition of a law?
6. Name an example of a field that is not considered a science.
7. Which of the following fields are studies of the natural universe?

    a. biophysics (a mix of biology and physics)

    b. art

    c. business

8. Which of the following fields are studies of the natural universe?

    a. accounting

    b. geochemistry (a mix of geology and chemistry)

    c. astronomy (the study of stars and planets [but not the earth])

9. Which of these statements are qualitative descriptions?

    a. The *Titanic* was the largest passenger ship built at that time.

    b. The population of the United States is about 328,000,000 people.

    c. The peak of Mount Everest is 29,035 feet above sea level.

10. Which of these statements are qualitative descriptions?

    a. A regular movie ticket in Cleveland costs $8.00.

    b. The weather in the Democratic Republic of the Congo is the wettest in all of Africa.

    c. The deepest part of the Pacific Ocean is the Mariana Trench.

11. Of the statements in Exercise 9, which are quantitative?

12. Of the statements in Exercise 10, which are quantitative?

Answers

1. Simply stated, the scientific method includes three steps: (1) stating a hypothesis, (2) testing the hypothesis, and (3) refining the hypothesis.

2. A hypothesis is a reasonable guess based on previous knowledge. Science does not use the word *hypothesis* to mean any random guess, but a reasonable one based on previous knowledge.

3. Scientists perform experiments to test their hypotheses because sometimes the nature of the natural universe is not obvious.

4. A theory is a general statement that explains a large number of observations. Many people improperly use the word *theory* to mean *hypothesis*.

5. A scientific law is a specific statement that is thought to be never violated by the entire natural universe. Everyday laws are arbitrary limits that society puts on its members.

6. English is not a science (despite its importance).

7. a. yes

    b. no

    c. no

8. a. no

    b. yes

    c. yes

9. a. qualitative

    b. not qualitative

    c. not qualitative

10. a. not qualitative

    b. qualitative

    c. qualitative

11. Statements b and c are quantitative.

12. Statement a is quantitative.

CHAPTER 2

Measurements

Opening Essay

Data suggest that a male child will weigh 50% of his adult weight at about 11 years of age. However, he will reach 50% of his adult height at only 2 years of age. It is obvious, then, that people eventually stop growing up but continue to grow out. Data also suggest that the average human height has been increasing over time. In industrialized countries, the average height of people increased 5.5 inches from 1810 to 1984. Most scientists attribute this simple, basic measurement of the human body to better health and nutrition.

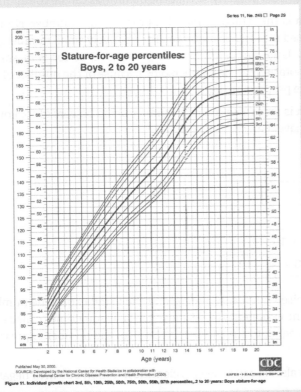

Source: "Figure 11. Individual growth chart 3rd, 5th, 10th, 25th, 50th, 75th, 90th, 95th, 97th percentiles, 2 to 20 years: Boys stature-for-age," *2000 CDC Growth Charts for the United States: Methods and Development*, Centers for Disease Control and Prevention, p. 29; https://www.cdc.gov/nchs/data/series/sr_11/sr11_246.pdf.

In 1983, an Air Canada airplane had to make an emergency landing because it unexpectedly ran out of fuel; ground personnel had filled the fuel tanks with a certain number of pounds of fuel, not kilograms of fuel. In 1999, the Mars Climate Orbiter spacecraft was lost attempting to orbit Mars because the thrusters were programmed in terms of English units, even though the engineers built the spacecraft using metric units. In 1993, a nurse mistakenly administered 23 units of morphine to a patient rather than the "2–3" units prescribed. (The patient survived.) These incidents occurred because people weren't paying attention to quantities.

Chemistry, like all sciences, is quantitative. It deals with *quantities*, things that have amounts and units. Dealing with quantities is very important in chemistry, as is relating quantities to each other. In this chapter, we will discuss how we deal with numbers and units, including how they are combined and manipulated.

2.1 Expressing Numbers

Learning Objective

1. Learn to express numbers properly.

Quantities have two parts: the number and the unit. The number tells "how many." It is important to be able to express numbers properly so that the quantities can be communicated properly.

standard notation

A straightforward expression of a number.

Standard notation is the straightforward expression of a number. Numbers such as 17, 101.5, and 0.00446 are expressed in standard notation. For relatively small numbers, standard notation is fine. However, for very large numbers, such as 324,000,000, or for very small numbers, such as 0.000000419, standard notation can be cumbersome because of the number of zeros needed to place nonzero numbers in the proper position.

scientific notation

An expression of a number using powers of 10.

Scientific notation is an expression of a number using powers of 10. Powers of 10 are used to express numbers that have many zeros:

10^0	= 1
10^1	= 10
10^2	= 100 = 10 × 10
10^3	= 1,000 = 10 × 10 × 10
10^4	= 10,000 = 10 × 10 × 10 × 10

exponent

The raised number to the right of a 10 indicating the number of factors of 10 in the original number.

and so forth. The raised number to the right of the 10 indicating the number of factors of 10 in the original number is the **exponent**. (Scientific notation is sometimes called *exponential notation*.) The exponent's value is equal to the number of zeros in the number expressed in standard notation.

Small numbers can also be expressed in scientific notation but with negative exponents:

10^{-1}	= 0.1 = 1/10
10^{-2}	= 0.01 = 1/100
10^{-3}	= 0.001 = 1/1,000
10^{-4}	= 0.0001 = 1/10,000

and so forth. Again, the value of the exponent is equal to the number of zeros in the denominator of the associated fraction. A negative exponent implies a decimal number less than one.

coefficient

The part of a number in scientific notation that is multiplied by a power of 10.

A number is expressed in scientific notation by writing the first nonzero digit, then a decimal point, and then the rest of the digits. The part of a number in scientific notation that is multiplied by a power of 10 is called the **coefficient**. Then determine the power of 10 needed to make that number into the original number and multiply the written number by the proper power of 10. For example, to write 79,345 in scientific notation,

$$79{,}345 = 7.9345 \times 10{,}000 = 7.9345 \times 10^4 \, 79{,}345 = 7.9345 \times 10{,}000 = 7.9345 \times 10^4$$

Thus, the number in scientific notation is 7.9345 × 10⁴. For small numbers, the same process is used, but the exponent for the power of 10 is negative:

$$0.000411 = 4.11 \times 1/10{,}000 = 4.11 \times 10^{-4}$$

Typically, the extra zero digits at the end or the beginning of a number are not included. (See Figure 2.1.)

Example 1

Express these numbers in scientific notation.

1. 306,000
2. 0.00884
3. 2,760,000
4. 0.000000559

Solution

1. The number 306,000 is 3.06 times 100,000, or 3.06 times 10^5. In scientific notation, the number is 3.06×10^5.

2. The number 0.00884 is 8.84 times 1/1,000, which is 8.84 times 10^{-3}. In scientific notation, the number is 8.84×10^{-3}.

3. The number 2,760,000 is 2.76 times 1,000,000, which is the same as 2.76 times 10^6. In scientific notation, the number is written as 2.76×10^6. Note that we omit the zeros at the end of the original number.

4. The number 0.000000559 is 5.59 times 1/10,000,000, which is 5.59 times 10^{-7}. In scientific notation, the number is written as 5.59×10^{-7}.

Test Yourself

Express these numbers in scientific notation.

1. 23,070
2. 0.0009706

Answers

1. 2.307×10^4
2. 9.706×10^{-4}

Another way to determine the power of 10 in scientific notation is to count the number of places you need to move the decimal point to get a numerical value between 1 and 10. The number of places equals the power of 10. This number is positive if you move the decimal point to the right and negative if you move the decimal point to the left:

$$56{,}900 = 5.69 \times 10^4 \qquad 0.000028 = 2.8 \times 10^{-5}$$
$$\quad 4 \; 3 \, 2 \, 1 \qquad\qquad\qquad 1 \, 2 \, 3 \, 4 \, 5$$

Many quantities in chemistry are expressed in scientific notation. When performing calculations, you may have to enter a number in scientific notation into a calculator. Be sure you know how to correctly enter a number in scientific notation into your calculator. Different models of calculators require different actions for properly entering scientific notation. If in doubt, consult your instructor immediately. (See Figure 2.2.)

FIGURE 2.2 Scientific Notation on a Calculator

This calculator shows only the coefficient and the power of 10 to represent the number in scientific notation. Thus, the number being displayed is 3.84951×10^{18}, or 3,849,510,000,000,000,000.

Source: © Thinkstock

Key Takeaways

- Standard notation expresses a number normally.
- Scientific notation expresses a number as a coefficient times a power of 10.
- The power of 10 is positive for numbers greater than 1 and negative for numbers between 0 and 1.

Exercises

1. Express these numbers in scientific notation.
   a. 56.9
   b. 563,100
   c. 0.0804
   d. 0.00000667

2. Express these numbers in scientific notation.
   a. −890,000
   b. 602,000,000,000
   c. 0.0000004099
   d. 0.000000000000011

3. Express these numbers in scientific notation.
   a. 0.00656

   b. 65,600

   c. 4,567,000

   d. 0.000005507

4. Express these numbers in scientific notation.

   a. 65

   b. −321.09

   c. 0.000077099

   d. 0.00000C000218

5. Express these numbers in standard notation.

   a. 1.381×10^5

   b. 5.22×10^{-7}

   c. 9.998×10^4

6. Express these numbers in standard notation.

   a. 7.11×10^{-2}

   b. 9.18×10^2

   c. 3.09×10^{-10}

7. Express these numbers in standard notation.

   a. 8.09×10^0

   b. 3.088×10^{-5}

   c. -4.239×10^2

8. Express these numbers in standard notation.

   a. 2.87×10^{-8}

   b. 1.78×10^{11}

   c. 1.381×10^{-23}

9. These numbers are not written in proper scientific notat on. Rewrite them so that they are in proper scientific notation.

   a. 72.44×10^3

   b. $9,943 \times 10^{-5}$

   c. $588,399 \times 10^2$

10. These numbers are not written in proper scientific notation. Rewrite them so that they are in proper scientific notation.

   a. 0.000077×10^{-7}

   b. 0.000111×10^8

   c. $602,000 \times 10^{18}$

11. These numbers are not written in proper scientific notation. Rewrite them so that they are in proper scientific notation.

   a. 345.1×10^2

   b. 0.234×10^{-3}

   c. $1,800 \times 10^{-2}$

12. These numbers are not written in proper scientific notation. Rewrite them so that they are in proper scientific notation.

   a. $8,099 \times 10^{-8}$

   b. 34.5×10^0

   c. 0.000332×10^4

13. Write these numbers in scientific notation by counting the number of places the decimal point is moved.

   a. 123,456.78

   b. 98,490

   c. 0.000000445

14. Write these numbers in scientific notation by counting the number of places the decimal point is moved.

   a. 0.000552

   b. 1,987

   c. 0.00000000887

15. Use your calculator to evaluate these expressions. Express the final answer in proper scientific notation.

   a. $456 \times (7.4 \times 10^8) = ?$

   b. $(3.02 \times 10^5) \div (9.04 \times 10^{15}) = ?$

   c. $0.0044 \times 0.000833 = ?$

16. Use your calculator to evaluate these expressions. Express the final answer in proper scientific notation.

   a. $98,000 \times 23,000 = ?$

   b. $98,000 \div 23,000 = ?$

   c. $(4.6 \times 10^{-5}) \times (2.09 \times 10^3) = ?$

17. Use your calculator to evaluate these expressions. Express the final answer in proper scientific notation.

   a. $45 \times 132 \div 882 = ?$

   b. $[(6.37 \times 10^4) \times (8.44 \times 10^{-4})] \div (3.2209 \times 10^{15}) = ?$

18. Use your calculator to evaluate these expressions. Express the final answer in proper scientific notation.

   a. $(9.09 \times 10^8) \div [(6.33 \times 10^9) \times (4.066 \times 10^{-7})] = ?$

   b. $9,345 \times 34.866 \div 0.00665 = ?$

Answers

1. a. 5.69×10^1

   b. 5.631×10^5

   c. 8.04×10^{-2}

   d. 6.67×10^{-6}

2. a. -8.9×10^5

   b. 6.02×10^{11}

   c. 4.099×10^{-7}

   d. 1.1×10^{-14}

3. a. 6.56×10^{-3}

   b. 6.56×10^4

   c. 4.567×10^6

   d. 5.507×10^{-6}

4. a. 6.5×10^1

   b. -3.2109×10^2

   c. 7.7099×10^{-5}

   d. 2.18×10^{-10}

5. a. 138,100

   b. 0.000000522

   c. 99,980

6. a. 0.0711

   b. 918

   c. 0.000000000309

7. a. 8.09

   b. 0.00003088

   c. −423.9

8. a. 0.0000000287

   b. 178,000,000,000

   c. 0.00000000000000000000001381

9. a. 7.244×10^{4}

   b. 9.943×10^{-2}

   c. 5.88399×10^{7}

10. a. 7.7×10^{-12}

   b. 1.11×10^{4}

   c. 6.02×10^{23}

11. a. 3.451×10^{4}

   b. 2.34×10^{-4}

   c. 1.8×10^{1}

12. a. 8.099×10^{-5}

   b. 3.45×10^{1}

   c. 3.32×10^{0}

13. a. 1.2345678×10^{5}

   b. 9.849×10^{4}

   c. 4.45×10^{-7}

14. a. 5.52×10^{-4}

   b. 1.987×10^{3}

   c. 8.87×10^{-9}

15. a. 3.3744×10^{11}

   b. 3.3407×10^{-11}

   c. 3.665×10^{-6}

16. a. 2.254×10^{9}

   b. 4.2608×10^{0}

   c. 9.614×10^{-2}

17. a. 6.7346×10^{0}

   b. 1.6691×10^{-14}

18. a. 3.5317×10^{5}

   b. 4.8995×10^{7}

2.2 Expressing Units

Learning Objectives

1. Learn the units that go with various quantities.
2. Express units using their abbreviations.
3. Make new units by combining numerical prefixes with units.

A number indicates "how much," but the unit indicates "of what." The "of what" is important when communicating a quantity. For example, if you were to ask a friend how close you are to Lake Erie and your friend says "six," then your friend isn't giving you complete information. Six *what*? Six miles? Six inches? Six city blocks? The actual distance to the lake depends on what units you use.

fundamental units

One of the seven basic units of SI used in science.

Chemistry, like most sciences, uses the International System of Units, or SI for short. (The letters *SI* stand for the French "le Système International d'unités.") SI specifies certain units for various types of quantities, based on seven **fundamental units** for various quantities. We will use most of the fundamental units in chemistry. Initially, we will deal with three fundamental units. The meter (abbreviated m) is the SI unit of length. It is a little longer than a yard (see Figure 2.3). The SI unit of mass is the kilogram (kg), which is about 2.2 pounds (lb). The SI unit of time is the second (s).

FIGURE 2.3 The Meter
The SI standard unit of length, the meter, is a little longer than a yard.

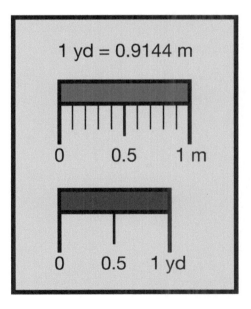

To express a quantity, you need to combine a number with a unit. If you have a length that is 2.4 m, then you express that length as simply 2.4 m. A mass of 15,000 kg can be expressed as 1.5×10^4 kg in scientific notation.

Sometimes, a given unit is not an appropriate size to easily express a quantity. For example, the width of a human hair is very small, and it doesn't make much sense to express it in meters. SI also defines a series of **numerical prefixes** that refer to multiples or fractions of a fundamental unit to make a unit more conveniently sized for a specific quantity. Table 2.1 lists the prefixes, their abbreviations, and their multiplicative factors. Some of the prefixes, such as kilo-, mega-, and giga-, represent more than one of the fundamental unit, while other prefixes, such as centi-, milli-, and micro-, represent fractions of the original unit. Note, too, that once again we are using powers of 10. Each prefix is a multiple of or fraction of a power of 10.

numerical prefix

A prefix used with a unit that refers to a multiple or fraction of a fundamental unit to make a more conveniently sized unit for a specific quantity.

TABLE 2.1 Multiplicative Prefixes for SI Units

Prefix	Abbreviation	Multiplicative Amount
giga-	G	1,000,000,000 ×
mega-	M	1,000,000 ×
kilo-	k	1,000 ×
deci-	d	1/10 ×
centi-	c	1/100 ×
milli-	m	1/1,000 ×
micro-	μ*	1/1,000,000 ×
nano-	n	1/1,000,000,000 ×
pico-	p	1/1,000,000,000,000 ×
* The letter μ is the Greek letter lowercase equivalent to an m and is called "mu" (pronounced "myoo").		

To use the fractions to generate new units, simply combine the prefix with the unit itself; the abbreviation for the new unit is the combination of the abbreviation for the prefix and the abbreviation of the unit. For example, the kilometer (km) is 1,000 × meter, or 1,000 m. Thus, 5 kilometers (5 km) is equal to 5,000 m. Similarly, a millisecond (ms) is 1/1,000 × second, or one-thousandth of a second. Thus, 25 ms is 25 thousandths of a second. You will need to become proficient in combining prefixes and units. (You may recognize that one of our fundamental units, the kilogram, automatically has a prefix-unit combination, the kilogram. The word *kilogram* means 1,000 g.)

In addition to the fundamental units, SI also allows for **derived units** based on a fundamental unit or units. There are many derived units used in science. For example, the derived unit for area comes from the idea that area is defined as width times height. Because both width and height are lengths, they both have the fundamental unit of meter, so the unit of area is meter × meter, or meter^2 (m^2). This is sometimes spoken as "square meters." A unit with a prefix can also be used to derive a unit for area, so we can also have cm^2, mm^2, or km^2 as acceptable units for area.

derived unit

A unit that is a product or a quotient of a fundamental unit.

Volume is defined as length times width times height, so it has units of meter × meter × meter or meter^3 (m^3), sometimes spoken as "cubic meters." The cubic meter is a rather large unit, however, so another unit is defined that is somewhat more manageable: the liter (L). A liter is 1/1,000th of a cubic meter and is a little more than 1 quart in volume (see Figure 2.4). Prefixes can also be used with the liter unit, so we can speak of milliliters (1/1,000th of a liter; mL) and kiloliters (1,000 L; kL).

FIGURE 2.4
The Liter
The SI unit of volume, the liter, is slightly larger than 1 quart.

Another definition of a liter is one-tenth of a meter cubed. Because one-tenth of a meter is 10 cm, then a liter is equal to 1,000 cm^3 (Figure 2.5). Because 1 L equals 1,000 mL, we conclude that 1 mL equals 1 cm^3; thus, these units are interchangeable.

FIGURE 2.5 The Size of 1 Liter
One liter equals 1,000 cm^3, so 1 cm^3 is the same as 1 mL.

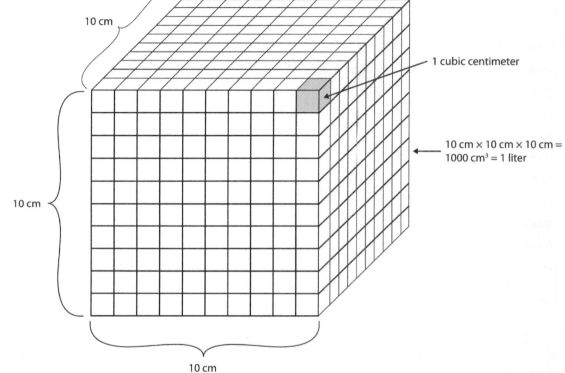

Units not only are multiplied together but also can be divided. For example, if you are traveling at one meter for every second of time elapsed, your velocity is 1 meter per second, or 1 m/s. The word *per* implies division, so velocity is determined by dividing a distance quantity by a time quantity. Other units for velocity include kilometers per hour (km/h) or even micrometers per nanosecond (μm/ns). Later, we will see other derived units that can be expressed as fractions.

Example 2

1. A human hair has a diameter of about 6.0×10^{-5} m. Suggest an appropriate unit for this measurement and write the diameter of a human hair in terms of that unit.
2. What is the velocity of a car if it travels 25 m in 5.0 s?

Solution

1. The scientific notation 10^{-5} is close to 10^{-6}, which defines the micro- prefix. Let us use micrometers as the unit for hair diameter. The number 6.0×10^{-5} can be written as 60×10^{-6}, and a micrometer is 10^{-6} m, so the diameter of a human hair is about 60 μm.
2. If velocity is defined as a distance quantity divided by a time quantity, then velocity is 25 meters/5.0 seconds. Dividing the numbers gives us 25/5.0 = 5.0, and dividing the units gives us meters/second, or m/s. The velocity is 5.0 m/s.

Test Yourself

1. Express the volume of an Olympic-sized swimming pool, 2,500,000 L, in more appropriate units.

2. A common garden snail moves about 6.1 m in 30 min. What is its velocity in meters per minute (m/min)?

Answers

1. 2.5 ML

2. 0.203 m/min

Key Takeaways

- Numbers tell "how much," and units tell "of what."
- Chemistry uses a set of fundamental units and derived units based on the SI system of units.
- Chemistry uses a set of prefixes that represent multiples or fractions of units.
- Units can be multiplied and divided to generate new units for quantities.

Exercises

1. Identify the unit in each quantity.

   a. 2 boxes of crayons

   b. 3.5 grams of gold

2. Identify the unit in each quantity.

   a. 32 oz of cheddar cheese

   b. 0.045 cm^3 of water

3. Identify the unit in each quantity.

   a. 9.58 s (the current world record in the 100 m dash)

   b. 6.16 m (the current world record in the pole vault)

4. Identify the unit in each quantity.

   a. 2 dozen eggs

   b. 2.4 km/s (the escape velocity of the moon, which is the velocity you need at the surface to escape the moon's gravity)

5. Indicate what multiplier each prefix represents.

   a. k

   b. m

   c. M

6. Indicate what multiplier each prefix represents.

   a. c

   b. G

   c. μ

7. Give the prefix that represents each multiplier.

   a. 1/1,000th ×

   b. 1,000 ×

   c. 1,000,000,000 ×

8. Give the prefix that represents each multiplier.

   a. 1/1,000,000,000th ×

b. 1/100th ×

c. 1,000,000 ×

9. Complete the following table with the missing information.

Unit	Abbreviation
kilosecond	
	mL
	Mg
centimeter	

10. Complete the following table with the missing information.

Unit	Abbreviation
kilometer per second	
second	
	cm^3
	μL
nanosecond	

11. Express each quantity in a more appropriate unit. There may be more than one acceptable answer.

a. 3.44×10^{-6} s

b. 3,500 L

c. 0.045 m

12. Express each quantity in a more appropriate unit. There may be more than one acceptable answer.

a. 0.000066 m/s (Hint: you need consider only the unit in the numerator.)

b. 4.66×10^6 s

c. 7,654 L

13. Express each quantity in a more appropriate unit. There may be more than one acceptable answer.

a. 43,600 mL

b. 0.0000044 m

c. 1,438 ms

14. Express each quantity in a more appropriate unit. There may be more than one acceptable answer.

a. 0.000000345 m^3

b. 47,000,000 mm^3

c. 0.00665 L

15. Multiplicative prefixes are used for other units as well, such as computer memory. The basic unit of computer memory is the byte (b). What is the unit for one million bytes?

16. You may have heard the terms *microscale* or *nanoscale* to represent the sizes of small objects. What units of length do you think are useful at these scales? What fractions of the fundamental unit of length are these units?

17. Acceleration is defined as a change in velocity per time. Propose a unit for acceleration in terms of the fundamental SI units.

18. Density is defined as the mass of an object divided by its volume. Propose a unit of density in terms of the fundamental SI units.

Answers

1.
   a. boxes of crayons
   b. grams of gold

3.
   a. seconds
   b. meters

5.
   a. 1,000 ×
   b. 1/1,000 ×
   c. 1,000,000 ×

7.
   a. milli-
   b. kilo-
   c. giga-

9.

Unit	Abbreviation
kilosecond	ks
milliliter	mL
megagram	Mg
centimeter	cm

11.
   a. 3.44 μs
   b. 3.5 kL
   c. 4.5 cm

13.
   a. 43.6 L
   b. 4.4 μm
   c. 1.438 s

15. megabytes (Mb)

17. meters/second^2

2.3 Significant Figures

Learning Objectives

1. Apply the concept of significant figures to limit a measurement to the proper number of digits.
2. Recognize the number of significant figures in a given quantity.
3. Limit mathematical results to the proper number of significant figures.

If you use a calculator to evaluate the expression 337/217, you will get the following:

$$\frac{337}{217} = 1.55299539171\ldots$$

and so on for many more digits. Although this answer is correct, it is somewhat presumptuous. You start with two values that each have three digits, and the answer has *twelve* digits? That does not make much sense.

Consider using a ruler to measure the width of an object, as shown in Figure 2.6. The object is definitely more than 1 cm long, so we know that the first digit in our measurement is 1. We see by counting the tick marks on the ruler that the object is at least three ticks after the 1. If each tick represents 0.1 cm, then we know the object is at least 1.3 cm wide. But our ruler does not have any more ticks between the 0.3 and the 0.4 marks, so we can't know exactly how much the next decimal place is. But with a practiced eye we can estimate it. Let us estimate it as about six-tenths of the way between the third and fourth tick marks, which estimates our hundredths place as 6, so we identify a measurement of 1.36 cm for the width of the object.

FIGURE 2.6 Expressing Width
What is the proper way to express the width of this object?

Does it make any sense to try to report a thousandths place for the measurement? No, it doesn't; we are not exactly sure of the hundredths place (after all, it was an estimate only), so it would be fruitless to estimate a thousandths place. Our best measurement, then, stops at the hundredths place, and we report 1.36 cm as proper measurement.

significant figures

The limit of the number of places a measurement can be properly expressed with.

This concept of reporting the proper number of digits in a measurement or a calculation is called **significant figures**. Significant figures (sometimes called significant digits) represent the limits of what values of a measurement or a calculation we are sure of. The convention for a measurement is that the quantity reported should be all known values and the first estimated value. The conventions for calculations are discussed as follows.

Example 3

Use each diagram to report a measurement to the proper number of significant figures.

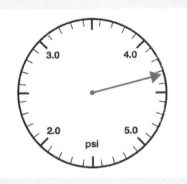

1.

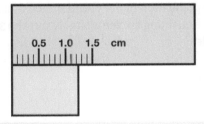

2.

Solution

1. The arrow is between 4.0 and 5.0, so the measurement is at least 4.0. The arrow is between the third and fourth small tick marks, so it's at least 0.3. We will have to estimate the last place. It looks like about one-third of the way across the space, so let us estimate the hundredths place as 3. Combining the digits, we have a measurement of 4.33 psi (psi stands for "pounds per square inch" and is a unit of pressure). We say that the measurement is reported to three significant figures.

2. The rectangle is at least 1.0 cm wide but certainly not 2.0 cm wide, so the first significant digit is 1. The rectangle's width is past the second tick mark but not the third; if each tick mark represents 0.1, then the rectangle is at least 0.2 in the next significant digit. We have to estimate the next place because there are no markings to guide us. It appears to be about halfway between 0.2 and 0.3, so we will estimate the next place to be a 5. Thus, the measured width of the rectangle is 1.25 cm. Again, the measurement is reported to three significant figures.

Test Yourself

What would be the reported width of this rectangle?

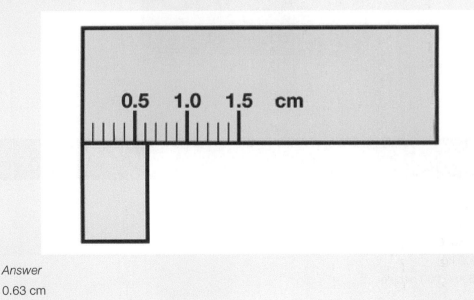

Answer

0.63 cm

In many cases, you will be given a measurement. How can you tell by looking what digits are significant? For example, the reported population of the United States is 328,000,000. Does that mean that it is *exactly* three hundred twenty-eight million, or is some estimation occurring?

The following conventions dictate which numbers in a reported measurement are significant and which are not significant:

1. Any nonzero digit is significant.

2. Any zeros between nonzero digits (i.e., embedded zeros) are significant.

3. Zeros at the end of a number without a decimal point (i.e., trailing zeros) are not significant; they serve only to put the significant digits in the correct positions. However, zeros at the end of any number with a decimal point are significant.

4. Zeros at the beginning of a decimal number (i.e., leading zeros) are not significant; again, they serve only to put the significant digits in the correct positions.

So, by these rules, the population figure of the United States has only three significant figures: the 3, the 2, and the 8. The remaining six zeros simply put the 328 in the millions position. (See Figure 2.7 for another example.)

FIGURE 2.7 Significant Figures
How many of the numbers in this display are actually significant?

Source: © Thinkstock

Example 4

Give the number of significant figures in each measurement.

1. 36.7 m
2. 0.006606 s
3. 2,002 kg
4. 306,490,000 people

Solution

1. By rule 1, all nonzero digits are significant, so this measurement has three significant figures.
2. By rule 4, the first three zeros are not significant but by rule 2 the zero between the sixes is; therefore, this number has four significant figures.
3. By rule 2, the two zeros between the twos are significant, so this measurement has four significant figures.
4. The four trailing zeros in the number are not significant, but the other five numbers are, so this number has five significant figures.

Test Yourself

Give the number of significant figures in each measurement.

1. 0.000601 m
2. 65.080 kg

Answers

1. three significant figures
2. five significant figures

How are significant figures handled in calculations? It depends on what type of calculation is being performed. If the calculation is an addition or a subtraction, the rule is as follows: limit the reported answer to the rightmost column that all numbers have significant figures in common. For example, if you were to add 1.2 and 4.71, we note that the first number stops its significant figures in the tenths column, while the second number stops its significant figures in the hundredths column. We therefore limit our answer to the tenths column.

1.2
4.41
5.61

↑ limit final answer to the tenths column: 5.6

We drop the last digit—the 1—because it is not significant to the final answer.

The dropping of positions in sums and differences brings up the topic of rounding. Although there are several conventions, in this text we will adopt the following rule: the final answer should be rounded up if the first dropped digit is 5 or greater and rounded down if the first dropped digit is less than 5.

77.2
10.46
87.66

↑ limit final answer to the tenths column and round up: 87.7

Example 5

Express the final answer to the proper number of significant figures.

1. 101.2 + 18.702 = ?
2. 202.88 − 1.013 = ?

Solution

1. If we use a calculator to add these two numbers, we would get 119.902. However, most calculators do not understand significant figures, and we need to limit the final answer to the tenths place. Thus, we drop the 02 and report a final answer of 119.9 (rounding down).
2. A calculator would answer 201.867. However, we have to limit our final answer to the hundredths place. Because the first number being dropped is 7, which is greater than 7, we round up and report a final answer of 201.87.

Test Yourself

Express the answer for 3.445 + 90.83 – 72.4 to the proper number of significant figures.

Answer

21.9

If the operations being performed are multiplication or division, the rule is as follows: limit the answer to the number of significant figures that the data value with the *least* number of significant figures has. So if we are dividing 23 by 448, which have two and three significant figures each, we should limit the final reported answer to two significant figures (the lesser of two and three significant figures):

$$\frac{23}{448} = 0.051339286... = 0.051$$

The same rounding rules apply in multiplication and division as they do in addition and subtraction.

Example 6

Express the final answer to the proper number of significant figures.

1. 76.4 × 180.4 = ?
2. 934.9 ÷ 0.00455 = ?

Solution

1. The first number has three significant figures, while the second number has four significant figures. Therefore, we limit our final answer to three significant figures: 76.4 × 180.4 = 13,782.56 = 13,800.
2. The first number has four significant figures, while the second number has three significant figures. Therefore we limit our final answer to three significant figures: 934.9 ÷ 0.00455 = 205,472.5275... = 205,000.

Test Yourself

Express the final answer to the proper number of significant figures.

1. 22.4 × 8.314 = ?
2. 1.381 ÷ 6.02 = ?

Answers

1. 186
2. 0.229

As you have probably realized by now, the biggest issue in determining the number of significant figures in a value is the zero. Is the zero significant or not? One way to unambiguously determine whether a zero is significant or not is to write a number in scientific notation. Scientific notation will include zeros in the coefficient of the number *only if they are significant*. Thus, the number 8.666×10^6 has four significant figures. However, the number 8.6660×10^6 has five significant figures. That last zero is significant; if it were not, it would not be written in the coefficient. So when in doubt about expressing the number of significant figures in a quantity, use scientific notation and include the number of zeros that are truly significant.

Key Takeaways

- Significant figures in a quantity indicate the number of known values plus one place that is estimated.
- There are rules for which numbers in a quantity are significant and which are not significant.
- In calculations involving addition and subtraction, limit significant figures based on the right-most place that all values have in common.
- In calculations involving multiplication and division, limit significant figures to the least number of significant figures in all the data values.

Exercises

1. Express each measurement to the correct number of significant figures.

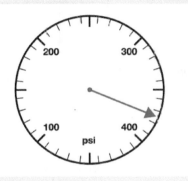

   a.

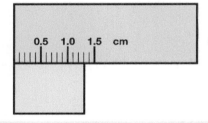

   b.

2. Express each measurement to the correct number of significant figures.

a.

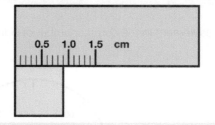

b.

3. How many significant figures do these numbers have?

   a. 23

   b. 23.0

   c. 0.00023

   d. 0.0002302

4. How many significant figures do these numbers have?

   a. 5.44×10^8

   b. 1.008×10^{-5}

   c. 43.09

   d. 0.0000001381

5. How many significant figures do these numbers have?

   a. 765,890

   b. 765,890.0

   c. 1.2000×10^5

   d. 0.0005060

6. How many significant figures do these numbers have?

   a. 0.009

   b. 0.0000009

   c. 65,444

   d. 65,040

7. Compute and express each answer with the proper number of significant figures, rounding as necessary.

   a. 56.0 + 3.44 = ?

   b. 0.00665 + 1.004 = ?

   c. 45.99 − 32.8 = ?

   d. 45.99 − 32.8 + 75.02 = ?

8. Compute and express each answer with the proper number of significant figures, rounding as necessary.

    a. 1.005 + 17.88 = ?

    b. 56,700 − 324 = ?

    c. 405,007 − 123.3 = ?

    d. 55.5 + 66.66 − 77.777 = ?

9. Compute and express each answer with the proper number of significant figures, rounding as necessary.

    a. 56.7 × 66.99 = ?

    b. 1.000 ÷ 77 = ?

    c. 1.000 ÷ 77.0 = ?

    d. 6.022 × 1.89 = ?

10. Compute and express each answer with the proper number of significant figures, rounding as necessary.

    a. 0.000440 × 17.22 = ?

    b. 203,000 ÷ 0.044 = ?

    c. 67 × 85.0 × 0.0028 = ?

    d. 999,999 ÷ 3,310 = ?

11. a. Write the number 87,449 in scientific notation with four significant figures.

    b. Write the number 0.000066600 in scientific notation with five significant figures.

12. a. Write the number 306,000,000 in scientific notation to the proper number of significant figures.

    b. Write the number 0.0000558 in scientific notation with two significant figures.

13. Perform each calculation and limit each answer to three significant figures

    a. 67,883 × 0.004321 = ?

    b. $(9.67 \times 10^3) \times 0.0055087 = ?$

14. Perform each calculation and limit each answer to four significant figures.

    a. 18,900 × 76.33 ÷ 0.00336 = ?

    b. 0.77604 ÷ 76,003 × 8.888 = ?

Answers

1. a. 375 psi
   b. 1.30 cm
2. a. 32.5 psi
   b. 0.91 cm
3. a. two
   b. three
   c. two
   d. four
4. a. three
   b. four
   c. four
   d. four
5. a. five
   b. seven
   c. five
   d. four

6. a. one
    b. one
    c. five
    d. four

7. a. 59.4
    b. 1.011
    c. 13.2
    d. 88.2

8. a. 18.89
    b. 56,400
    c. 404,884
    d. 44.4

9. a. 3.80×10^3
    b. 0.013
    c. 0.0130
    d. 11.4

10. a. 0.00758
    b. 4,600,000
    c. 16
    d. 302

11. a. 8.745×10^4
    b. 6.6600×10^{-5}

12. a. 3.06×10^8
    b. 5.6×10^{-5}

13. a. 293
    b. 53.3

14. a. 4.29×10^8
    b. 9.075×10^{-5}

2.4 Converting Units

Learning Objective

1. Convert from one unit to another unit of the same type.

In Section 2, we showed some examples of how to replace initial units with other units of the same type to get a numerical value that is easier to comprehend. In this section, we will formalize the process.

Consider a simple example: how many feet are there in 4 yards? Most people will almost automatically answer that there are 12 feet in 4 yards. How did you make this determination? Well, if there are 3 feet in 1 yard and there are 4 yards, then there are 4 × 3 = 12 feet in 4 yards.

This is correct, of course, but it is informal. Let us formalize it in a way that can be applied more generally. We know that 1 yard (yd) equals 3 feet (ft):

$$1 \text{ yd} = 3 \text{ ft}$$

In math, this expression is called an *equality*. The rules of algebra say that you can change (i.e., multiply or divide or add or subtract) the equality (as long as you don't divide by zero) and the new expression will still be an equality. For example, if we divide both sides by 2, we get

$$\frac{1}{2}\text{yd} = \frac{3}{2}\text{ ft}$$

We see that one-half of a yard equals 3/2, or one and a half, feet—something we also know to be true, so the above equation is still an equality. Going back to the original equality, suppose we divide both sides of the equation by 1 yard (number *and* unit):

$$\frac{1 \text{ yd}}{1 \text{ yd}} = \frac{3 \text{ ft}}{1 \text{ yd}}$$

The expression is still an equality, by the rules of algebra. The left fraction equals 1. It has the same quantity in the numerator and the denominator, so it must equal 1. The quantities in the numerator and denominator cancel, both the number *and* the unit:

$$\frac{\cancel{1 \text{ yd}}}{\cancel{1 \text{ yd}}} = \frac{3 \text{ ft}}{1 \text{ yd}}$$

When everything cancels in a fraction, the fraction reduces to 1:

$$1 = \frac{3 \text{ ft}}{1 \text{ yd}}$$

We have an expression, $\frac{3 \text{ ft}}{1 \text{ yd}}$, that equals 1. This is a strange way to write 1, but it makes sense: 3 ft equal 1 yd, so the quantities in the numerator and denominator are the same quantity, just expressed with different units. The expression $\frac{3 \text{ ft}}{1 \text{ yd}}$ is called a **conversion factor**, and it is used to formally change the unit of a quantity into another unit. (The process of converting units in such a formal fashion is sometimes called *dimensional analysis* or the *factor label method*.)

> **conversion factor**
>
> A fraction that can be used to convert a quantity from one unit to another.

To see how this happens, let us start with the original quantity:

$$4 \text{ yd}$$

Now let us multiply this quantity by 1. When you multiply anything by 1, you don't change the value of the quantity. Rather than multiplying by just 1, let us write 1 as $\frac{3 \text{ ft}}{1 \text{ yd}}$:

$$4 \text{ yd} \times \frac{3 \text{ ft}}{1 \text{ yd}}$$

The 4 yd term can be thought of as $\frac{4 \text{ yd}}{1}$; that is, it can be thought of as a fraction with 1 in the denominator. We are essentially multiplying fractions. If the same thing appears in the numerator and denominator of a fraction, they cancel. In this case, what cancels is the unit *yard*:

$$4 \cancel{\text{ yd}} \times \frac{3 \text{ ft}}{1 \cancel{\text{ yd}}}$$

That is all that we can cancel. Now, multiply and divide all the numbers to get the final answer:

$$\frac{4 \times 3 \text{ ft}}{1} = \frac{12 \text{ ft}}{1} = 12 \text{ ft}$$

Again, we get an answer of 12 ft, just as we did originally. But in this case, we used a more formal procedure that is applicable to a variety of problems.

How many millimeters are in 14.66 m? To answer this, we need to construct a conversion factor between millimeters and meters and apply it correctly to the original quantity. We start with the definition of a millimeter, which is

$$1 \text{ mm} = 1/1{,}000 \text{ m}$$

The 1/1,000 is what the prefix *milli-* means. Most people are more comfortable working without fractions, so we will rewrite this equation by bringing the 1,000 into the numerator of the other side of the equation:

$$1{,}000 \text{ mm} = 1 \text{ m}$$

Now we construct a conversion factor by dividing one quantity into both sides. But now a question arises: which quantity do we divide by? It turns out that we have two choices, and the two choices will give us different conversion factors, both of which equal 1:

$$\frac{1{,}000 \text{ mm}}{1{,}000 \text{ mm}} = \frac{1 \text{ m}}{1{,}000 \text{ mm}} \quad \text{or} \quad \frac{1{,}000 \text{ mm}}{1 \text{ m}} = \frac{1 \text{ m}}{1 \text{ m}}$$

$$1 = \frac{1 \text{ m}}{1{,}000 \text{ mm}} \quad \text{or} \quad \frac{1{,}000 \text{ mm}}{1 \text{ m}} = 1$$

Which conversion factor do we use? The answer is based on *what unit you want to get rid of in your initial quantity*. The original unit of our quantity is meters, which we want to convert to millimeters. Because the original unit is assumed to be in the numerator, to get rid of it, we want the meter unit in the *denominator*; then they will cancel. Therefore, we will use the second conversion factor. Canceling units and performing the mathematics, we get

$$14.66 \ \cancel{\text{m}} \times \frac{1{,}000 \text{ mm}}{1 \ \cancel{\text{m}}} = 14{,}660 \text{ mm}$$

Note how m cancels, leaving mm, which is the unit of interest.

The ability to construct and apply proper conversion factors is a very powerful mathematical technique in chemistry. You need to master this technique if you are going to be successful in this and future courses.

Example 7

1. Convert 35.9 kL to liters.
2. Convert 555 nm to meters.

Solution

1. We will use the fact that 1 kL = 1,000 L. Of the two conversion factors that can be defined, the one that will work is $\frac{1,000 \text{ L}}{1 \text{ kL}}$. Applying this conversion factor, we get:

$$35.9 \text{ } \cancel{\text{kL}} \times \frac{1,000 \text{ L}}{1 \text{ } \cancel{\text{kL}}} = 35,900 \text{ L}$$

2. We will use the fact that 1 nm = 1/1,000,000,000 m, which we will rewrite as 1,000,000,000 nm = 1 m, or 10^9 nm = 1 m. Of the two possible conversion factors, the appropriate one has the nm unit in the denominator: $\frac{1 \text{ m}}{10^9 \text{ nm}}$. Applying this conversion factor, we get:

$$555 \text{ } \cancel{\text{nm}} \times \frac{1 \text{ m}}{10^9 \text{ } \cancel{\text{nm}}} = 0.000000555 \text{ m} = 5.55 \times 10^{-7} \text{ m}$$

In the final step, we expressed the answer in scientific notation.

Test Yourself

1. Convert 67.08 µL to liters.
2. Convert 56.8 m to kilometers.

Answers

1. 6.708×10^{-5} L
2. 5.68×10^{-2} km

What if we have a derived unit that is the product of more than one unit, such as m^2? Suppose we want to convert square meters to square centimeters? The key is to remember that m^2 means m × m, which means we have *two* meter units in our derived unit. That means we have to include *two* conversion factors, one for each appearance of the unit. For example, to convert 17.6 m^2 to square centimeters, we perform the conversion as follows:

$$17.6 \text{ m}^2 = 17.6 \left(\cancel{\text{m}} \times \cancel{\text{m}} \right) \times \frac{100 \text{ cm}}{1 \text{ } \cancel{\text{m}}} \times \frac{100 \text{ cm}}{1 \text{ } \cancel{\text{m}}} = 176,000 \text{ cm} \times \text{cm} = 1.76 \times 10^5 \text{ cm}^2$$

Example 8

How many cubic centimeters are in 0.883 m^3?

Solution

With an exponent of 3, we have three length units, so by extension we need to use three conversion factors between meters and centimeters. Thus, we have:

$$0.883 \text{ } \cancel{\text{m}^3} \times \frac{100 \text{ cm}}{1 \text{ } \cancel{\text{m}}} \times \frac{100 \text{ cm}}{1 \text{ } \cancel{\text{m}}} \times \frac{100 \text{ cm}}{1 \text{ } \cancel{\text{m}}} = 883,000 \text{ cm}^3 = 8.83 \times 10^5 \text{ cm}^3$$

You should demonstrate to yourself that the three meter units do indeed cancel.

Test Yourself

How many cubic millimeters are present in 0.0923 m^3?

Answer

9.23×10^7 mm^3

Suppose the unit you want to convert is in the denominator of a derived unit what then? Then, in the conversion factor, the unit you want to remove must be in the *numerator*. This will cancel with the original unit in the denominator and introduce a new unit in the denominator. The following example illustrates this situation.

Example 9

Convert 88.4 m/min to meters/second.

Solution

We want to change the unit in the denominator from minutes to seconds. Because there are 60 seconds in 1 minute (60 s = 1 min), we construct a conversion factor so that the unit we want to remove, minutes, is in the numerator: $\frac{1 \text{ min}}{60 \text{ s}}$. Apply and perform the math:

$$\frac{88.4 \text{ m}}{\cancel{\text{min}}} \times \frac{1 \cancel{\text{min}}}{60 \text{ s}} = 1.47 \text{ m/s}$$

Notice how the 88.4 automatically goes in the numerator. That's because any number can be thought of as being in the numerator of a fraction divided by 1.

Test Yourself

Convert 0.203 m/min to meters/second.

Answer

0.00338 m/s or 3.38×10^{-3} m/s

FIGURE 2.8
How Fast Is Fast?
A common garden snail moves at a rate of about 0.2 m/min, which is about 0.003 m/s, which is 3 mm/s!

Source: © Thinkstock

Sometimes there will be a need to convert from one unit with one numerical prefix to another unit with a different numerical prefix. How do we handle those conversions? Well, you could memorize the conversion factors that interrelate all numerical prefixes. Or you can go the easier route: first convert the quantity to the base unit, the unit with no numerical prefix, using the definition of the original prefix. Then convert the quantity in the base unit to the desired unit using the definition of the second prefix. You can do the conversion in two separate steps or as one long algebraic step. For example, to convert 2.77 kg to milligrams:

$$2.77 \cancel{\text{kg}} \times \frac{1{,}000 \text{ g}}{1 \cancel{\text{kg}}} = 2{,}770 \text{ g} \quad \text{(convert to the base unit of grams)}$$

$$2{,}770 \cancel{\text{g}} \times \frac{1{,}000 \text{ mg}}{1 \cancel{\text{g}}} = 2{,}770{,}000 \text{ mg} = 2.77 \times 10^6 \text{ mg} \quad \text{(convert to desired unit)}$$

Alternatively, it can be done in a single multistep process:

$$2.77 \cancel{\text{kg}} \times \frac{1{,}000 \cancel{\text{g}}}{1 \cancel{\text{kg}}} \times \frac{1{,}000 \text{ mg}}{1 \cancel{\text{g}}} = 2{,}770{,}000 \text{ mg} = 2.77 \times 10^6 \text{ mg}$$

You get the same answer either way.

Example 10

How many nanoseconds are in 368.09 μs?

Solution

You can either do this as a one-step conversion from microseconds to nanoseconds or convert to the base unit first and then to the final desired unit. We will use the second method here, showing the two steps in a single line. Using the definitions of the prefixes *micro-* and *nano-*,

$$368.09 \ \mu s \times \frac{1 \ s}{1,000,000 \ \mu s} \times \frac{1,000,000,000 \ ns}{1 \ s} = 368,090 \ ns = 3.6809 \times 10^5 \ ns$$

Test Yourself

How many milliliters are in 607.8 kL?

Answer

6.078×10^8 mL

When considering the significant figures of a final numerical answer in a conversion, there is one important case where a number does not impact the number of significant figures in a final answer—the so-called **exact number**. An exact number is a number from a defined relationship, not a measured one. For example, the prefix *kilo-* means 1,000—*exactly* 1,000, no more or no less. Thus, in constructing the conversion factor

$$\frac{1,000 \ g}{1 \ kg}$$

neither the 1,000 nor the 1 enter into our consideration of significant figures. The numbers in the numerator and denominator are defined exactly by what the prefix *kilo-* means. Another way of thinking about it is that these numbers can be thought of as having an infinite number of significant figures, such as

$$\frac{1,000.0000000000 \dots \ g}{1.0000000000 \dots \ kg}$$

The other numbers in the calculation will determine the number of significant figures in the final answer.

exact number

A number from a defined relationship that technically has an infinite number of significant figures.

Example 11

A rectangular plot in a garden has the dimensions 36.7 cm by 128.8 cm. What is the area of the garden plot in square meters? Express your answer in the proper number of significant figures.

Solution

Area is defined as the product of the two dimensions, which we then have to convert to square meters and express our final answer to the correct number of significant figures, which in this case will be three.

$$36.7 \ cm \times 128.8 \ cm \times \frac{1 \ m}{100 \ cm} \times \frac{1 \ m}{100 \ cm} = 0.472696 \ m^2 = 0.473 \ m^2$$

The 1 and 100 in the conversion factors do not affect the determination of significant figures because they are exact numbers, defined by the centi- prefix.

Test Yourself

What is the volume of a block in cubic meters whose dimensions are 2.1 cm × 34.0 cm × 118 cm?

Answer

0.0084 m^3

Chemistry Is Everywhere: The Gimli Glider

On July 23, 1983, an Air Canada Boeing 767 jet had to glide to an emergency landing at Gimli Industrial Park Airport in Gimli, Manitoba, because it unexpectedly ran out of fuel during flight. There was no loss of life in the course of the emergency landing, only some minor injuries associated in part with the evacuation of the craft after landing. For the remainder of its operational life (the plane was retired in 2008), the aircraft was nicknamed "the Gimli Glider."

The Gimli Glider is the Boeing 767 that ran out of fuel and glided to safety at Gimli Airport. The aircraft ran out of fuel because of confusion over the units used to express the amount of fuel.

Source: By Aca-767-C-GAUN-604-080201-01-8.jpg: Akradeckiderivative work: Altair78 (Aca-767-C-GAUN-604-080201-01-8.jpg) [CC BY-SA 3.0 (https://creativecommons.org/ licenses/by-sa/3.0) or GFDL (http://www.gnu.org/copyleft/fdl.html)], via Wikimedia Commons; https://commons.wikimedia.org/wiki/File:Air_Canada_767_C-GAUN_Gimli_ Glider.jpg

The 767 took off from Montreal on its way to Ottawa, ultimately heading for Edmonton, Canada. About halfway through the flight, all the engines on the plane began to shut down because of a lack of fuel. When the final engine cut off, all electricity (which was generated by the engines) was lost; the plane became, essentially, a powerless glider. Captain Robert Pearson was an experienced glider pilot, although he had never flown a glider the size of a 767. First Officer Maurice Quintal quickly determined that the aircraft would not be able make it to Winnipeg, the next large airport. He suggested his old Royal Air Force base at Gimli Station, one of whose runways was still being used as a community airport. Between the efforts of the pilots and the flight crew, they managed to get the airplane safely on the ground (although with buckled landing gear) and all passengers off safely.

What happened? At the time, Canada was transitioning from the older English system to the metric system. The Boeing 767s were the first aircraft whose gauges were calibrated in the metric system of units (liters and kilograms) rather than the English system of units (gallons and pounds). Thus, when the fuel gauge read 22,300, the gauge meant kilograms, but the ground crew mistakenly fueled the plane with 22,300 *pounds* of fuel. This ended up being just less than half of the fuel needed to make the trip, causing the engines to quit about halfway to Ottawa. Quick thinking and extraordinary skill saved the lives of 61 passengers and 8 crew members—an incident that would not have occurred if people were watching their units.

Key Takeaways

- Units can be converted to other units using the proper conversion factors.
- Conversion factors are constructed from equalities that relate two different units.
- Conversions can be a single step or multistep.
- Unit conversion is a powerful mathematical technique in chemistry that must be mastered.
- Exact numbers do not affect the determination of significant figures.

Exercises

1. Write the two conversion factors that exist between the two given units.
   a. milliliters and liters
   b. microseconds and seconds
   c. kilometers and meters

2. Write the two conversion factors that exist between the two given units.
   a. kilograms and grams
   b. milliseconds and seconds
   c. centimeters and meters

3. Perform the following conversions.
   a. 5.4 km to meters
   b. 0.665 m to millimeters
   c. 0.665 m to kilometers

4. Perform the following conversions.
   a. 90.6 mL to liters
   b. 0.00066 ML to liters
   c. 750 L to kiloliters

5. Perform the following conversions.
   a. 17.8 µg to grams
   b. 7.22×10^2 kg to grams
   c. 0.00118 g to nanograms

6. Perform the following conversions.
   a. 833 ns to seconds
   b. 5.809 s to milliseconds
   c. 2.77×10^6 s to megaseconds

7. Perform the following conversions.
   a. 9.44 m^2 to square centimeters
   b. 3.44×10^8 mm^3 to cubic meters

8. Perform the following conversions.

    a. 0.00444 cm^3 to cubic meters

    b. 8.11 × 10^2 m^2 to square nanometers

9. Why would it be inappropriate to convert square centimeters to cubic meters?

10. Why would it be inappropriate to convert from cubic meters to cubic seconds?

11. Perform the following conversions.

    a. 45.0 m/min to meters/second

    b. 0.000444 m/s to micrometers/second

    c. 60.0 km/h to kilometers/second

12. Perform the following conversions.

    a. 3.4 × 10^2 cm/s to centimeters/minute

    b. 26.6 mm/s to millimeters/hour

    c. 13.7 kg/L to kilograms/milliliters

13. Perform the following conversions.

    a. 0.674 kL to milliliters

    b. 2.81 × 10^{12} mm to kilometers

    c. 94.5 kg to milligrams

14. Perform the following conversions.

    a. 6.79 × 10^{-6} kg to micrograms

    b. 1.22 mL to kiloliters

    c. 9.508 × 10^{-9} ks to milliseconds

15. Perform the following conversions.

    a. 6.77 × 10^{14} ms to kiloseconds

    b. 34,550,000 cm to kilometers

16. Perform the following conversions.

    a. 4.701 × 10^{15} mL to kiloliters

    b. 8.022 × 10^{-11} ks to microseconds

17. Perform the following conversions. Note that you will have to convert units in both the numerator and the denominator.

    a. 88 ft/s to miles/hour (Hint: use 5,280 ft = 1 mi.)

    b. 0.00667 km/h to meters/second

18. Perform the following conversions. Note that you will have to convert units in both the numerator and the denominator.

    a. 3.88 × 10^2 mm/s to kilometers/hour

    b. 1.004 kg/L to grams/milliliter

19. What is the area in square millimeters of a rectangle whose sides are 2.44 cm × 6.077 cm? Express the answer to the proper number of significant figures.

20. What is the volume in cubic centimeters of a cube with sides of 0.774 m? Express the answer to the proper number of significant figures.

21. The formula for the area of a triangle is 1/2 × base × height. What is the area of a triangle in square centimeters if its base is 1.007 m and its height is 0.665 m? Express the answer to the proper number of significant figures.

22. The formula for the area of a triangle is 1/2 × base × height. What is the area of a triangle in square meters if its base is 166 mm and its height is 930.0 mm? Express the answer to the proper number of significant figures.

Answers

1. a. $\dfrac{1{,}000 \text{ mL}}{1 \text{ L}}$ and $\dfrac{1 \text{ L}}{1{,}000 \text{ mL}}$

    b. $\dfrac{1{,}000{,}000 \text{ }\mu s}{1 \text{ s}}$ and $\dfrac{1 \text{ s}}{1{,}000{,}000 \text{ }\mu s}$

    c. $\dfrac{1{,}000 \text{ m}}{1 \text{ km}}$ and $\dfrac{1 \text{ km}}{1{,}000 \text{ m}}$

2. a. $\dfrac{1{,}000 \text{ g}}{1 \text{ kg}}$ and $\dfrac{1 \text{ kg}}{1{,}000 \text{ g}}$

    b. $\dfrac{1{,}000 \text{ ms}}{1 \text{ s}}$ and $\dfrac{1 \text{ s}}{1{,}000 \text{ ms}}$

    c. $\dfrac{100 \text{ cm}}{1 \text{ m}}$ and $\dfrac{1 \text{ m}}{100 \text{ cm}}$

3. a. 5,400 m

    b. 665 mm

    c. 6.65×10^{-4} km

4. a. 0.0906 L

    b. 660 L

    c. 0.75 kL

5. a. 1.78×10^{-5} g

    b. 7.22×10^{5} g

    c. 1.18×10^{6} ng

6. a. 8.33×10^{-7} s

    b. 5.809×10^{3} ms

    c. 2.77 Ms

7. a. 94,400 cm^2

    b. 0.344 m^3

8. a. 4.44×10^{-9} m^3

    b. 8.11×10^{20} nm^2

9. One is a unit of area, and the other is a unit of volume.

10. One is a unit of volume, and the other is a unit of time cubed.

11. a. 0.75 m/s

    b. 444 µm/s

    c. 1.666×10^{-2} km/s

12. a. 2.04×10^{4} cm/min

    b. 95,760 mm/h

    c. 0.0137 kg/mL

13. a. 674,000 mL

    b. 2.81×10^{6} km

    c. 9.45×10^{7} mg

14. a. 6.79×10^{3} µg

    b. 1.22×10^{-6} kL

    c. 9.508×10^{-3} ms

15. a. 6.77×10^{8} ks

    b. 345.5 km

16. a. 4.701×10^9 kL
    b. 8.022×10^{-2} µs
17. a. 6.0×10^1 mi/h
    b. 0.00185 m/s
18. a. 1.3968 km/h
    b. 1.004 g/mL
19. 1.48×10^3 mm^2
20. 4.64×10^5 cm^3
21. 3.35×10^3 cm^2
22. 7.72×10^{-2} m^2

2.5 Other Units: Temperature, Energy, and Density

Learning Objectives

1. Learn about the various temperature scales that are commonly used in chemistry.
2. Define density and use it as a conversion factor.

temperature

A measure of the average amount of kinetic energy a system contains.

degree

The unit of temperature scales.

There are other units in chemistry that are important, and we will cover others in the course of the entire book. One of the fundamental quantities in science is temperature. **Temperature** is a measure of the average amount of energy of motion, or *kinetic energy*, a system contains. Temperatures are expressed using scales that use units called **degrees**, and there are several temperature scales in use. In the United States, the commonly used temperature scale is the *Fahrenheit scale* (symbolized by °F and spoken as "degrees Fahrenheit"). On this scale, the freezing point of liquid water (the temperature at which liquid water turns to solid ice) is 32°F, and the boiling point of water (the temperature at which liquid water turns to steam) is 212°F.

Science also uses other scales to express temperature. The Celsius scale (symbolized by °C and spoken as "degrees Celsius") is a temperature scale where 0°C is the freezing point of water and 100°C is the boiling point of water; the scale is divided into 100 divisions between these two landmarks and extended higher and lower. By comparing the Fahrenheit and Celsius scales, a conversion between the two scales can be determined:

$$°C = (°F - 32) \times \tfrac{5}{9}$$
$$°F = \left(°C \times \tfrac{9}{5}\right) + 32$$

Using these formulas, we can convert from one temperature scale to another. The number 32 in the formulas is exact and does not count in significant figure determination.

Example 12

1. What is 98.6°F in degrees Celsius?
2. What is 25.0°C in degrees Fahrenheit?

Solution

1. Using the first formula from above, we have:

$$°C = (98.6 - 32) \times \frac{5}{9} = 66.6 \times \frac{5}{9} = 37.0\,°C$$

2. Using the second formula from above, we have:

$$°F = \left(25.0 \times \frac{9}{5}\right) + 32 = 45.0 + 32 = 77.0\,°F$$

Test Yourself

1. Convert 0°F to degrees Celsius.
2. Convert 212°C to degrees Fahrenheit.

Answers

1. −17.8°C
2. 414°F

The fundamental unit of temperature (another fundamental unit of science, bringing us to four) in SI is the **kelvin** (K). The Kelvin temperature scale (note that the name of the scale capitalizes the word *Kelvin*, but the unit itself is lowercase) uses degrees that are the same size as the Celsius degree, but the numerical scale is shifted up by 273.15 units. That is, the conversion between the Kelvin and Celsius scales is as follows:

kelvin
The fundamental unit of temperature in SI.

$$K = °C + 273.15$$

$$°C = K - 273.15$$

For most purposes, it is acceptable to use 273 instead of 273.15. Note that the Kelvin scale does not use the word *degrees*; a temperature of 295 K is spoken of as "two hundred ninety-five kelvins" and not "two hundred ninety-five degrees Kelvin."

The reason that the Kelvin scale is defined this way is because there exists a minimum possible temperature called **absolute zero**. The Kelvin temperature scale is set so that 0 K is absolute zero, and temperature is counted upward from there. Normal room temperature is about 295 K, as seen in the following example.

absolute zero
The minimum possible temperature, labeled 0 K (zero kelvins).

Example 13

If normal room temperature is 72.0°F, what is room temperature in degrees Celsius and kelvins?

Solution

First, we use the formula to determine the temperature in degrees Celsius:

$$°C = (72.0 - 32) \times \frac{5}{9} = 40.0 \times \frac{5}{9} = 22.2\,°C$$

Then we use the appropriate formula above to determine the temperature in the Kelvin scale:

$$K = 22.2\,°C + 273.15 = 295.4\ K$$

So, room temperature is about 295 K.

Test Yourself

What is 98.6°F on the Kelvin scale?

Answer

310.2 K

Figure 2.9 compares the three temperature scales. Note that science uses the Celsius and Kelvin scales almost exclusively; virtually no practicing chemist expresses laboratory-measured temperatures with the Fahrenheit scale. (In fact, the United States is one of the few countries in the world that still uses the Fahrenheit scale on a daily basis. The other two countries are Liberia and Myanmar [formerly Burma]. People driving near the borders of Canada or Mexico may pick up local radio stations on the other side of the border that express the daily weather in degrees Celsius, so don't get confused by their weather reports.)

FIGURE 2.9 Fahrenheit, Celsius, and Kelvin Temperatures
A comparison of the three temperature scales.

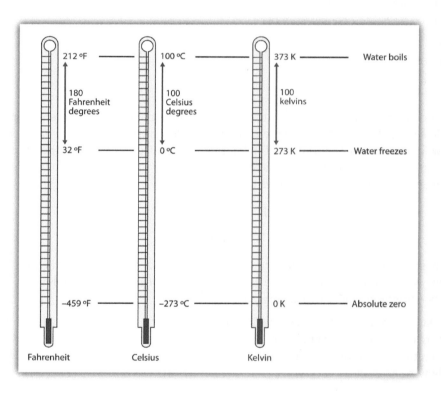

energy

The ability to do work or change temperature.

Energy is the ability to do work or to change temperature or phase. An old unit of energy which is still used in come circumstances is the *calorie*, which was originally defined as the amount of energy needed to raise the temperature of 1 gram of water by 1°C. A preferred unit of energy is the *joule* (abbreviation J). There are about 4 joules per calorie, so it is easy to convert from one energy unit to another. Energy will be an issue in several topics discussed in this book, and a later chapter will focus on how energy impacts chemistry.

density

A physical property defined as a substance's mass divided by its volume.

Density is a physical property that is defined as a substance's mass divided by its volume:

$$\text{density} = \frac{\text{mass}}{\text{volume}} \text{ or } d = \frac{m}{V}$$

Density is usually a measured property of a substance, so its numerical value affects the significant figures in a calculation. Notice that density is defined in terms of two dissimilar units, mass and volume. That means that density overall has derived units, just like velocity. Common units for density include g/mL, g/cm^3, g/L, kg/L, and even kg/m^3. Densities for some common substances are listed in Table 2.2.

TABLE 2.2 Densities of Some Common Substances

Substance	Density (g/mL or g/cm^3)
water	1.0
gold	19.3
mercury	13.6
air	0.0012
cork	0.22–0.26
aluminum	2.7
iron	7.87

Because of how it is defined, density can act as a conversion factor for switching between units of mass and volume. For example, suppose you have a sample of aluminum that has a volume of 7.88 cm^3. How can you determine what mass of aluminum you have without measuring it? You can use the volume to calculate it. If you multiply the given volume by the known density (from Table 2.2), the volume units will cancel and leave you with mass units, telling you the mass of the sample:

$$7.88 \ \cancel{cm^3} \times \frac{2.7 \ g}{\cancel{cm^3}} = 21 \ g \text{ of aluminum}$$

where we have limited our answer to two significant figures.

Example 14

What is the mass of 44.6 mL of mercury?

Solution

Use the density from Table 2.2 as a conversion factor to go from volume to mass:

$$44.6 \ \cancel{mL} \times \frac{13.6 \ g}{\cancel{mL}} = 607 \ g$$

The mass of the mercury is 607 g.

Test Yourself

What is the mass of 25.0 cm^3 of iron?

Answer

197 g

Density can also be used as a conversion factor to convert mass to volume—but care must be taken. We have already demonstrated that the number that goes with density normally goes in the numerator when density is written as a fraction. Take the density of gold, for example:

$$d = 19.3 \ g/mL = \frac{19.3 \ g}{mL}$$

Although this was not previously pointed out, it can be assumed that there is a 1 in the denominator:

$$d = 19.\,3 \text{ g/mL} = \frac{19.3 \text{ g}}{1 \text{ mL}}$$

That is, the density value tells us that we have 19.3 grams for every 1 milliliter of volume, and the 1 is an exact number. When we want to use density to convert from mass to volume, the numerator and denominator of density need to be switched—that is, we must take the *reciprocal* of the density. In so doing, we move not only the units but also the numbers:

$$\frac{1}{d} = \frac{1 \text{ mL}}{19.3 \text{ g}}$$

This reciprocal density is still a useful conversion factor, but now the mass unit will cancel and the volume unit will be introduced. Thus, if we want to know the volume of 45.9 g of gold, we would set up the conversion as follows:

$$45.\,9 \text{ g} \times \frac{1 \text{ mL}}{19.3 \text{ g}} = 2.\,38 \text{ mL}$$

Note how the mass units cancel, leaving the volume unit, which is what we're looking for.

Example 15

A cork stopper from a bottle of wine has a mass of 3.78 g. If the density of cork is 0.22 g/cm^3, what is the volume of the cork?

Solution

To use density as a conversion factor, we need to take the reciprocal so that the mass unit of density is in the denominator. Taking the reciprocal, we find:

$$\frac{1}{d} = \frac{1 \text{ cm}^3}{0.22 \text{ g}}$$

We can use this expression as the conversion factor. So:

$$3.\,78 \text{ g} \times \frac{1 \text{ cm}^3}{0.22 \text{ g}} = 17.\,2 \text{ cm}^3$$

Test Yourself

What is the volume of 3.78 g of gold?

Answer

0.196 cm^3

Care must be used with density as a conversion factor. Make sure the mass units are the same, or the volume units are the same, before using density to convert to a different unit. Often, the unit of the given quantity must first be converted to the appropriate unit before applying density as a conversion factor.

Food and Drink App: Cooking Temperatures

Because degrees Fahrenheit is the common temperature scale in the United States, kitchen appliances, such as ovens, are calibrated in that scale. A cool oven may be only 150°F, while a cake may be baked at 350°F and a chicken roasted at 400°F. The broil setting on many ovens is 500°F, which is typically the highest temperature setting on a household oven.

People who live at high altitudes, typically 2,000 ft above sea level or higher, are sometimes urged to use slightly different cooking instructions on some products, such as cakes and bread, because water boils at a lower temperature the higher in altitude you go, meaning that foods cook slower. For example, in Cleveland water typically boils at 212°F (100°C), but in Denver, the Mile-High City, water boils at about 200°F (93.3°C), which can significantly lengthen cooking times. Good cooks need to be aware of this.

At the other end is pressure cooking. A pressure cooker is a closed vessel that allows steam to build up additional pressure, which increases the temperature at which water boils. A good pressure cooker can get to temperatures as high as 252°F (122°C); at these temperatures, food cooks much faster than it normally would. Great care must be used with pressure cookers because of the high pressure and high temperature. (When a pressure cooker is used to sterilize medical instruments, it is called an *autoclave*.)

Other countries use the Celsius scale for everyday purposes. Therefore, oven dials in their kitchens are marked in degrees Celsius. It can be confusing for US cooks to use ovens abroad—a 425°F oven in the United States is equivalent to a 220°C oven in other countries. These days, many oven thermometers are marked with both temperature scales.

This oven thermometer shows both Fahrenheit (outer scale) and Celsius (inner scale) temperatures. Recipes for cooking food in an oven can use very different numbers, depending on the country you're in.

Source: © Thinkstock

Exercises

1. Perform the following conversions.
   a. 255°F to degrees Celsius
   b. −255°F to degrees Celsius

    c. 50.0°C to degrees Fahrenheit

    d. −50.0°C to degrees Fahrenheit

2. Perform the following conversions.

    a. 1,065°C to degrees Fahrenheit

    b. −222°C to degrees Fahrenheit

    c. 400.0°F to degrees Celsius

    d. 200.0°F to degrees Celsius

3. Perform the following conversions.

    a. 100.0°C to kelvins

    b. −100.0°C to kelvins

    c. 100 K to degrees Celsius

    d. 300 K to degrees Celsius

4. Perform the following conversions.

    a. 1,000.0 K to degrees Celsius

    b. 50.0 K to degrees Celsius

    c. 37.0°C to kelvins

    d. −37.0°C to kelvins

5. Convert 0 K to degrees Celsius. What is the significance of the temperature in degrees Celsius?

6. Convert 0 K to degrees Fahrenheit. What is the significance of the temperature in degrees Fahrenheit?

7. The hottest temperature ever recorded on the surface of the earth was 136°F in Libya in 1922. What is the temperature in degrees Celsius and in kelvins?

8. The coldest temperature ever recorded on the surface of the earth was −128.6°F in Vostok, Antarctica, in 1983. What is the temperature in degrees Celsius and in kelvins?

9. Give at least three possible units for density.

10. What are the units when density is inverted? Give three examples.

11. A sample of iron has a volume of 48.2 cm^3. What is its mass?

12. A sample of air has a volume of 1,015 mL. What is its mass?

13. The volume of hydrogen used by the *Hindenburg*, the German airship that exploded in New Jersey in 1937, was 2.000×10^8 L. If hydrogen gas has a density of 0.0899 g/L, what mass of hydrogen was used by the airship?

14. The volume of an Olympic-sized swimming pool is 2.50×10^9 cm^3. If the pool is filled with alcohol (d = 0.789 g/cm^3), what mass of alcohol is in the pool?

15. A typical engagement ring has 0.77 cm^3 of gold. What mass of gold is present?

16. A typical mercury thermometer has 0.039 mL of mercury in it. What mass of mercury is in the thermometer?

17. What is the volume of 100.0 g of lead if lead has a density of 11.34 g/cm^3?

18. What is the volume of 255.0 g of uranium if uranium has a density of 19.05 g/cm^3?

19. What is the volume in liters of 222 g of neon if neon has a density of 0.900 g/L?

20. What is the volume in liters of 20.5 g of sulfur hexafluoride if sulfur hexafluoride has a density of 6.164 g/L?

21. Which has the greater volume, 100.0 g of iron (d = 7.87 g/cm^3) or 75.0 g of gold (d = 19.3 g/cm^3)?

22. Which has the greater volume, 100.0 g of hydrogen gas (d = 0.0000899 g/cm^3) or 25.0 g of argon gas (d = 0.00178 g/cm^3)?

Answers

1. a. 124°C
   b. −159°C
   c. 122°F
   d. −58°F
2. a. 1,949°F
   b. −368°F
   c. 204°C
   d. 93°C
3. a. 373 K
   b. 173 K
   c. −173°C
   d. 27°C
4. a. 727°C
   b. −223°C
   c. 310 K
   d. 236 K
5. −273°C. This is the lowest possible temperature in degrees Celsius.
6. −459°F. This is the lowest possible temperature in degrees Fahrenheit.
7. 57.8°C; 331 K
8. −89°C; 184 K
9. g/mL, g/L, and kg/L (answers will vary)
10. L/g, mL/g, and L/kg (answers will vary)
11. 379 g
12. 1.2 g
13. 1.80×10^7 g
14. 1.97×10^9 g
15. 15 g
16. 0.53 g
17. 8.818 cm^3
18. 13.39 cm^3
19. 247 L
20. 3.33 L
21. The 100.0 g of iron has the greater volume.
22. The hydrogen has the larger volume.

2.6 End-of-Chapter Material

Additional Exercises

1. Evaluate 0.00000000552 × 0.0000000006188 and express the answer in scientific notation. You may have to rewrite the original numbers in scientific notation first.

2. Evaluate 333,999,500,000 ÷ 0.00000000003396 and express the answer in scientific notation. You may need to rewrite the original numbers in scientific notation first.

3. Express the number 6.022×10^{23} in standard notation.

4. Express the number 6.626×10^{-34} in standard notation.

5. When powers of 10 are multiplied together, the powers are added together. For example, $10^2 \times 10^3 = 10^{2+3} = 10^5$. With this in mind, can you evaluate $(4.506 \times 10^4) \times (1.003 \times 10^2)$ without entering scientific notation into your calculator?

6. When powers of 10 are divided into each other, the bottom exponent is subtracted from the top exponent. For example, $10^5/10^3 = 10^{5-3} = 10^2$. With this in mind, can you evaluate $(8.552 \times 10^6) \div (3.129 \times 10^3)$ without entering scientific notation into your calculator?

7. Consider the quantity two dozen eggs. Is the number in this quantity "two" or "two dozen"? Justify your choice.

8. Consider the quantity two dozen eggs. Is the unit in this quantity "eggs" or "dozen eggs"? Justify your choice.

9. Fill in the blank: 1 km = _____ μm.

10. Fill in the blank: 1 Ms = _____ ns.

11. Fill in the blank: 1 cL = _____ ML.

12. Fill in the blank: 1 mg = _____ kg.

13. Express 67.3 km/h in meters/second.

14. Express 0.00444 m/s in kilometers/hour.

15. Using the idea that 1.602 km = 1.000 mi, convert a speed of 60.0 mi/h into kilometers/hour.

16. Using the idea that 1.602 km = 1.000 mi, convert a speed of 60.0 km/h into miles/hour.

17. Convert 52.09 km/h into meters/second.

18. Convert 2.155 m/s into kilometers/hour.

19. Use the formulas for converting degrees Fahrenheit into degrees Celsius to determine the relative size of the Fahrenheit degree over the Celsius degree.

20. Use the formulas for converting degrees Celsius into kelvins to determine the relative size of the Celsius degree over kelvins.

21. What is the mass of 12.67 L of mercury?

22. What is the mass of 0.663 m^3 of air?

23. What is the volume of 2.884 kg of gold?

24. What is the volume of 40.99 kg of cork? Assume a density of 0.22 g/cm^3.

Answers

1. 3.42×10^{-18}

2. 9.835×10^{21}

3. 602,200,000,000,000,000,000,000

4. 0.0000000000000000000000000000000006626

5. 4.520×10^6

6. 2.733×10^3

7. The quantity is two; dozen is the unit.

8. The unit is dozen eggs.

9. 1,000,000,000

10. 10^{15}

11. 1/100,000,000

12. 10^{-6}

13. 18.7 m/s

14. 0.0160 km/h

15. 96.1 km/h

16. 37.5 mi/h

17. 14.47 m/s

18. 7.758 km/hr

19. One Fahrenheit degree is nine-fifths the size of a Celsius degree.

20. Celsius degrees and kelvins are the same size.

21. 1.72×10^5 g

22. 796 g

23. 149 mL

24. 1.9×10^5 cm^3

CHAPTER 3
Fundamentals of Atomic Theory

Opening Essay

Although not an SI unit, the angstrom (Å) is a useful unit of length. It is one ten-billionth of a meter, or 10^{-10} m. Why is it a useful unit? The ultimate particles that compose all matter are about 10^{-10} m in size, or about 1 Å. This makes the angstrom a natural—though not approved—unit for describing these particles.

The angstrom unit is named after Anders Jonas Ångström, a nineteenth-century Swedish physicist. Ångström's research dealt with light being emitted by glowing objects, including the sun. Ångström studied the brightness of the different colors of light that the sun emitted and was able to deduce that the sun is composed of the same kinds of matter that are present on the earth. By extension, we now know that all matter throughout the universe is similar to the matter that exists on our own planet.

Anders Jonas Ångstrom, a Swedish physicist, studied the light coming from the sun. His contributions to science were sufficient to have a tiny unit of length named after him, the angstrom, which is one ten-billionth of a meter.

Sources: https://commons.wikimedia.org/wiki/File:Anders_Jonas_Ã...ngstÃ¶m_-_001. png#file; Photo of the sun courtesy of NASA's Solar Dynamics Observatory http:// commons.wikimedia.org/wiki/File:The_Sun_by_the_Atmospheric_Imaging_Assembly_of_ NASA's_Solar_Dynamics_Observatory_-_20100801.jpg.

The basic building block of all matter is the atom. Curiously, the idea of atoms was first proposed in the fifth century BCE, when the Greek philosophers Leucippus and Democritus proposed their existence in a surprisingly modern fashion. However, their ideas never took hold among their contemporaries, and it wasn't until the early 1800s that enough evidence amassed to make scientists reconsider the idea. Today, the concept of the atom is central to the study of matter.

3.1 The Atom and Its Parts

Learning Objectives

1. State the modern atomic theory.
2. Learn how atoms are constructed.

atom

The smallest piece of an element that maintains the identity of that element.

modern atomic theory

The concept that atoms play a fundamental role in chemistry.

electron

A tiny subatomic particle with a negative charge.

proton

A subatomic particle with a positive charge.

neutron

A subatomic particle with no charge.

The smallest piece of an element that maintains the identity of that element is called an **atom**. Individual atoms are extremely small. It would take about fifty million atoms in a row to make a line that is 1 cm long. The period at the end of a printed sentence has several million atoms in it. Atoms are so small that it is difficult to believe that all matter is made from atoms—but it is.

The concept that atoms play a fundamental role in chemistry is formalized by the **modern atomic theory**, first stated by John Dalton, an English scientist, in 1808. It consists of three parts:

1. All matter is composed of atoms.
2. Atoms of the same element are the same; atoms of different elements are different.
3. Atoms combine in whole-number ratios to form compounds.

These concepts form the basis of chemistry.

Although the word *atom* comes from a Greek word that means "indivisible," we understand now that atoms themselves are composed of smaller parts called *subatomic particles*. The first part to be discovered was the **electron**, a tiny subatomic particle with a negative charge. It is often represented as e^-, with the right superscript showing the negative charge. Later, two larger particles were discovered. The **proton** is a more massive (but still tiny) subatomic particle with a positive charge, represented as p^+. The **neutron** is a subatomic particle with about the same mass as a proton but no charge. It is represented as either n or n^0. We now know that all atoms of all elements are composed of electrons, protons, and (with one exception) neutrons. Table 3.1 summarizes the properties of these three subatomic particles.

TABLE 3.1 Properties of the Three Subatomic Particles

Name	Symbol	Mass (approx.; kg)	Charge
Proton	p^+	1.6×10^{-27}	1+
Neutron	n, n^0	1.6×10^{-27}	none
Electron	e^-	9.1×10^{-31}	1−

nuclear model

The model of an atom that has the protons and neutrons in a central nucleus with the electrons in orbit about the nucleus.

nucleus

The center of an atom that contains protons and neutrons.

How are these particles arranged in atoms? They are not arranged at random. Experiments by Ernest Rutherford in England in the 1910s pointed to a **nuclear model** of the atom. The relatively massive protons and neutrons are collected in the center of an atom, in a region called the **nucleus** of the atom (plural *nuclei*). The tiny electrons are outside the nucleus and spend their time orbiting in space about the nucleus. (See Figure 3.1.)

FIGURE 3.1 The Structure of the Atom
Atoms have protons and neutrons in the center, making the nucleus, while the electrons orbit the nucleus.

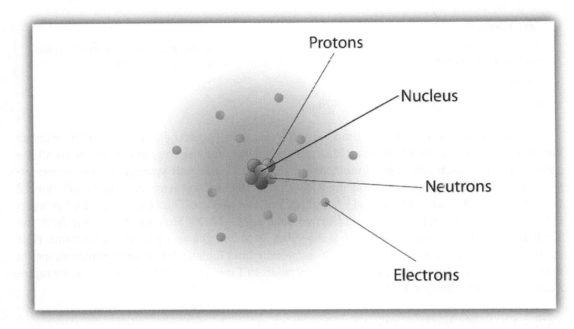

The modern atomic theory states that atoms of one element are the same, while atoms of different elements are different. What makes atoms of different elements different? The fundamental characteristic that all atoms of the same element share is the *number of protons*. All atoms of hydrogen have one and only one proton in the nucleus; all atoms of iron have 26 protons in the nucleus. This number of protons is so important to the identity of an atom that it is called the **atomic number** of the element. Thus, hydrogen has an atomic number of 1, while iron has an atomic number of 26. Each element has its own characteristic atomic number.

Atoms of the same element can have different numbers of neutrons, however. Atoms of the same element (i.e., atoms with the same number of protons) with different numbers of neutrons are called **isotopes**. Most naturally occurring elements exist as isotopes. For example, most hydrogen atoms have a single proton in their nucleus. However, a small number (about one in a million) of hydrogen atoms have a proton and a neutron in their nuclei. This particular isotope of hydrogen is called deuterium. A very rare form of hydrogen has one proton and two neutrons in the nucleus; this isotope of hydrogen is called tritium. The sum of the number of protons and neutrons in the nucleus is called the **mass number** of the isotope.

Neutral atoms have the same number of electrons as they have protons, so their overall electrical charge is zero. However, as we shall see later, this will not always be the case.

atomic number

The number of protons in an atom.

isotopes

Atoms of the same element that have different numbers of neutrons.

mass number

The sum of the number of protons and neutrons in a nucleus.

Example 1

1. The most common carbon atoms have six protons and six neutrons in their nuclei. What are the atomic number and the mass number of these carbon atoms?
2. An isotope of uranium has an atomic number of 92 and a mass number of 235. What are the number of protons and neutrons in the nucleus of this atom?

Solution

1. If a carbon atom has six protons in its nucleus, its atomic number is 6. If it also has six neutrons in the nucleus, then the mass number is 6 + 6, or 12.
2. If the atomic number of uranium is 92, then that is the number of protons in the nucleus. Because the mass number is 235, we subtract the number of protons from the mass number

to get the number of neutrons. As such, the number of neutrons in the nucleus is 235 − 92, or 143.

Test Yourself

The number of protons in the nucleus of a tin atom is 50, while the number of neutrons in the nucleus is 68. What are the atomic number and the mass number of this isotope?

Answer

Atomic number = 50, mass number = 118

atomic symbol

A one- or two-letter representation of the name of an element.

When referring to an atom, we simply use the element's name: the term *sodium* refers to the element as well as an atom of sodium. But it can be unwieldy to use the name of elements all the time. Instead, chemistry defines a symbol for each element. The **atomic symbol** is a one- or two-letter abbreviation of the name of the element. By convention, the first letter of an element's symbol is always capitalized, while the second letter (if present) is lowercase. Thus, the symbol for hydrogen is H, the symbol for sodium is Na, and the symbol for nickel is Ni. Most symbols come from the English name of the element, although some symbols come from an element's Latin name. (The symbol for sodium, Na, comes from its Latin name, *natrium*.) Table 3.2 lists some common elements and their symbols. You should memorize the symbols in Table 3.2, as this is how we will be representing elements throughout chemistry.

TABLE 3.2 Names and Symbols of Common Elements

Element Name	Symbol	Element Name	Symbol
Aluminum	Al	Mercury	Hg
Argon	Ar	Molybdenum	Mo
Arsenic	As	Neon	Ne
Barium	Ba	Nickel	Ni
Beryllium	Be	Nitrogen	N
Bismuth	Bi	Oxygen	O
Boron	B	Palladium	Pd
Bromine	Br	Phosphorus	P
Calcium	Ca	Platinum	Pt
Carbon	C	Potassium	K
Chlorine	Cl	Radium	Ra
Chromium	Cr	Radon	Rn
Cobalt	Co	Rubidium	Rb
Copper	Cu	Scandium	Sc
Fluorine	F	Selenium	Se
Gallium	Ga	Silicon	Si
Germanium	Ge	Silver	Ag
Gold	Au	Sodium	Na
Helium	He	Strontium	Sr
Hydrogen	H	Sulfur	S
Iodine	I	Tantalum	Ta
Iridium	Ir	Tin	Sn
Iron	Fe	Titanium	Ti
Krypton	Kr	Tungsten	W

Element Name	Symbol	Element Name	Symbol
Lead	Pb	Uranium	U
Lithium	Li	Xenon	Xe
Magnesium	Mg	Zinc	Zn
Manganese	Mn	Zirconium	Zr

There is an easy way to represent isotopes using the atomic symbols. We use the construction

$$_{Z}^{A}\text{X}$$

where X is the symbol of the element, A is the mass number, and Z is the atomic number. Thus, for the isotope of carbon that has 6 protons and 6 neutrons, the symbol is

$$_{6}^{12}\text{C}$$

where C is the symbol for carbon, 6 represents its atomic number, and 12 represents the mass number.

Example 2

1. What is the symbol for an isotope of uranium that has an atomic number of 92 and a mass number of 235?
2. How many protons and neutrons are in $_{26}^{56}\text{Fe}$?

Solution

1. The symbol for this isotope is $_{92}^{235}\text{U}$.
2. This iron atom has 26 protons and 56 − 26 = 30 neutrons.

Test Yourself

How many protons are in $_{11}^{23}\text{Na}$?

Answer

11 protons

It is also common to state the mass number after the name of an element to indicate a particular isotope. *Carbon-12* represents an isotope of carbon with 6 protons and 6 neutrons, while *uranium-238* is an isotope of uranium that has 146 neutrons.

Key Takeaways

- Chemistry is based on the modern atomic theory, which states that all matter is composed of atoms.
- Atoms themselves are composed of protons, neutrons, and electrons.
- Each element has its own atomic number, which is equal to the number of protons in its nucleus.
- Isotopes of an element contain different numbers of neutrons.
- Elements are represented by an atomic symbol.

Exercises

1. List the three statements that make up the modern atomic theory.
2. Explain how atoms are composed.
3. Which is larger, a proton or an electron?
4. Which is larger, a neutron or an electron?
5. What are the charges for each of the three subatomic particles?
6. Where is most of the mass of an atom located?
7. Sketch a diagram of a boron atom, which has five protons and six neutrons in its nucleus.
8. Sketch a diagram of a helium atom, which has two protons and two neutrons in its nucleus.
9. Define *atomic number*. What is the atomic number for a boron atom?
10. What is the atomic number of helium?
11. Define *isotope* and give an example.
12. What is the difference between deuterium and tritium?
13. Which pair represents isotopes?

    a. ^4_2He and ^3_2He

    b. $^{56}_{26}\text{Fe}$ and $^{56}_{25}\text{Mn}$

    c. $^{28}_{14}\text{Si}$ and $^{31}_{15}\text{P}$

14. Which pair represents isotopes?

    a. $^{40}_{20}\text{Ca}$ and $^{40}_{19}\text{K}$

    b. $^{56}_{26}\text{Fe}$ and $^{58}_{26}\text{Fe}$

    c. $^{238}_{92}\text{U}$ and $^{235}_{92}\text{U}$

15. Give complete symbols of each atom, including the atomic number and the mass number.

    a. an oxygen atom with 8 protons and 8 neutrons

    b. a potassium atom with 19 protons and 20 neutrons

    c. a lithium atom with 3 protons and 4 neutrons

16. Give complete symbols of each atom, including the atomic number and the mass number.

    a. a magnesium atom with 12 protons and 12 neutrons

    b. a magnesium atom with 12 protons and 13 neutrons

    c. a xenon atom with 54 protons and 77 neutrons

17. Americium-241 is an isotope used in smoke detectors. What is the complete symbol for this isotope?
18. Carbon-14 is an isotope used to perform radioactive dating tests on previously living material. What is the complete symbol for this isotope?
19. Give atomic symbols for each element.

    a. sodium

    b. argon

    c. nitrogen

    d. radon

20. Give atomic symbols for each element.

    a. silver

    b. gold

    c. mercury

    d. iodine

21. Give the name of the element.

    a. Si

    b. Mn

    c. Fe

    d. Cr

22. Give the name of the element.

    a. F

    b. Cl

    c. Br

    d. I

Answers

1. All matter is composed of atoms; atoms of the same element are the same, and atoms of different elements are different; atoms combine in whole-number ratios to form compounds.

2. Atoms have protons and neutrons together at the center of an atom, and electrons orbit space about the nucleus.

3. A proton is larger than an electron.

4. A neutron is larger than an electron.

5. proton: 1+; electron: 1–; neutron: 0

6. Most of the mass of an atom is located in the nucleus.

7.
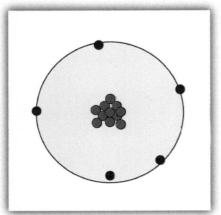

8.
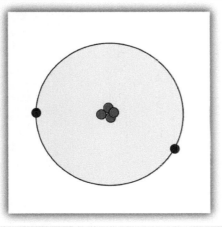

9. The atomic number is the number of protons in a nucleus. Boron has an atomic number of five.

10. The atomic number of helium is two.

11. Isotopes are atoms of the same element but with different numbers of neutrons. ^1_1H and ^2_1H are examples.

12. Deuterium has one neutron in the nucleus, and tritium has two neutrons.

13. a. isotopes
    b. not isotopes
    c. not isotopes

14. a. not isotopes
    b. isotopes
    c. isotopes

15. a. $^{16}_8O$

    b. $^{39}_{19}K$

    c. ^7_3Li

16. a. $^{24}_{12}Mg$

    b. $^{25}_{12}Mg$

    c. $^{131}_{54}Xe$

17. $^{241}_{95}Am$

18. $^{14}_6C$

19. a. Na
    b. Ar
    c. N
    d. Rn

20. a. Ag
    b. Au
    c. Hg
    d. I

21. a. silicon
    b. manganese
    c. iron
    d. chromium

22. a. fluorine
    b. chlorine
    c. bromine
    d. iodine

3.2 Masses of Atoms

Learning Objective

1. Express the masses of atoms.

Because matter is defined as anything that has mass and takes up space, it should not be surprising to learn that atoms have mass.

Individual atoms, however, are very small, so the masses of individual atoms are also very small. For macroscopic objects, we use units such as grams and kilograms to state their masses, but these units are much too big to comfortably describe the masses of individual atoms and molecules. Another scale is needed.

The **atomic mass unit** (u; some texts use amu, but this older style is no longer accepted) is defined as one-twelfth of the mass of a carbon-12 atom, an isotope of carbon that has six protons and six neutrons in its nucleus. By this scale, the mass of a proton is 1.00728 u, the mass of a neutron is 1.00866 u, and the mass of an electron is 0.000549 u. There will not be much error if you estimate the mass of an atom by simply counting the total number of protons and neutrons in the nucleus (i.e., identify its mass number) and ignore the electrons. Thus, the mass of carbon-12 is about 12 u, the mass of oxygen-16 is about 16 u, and the mass of uranium-238 is about 238 u. More exact masses are found in scientific references—for example, the exact mass of uranium-238 is 238.050788 u, so you can see that we are not far off by using the whole-number value as the mass of the atom.

What is the mass of an element? This is somewhat more complicated because most elements exist as a mixture of isotopes, each of which has its own mass. Thus, although it is easy to speak of the mass of an atom, when talking about the mass of an element, we must take the isotopic mixture into account.

The **atomic mass** of an element is a weighted average of the masses of the isotopes that compose an element. What do we mean by a weighted average? Well, consider an element that consists of two isotopes, 50% with mass 10 u and 50% with mass 11 u. A weighted average is found by multiplying each mass by its fractional occurrence (in decimal form) and then adding all the products. The sum is the weighted average and serves as the formal atomic mass of the element. In this example, we have the following:

> **atomic mass unit**
>
> One-twelfth of the mass of a carbon-12 atom.

> **atomic mass**
>
> The weighted average of the masses of the isotopes that compose an element.

0.50 × 10 u = 5.0 u
0.50 × 11 u = <u>5.5 u</u>
Sum   = 10.5 u = the atomic mass of our element

Note that no atom in our hypothetical element has a mass of 10.5 u; rather, that is the average mass of the atoms, weighted by their percent occurrence.

This example is similar to a real element. Boron exists as about 20% boron-10 (five protons and five neutrons in the nuclei) and about 80% boron-11 (five protons and six neutrons in the nuclei). The atomic mass of boron is calculated similarly to what we did for our hypothetical example, but the percentages are different:

0.20 × 10 u = 2.0 u
0.80 × 11 u = <u>8.8 u</u>
Sum   = 10.8 u = the atomic mass of boron

Thus, we use 10.8 u for the atomic mass of boron.

Virtually all elements exist as mixtures of isotopes, so atomic masses may vary significantly from whole numbers. Table 3.3 lists the atomic masses of some elements; a more expansive table is in Appendix A. The atomic masses in Table 3.3 are listed to three decimal places where possible, but in most cases, only one or two decimal places are needed. Note that many of the atomic masses, especially the larger ones, are not very close to whole numbers. This is, in part, the effect of an increasing number of naturally occurring isotopes as the atoms increase in size. (The record number is ten isotopes for tin.)

TABLE 3.3 Selected Atomic Masses of Some Elements

Element Name	Atomic Mass (u)	Element Name	Atomic Mass (u)
Aluminum	26.981	Molybdenum	95.94
Argon	39.948	Neon	20.180
Arsenic	74.922	Nickel	58.693
Barium	137.327	Nitrogen	14.007
Beryllium	9.012	Oxygen	15.999
Bismuth	208.980	Palladium	106.42
Boron	10.811	Phosphorus	30.974
Bromine	79.904	Platinum	195.084
Calcium	40.078	Potassium	39.098
Carbon	12.011	Radium	n/a
Chlorine	35.453	Radon	n/a
Cobalt	58.933	Rubidium	85.468
Copper	63.546	Scandium	44.956
Fluorine	18.998	Selenium	78.96
Gallium	69.723	Silicon	28.086
Germanium	72.64	Silver	107.868
Gold	196.967	Sodium	22.990
Helium	4.003	Strontium	87.62
Hydrogen	1.008	Sulfur	32.065
Iodine	126.904	Tantalum	180.948
Iridium	192.217	Tin	118.710
Iron	55.845	Titanium	47.867
Krypton	83.798	Tungsten	183.84
Lead	207.2	Uranium	238.029
Lithium	6.941	Xenon	131.293
Magnesium	24.305	Zinc	65.409
Manganese	54.938	Zirconium	91.224
Mercury	200.59	Molybdenum	95.94
Note: Atomic mass is given to three decimal places, if known.			

Chemistry is Everywhere: Atoms in Space

In the first part of the 20th century, scientists figured out the ultimate energy source of the sun. Hydrogen atoms were being converted to helium atoms under conditions of tremendous pressure and temperature, and in doing so were giving off huge amounts of energy. (This process is called nuclear fusion, and it will be covered in Chapter 16.) It is estimated that 600 million tons of hydrogen is converted into helium *every second*. While that sounds like a lot, the sun is large enough that it can continue doing this for about *5 billion* more years.

As you might expect, because the sun is so hot, hydrogen atoms and nuclei (and to a lesser extent, helium atoms and nuclei) are slowly boiling off the surface of the sun and streaming into space: This is the *solar wind*. However, as a "wind" it's not very strong: only about a millionth of a billionth of Earth's normal atmospheric pressure, although this can vary with time. It is enough, though, to strip any atmosphere from the planet Mercury, close to the sun, and even Mars, which is significantly farther away. Why, then, does Earth have an atmosphere?

The reason is because Earth has a magnetic field, likely due to a partially-liquid planetary core. The magnetic field causes atomic nuclei of the solar wind, with their positive charge, to curve around the planet rather than hitting it. It's not completely effective: Auroras are caused by the interactions of solar wind (hydrogen atoms and nuclei) with the upper parts of the atmosphere. However, auroras typically occur near the North and South Poles, where the Earth's magnetic field is emitted.

Photo of aurora borealis viewed from Estonia.

Source: By Kristian Pikner [CC BY-SA 4.0 (https://creativecommons.org/licenses/by-sa/4.0)], from Wikimedia Commons

What about Venus, which has a small planetary magnetic field? Actually, the solar wind hasn't so much removed Venus' atmosphere as much as changed its composition: It is mostly carbon dioxide, which is a relatively massive gas. Planetary scientists speculate that any hydrogen that might have been present in Venus' atmosphere was literally blown away by the solar wind over the eons.

Because all stars are emitting their own solar winds, interstellar space is full of hydrogen and helium particles. The point at which our sun's solar wind drops to the same pressure as that of interstellar space is called the *heliopause*. At present, only two objects of human construction have passed the heliopause: The spacecraft *Voyager 1*, launched in September 1977, and *Voyager 2*, launched a month earlier (ironically, given the numbering).

Key Takeaways

- The atomic mass unit (u) is a unit that describes the masses of individual atoms and molecules.
- The atomic mass is the weighted average of the masses of all isotopes of an element.

Exercises

1. Define *atomic mass unit*. What is its abbreviation?
2. Define *atomic mass*. What is its unit?
3. Estimate the mass, in whole numbers, of each isotope.
   a. hydrogen-1
   b. hydrogen-3
   c. iron-56
4. Estimate the mass, in whole numbers, of each isotope.
   a. phosphorus-31
   b. carbon-14
   c. americium-241
5. Determine the atomic mass of each element, given the isotopic composition.
   a. lithium, which is 92.4% lithium-7 (mass 7.016 u) and 7.60% lithium-6 (mass 6.015 u)
   b. oxygen, which is 99.76% oxygen-16 (mass 15.995 u), 0.038% oxygen-17 (mass 16.999 u), and 0.205% oxygen-18 (mass 17.999 u)
6. Determine the atomic mass of each element, given the isotopic composition.
   a. neon, which is 90.48% neon-20 (mass 19.992 u), 0.27% neon-21 (mass 20.994 u), and 9.25% neon-22 (mass 21.991 u)
   b. uranium, which is 99.27% uranium-238 (mass 238.051 u) and 0.720% uranium-235 (mass 235.044 u)
7. How far off would your answer be from Exercise 5a if you used whole-number masses for individual isotopes of lithium?
8. How far off would your answer be from Exercise 6b if you used whole-number masses for individual isotopes of uranium?

Answers

1. The atomic mass unit is defined as one-twelfth of the mass of a carbon-12 atom. Its abbreviation is u.
2. Atomic mass is the weighted average of the masses of the isotopes of an element. It has units of u.
3. a. 1
   b. 3
   c. 56
4. a. 31
   b. 14
   c. 241
5. a. 6.940 u
   b. 16.000 u
6. a. 20.18 u
   b. 238.01 u
7. We would get 6.924 u.
8. We would get 237.95 u.

3.3 The Periodic Table

Learning Objectives

1. Recognize the periodic table as the organizing tool for the elements.
2. Learn some of the terms for rows and columns of the periodic table.

The modern definition of a chemical element was proposed by Antoine Lavoisier (Figure 3.2) in 1789 in his book *Traité élémentaire de chimie* (*Elements of Chemistry*). In that book, Lavoisier listed 33 things that he considered elements; modern chemistry recognizes that 23 of the items on his list are actually chemical elements.

FIGURE 3.2 Painting of Antoine Lavoisier and his wife, Anne-Marie
Antoine Lavoisier was a French scientist who formulated the modern definition of a chemical element. Although his wife, Anne-Marie, helped him in his scientific work, it was the connections to her family that led to Lavoisier being guillotined during the French Revolution in 1794.

Source: By Jacques-Louis David - Metropolitan Museum of Art, online database: entry 436106 (accession number: 1977.10), Public Domain, https://commons.wikimedia.org/w/index.php?curid=28550

Using the modern definition, over the next few decades dozens of new elements were discovered. (Curiously, the last naturally-existing stable element to be verified was rhenium, finally isolated in macroscopic amounts in 1927.) Over time, scientists noted certain similarities in the behavior of certain sets of elements. For example, the elements chlorine, bromine, and iodine always combined with other elements in similar proportions. Likewise, sodium, lithium, and potassium exhibited certain chemical similarities.

In time, scientists began to arrange these sets of elements in a way as to organize them by their chemical properties. The most successful attempt was made by Russian chemist Dmitri Mendeleev

(Figure 3.3), who presented his version in 1869. While Mendeleev got a few things wrong (for example, he listed his elements by atomic mass, which we know now to be incorrect), he also took the bold step of leaving blanks in his arrangement where he proposed elements that had not been discovered yet—and then he had the audacity to predict their properties, some of which proved to be very close once the elements were discovered.

Since then, more elements have been discovered and Mendeleev's original arrangement has been modernized and updated into what we call the **periodic table**. A modern periodic table is shown in Figure 3.4. The periodic table is one of the most useful tools in chemistry, indeed perhaps all of science.

Although periodic tables come in many styles, most of them contain certain minimum information. Every box on the periodic table refers to an individual element. Each box usually contains the following information about the element: Its symbol, its name, its atomic number, and its atomic mass (Figure 3.5). Right from the start, a periodic table collects some crucial information about each element.

FIGURE 3.3
Dmitri Mendeleev (1834 - 1907)

Mendeleev constructed one of the first successful periodic tables in the 1860s.

Source: [Public domain], via Wikimedia Commons; https://commons.wikimedia.org/wiki/File:Dmitri_Mendeleev_1890s.jpg.

periodic table

A chart that arranges all of the chemical elements into rows and columns.

FIGURE 3.4 The Periodic Table

Source: "IUPAC Periodic Table of the Elements," International Union of Pure and Applied Chemistry; https://iupac.org/cms/wp-content/uploads/2018/12/IUPAC_Periodic_Table-01Dec18.pdf.

FIGURE 3.5 Carbon atom information

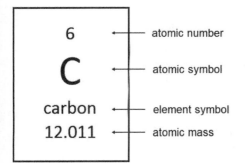

- 6 — atomic number
- C — atomic symbol
- carbon — element symbol
- 12.011 — atomic mass

Looking at Figure 3.4, the first thing to note about the periodic table is that if you trace the elements in each row, from left to right, you will see that the elements are ordered by atomic number (remember Mendeleev's error, mentioned previously?). However, each row contains a different number of elements, at least at first. The first row contains only two elements, hydrogen and helium. The second and third rows have eight elements, lithium through neon and sodium through argon, respectively. The elements are separated in a strange way, for reasons that will become clear in the next chapter. The fourth row contains eighteen elements, and so forth.

Each row of elements is called a **period**. Laid out the way they are, the elements in each row are in positions so that the elements in each column have similar chemical properties, as had been noted by earlier scientists. Each column of elements in the periodic table is called a **group** (sometimes also called a *family*). Each group in the periodic table is labeled at the top with a number called the **group number** (some older versions of the periodic table use a Roman numeral/letter combination). Some groups have names that are well-known to chemists. Group 1, the first column of elements in the periodic table (except hydrogen), are called the *alkali metals*, while the elements in Group 2 are called the *alkaline earth metals*. Group 16, headed by the element oxygen, are called the *chalcogens*, while Group 17, headed by fluorine, are called the *halogens*. The last group of elements, Group 18, is composed of a set of gases that are very chemically unreactive; because of this, they are called the *noble gases*.

Figure 3.4 shows two rows apart from the main body of the periodic table, elements having atomic numbers 57 through 71 and elements 89 through 103. These two rows actually belong in periods six and seven, respectively, but putting them there would make the periodic table too long to display conveniently. By convention, these fourteen columns are shown separately, usually underneath the other elements. These parts of the periods also have common names: The first row is called the *lanthanide series* and the second row is called the *actinide series*, in each case after the first element in each row.

period

A row of elements in the periodic table.

group

A column of elements in the periodic table.

group number

The numerical label of each column in the periodic table.

Example 3

Use the element symbol to determine which period and group it is in. See Figure 3.4.

1. Na
2. S

Solution

1. Na, which is the element sodium, is in the first column and third row. It is an alkali metal in the third period of the periodic table.
2. S stands for sulfur, and it is in the third row and is in Group 16. Sulfur is in the third period and is a chalcogen.

Test Yourself

What column and period is the element tin, symbol Sn, in?

Answer

The fifth period and in Group 14.

The periodic table shows some other interesting groupings as well. The elements in the upper right corner of the periodic table (as well as hydrogen) are all **nonmetals**— they share certain properties, like an inability to conduct heat or electricity well, are brittle when solid, and have a variety of colors. Only 20 or so elements are considered nonmetals. The remaining elements, going all the way to the left side of the periodic table, are **metals**—they share such characteristics as a silvery color, good conductors of heat and electricity, can be beaten into thin sheets (a property called "malleable") and drawn into wires (a property called "ductile"). They are typically solids at room temperature and are usually rather hard. Of course, not all metals or nonmetals have all of these properties. For example, gold and copper are not silvery-colored, and mercury is a liquid at room temperature. Carbon, a nonmetal, is actually a good conductor of heat and electricity. However, the separation of elements into metals and nonmetals demonstrates another useful application of the periodic table.

nonmetals

Elements that share certain properties, like inability to conduct heat or electricity well, brittle as a solid, and a range of colors.

metals

Elements that share a variety of properties, such as a silvery color, being good conductors of electricity and heat, ability to be beaten into thin sheets or drawn into thin wires.

Food and Drink App: Strontium in Radioactive Releases

Intentional above-ground nuclear testing has not been conducted in decades, although there have been a few well-publicized accidental release of nuclear materials. One of the concerns with release of nuclear materials is the presence of a radioactive isotope of the element strontium having a mass number 90: ^{90}Sr, or strontium-90. Why does this element cause special concern?

The elements calcium and strontium are in the same column of the periodic table, meaning that they have similar chemical properties.

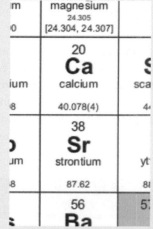

Source: Reproduced by permission of International Union of Pure and Applied Chemistry.

A look at the periodic table explains why. The element strontium is just underneath the element calcium in the periodic table, meaning that strontium and calcium have similar chemical properties—that's one of the purposes of the periodic table, after all. What this implies is that strontium can replace calcium where calcium would normally be present. In the case of the human body, that would be the bones, and in the case of *radioactive* strontium replacing calcium, that would cause certain health issues, like bone and bone marrow cancer. Because of this, ^{90}Sr is considered one of the more hazardous isotopes of environmental radioactive contamination. In fact, measurements of ^{90}Sr in children's teeth in the 1950s was one factor that convinced the nuclear powers to ban above-ground nuclear testing.

Ironically, ^{90}Sr is also used to treat bone cancer that develops from other sources. The fact that strontium-90 is both a cause and a treatment is only one demonstration of the dual application of many modern technologies.

The periodic table has an unusual shape to it. The scientists developing it in the late 1800s couldn't explain why, in part because new elements were still being discovered. It wasn't until the 1920s and 1930s that the reason for its unusual shape was understood. We will cover this topic in Chapter 4.

Key Takeaway

- The periodic table is a chart that organizes all the elements.

Exercises

1. How many periods does the modern periodic table have?
2. How many groups does the modern periodic table have?

3. What is the name of Group 2 of the periodic table?
4. What is the name of Group 17 of the periodic table?
5. Name the element in the second period that has similar chemical properties to strontium.
6. Name the element in the fifth period that has similar chemical properties to oxygen.
7. Name the noble gas in the fourth period of the periodic table.
8. Name the alkali metal in the sixth period of the periodic table.
9. List some general properties of metals.
10. List some general properties of nonmetals.

Answers

1. seven
2. eighteen
3. alkaline earth metals
4. halogens
5. beryllium
6. tellurium
7. krypton
8. caesium (usually spelled "cesium" in the US)
9. good conductors of heat; good conductors of electricity; malleable; ductile; silvery-colored
10. poor conductors of heat; poor conductors of electricity; brittle when solid; variety of colors

3.4 End-of-Chapter Material

Additional Exercises

1. How many electrons does it take to equal the mass of one proton?
2. How many protons does it take to equal the mass of a neutron?
3. Dalton's initial version of the modern atomic theory says that all atoms of the same element are the same. Is this actually correct? Why or why not?
4. How are atoms of the same element the same? How are atoms of the same element different?
5. Give complete atomic symbols for the three known isotopes of hydrogen.
6. A rare isotope of helium has a single neutron in its nucleus. Write the complete atomic symbol of this isotope.
7. Use its place on the periodic table to determine if indium, In, atomic number 49, is a metal or a nonmetal.
8. Only a few atoms of astatine, At, atomic number 85, have been detected. On the basis of its position on the periodic table, would you expect it to be a metal or a nonmetal?
9. Americium-241 is a crucial part of many smoke detectors. How many neutrons are present in its nucleus?
10. Potassium-40 is a radioactive isotope of potassium that is present in the human body. How many neutrons are present in its nucleus?

11. Determine the atomic mass of ruthenium from the given abundance and mass data.

Ruthenium-96	5.54%	95.907 u
Ruthenium-98	1.87%	97.905 u
Ruthenium-99	12.76%	98.906 u
Ruthenium-100	12.60%	99.904 u
Ruthenium-101	17.06%	100.906 u
Ruthenium-102	31.55%	101.904 u
Ruthenium-104	18.62%	103.905 u

12. Determine the atomic mass of tellurium from the given abundance and mass data.

Tellurium-120	0.09%	119.904 u
Tellurium-122	2.55%	121.903 u
Tellurium-123	0.89%	122.904 u
Tellurium-124	4.74%	123.903 u
Tellurium-125	7.07%	124.904 u
Tellurium-126	18.84%	125.903 u
Tellurium-128	31.74%	127.904 u
Tellurium-130	34.08%	129.906 u

13. One atomic mass unit has a mass of 1.6605×10^{-24} g. What is the mass of one atom of sodium?

14. One atomic mass unit has a mass of 1.6605×10^{-24} g. What is the mass of one atom of uranium?

Answers

1. about 1,800 electrons

3. It is not strictly correct because of the existence of isotopes.

5. $^{1}_{1}\text{H}$, $^{2}_{1}\text{H}$, and $^{3}_{1}\text{H}$

7. It is a metal.

9. 146 neutrons

11. 101.065 u

13. 3.817×10^{-23} g

CHAPTER 4
Electronic Structure

Opening Essay

Normal light microscopes can magnify objects up to about 1,500 times. Electron microscopes can magnify objects up to 1,000,000 times. Why can electron microscopes magnify images so much?

A microscope's resolution depends on the wavelength of light used. The smaller the wavelength, the more a microscope can magnify. Light is a wave, and, as such, it has a wavelength associated with it. The wavelength of visible light, which is detected by the eyes, varies from about 700 nm to about 400 nm. (Recall that a nanometer, nm, is one-billionth of a meter.)

One of the startling conclusions about modern science is that electrons also act as waves. However, the wavelength of electrons is much, much shorter—about 0.5 to 1 nm. This allows electron microscopes to magnify 600–700 times more than light microscopes. This allows us to see even smaller features in a world that is invisible to the naked eye.

(a) A simple light microscope can magnify up to 1,500 times. (b) An electron microscope can magnify up to 1,000,000 times. (c) Flu viruses imaged by an electron microscope. The virus is about 100 nm in diameter.

Source: © Thinkstock

Atoms are at the heart of chemistry, and the way they behave in the presence of other atoms is what chemical reactions are all about. Atoms act the way they do because of their structure. We already know that atoms are composed of protons, neutrons, and electrons. Protons and neutrons are located in the nucleus, and electrons orbit around the nucleus. But we need to know more about how electrons are arranged in atoms to understand why atoms react the way they do.

Virtually everything we know about atoms ultimately comes from light. Before we can understand the composition of atoms (especially electrons), we need to understand the properties of light.

4.1 Light

wavelength

The distance between corresponding points in two adjacent light cycles.

frequency

The number of cycles of light that pass a given point in one second.

What we know as light is more properly called *electromagnetic radiation*. We know from experiments that light acts as a wave. As such, it can be described as having a frequency and a wavelength. The **wavelength** of light is the distance between corresponding points in two adjacent light cycles, and the **frequency** of light is the number of cycles of light that pass a given point in one second. Wavelength is typically represented by λ, the lowercase Greek letter *lambda*, while frequency is represented by ν, the lowercase Greek letter *nu* (although it looks like a Roman "vee," it is actually the Greek equivalent of the letter "en"). Wavelength has units of length (meters, centimeters, etc.), while frequency has units of *per second*, written as s^{-1} and sometimes called a *hertz* (Hz). Figure 4.1 shows how these two characteristics are defined.

FIGURE 4.1 Characteristics of Light Waves
Light acts as a wave and can be described by a wavelength λ and a frequency ν.

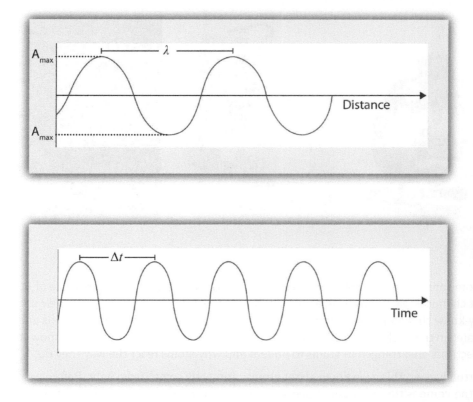

One property of waves is that their speed is equal to their wavelength times their frequency. That means we have

$$\text{speed} = \lambda\nu$$

For light, however, speed is actually a universal constant when light is traveling through a vacuum (or, to a very good approximation, air). The measured speed of light (c) in a vacuum is 2.9979×10^8 m/s, or about 3.00×10^8 m/s. Thus, we have

$$c = \lambda \nu$$

Because the speed of light is a constant, the wavelength and the frequency of light are related to each other: as one increases, the other decreases and vice versa. We can use this equation to calculate what one property of light has to be when given the other property.

Example 1

What is the frequency of light if its wavelength is 5.55×10^{-7} m?

Solution

We use the equation that relates the wavelength and frequency of light with its speed. We have

$$3.00 \times 10^8 \, \text{m/s} = \left(5.55 \times 10^{-7} \text{m}\right) \nu$$

We divide both sides of the equation by 5.55×10^{-7} m and get

$$\nu = 5.41 \times 10^{14} \, \text{s}^{-1}$$

Note how the m units cancel, leaving s in the denominator. A unit in a denominator is indicated by a –1 exponent—s^{-1}—and read as "per second."

Test Yourself

What is the wavelength of light if its frequency is 1.55×10^{10} s^{-1}?

Answer

0.0194 m, or 19.4 mm

Light also behaves like a package of energy. It turns out that for light, the energy of the "package" of energy is proportional to its frequency. (For most waves, energy is proportional to wave amplitude, or the height of the wave.) The mathematical equation that relates the energy (E) of light to its frequency is

$$E = h\nu$$

where ν is the frequency of the light, and h is a constant called **Planck's constant**. Its value is 6.626×10^{-34} J·s—a very small number that is another fundamental constant of our universe, like the speed of light. The units on Planck's constant may look unusual, but these units are required so that the algebra works out.

Planck's constant

The proportionality constant between the frequency and the energy of light.

Example 2

What is the energy of light if its frequency is 1.55×10^{10} s^{-1}?

Solution

Using the formula for the energy of light, we have

$$E = (6.626 \times 10^{-34} \, \text{J} \cdot \text{s})(1.55 \times 10^{10} \, \text{s}^{-1})$$

Seconds are in the numerator and the denominator, so they cancel, leaving us with joules, the unit of energy. So

$$E = 1.03 \times 10^{-23} \, \text{J}$$

This is an extremely small amount of energy—but this is for only one light wave.

Test Yourself

What is the frequency of a light wave if its energy is 4.156×10^{-20} J?

Answer

6.27×10^{13} s^{-1}

photon

The name of a wave of light acting as a particle.

electromagnetic spectrum

The full span of the possible wavelengths, frequencies, and energies of light.

Because a light wave behaves like a little particle of energy, light waves have a particle-type name: the **photon**. It is not uncommon to hear light described as photons.

Wavelengths, frequencies, and energies of light span a wide range; the entire range of possible values for light is called the **electromagnetic spectrum**. We are mostly familiar with visible light, which is light having a wavelength range between about 400 nm and 700 nm. Light can have much longer and much shorter wavelengths than this, with corresponding variations in frequency and energy. Figure 4.2 shows the entire electromagnetic spectrum and how certain regions of the spectrum are labeled. You may already be familiar with some of these regions; they are all light—with different frequencies, wavelengths, and energies.

FIGURE 4.2 The Electromagnetic Spectrum
The electromagnetic spectrum, with its various regions labeled. The borders of each region are approximate.

Electromagnetic Spectrum

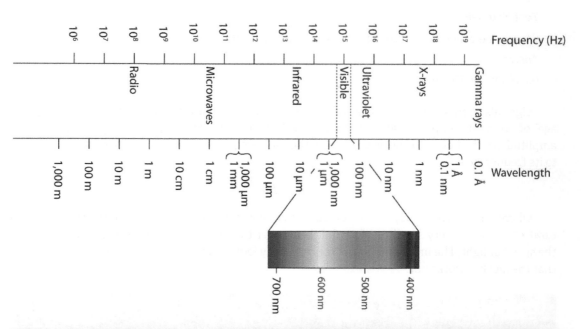

Key Takeaways

- Light acts like a wave, with a frequency and a wavelength.
- The frequency and wavelength of light are related by the speed of light, a constant.
- Light acts like a particle of energy, whose value is related to the frequency of light.

Exercises

1. Describe the characteristics of a light wave.
2. What is a characteristic of a particle of light?

3. What is the frequency of light if its wavelength is 7.33×10^{-5} m?
4. What is the frequency of light if its wavelength is 1.226 m?
5. What is the frequency of light if its wavelength is 733 nm?
6. What is the frequency of light if its wavelength is 8.528 cm?
7. What is the wavelength of light if its frequency is 8.19×10^{14} s^{-1}?
8. What is the wavelength of light if its frequency is 3.66×10^{6} s^{-1}?
9. What is the wavelength of light if its frequency is 1.009×10^{6} Hz?
10. What is the wavelength of light if its frequency is 3.79×10^{-3} Hz?
11. What is the energy of a photon if its frequency is 5.55×10^{13} s^{-1}?
12. What is the energy of a photon if its frequency is 2.06×10^{18} s^{-1}?
13. What is the energy of a photon if its wavelength is 5.88×10^{-4} m?
14. What is the energy of a photon if its wavelength is 1.888×10^{2} m?

Answers

1. Light has a wavelength and a frequency.
2. It has a certain amount of energy.
3. 4.09×10^{12} s^{-1}
4. 2.45×10^{8} s^{-1}
5. 4.09×10^{14} s^{-1}
6. 3.52×10^{9} s^{-1}
7. 3.66×10^{-7} m
8. 82.0 m
9. 297 m
10. 7.92×10^{10} m
11. 3.68×10^{-20} J
12. 1.36×10^{-15} J
13. 3.38×10^{-22} J
14. 1.05×10^{-27} J

4.2 Quantum Numbers for Electrons

Learning Objectives

1. Explain what spectra are.
2. Learn the quantum numbers that are assigned to electrons.

There are two fundamental ways of generating light: either heat an object up so hot it glows or pass an electrical current through a sample of matter (usually a gas). Incandescent lights and fluorescent lights generate light using these two methods, respectively.

continuous spectrum

An image that contains all colors of light.

line spectrum

An image that contains only certain colors of light.

A hot object gives off a continuum of light. We notice this when the visible portion of the electromagnetic spectrum is passed through a prism: the prism separates light into its constituent colors, and all colors are present in a continuous rainbow (part (a) in Figure 4.3). This image is known as a **continuous spectrum**. However, when electricity is passed through a gas and light is emitted and this light is passed though a prism, we see only certain lines of light in the image (part (b) in Figure 4.3). This image is called a **line spectrum**. It turns out that every element has its own unique, characteristic line spectrum.

FIGURE 4.3 Continuous and Line Spectra
(a) A glowing object gives off a full rainbow of colors, which are noticed only when light is passed through a prism to make a continuous spectrum. (b) However, when electricity is passed through a gas, only certain colors of light are emitted. Here are the colors of light in the line spectrum of Hg.

(a)

(b)

Why does the light emitted from an electrically excited gas have only certain colors, while light given off by hot objects has a continuous spectrum? For a long time, it was not well explained. Particularly simple was the spectrum of hydrogen gas, which could be described easily by an equation; no other element has a spectrum that is so predictable (Figure 4.4). Late-nineteenth-century scientists found that the positions of the lines obeyed a pattern given by the equation

$$\frac{1}{\lambda} = (109{,}700 \text{ cm}^{-1}) \left(\frac{1}{4} - \frac{1}{n^2} \right)$$

where n = 3, 4, 5, 6,..., but they could not explain why this was so.

FIGURE 4.4 Hydrogen Spectrum
The spectrum of hydrogen was particularly simple and could be predicted by a simple mathematical expression.

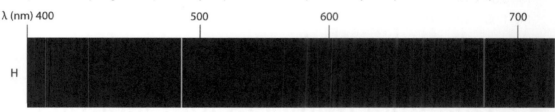

λ (nm) 400   500   600   700

H

quantum number

An index that corresponds to a property of an electron, like its energy.

quantized

When a quantity is restricted to having only certain values.

In 1913, the Danish scientist Niels Bohr suggested a reason why the hydrogen atom spectrum looked this way. He suggested that the electron in a hydrogen atom could not have any random energy, having *only* certain fixed values of energy that were indexed by the number n (the same n in the equation above and now called a **quantum number**). Quantities that have certain specific values are called **quantized** values. Bohr suggested that the energy of the electron in hydrogen was quantized because it was in a specific orbit. Because the energies of the electron can have only certain values, the changes in energies can have only certain values (somewhat similar to a staircase: not only are the stair steps set at specific heights but the height between steps is fixed). Finally, Bohr suggested that the energy of light emitted from electrified hydrogen gas was equal to the energy difference of the electron's energy states:

$$E_{\text{light}} = h\nu = \Delta E_{\text{electron}}$$

This means that only certain frequencies (and thus, certain wavelengths) of light are emitted. Figure 4.5 shows a model of the hydrogen atom based on Bohr's ideas.

FIGURE 4.5 Bohr's Model of the Hydrogen Atom
Bohr's description of the hydrogen atom had specific orbits for the electron, which had quantized energies.

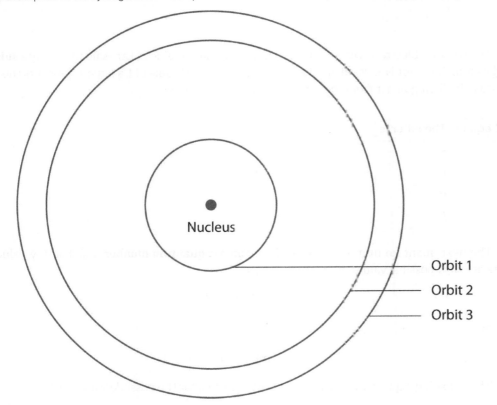

Nucleus

Orbit 1
Orbit 2
Orbit 3

Bohr's ideas were useful but were applied only to the hydrogen atom. However, later researchers generalized Bohr's ideas into a new theory called **quantum mechanics**, which explains the behavior of electrons as if they were acting as a wave, not as particles. Quantum mechanics predicts two major things: quantized energies for electrons of all atoms (not just hydrogen) and an organization of electrons within atoms. Electrons are no longer thought of as being randomly distributed around a nucleus or restricted to certain orbits (in that regard, Bohr was wrong). Instead, electrons are collected into groups and subgroups that explain much about the chemical behavior of the atom.

In the quantum-mechanical model of an atom, the state of an electron is described by four quantum numbers, not just the one predicted by Bohr. The first quantum number is called the **principal quantum number** (n). The principal quantum number largely determines the energy of an electron. Electrons in the same atom that have the same principal quantum number are said to occupy an electron **shell** of the atom. The principal quantum number can be any nonzero positive integer: 1, 2, 3, 4,....

Within a shell, there may be multiple possible values of the next quantum number, the **angular momentum quantum number** (l). The l quantum number has a minor effect on the energy of the electron but also affects the spatial distribution of the electron in three-dimensional space—that is, the shape of an electron's distribution in space. The value of the l quantum number can be any integer between 0 and $n - 1$:

$$\ell = 0, 1, 2, \ldots, n - 1$$

Thus, for a given value of n, there are different possible values of l:

quantum mechanics

The theory of electrons that treats them as a wave.

principal quantum number

The index that largely determines the energy of an electron in an atom. Represented by n.

shell

A term used to describe electrons with the same principal quantum number.

angular momentum quantum number

An index that affects the energy and the spatial distribution of an electron in an atom. Represented by ℓ.

If n equals	ℓ can be
1	0
2	0 or 1
3	0, 1, or 2
4	0, 1, 2, or 3

subshell

A term used to describe electrons in a shell that have the same angular momentum quantum number.

and so forth. Electrons within a shell that have the same value of l are said to occupy a **subshell** in the atom. Commonly, instead of referring to the numerical value of l, a letter represents the value of l (to help distinguish it from the principal quantum number):

If ℓ equals	The letter is
0	s
1	p
2	d
3	f

magnetic quantum number

The index that determines the orientation of the electron's spatial distribution. Represented by m_ℓ .

The next quantum number is called the **magnetic quantum number** (m_l). For any value of l, there are 2l + 1 possible values of m_l, ranging from –l to l:

$$-\ell \le m_\ell \le \ell$$

or

$$|m_\ell| \le \ell$$

The following explicitly lists the possible values of m_l for the possible values of l:

If ℓ equals	The m_ℓ values can be
0	0
1	–1, 0, or 1
2	–2, –1, 0, 1, or 2
3	–3, –2, –1, 0, 1, 2, or 3

orbital

The specific set of principal, angular momentum, and magnetic quantum numbers for an electron.

The particular value of m_l dictates the orientation of an electron's distribution in space. When l is zero, m_l can be only zero, so there is only one possible orientation. When l is 1, there are three possible orientations for an electron's distribution. When l is 2, there are five possible orientations of electron distribution. This goes on and on for other values of l, but we need not consider any higher values of l here. Each value of m_l designates a certain **orbital**. Thus, there is only one orbital when l is zero, three orbitals when l is 1, five orbitals when l is 2, and so forth. The m_l quantum number has no effect on the energy of an electron unless the electrons are subjected to a magnetic field—hence its name.

The l quantum number dictates the general shape of electron distribution in space (Figure 4.6). Any s orbital is spherically symmetric (part (a) in Figure 4.6), and there is only one orbital in any s subshell. Any p orbital has a two-lobed, dumbbell-like shape (part (b) in Figure 4.6); because there are three of them, we normally represent them as pointing along the x-, y-, and z-axes of Cartesian space. The d orbitals are four-lobed rosettes (part (c) in Figure 4.6); they are oriented differently in space (the one labeled d_{z^2} has two lobes and a torus instead of four lobes, but it is equivalent to the other orbitals). When there is more than one possible value of m_l, each orbital is labeled with one of the possible values. It should be noted that the diagrams in Figure 4.6 are estimates of the electron distribution in space, not surfaces electrons are fixed on.

FIGURE 4.6 Electron Orbitals
(a) The lone *s* orbital is spherical in distribution. (b) The three *p* orbitals are shaped like dumbbells, and each one points in a different direction. (c) The five *d* orbitals are rosette in shape, except for the d_{z^2} orbital, which is a "dumbbell + torus" combination. They are all oriented in different directions.

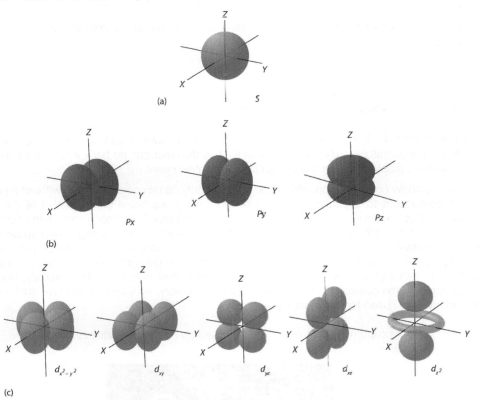

(a)   *s*

(b)   *Px*   *Py*   *Pz*

(c) $d_{x^2-y^2}$ d_{xy} d_{yz} d_{xz} d_{z^2}

The final quantum number is the **spin quantum number** (m_s). Electrons and other subatomic particles behave as if they are spinning (we cannot tell if they really are, but they behave as if they are). Electrons themselves have two possible spin states, and because of mathematics, they are assigned the quantum numbers +1/2 and –1/2. These are the only two possible choices for the spin quantum number of an electron.

Example 3

Of the set of quantum numbers {n, ℓ, m_ℓ, m_s}, which are possible and which are not allowed?

1. {3, 2, 1, +1/2}
2. {2, 2, 0, –1/2}
3. {3, –1, 0, +1/2}

Solution

1. The principal quantum number *n* must be an integer, which it is here. The quantum number ℓ must be less than *n*, which it is. The m_ℓ quantum number must be between $-\ell$ and ℓ, which it is. The spin quantum number is +1/2, which is allowed. Because this set of quantum numbers follows all restrictions, it is possible.

2. The quantum number *n* is an integer, but the quantum number ℓ must be less than *n*, which it is not. Thus, this is not an allowed set of quantum numbers.

3. The principal quantum number *n* is an integer, but ℓ is not allowed to be negative. Therefore this is not an allowed set of quantum numbers.

Test Yourself

Of the set of quantum numbers {n, ℓ, m_ℓ, m_s}, which are possible and which are not allowed?

1. {4, 2, –2, 1}
2. {3, 1, 0, –1/2}

Answers

1. Spin must be either +1/2 or –1/2, so this set of quantum number is not allowed.
2. allowed

Chemistry Is Everywhere: Neon Lights

A neon light is basically an electrified tube with a small amount of gas in it. Electricity excites electrons in the gas atoms, which then give off light as the electrons go back into a lower energy state. However, many so-called "neon" lights don't contain neon!

Although we know now that a gas discharge gives off only certain colors of light, without a prism or other component to separate the individual light colors, we see a composite of all the colors emitted. It is not unusual for a certain color to predominate. True neon lights, with neon gas in them, have a reddish-orange light due to the large amount of red-, orange-, and yellow-colored light emitted. However, if you use krypton instead of neon, you get a whitish light, while using argon yields a blue-purple light. A light filled with nitrogen gas glows purple, as does a helium lamp. Other gases—and mixtures of gases—emit other colors of light. Ironically, despite its importance in the development of modern electronic theory, hydrogen lamps emit little visible light and are rarely used for illumination purposes.

The different colors of these "neon" lights are caused by gases other than neon in the discharge tubes.

Source: © Thinkstock

Key Takeaways

- Electrons in atoms have quantized energies.
- The state of electrons in atoms is described by four quantum numbers.

Exercises

1. Differentiate between a continuous spectrum and a line spectrum.
2. Under what circumstances is a continuous spectrum formed? Under what circumstances is a line spectrum formed?
3. What is the wavelength of light from the hydrogen atom spectrum when $n = 3$?
4. What is the wavelength of light from the hydrogen atom spectrum when $n = 5$?
5. What are the restrictions on the principal quantum number?
6. What are the restrictions on the angular momentum quantum number?

7. What are the restrictions on the magnetic quantum number?

8. What are the restrictions on the spin quantum number?

9. What are the possible values for ℓ when $n = 5$?

10. What are the possible values for ℓ when $n = 1$?

11. What are the possible values for m_ℓ when $\ell = 3$?

12. What are the possible values for m_ℓ when $\ell = 6$?

13. Describe the shape of an s orbital.

14. Describe the shape of a p orbital.

15. Which of these sets of quantum numbers is allowed? If it is not, explain why.

   a. {4, 1, −2, +1/2}

   b. {2, 0, 0, −1/2}

16. Which of these sets of quantum numbers is allowed? If it is not, explain why.

   a. {5, 2, −1, −1/2}

   b. {3, −1, −1, −1/2}

Answers

1. A continuous spectrum is a range of light frequencies or wavelengths; a line spectrum shows only certain frequencies or wavelengths.

2. A continuous spectrum is formed from light coming from a hot object; a line spectrum is formed from light coming from an electrically excited gas.

3. 6.56×10^{-7} m, or 656 nm

4. 4.34×10^{-7} m, or 434 nm

5. The principal quantum number is restricted to being a positive whole number.

6. ℓ must be less than n.

7. The absolute value of m_ℓ must be less than or equal to ℓ: $|m_\ell| \leq \ell$.

8. m_s can be only +1/2 or −1/2.

9. ℓ can be 0, 1, 2, 3, or 4.

10. ℓ can be 0 only.

11. m_ℓ can be −3, −2, −1, 0, 1, 2, or 3.

12. m_ℓ can be −6, −5, −4, −3, −2, −1, 0, 1, 2, 3, 4, 5, or 6.

13. An s orbital is spherical in shape.

14. A p orbital has a dumbbell-like shape.

15. a. Because $|m_\ell|$ must be less than ℓ, this set of quantum numbers is not allowed.

   b. allowed

16. a. allowed

   b. Because ℓ must be a positive number, this set of quantum numbers is not allowed.

4.3 Organization of Electrons in Atoms

Learning Objectives

1. Learn how electrons are organized in atoms.
2. Represent the organization of electrons by an electron configuration.

Pauli exclusion principle

No two electrons in an atom can have the same set of four quantum numbers.

Now that you know that electrons have quantum numbers, how are they arranged in atoms? The key to understanding electronic arrangement is summarized in the **Pauli exclusion principle**: no two electrons in an atom can have the same set of four quantum numbers. This dramatically limits the number of electrons that can exist in a shell or a subshell.

Electrons are typically organized around an atom by starting at the lowest possible quantum numbers first, which are the shells-subshells with lower energies. Consider H, an atom with a single electron only. Under normal conditions, the single electron would go into the $n = 1$ shell, which has only a single s subshell with one orbital (because m_l can equal only 0). The convention is to label the shell-subshell combination with the number of the shell and the letter that represents the subshell. Thus, the electron goes in the 1s shell-subshell combination. It is usually not necessary to specify the m_l or m_s quantum numbers, but for the H atom, the electron has $m_l = 0$ (the only possible value) and an m_s of either +1/2 or –1/2.

The He atom has two electrons. The second electron can also go into the 1s shell-subshell combination but only if its spin quantum number is different from the first electron's spin quantum number. Thus, the sets of quantum numbers for the two electrons are {1, 0, 0, +1/2} and {1, 0, 0, –1/2}. Notice that the overall set is different for the two electrons, as required by the Pauli exclusion principle.

The next atom is Li, with three electrons. However, now the Pauli exclusion principle implies that we cannot put that electron in the 1s shell-subshell because no matter how we try, this third electron would have the same set of four quantum numbers as one of the first two electrons. So this third electron must be assigned to a different shell-subshell combination. However, the $n = 1$ shell doesn't have another subshell; it is restricted to having just l = 0, or an s subshell. Therefore, this third electron has to be assigned to the $n = 2$ shell, which has an s (l = 0) subshell and a p (l = 1) subshell. Again, we usually start with the lowest quantum number, so this third electron is assigned to the 2s shell-subshell combination of quantum numbers.

The Pauli exclusion principle has the net effect of limiting the number of electrons that can be assigned a shell-subshell combination of quantum numbers. For example, in any s subshell, no matter what the shell number, there can be a maximum of only two electrons. Once the s subshell is filled up, any additional electrons must go to another subshell in the shell (if it exists) or to higher-numbered shell. A similar analysis shows that a p subshell can hold a maximum of six electrons. A d subshell can hold a maximum of 10 electrons, while an f subshell can have a maximum of 14 electrons. By limiting subshells to these maxima, we can distribute the available electrons to their shells and subshells.

Example 4

How would the six electrons for C be assigned to the n and ℓ quantum numbers?

Solution

The first two electrons go into the $1s$ shell-subshell combination. Two additional electrons can go into the $2s$ shell-subshell, but now this subshell is filled with the maximum number of electrons. The $n = 2$ shell also has a p subshell, so the remaining two electrons can go into the $2p$ subshell. The $2p$ subshell is not completely filled because it can hold a maximum of six electrons.

Test Yourself

How would the 11 electrons for Na be assigned to the n and ℓ quantum numbers?

Answer

Two $1s$ electrons, two $2s$ electrons, six $2p$ electrons, and one $3s$ electron

Now that we see how electrons are partitioned among the shells and subshells, we need a more concise way of communicating this partitioning. Chemists use an **electron configuration** to represent the organization of electrons in shells and subshells in an atom. An electron configuration simply lists the shell and subshell labels, with a right superscript giving the number of electrons in that subshell. The shells and subshells are listed in the order of filling.

For example, an H atom has a single electron in the $1s$ subshell. Its electron configuration is

$$\text{H} : 1s^1$$

He has two electrons in the $1s$ subshell. Its electron configuration is

$$\text{He} : 1s^2$$

The three electrons for Li are arranged in the $1s$ subshell (two electrons) and the $2s$ subshell (one electron). The electron configuration of Li is

$$\text{Li} : 1s^2 2s^1$$

Be has four electrons, two in the $1s$ subshell and two in the $2s$ subshell. Its electron configuration is

$$\text{Be} : 1s^2 2s^2$$

Now that the $2s$ subshell is filled, electrons in larger atoms must go into the $2p$ subshell, which can hold a maximum of six electrons. The next six elements progressively fill up the $2p$ subshell:

$$\text{B} : 1s^2 2s^2 2p^1$$

$$\text{C} : 1s^2 2s^2 2p^2$$

$$\text{N} : 1s^2 2s^2 2p^3$$

$$\text{O} : 1s^2 2s^2 2p^4$$

$$\text{F} : 1s^2 2s^2 2p^5$$

$$\text{Ne} : 1s^2 2s^2 2p^6$$

Now that the $2p$ subshell is filled (all possible subshells in the $n = 2$ shell), the next electron for the next-larger atom must go into the $n = 3$ shell, s subshell.

electron configuration

The representation of the organization of electrons in shells and subshells in an atom.

Example 5

What is the electron configuration for Na, which has 11 electrons?

Solution

The first two electrons occupy the $1s$ subshell. The next two occupy the $2s$ subshell, while the next six electrons occupy the $2p$ subshell. This gives us 10 electrons so far, with 1 electron left. This last electron goes into the $n = 3$ shell, s subshell. Thus, the electron configuration of Na is $1s^2 2s^2 2p^6 3s^1$.

Test Yourself

What is the electron configuration for Mg, which has 12 electrons?

Answer

$1s^2 2s^2 2p^6 3s^2$

For larger atoms, the electron arrangement becomes more complicated. This is because after the $3p$ subshell is filled, filling the $4s$ subshell first actually leads to a lesser overall energy than filling the $3d$ subshell. Recall that while the principal quantum number largely dictates the energy of an electron, the angular momentum quantum number also has an impact on energy; by the time we get to the $3d$ and $4s$ subshells, we see overlap in the filling of the shells. Thus, after the $3p$ subshell is completely filled (which occurs for Ar), the next electron for K occupies the $4s$ subshell, not the $3d$ subshell:

$$\text{K}: 1s^2 2s^2 2p^6 3s^2 3p^6 4s^1, \text{ not } 1s^2 2s^2 2p^6 3s^2 3p^6 3d^1$$

For larger and larger atoms, the order of filling the shells and subshells seems to become even more complicated. There are some useful ways to remember the order, like that shown in Figure 4.7. If you follow the arrows in order, they pass through the subshells in the order that they are filled with electrons in larger atoms. Initially, the order is the same as the expected shell-subshell order, but for larger atoms, there is some shifting around of the principal quantum numbers. However, Figure 4.7 gives a valid ordering of filling subshells with electrons for most atoms.

FIGURE 4.7 Electron Shell Filling Order
Starting with the top arrow, follow each arrow. The subshells you reach along each arrow give the ordering of filling of subshells in larger atoms. The $n = 5$ and higher shells have more subshells, but only those subshells that are needed to accommodate the electrons of the known elements are given.

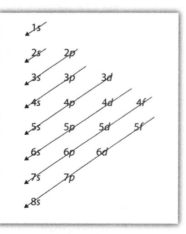

Example 6

What is the predicted electron configuration for Sn, which has 50 electrons?

Solution

We will follow the chart in Figure 4.7 until we can accommodate 50 electrons in the subshells in the proper order:

$$\text{Sn: } 1s^2 2s^2 2p^6 3s^2 3p^6 4s^2 3d^{10} 4p^6 5s^2 4d^{10} 5p^2$$

Verify by adding the superscripts, which indicate the number of electrons: 2 + 2 + 6 + 2 + 6 + 2 + 10 + 6 + 2 + 10 + 2 = 50, so we have placed all 50 electrons in subshells in the proper order.

Test Yourself

What is the electron configuration for Ba, which has 56 electrons?

Answer

$1s^2 2s^2 2p^6 3s^2 3p^6 4s^2 3d^{10} 4p^6 5s^2 4d^{10} 5p^6 6s^2$

As the previous example demonstrated, electron configurations can get fairly long. An **abbreviated electron configuration** uses one of the elements from the last column of the periodic table, which contains what are called the *noble gases*, to represent the core of electrons up to that element. Then the remaining electrons are listed explicitly. For example, the abbreviated electron configuration for Li, which has three electrons, would be

$$\text{Li: } [\text{He}]2s^1$$

where [He] represents the two-electron core that is equivalent to He's electron configuration. The square brackets represent the electron configuration of a noble gas. This is not much of an abbreviation. However, consider the abbreviated electron configuration for W, which has 74 electrons:

$$\text{W: } [\text{Xe}]6s^2 4f^{14} 5d^4$$

This is a significant simplification over an explicit listing of all 74 electrons. So for larger elements, the abbreviated electron configuration can be a very useful shorthand.

abbreviated electron configuration

An electron configuration that uses one of the noble gases to represent the core of electrons up to that element.

Example 7

What is the abbreviated electron configuration for P, which has 15 electrons?

Solution

With 15 electrons, the electron configuration of P is:

$$\text{P: } 1s^2 2s^2 2p^6 3s^2 3p^3$$

The first immediate noble gas is Ne, which has an electron configuration of $1s^2 2s^2 2p^6$. Using the electron configuration of Ne to represent the first 10 electrons, the abbreviated electron configuration of P is:

$$\text{P: } [\text{Ne}]3s^2 3p^3$$

Test Yourself

What is the abbreviated electron configuration for Rb, which has 37 electrons?

Answer

$[\text{Kr}]5s^1$

There are some exceptions to the rigorous filling of subshells by electrons. In many cases, an electron goes from a higher-numbered shell to a lower-numbered but later-filled subshell to fill the later-filled subshell. One example is Ag. With 47 electrons, its electron configuration is predicted to be:

$$\text{Ag: } [\text{Kr}]5s^2 4d^9$$

However, experiments have shown that the electron configuration is actually:

$$Ag: [Kr]5s^1 4d^{10}$$

This, then, qualifies as an exception to our expectations. At this point, you do not need to memorize the exceptions; but if you come across one, understand that it is an exception to the normal rules of filling subshells with electrons, which can happen.

Key Takeaways

- The Pauli exclusion principle limits the number of electrons in the subshells and shells.
- Electrons in larger atoms fill shells and subshells in a regular pattern that we can follow.
- Electron configurations are a shorthand method of indicating what subshells electrons occupy in atoms.
- Abbreviated electron configurations are a simpler way of representing electron configurations for larger atoms.
- Exceptions to the strict filling of subshells with electrons occur.

Exercises

1. Give two possible sets of four quantum numbers for the electron in an H atom.
2. Give the possible sets of four quantum numbers for the electrons in a Li atom.
3. How many subshells are completely filled with electrons for Na? How many subshells are unfilled?
4. How many subshells are completely filled with electrons for Mg? How many subshells are unfilled?
5. What is the maximum number of electrons in the entire $n = 2$ shell?
6. What is the maximum number of electrons in the entire $n = 4$ shell?
7. Write the complete electron configuration for each atom.
    a. Si, 14 electrons
    b. Sc, 21 electrons
8. Write the complete electron configuration for each atom.
    a. Br, 35 electrons
    b. Be, 4 electrons
9. Write the complete electron configuration for each atom.
    a. Cd, 48 electrons
    b. Mg, 12 electrons
10. Write the complete electron configuration for each atom.
    a. Cs, 55 electrons
    b. Ar, 18 electrons
11. Write the abbreviated electron configuration for each atom in Exercise 7.
12. Write the abbreviated electron configuration for each atom in Exercise 8.
13. Write the abbreviated electron configuration for each atom in Exercise 9.
14. Write the abbreviated electron configuration for each atom in Exercise 10.

Answers

1. {1, 0, 0, 1/2} and [1, 0, 0, –1/2}
2. {1, 0, 0, 1/2}, {1, 0, 0, –1/2}, and {2, 0, 0, 1/2} or {1, 0, 0, 1/2}, {1, 0, 0. –1/2}, and {2, 0, 0, –1/2}
3. Three subshells (1s, 2s, 2p) are completely filled, and one shell (3s) is partially filled.
4. Three subshells (1s, 2s, 2p) are completely filled, and one shell (3s) is partially filled.
5. 8 electrons
6. 32 electrons
7. a. $1s^2 2s^2 2p^6 3s^2 3p^2$

    b. $1s^2 2s^2 2p^6 3s^2 3p^6 4s^2 3d^1$
8. a. $1s^2 2s^2 2p^6 3s^2 3p^6 4s^2 3d^{10} 4p^5$

    b. $1s^2 2s^2$
9. a. $1s^2 2s^2 2p^6 3s^2 3p^6 4s^2 3d^{10} 4p^6 5s^2 4d^{10}$

    b. $1s^2 2s^2 2p^6 3s^2$
10. a. $1s^2 2s^2 2p^6 3s^2 3p^6 4s^2 3d^{10} 4p^6 5s^2 4d^{10} 5p^6 6s^1$

    b. $1s^2 2s^2 2p^6 3s^2 3p^6$
11. a. $[Ne]3s^2 3p^2$

    b. $[Ar]4s^2 3d^1$
12. a. $[Ar]4s^2 3d^{10} 4p^5$

    b. $[He]2s^2$
13. a. $[Kr]5s^2 4d^{10}$

    b. $[Ne]3s^2$
14. a. $[Xe]6s^1$

    b. $[Ar]$

4.4 Electronic Structure and the Periodic Table

Learning Objectives

1. Relate the electron configurations of the elements to the shape of the periodic table.
2. Determine the expected electron configuration of an element by its place on the periodic table.

In Chapter 3, we introduced the periodic table as a tool for organizing the known chemical elements. A periodic table is shown in Figure 4.8. The elements are listed by atomic number (the number of protons in the nucleus), and elements with similar chemical properties are grouped together in columns.

FIGURE 4.8 Periodic Table

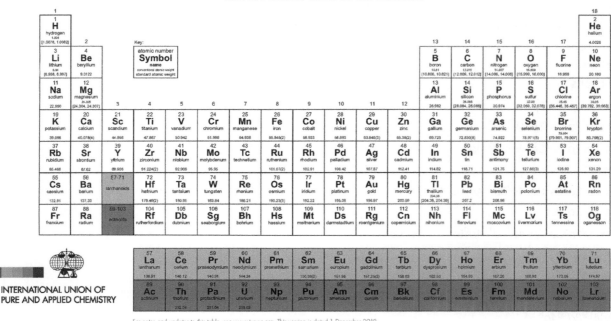

IUPAC Periodic Table of the Elements

Source: "IUPAC Periodic Table of the Elements," International Union of Pure and Applied Chemistry; https://iupac.org/cms/wp-content/uploads/2018/12/IUPAC_Periodic_Table-01Dec18.pdf.

Why does the periodic table have the structure it does? The answer is rather simple, if you understand electron configurations: *the shape of the periodic table mimics the filling of the sub-shells with electrons.*

Let us start with H and He. Their electron configurations are $1s^1$ and $1s^2$, respectively; with He, the $n = 1$ shell is filled. These two elements make up the first row of the periodic table (see Figure 4.9).

FIGURE 4.9 The 1s Subshell
H and He represent the filling of the 1s subshell.

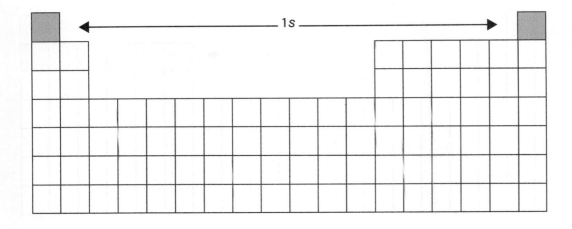

The next two electrons, for Li and Be, would go into the 2s subshell. Figure 4.10 shows that these two elements are adjacent on the periodic table.

FIGURE 4.10 The 2s Subshell
In Li and Be, the 2s subshell is being filled.

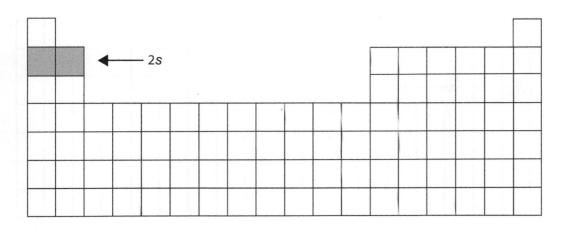

For the next six elements, the 2p subshell is being occupied with electrons. On the right side of the periodic table, these six elements (B through Ne) are grouped together (Figure 4.11).

FIGURE 4.11 The 2*p* Subshell
For B through Ne, the 2*p* subshell is being occupied.

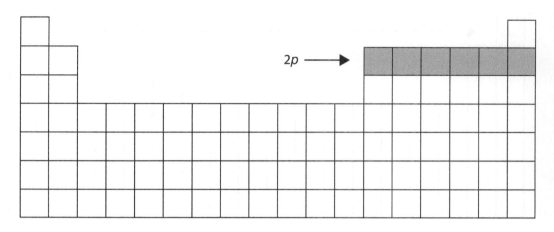

The next subshell to be filled is the 3*s* subshell. The elements when this subshell is being filled, Na and Mg, are back on the left side of the periodic table (Figure 4.12).

FIGURE 4.12 The 3*s* Subshell
Now the 3*s* subshell is being occupied.

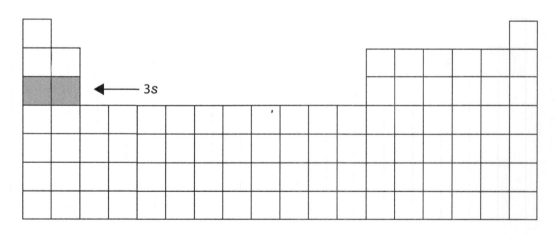

Next, the 3*p* subshell is filled with the next six elements (Figure 4.13).

FIGURE 4.13 The 3*p* Subshell
Next, the 3*p* subshell is filled with electrons.

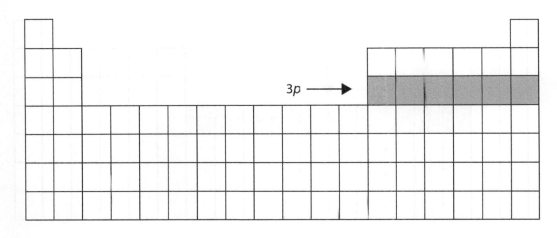

Instead of filling the 3*d* subshell next, electrons go into the 4*s* subshell (Figure 4.14).

FIGURE 4.14 The 4*s* Subshell
The 4*s* subshell is filled before the 3*d* subshell. This is reflected in the structure of the periodic table.

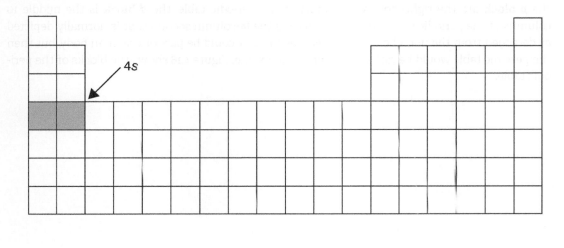

After the 4*s* subshell is filled, the 3*d* subshell is filled with up to 10 electrons. This explains the section of 10 elements in the middle of the periodic table (Figure 4.15).

FIGURE 4.15 The 3*d* Subshell
The 3*d* subshell is filled in the middle section of the periodic table.

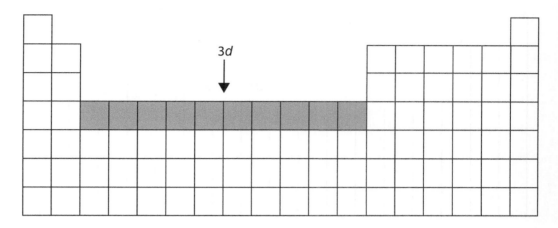

And so forth. As we go across the rows of the periodic table, the overall shape of the table outlines how the electrons are occupying the shells and subshells.

The first two columns on the left side of the periodic table are where the *s* subshells are being occupied. Because of this, the first two rows of the periodic table are labeled the **s block**. Similarly, the **p block** are the right-most six columns of the periodic table, the **d block** is the middle 10 columns of the periodic table, while the **f block** is the 14-column section that is normally depicted as detached from the main body of the periodic table. It could be part of the main body, but then the periodic table would be rather long and cumbersome. Figure 4.16 shows the blocks of the periodic table.

s block

The columns of the periodic table in which **s** subshells are being occupied.

p block

The columns of the periodic table in which **p** subshells are being occupied.

d block

The columns of the periodic table in which **d** subshells are being occupied.

f block

The columns of the periodic table in which **f** subshells are being occupied.

FIGURE 4.16 Blocks on the Periodic Table

The periodic table is separated into blocks depending on which subshell is being filled for the atoms that belong in that section.

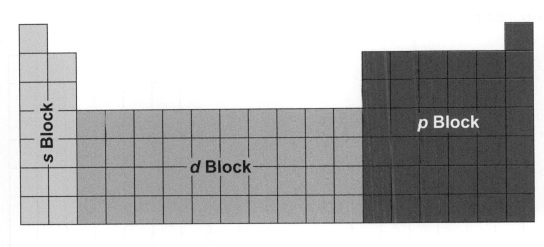

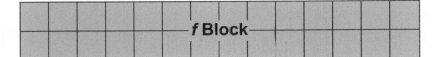

The electrons in the highest-numbered shell, plus any electrons in the last unfilled subshell, are called **valence electrons**; the highest-numbered shell is called the **valence shell**. (The inner electrons are called *core electrons*.) The valence electrons largely control the chemistry of an atom. If we look at just the valence shell's electron configuration, we find that in each column, the valence shell's electron configuration is the same. For example, take the elements in the first column of the periodic table: H, Li, Na, K, Rb, and Cs. Their electron configurations (abbreviated for the larger atoms) are as follows, with the valence shell electron configuration highlighted:

H:	$1s^1$
Li:	$1s^2 2s^1$
Na:	$[\text{Ne}]3s^1$
K:	$[\text{Ar}]4s^1$
Rb:	$[\text{Kr}]5s^1$
Cs:	$[\text{Xe}]6s^1$

valence electrons

The electrons in the highest-numbered shell, plus any electrons in the last unfilled subshell.

valence shell

The highest-numbered shell in an atom that contains electrons.

They all have a similar electron configuration in their valence shells: a single s electron. Because much of the chemistry of an element is influenced by valence electrons, we would expect that these elements would have similar chemistry—*and they do*. The organization of electrons in atoms explains not only the shape of the periodic table but also the fact that elements in the same column of the periodic table have similar chemistry.

The same concept applies to the other columns of the periodic table. Elements in each column have the same valence shell electron configurations, and the elements have some similar chemical properties. This is strictly true for all elements in the s and p blocks. In the d and f blocks, because there are exceptions to the order of filling of subshells with electrons, similar valence shells are not absolute in these blocks. However, many similarities do exist in these blocks, so a similarity in chemical properties is expected.

Similarity of valence shell electron configuration implies that we can determine the electron configuration of an atom solely by its position on the periodic table. Consider Se, as shown in Figure

4.17. It is in the fourth column of the *p* block. This means that its electron configuration should end in a p^4 electron configuration. Indeed, the electron configuration of Se is $[Ar]4s^2 3d^{10} 4p^4$, as expected.

FIGURE 4.17 Selenium on the Periodic Table

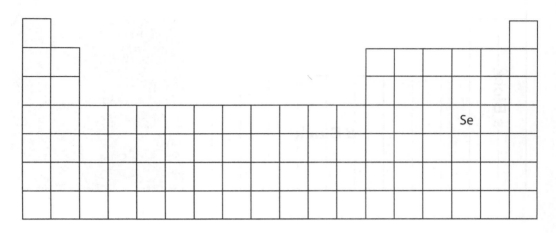

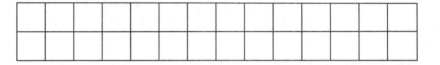

Example 8

From the element's position on the periodic table, predict the valence shell electron configuration for each atom. See Figure 4.18.

1. Ca
2. Sn

Solution

1. Ca is located in the second column of the *s* block. We would expect that its electron configuration should end with s^2. Calcium's electron configuration is $[Ar]4s^2$.

2. Sn is located in the second column of the *p* block, so we expect that its electron configuration would end in p^2. Tin's electron configuration is $[Kr]5s^2 4d^{10} 5p^2$.

Test Yourself

From the element's position on the periodic table, predict the valence shell electron configuration for each atom. See Figure 4.18.

1. Ti
2. Cl

Answer

1. $[Ar]4s^2 3d^2$
2. $[Ne]3s^2 3p^5$

FIGURE 4.18 Various Elements on the Periodic Table

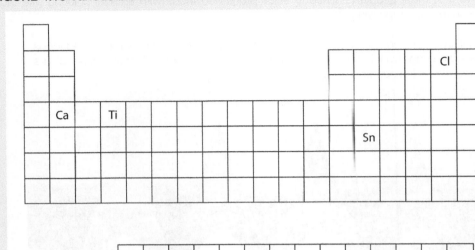

Food and Drink App: Artificial Colors

The color of objects comes from a different mechanism than the colors of neon and other discharge lights. Although colored lights produce their colors, objects are colored because they preferentially reflect a certain color from the white light that shines on them. A red tomato, for example, is bright red because it reflects red light while absorbing all the other colors of the rainbow.

Many foods, such as tomatoes, are highly colored; in fact, the common statement "you eat with your eyes first" is an implicit recognition that the visual appeal of food is just as important as its taste. But what about processed foods?

Many processed foods have food colorings added to them. There are two types of food colorings: natural and artificial. Natural food colorings include caramelized sugar for brown; annatto, turmeric, and saffron for various shades of orange or yellow; betanin from beets for purple; and even carmine, a deep red dye that is extracted from the cochineal, a small insect that is a parasite on cacti in Central and South America. (That s right: you may be eating bug juice!)

Some colorings are artificial. In the United States, the Food and Drug Administration currently approves only seven compounds as artificial colorings in food, beverages, and cosmetics:

1. FD&C Blue #1: Brilliant Blue FCF
2. FD&C Blue #2: Indigotine
3. FD&C Green #3: Fast Green FCF
4. RD&C Red #3: Erythrosine
5. FD&C Red #40: Allura Red AC
6. FD&C Yellow #5: Tartrazine
7. FD&C Yellow #6: Sunset Yellow FCF

Lower-numbered colors are no longer on the market or have been removed for various reasons. Typically, these artificial colorings are large molecules that absorb certain colors of light very strongly, making them useful even at very low concentrations in foods and cosmetics. Even at such low amounts, some critics claim that a small portion of the population (especially children) is sensitive to artificial colorings and urge that their use be curtailed or halted. However, formal studies of artificial colorings and their effects on behavior have been inconclusive or contradictory. Despite this, most people continue to enjoy processed foods with artificial coloring (like those shown in the accompanying figure).

Artificial food colorings are found in a variety of food products, such as processed foods, candies, and egg dyes. Even pet foods have artificial food coloring in them, although it's likely that the animal doesn't care!

Source: Photo courtesy of Matthew Bland, http://www.flickr.com/photos/matthewbland/3111904731.

Key Takeaways

- The arrangement of electrons in atoms is responsible for the shape of the periodic table.
- Electron configurations can be predicted by the position of an atom on the periodic table.

Exercises

1. Where on the periodic table are *s* subshells being occupied by electrons?
2. Where on the periodic table are *d* subshells being occupied by electrons?
3. In what block is Ra found?
4. In what block is Br found?
5. What are the valence shell electron configurations of the elements in the second column of the periodic table?
6. What are the valence shell electron configurations of the elements in the next-to-last column of the periodic table?
7. What are the valence shell electron configurations of the elements in the first column of the *p* block?
8. What are the valence shell electron configurations of the elements in the last column of the *p* block?
9. From the element's position on the periodic table, predict the electron configuration of each atom.

    a. Sr

    b. S

10. From the element's position on the periodic table, predict the electron configuration of each atom.

    a. Fe

    b. Ba

11. From the element's position on the periodic table, predict the electron configuration of each atom.

    a. V

    b. Ar

12. From the element's position on the periodic table, predict the electron configuration of each atom.

    a. Cl

    b. K

13. From the element's position on the periodic table, predict the electron configuration of each atom.

    a. Ge

    b. C

14. From the element's position on the periodic table, predict the electron configuration of each atom.

    a. Mg

    b. I

Answers

1. the first two columns
2. the middle section (transition metals)
3. the s block
4. the p block
5. ns^2
6. ns^2np^5
7. ns^2np^1
8. ns^2np^6
9. a. $1s^22s^22p^63s^23p^64s^23d^{10}4p^65s^2$
   b. $1s^22s^22p^63s^23p^4$
10. a. $1s^22s^22p^63s^23p^64s^23d^6$
    b. $1s^22s^22p^63s^23p^64s^23d^{10}4p^65s^24d^{10}5p^66s^2$
11. a. $1s^22s^22p^63s^23p^64s^23d^3$
    b. $1s^22s^22p^63s^23p^6$
12. a. $1s^22s^22p^63s^23p^5$
    b. $1s^22s^22p^63s^23p^64s^1$

13. a. $1s^22s^22p^63s^23p^64s^23d^{10}4p^2$

    b. $1s^22s^22p^2$

14. a. $1s^22s^22p^63s^2$

    b. $1s^22s^22p^63s^23p^64s^23d^{10}4p^65s^24d^{10}5p^5$

4.5 Periodic Trends

Learning Objective

1. Be able to state how certain properties of atoms vary based on their relative position on the periodic table.

periodic trends

Variation of properties versus position on the periodic table.

One of the reasons the periodic table is so useful is because its structure allows us to qualitatively determine how some properties of the elements vary versus their position on the periodic table. The variation of properties versus position on the periodic table is called **periodic trends**. There is no other tool in science that allows us to judge relative properties of a class of objects like this, which makes the periodic table a very useful tool. Many periodic trends are general. There may be a few points where an opposite trend is seen, but there is an overall trend when considered across a whole row or down a whole column of the periodic table.

atomic radius

An indication of the size of the atom.

The first periodic trend we will consider atomic radius. The **atomic radius** is an indication of the size of an atom. Although the concept of a definite radius of an atom is a bit fuzzy, atoms behave as if they have a certain radius. Such radii can be estimated from various experimental techniques, such as the x-ray crystallography of crystals.

As you go down a column of the periodic table, the atomic radii increase. This is because the valence electron shell is getting larger and there is a larger principal quantum number, so the valence shell lies physically farther away from the nucleus. This trend can be summarized as follows:

$$\text{as} \downarrow \text{PT, atomic radius} \uparrow$$

where PT stands for periodic table. Going across a row on the periodic table, left to right, the trend is different. This is because although the valence shell maintains the same principal quantum number, the number of protons—and hence the nuclear charge—is increasing as you go across the row. The increasing positive charge casts a tighter grip on the valence electrons, so as you go across the periodic table, the atomic radii decrease. Again, we can summarize this trend as follows:

$$\text{as} \rightarrow \text{PT, atomic radius} \downarrow$$

Figure 4.19 shows spheres representing the atoms of the s and p blocks from the periodic table to scale, showing the two trends for the atomic radius.

FIGURE 4.19 Atomic Radii Trends on the Periodic Table
Although there are some reversals in the trend (e.g., see Po in the bottom row), atoms generally get smaller as you go across the periodic table and larger as you go down any one column. Numbers are the radii in pm. Numbers in parentheses are estimates.

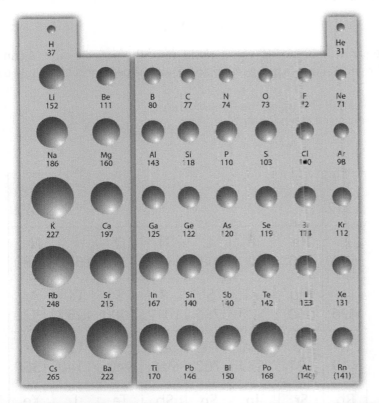

Example 9

Referring only to a periodic table and not to Figure 4.19, which atom is larger in each pair?

1. Si or S
2. S or Te

Solution

1. Si is to the left of S on the periodic table, so it is larger because as you go across the row, the atoms get smaller.
2. S is above Te on the periodic table, so Te is larger because as you go down the column, the atoms get larger.

Test Yourself

Referring only to a periodic table and not to Figure 4.19, which atom is smaller, Ca or Br?

Answer

Br

Ionization energy (IE) is the amount of energy required to remove an electron from an atom in the gas phase (the label "(g)" means "gas phase"):

$$A(g) \rightarrow A^+(g) + e^- \qquad \text{energy required} \equiv IE$$

Ionization energy is always positive because the removal of an electron always requires that energy be put into the atom. IE also shows periodic trends. As you go down the periodic table, it becomes easier to remove an electron from an atom (i.e., IE decreases) because the valence electron is farther away from the nucleus. Thus,

ionization energy (IE)

The amount of energy required to remove an electron from an atom in the gas phase.

$$\text{as} \downarrow \text{PT, IE} \downarrow$$

However, as you go across the periodic table and the electrons get drawn closer in, it takes more energy to remove an electron; as a result, IE increases:

$$\text{as} \rightarrow \text{PT, IE} \uparrow$$

Figure 4.20 shows values of IE versus position on the periodic table. Again, the trend isn't absolute, but the general trends going across and down the periodic table should be obvious.

FIGURE 4.20 Ionization Energy on the Periodic Table
Values are in kilojoules per unit amount of atoms.

H 1312							He 2372
Li 520	Be 899	B 800	C 1086	N 1402	O 1314	F 1681	Ne 2080
Na 496	Mg 160	Al 578	Si 786	P 1012	S 1000	Cl 1251	Ar 1520
K 419	Ca 197	Ga 579	Ge 762	As 946	Se 940	Br 1140	Kr 1350
Rb 403	Sr 550	In 558	Sn 708	Sb 833	Te 870	I 1008	Xe 1170
Cs 376	Bi 503	Ti 590	Pb 715	Bi 703	Po 812	At 890	Rn 1040

IE also shows an interesting trend within a given atom. This is because more than one IE can be defined by removing successive electrons (if the atom has them to begin with):

$$A(g) \rightarrow A^+(g) + e^- \qquad IE_1$$

$$A^+(g) \rightarrow A^{2+}(g) + e^- \qquad IE_2$$

$$A^{2+}(g) \rightarrow A^{3+}(g) + e^- \qquad IE_3$$

and so forth.

Each successive IE is larger than the previous because an electron is being removed from an atom with a progressively larger positive charge. However, IE takes a large jump when a successive ionization goes down into a new shell. For example, the following are the first three IEs for Mg, whose electron configuration is $1s^2 2s^2 2p^6 3s^2$:

$$Mg(g) \rightarrow Mg^+(g) + e^- \qquad IE_1 = 738 \text{ kJ/mol}$$

$$Mg^+(g) \rightarrow Mg^{2+}(g) + e^- \qquad IE_2 = 1,450 \text{ kJ/mol}$$

$$Mg^{2+}(g) \rightarrow Mg^{3+}(g) + e^- \qquad IE_3 = 7,734 \text{ kJ/mol}$$

The second IE is twice the first, which is not a surprise: the first IE involves removing an electron from a neutral atom, while the second one involves removing an electron from a positive ion. The third IE, however, is over *five times* the previous one. Why is it so much larger? Because the first two electrons are removed from the $3s$ subshell, but the third electron has to be removed from the $n = 2$ shell (specifically, the $2p$ subshell, which is lower in energy than the $n = 3$ shell). Thus, it takes much more energy than just overcoming a larger ionic charge would suggest. It is trends like this that demonstrate that electrons are organized in atoms in groups.

Example 10

Which atom in each pair has the larger IE?

1. Ca or Sr
2. K or K^+

Solution

1. Because Sr is below Ca on the periodic table, it is easier to remove an electron from it; thus, Ca has the higher IE.

2. Because K^+ has a positive charge, it will be harder to remove another electron from it, so its IE is larger than that of K. Indeed, it will be significantly larger because the next electron in K^+ to be removed comes from another shell.

Test Yourself

Which atom has the lower ionization energy, C or F?

Answer

C

The opposite of IE is described by **electron affinity (EA)**, which is the energy change when a gas-phase atom accepts an electron:

$$A(g) + e^- \rightarrow A^-(g) \qquad \text{energy change} \equiv EA$$

EA is also usually expressed in kJ/mol. EA also demonstrates some periodic trends, although they are less obvious than the other periodic trends discussed previously. Generally, as you go across the periodic table, EA increases its magnitude:

$$\text{as} \rightarrow PT, \ EA \uparrow$$

There is not a definitive trend as you go down the periodic table; sometimes EA increases, sometimes it decreases. Figure 4.21 shows EA values versus position on the periodic table for the *s*- and *p*-block elements. The trend isn't absolute, especially considering the large positive EA values for the second column. However, the general trend going across the periodic table should be obvious.

electron affinity (EA)

The energy change when a gas-phase atom accepts an electron.

FIGURE 4.21 Electron Affinity on the Periodic Table

Values are in kilojoules per unit amount of atoms.

H -73						
Li -60	**Be** 241	**B** -27	**C** -122	**N** ~0	**O** -141	**F** -328
Na -53	**Mg** 230	**Al** -43	**Si** -134	**P** -72	**S** -200	**Cl** -349
K -48	**Ca** 156	**Ga** -29	**Ge** -119	**As** -78	**Se** -195	**Br** -325
Rb -47	**Sr** 167	**In** -29	**Sn** -107	**Sb** -103	**Te** -190	**I** -295
Cs -46	**Ba** 52	**Ti** -19	**Pb** -35	**Bi** -91		

Example 11

Predict which atom in each pair will have the highest magnitude of EA.

1. C or F
2. Na or S

Solution

1. C and F are in the same row on the periodic table, but F is farther to the right. Therefore, F should have the larger magnitude of EA.

2. Na and S are in the same row on the periodic table, but S is farther to the right. Therefore, S should have the larger magnitude of EA.

Test Yourself

Predict which atom will have the highest magnitude of EA, As or Br.

Answer

Br

Key Takeaway

- Certain properties—notably atomic radius, IE, and EA—can be qualitatively understood by the positions of the elements on the periodic table.

Exercises

1. Write a chemical equation with an IE energy change.
2. Write a chemical equation with an EA energy change.
3. State the trends in atomic radii as you go across and down the periodic table.
4. State the trends in IE as you go across and down the periodic table.
5. Which atom of each pair is larger?
   a. Na or Cs
   b. N or Bi
6. Which atom of each pair is larger?
   a. C or Ge
   b. Be or Ba
7. Which atom of each pair is larger?
   a. K or Cl
   b. Ba or Bi
8. Which atom of each pair is larger?
   a. Si or S
   b. H or He
9. Which atom has the higher IE?
   a. Na or S
   b. Ge or Br
10. Which atom has the higher IE?
    a. C or Ne
    b. Rb or I
11. Which atom has the higher IE?
    a. Li or Cs
    b. Se or O
12. Which atom has the higher IE?
    a. Al or Ga
    b. F or I
13. A third-row element has the following successive IEs: 738; 1,450; 7,734; and 10,550 kJ/mol. Identify the element.
14. A third-row element has the following successive IEs: 1,012; 1,903; 2,912; 4,940; 6,270; and 21,300 kJ/mol. Identify the element.
15. For which successive IE is there a large jump in IE for Ca?
16. For which successive IE is there a large jump in IE for Al?
17. Which atom has the greater magnitude of EA?
    a. C or F
    b. Al or Cl
18. Which atom has the greater magnitude of EA?
    a. K or Br
    b. Mg or S

Answers

1. $Na(g) \rightarrow Na^+(g) + e^-$ energy change = IE (answers will vary)

2. $F(g) + e^- \rightarrow F^-(g)$ energy change = EA (answers will vary)

3. As you go across, atomic radii decrease; as you go down, atomic radii increase.

4. IE increases as you go across the periodic table and decreases as you go down.

5. a. Cs
   b. Bi

6. a. Ge
   b. Ba

7. a. K
   b. Ba

8. a. Si
   b. H

9. a. S
   b. Br

10. a. Ne
    b. I

11. a. Li
    b. O

12. a. Al
    b. F

13. Mg

14. P

15. The third IE shows a large jump in Ca.

16. The fourth IE shows a large jump in Al.

17. a. F
    b. Cl

18. a. Br
    b. S

4.6 End-of-Chapter Material

Additional Exercises

1. What is the frequency of light if its wavelength is 1.00 m?

2. What is the wavelength of light if its frequency is 1.00 s^{-1}?

3. What is the energy of a photon if its wavelength is 1.00 meter?

4. What is the energy of a photon if its frequency is 1.00 s^{-1}?

5. If visible light is defined by the wavelength limits of 400 nm and 700 nm, what is the energy range for visible light photons?

6. Domestic microwave ovens use microwaves that have a wavelength of 122 mm. What is the energy of one photon of this microwave?

7. Use the equation for the wavelengths of the lines of light in the H atom spectrum to calculate the wavelength of light emitted when n is 7 and 8.

8. Use the equation for the wavelengths of the lines of light in the H atom spectrum to calculate the wavelengths of light emitted when n is 5 and 6.

9. Make a table of all the possible values of the four quantum numbers when the principal quantum number $n = 5$.

10. Make a table of all the possible values of m_ℓ and m_s when $\ell = 4$. What is the lowest value of the principal quantum number for this to occur?

11. a. Predict the electron configurations of Sc through Zn.

    b. From a source of actual electron configurations, determine how many exceptions there are from your predictions in part a.

12. a. Predict the electron configurations of Ga through Kr.

    b. From a source of actual electron configurations, determine how many exceptions there are from your predictions in part a.

13. Recently, Russian chemists reported experimental evidence of element 117. Use the periodic table to predict its valence shell electron configuration.

14. Bi (atomic number 83) is used in some stomach discomfort relievers. Using its place on the periodic table, predict its valence shell electron configuration.

15. Which atom has a higher ionization energy (IE), C or P?

16. Which atom has a higher IE, F or As?

17. Which atom has a smaller radius, As or Cl?

18. Which atom has a smaller radius, K or F?

19. How many IEs does an H atom have? Write the chemical reactions for the successive ionizations.

20. How many IEs does a Be atom have? Write the chemical reactions for the successive ionizations.

21. Based on what you know of electrical charges, do you expect Na^+ to be larger or smaller than Na?

22. Based on what you know of electrical charges, do you expect Cl^- to be larger or smaller than Cl?

Answers

1. $3.00 \times 10^8 \text{ s}^{-1}$

2. $3.00 \times 10^8 \text{ m}$

3. $1.99 \times 10^{-22} \text{ J}$

4. $6.626 \times 10^{-34} \text{ J}$

5. $4.97 \times 10^{-19} \text{ J}$ to $2.84 \times 10^{-19} \text{ J}$

6. $1.63 \times 10^{-24} \text{ J}$

7. $3.97 \times 10^{-7} \text{ m}$ and $3.89 \times 10^{-7} \text{ m}$, respectively

8. 4.34×10^{-7} and $4.10 \times 10^{-7} \text{ m}$, respectively

9.

n	ℓ	m_ℓ	m_s
5	0	0	1/2 or −1/2
5	1	−1, 0, 1	1/2 or −1/2

n	ℓ	m_ℓ	m_s
5	2	-2, -1, 0, 1, 2	1/2 or -1/2
5	3	-3, -2, -1, 0, 1, 2, 3	1/2 or -1/2
5	4	-4, -3, -2, -1, 0, 1, 2, 3, 4	1/2 or -1/2

10.

ℓ	m_ℓ	m_s
4	-4	1/2 or -1/2
4	-3	1/2 or -1/2
4	-2	1/2 or -1/2
4	-1	1/2 or -1/2
4	0	1/2 or -1/2
4	1	1/2 or -1/2
4	2	1/2 or -1/2
4	3	1/2 or -1/2
4	4	1/2 or -1/2

Lowest value of n when this occurs: $n = 5$.

11. a. The electron configurations are predicted to end in $3d^1$, $3d^2$, $3d^3$, $3d^4$, $3d^5$, $3d^6$, $3d^7$, $3d^8$, $3d^9$, and $3d^{10}$.

  b. Cr and Cu are exceptions.

12. a. Electron configurations should end in $4p^1$, $4p^2$, $4p^3$, $4p^4$, $4p^5$, and $4p^6$.

  b. There are no exceptions.

13. Element 117's valence shell electron configuration should be $7s^27p^5$.

14. Bi's valence shell electron configuration is $6s^26p^3$.

15. O

16. F

17. Cl

18. F

19. H has only one IE: $H \rightarrow H^+ + e^-$

20. Be has four IEs:

  $Be \rightarrow Be^+ + e^-$ IE_1

  $Be^+ \rightarrow Be^{2+} + e^-$ IE_2

  $Be^{2+} \rightarrow Be^{3+} + e^-$ IE_3

  $Be^{3+} \rightarrow Be^{4+} + e^-$ IE_4

21. smaller

22. larger

CHAPTER 5
Molecules and Bonds

Opening Essay

Diamond is the hardest natural material known on earth. Yet diamond is just pure carbon. What is special about this element that makes diamond so hard?

Bonds. Chemical bonds.

In a perfect diamond crystal, each C atom makes four connections—bonds—to four other C atoms in a three-dimensional matrix. Four is the greatest number of bonds that is commonly made by atoms, so C atoms maximize their interactions with other atoms. This three-dimensional array of connections extends throughout the diamond crystal, making it essentially one large molecule. Breaking a diamond means breaking every bond at once.

Also, the bonds are moderately strong. There are stronger interactions known, but the carbon-carbon connection is fairly strong itself. Not only does a person have to break many connections at once, but also the bonds are strong connections from the start.

There are other substances that have similar bonding arrangements as diamond does. The substances known as silicon dioxide and boron nitride have some similarities, but neither of them comes close to the ultimate hardness of diamond.

Diamond is the hardest known natural substance and is composed solely of the element carbon.

Source: © Thinkstock

How do atoms make compounds? Typically they join together in such a way that they lose their identities as elements and adopt a new identity as a compound. These joins are called *chemical bonds*. But how do atoms join together? Ultimately, it all comes down to electrons: Electrons make chemistry happen.

5.1 Ions and Ionic Compounds

Learning Objectives

1. Know how ions form.
2. Learn the characteristic charges that ions have.

3. Construct a proper formula for an ionic compound.
4. Generate a proper name for an ionic compound.

As mentioned in Chapter 1, a compound is the combination of two or more elements to make a substance with new chemical and physical properties. There are two basic types of compounds, which are classified as ionic or covalent.

So far, we have discussed atoms that are electrically neutral. They have the same number of electrons as protons, so the negative charges of the electrons is balanced by the positive charges of the protons. However, this is not always the case. Electrons can move from one atom to another; when they do, species with overall electric charges are formed. Such species are called **ions**. Species with overall positive charges are termed **cations**, while species with overall negative charges are called **anions**. Remember that ions are formed only when *electrons* move from one atom to another; a proton never moves from one atom to another to make an ion. Compounds formed from positive and negative ions are called **ionic compounds**. Such compounds form because, from elementary physics, *opposite charges attract each other*. Thus, all ionic compounds will be formed from both cations and anions.

Individual atoms can gain or lose electrons. When they do, they become *monatomic* ions. When atoms gain or lose electrons, they usually gain or lose a characteristic number of electrons and so take on a characteristic overall charge. Table 5.1 lists some common ions in terms of how many electrons they lose (making cations) or gain (making anions). There are several things to notice about the ions in Table 5.1. First, each element that forms cations is a metal, except for one (hydrogen), while each element that forms anions is a nonmetal. This is actually one of the chemical properties of metals and nonmetals: metals tend to form cations, while nonmetals tend to form anions. Second, most atoms form ions of a single characteristic charge. When sodium atoms form ions, they always form a 1+ charge, never a 2+ or 3+ or even 1– charge. Thus, if you commit the information in Table 5.1 to memory, you will always know what charges most atoms form. (Later, we will discuss *why* atoms form the charges they do.)

ion

A species with an overall electric charge.

cation

A species with an overall positive charge.

anion

A species with an overall negative charge.

ionic compound

A compound formed from positive and negative ions.

TABLE 5.1 Monatomic Ions of Various Charges

Ions formed by losing a single electron	H^+
	Na^+
	K^+
	Rb^+
	Ag^+
	Au^+
Ions formed by losing two electrons	Mg^{2+}
	Ca^{2+}
	Sr^{2+}
	Fe^{2+}
	Co^{2+}
	Ni^{2+}
	Cu^{2+}
	Zn^{2+}
	Sn^{2+}
	Hg^{2+}

		Pb^{2+}
Ions formed by losing three electrons		Sc^{3+}
		Fe^{3+}
		Co^{3+}
		Ni^{3+}
		Au^{3+}
		Al^{3+}
		Cr^{3+}
Ions formed by losing four electrons		Ti^{4+}
		Sn^{4+}
		Pb^{4+}
Ions formed by gaining a single electron		F^-
		Cl^-
		Br^-
		I^-
Ions formed by gaining two electrons		O^{2-}
		S^{2-}
		Se^{2-}
Ions formed by gaining three electrons		N^{3-}
		P^{3-}

Third, there are some exceptions to the previous point. A few elements, all metals, can form more than one possible charge. For example, iron atoms can form 2+ cations or 3+ cations. Cobalt is another element that can form more than one possible charged ion (2+ and 3+), while lead can form 2+ or 4+ cations. Unfortunately, there is little understanding which two charges a metal atom may take, so it is best to just memorize the possible charges a particular element can have.

Note the convention for indicating an ion. The magnitude of the charge is listed as a right superscript next to the symbol of the element. If the charge is a single positive or negative one, the number 1 is not written; if the magnitude of the charge is greater than 1, then the number is written *before* the + or – sign. An element symbol without a charge written next to it is assumed to be the uncharged atom.

Naming an ion is straightforward. For a cation, simply use the name of the element and add the word *ion* (or if you want to be more specific, add *cation*) after the element's name. So Na^+ is the sodium ion; Ca^{2+} is the calcium ion. If the element has more than one possible charge, the value of the charge comes after the element name and before the word *ion*. Thus, Fe^{2+} is the iron two ion, while Fe^{3+} is the iron three ion. In print, we use roman numerals in parentheses to represent the charge on the ion, so these two iron ions would be represented as the iron(II) cation and the iron(III) cation, respectively.

For a monatomic anion, use the stem of the element name and append the suffix -*ide* to it, and then add *ion*. Thus, Cl^- is the chloride ion, and N^{3-} is the nitride ion.

Example 1

Name each species.

1. O^{2-}
2. Co
3. Co^{2+}

Solution

1. This species has a 2– charge on it, so it is an anion. Anions are named using the stem of the element name with the suffix *-ide* added. This is the oxide anion.
2. Because this species has no charge, it is an atom in its elemental form. This is cobalt.
3. In this case, there is a 2+ charge on the atom, so it is a cation. We note from Table 5.1 that cobalt cations can have two possible charges, so the name of the ion must specify which charge the ion has. This is the cobalt(II) cation.

Test Yourself

Name each species.

1. P^{3-}
2. Sr^{2+}

Answers

1. the phosphide anion
2. the strontium cation

chemical formula

A list of elements in a compound.

ionic formula

The chemical formula for an ionic compound.

We use the symbols of the elements to list the elements in a compound. This list is called a **chemical formula**. Chemical formulas for ionic compounds are called **ionic formulas**. A proper ionic formula has a cation and an anion in it; an ionic compound is never formed between two cations only or two anions only. The key to writing proper ionic formulas is simple: the total positive charge from the cation(s) must balance the total negative charge from the anion(s). Because the charges on the ions are characteristic, sometimes we have to have more than one of a cation or an anion to balance the overall positive and negative charges. It is conventional to use the lowest ratio of ions that are needed to balance the charges.

For example, consider the ionic compound between Na^+ and Cl^-. Each ion has a single charge, one positive and one negative, so we need only one ion of each to balance the overall charge. When writing the ionic formula, we follow two additional conventions: (1) write the formula for the cation first and the formula for the anion next, but (2) do not write the charges on the ions. Thus, for the compound between Na^+ and Cl^-, we have the ionic formula NaCl (Figure 5.1). The formula Na_2Cl_2 also has balanced charges, but the convention is to use the lowest ratio of ions, which would be one of each. There is one final convention: Do not write a subscripted "1" if there is only one ion; if no subscript is present, it is assumed that there is only a single atom of that element present. For the ionic compound between magnesium cations (Mg^{2+}) and oxide anions (O^{2-}), again we need only one of each ion to balance the charges. By convention, the formula is MgO.

For the ionic compound between Mg^{2+} ions and Cl^- ions, we must consider the fact that the charges have different magnitudes, 2+ on the magnesium ion and 1- on the chloride ion. To balance the charges with the lowest number of ions possible, we need to have two chloride ions to balance the charge on the one magnesium ion. Rather than write the formula MgClCl, we combine the two chloride ions and write it with a 2 subscript: $MgCl_2$.

Example 2

Write the proper ionic formula for each of the two given ions.

1. Ca^{2+} and Cl^-
2. Al^{3+} and F^-
3. Al^{3+} and O^{2-}

Solution

1. We need two Cl^- ions to balance the charge on one Ca^{2+} ion, so the proper ionic formula is $CaCl_2$.
2. We need three F^- ions to balance the charge on the Al^{3+} ion, so the proper ionic formula is AlF_3.
3. With Al^{3+} and O^{2-}, note that neither charge is a perfect multiple of the other. This means we have to go to a least common multiple, which in this case will be six. To get a total of 6+, we need two Al^{3+} ions; to get 6-, we need three O^{2-} ions. Hence the proper ionic formula is Al_2O_3.

Test Yourself

Write the proper ionic formulas for each of the two given ions.

1. Fe^{2+} and S^{2-}
2. Fe^{3+} and S^{2-}

Answers

1. FeS
2. Fe_2S_3

Naming ionic compounds is simple: combine the name of the cation and the name of the anion, in both cases omitting the word *ion*. *Do not use numerical prefixes if there is more than one ion necessary to balance the charges.* NaCl is sodium chloride, a combination of the name of the cation (sodium) and the anion (chloride). MgO is magnesium oxide. $MgCl_2$ is magnesium chloride—*not* magnesium dichloride.

In naming ionic compounds whose cations can have more than one possible charge, we must also include the charge, in parentheses and in roman numerals, as part of the name. Hence FeS is iron(II) sulfide, while Fe_2S_3 is iron(III) sulfide. Again, no numerical prefixes appear in the name. The number of ions in the formula is dictated by the need to balance the positive and negative charges.

Example 3

Name each ionic compound.

1. $CaCl_2$
2. AlF_3
3. Co_2O_3

Solution

FIGURE 5.1
NaCl = Table Salt
The ionic compound NaCl is very common.

Source: © Thinkstock

1. Using the names of the ions, this ionic compound is named calcium chloride. *It is not calcium(II) chloride* because calcium forms only one cation when it forms an ion, and it has a characteristic charge of 2+.

2. The name of this ionic compound is aluminum fluoride.

3. We know that cobalt can have more than one possible charge; we just need to determine what it is. Oxide always has a 2− charge, so with three oxide ions, we have a total negative charge of 6−. This means that the two cobalt ions have to contribute 6+, which for two cobalt ions means that each one is 3+. Therefore, the proper name for this ionic compound is cobalt(III) oxide.

Test Yourself

Name each ionic compound.

1. Sc_2O_3
2. AgCl

Answers

1. scandium oxide
2. silver chloride

How do you know whether a formula—and by extension, a name—is for an ionic compound? Ionic compounds form between metals and nonmetals. The periodic table (Figure 3.4) can be used to determine which elements are metals and nonmetals—metals are on one side (the left three-quarters), nonmetals are on the other (the upper right corner). This is another example of the usefulness of the periodic table.

polyatomic ion

An ion that contains more than one atom.

There also exists a group of ions that contain more than one atom. These are called **polyatomic ions**. Table 5.2 lists the formulas, charges, and names of some common polyatomic ions. Only one of them, the ammonium ion, is a cation; the rest are anions. Most of them also contain oxygen atoms, so sometimes they are referred to as *oxyanions*. Some of them, such as nitrate and nitrite, and sulfate and sulfite, have very similar formulas and names, so care must be taken to get the formulas and names correct. Note that the -ite polyatomic ion has one less oxygen atom in its formula than the -ate ion but with the same ionic charge.

TABLE 5.2 Common Polyatomic Ions

Name	Formula and Charge	Name	Formula and Charge
ammonium	NH_4^+	hydroxide	OH^-
acetate	$C_2H_3O_2^-$, or CH_3COO^-	nitrate	NO_3^-
bicarbonate (hydrogen carbonate)	HCO_3^-	nitrite	NO_2^-
bisulfate (hydrogen sulfate)	HSO_4^-	peroxide	O_2^{2-}
carbonate	CO_3^{2-}	perchlorate	ClO_4^-
chlorate	ClO_3^-	phosphate	PO_4^{3-}
chromate	CrO_4^{2-}	sulfate	SO_4^{2-}
cyanide	CN^-	sulfite	SO_3^{2-}
dichromate	$Cr_2O_7^{2-}$	triiodide	I_3^-

The naming of ionic compounds that contain polyatomic ions follows the same rules as the naming for other ionic compounds: simply combine the name of the cation and the name of the anion. Do not use numerical prefixes in the name if there is more than one polyatomic ion; the only exception to this is if the name of the ion itself contains a numerical prefix, such as dichromate or triiodide.

Writing the formulas of ionic compounds with polyatomic ions has one important difference. If more than one polyatomic ion is needed to balance the overall charge in the formula, enclose the formula of the polyatomic ion in parentheses and write the proper numerical subscript to the right and *outside* the parentheses. Thus, the formula between calcium ions, Ca^{2+}, and nitrate ions, NO_3^-, is properly written $Ca(NO_3)_2$, not $CaNO_{32}$ or CaN_2O_6. Use parentheses where required. The name of this ionic compound is simply calcium nitrate.

Example 4

Write the proper formula and give the proper name for each ionic compound formed between the two listed ions.

1. NH_4^+ and S^{2-}
2. Al^{3+} and PO_4^{3-}
3. Fe^{2+} and PO_4^{3-}

Solution

1. Because the ammonium ion has a 1+ charge and the sulfide ion has a 2– charge, we need two ammonium ions to balance the charge on a single sulfide ion. Enclosing the formula for the ammonium ion in parentheses, we have $(NH_4)_2S$. The compound's name is ammonium sulfide.
2. Because the ions have the same magnitude of charge, we need only one of each to balance the charges. The formula is $AlPO_4$, and the name of the compound is aluminum phosphate.
3. Neither charge is an exact multiple of the other, so we have to go to the least common multiple of 6. To get 6+, we need three iron(II) ions, and to get 6–, we need two phosphate ions. The proper formula is $Fe_3(PO_4)_2$, and the compound's name is iron(II) phosphate.

Test Yourself

Write the proper formula and give the proper name for each ionic compound formed between the two listed ions.

1. NH_4^+ and PO_4^{3-}
2. Co^{3+} and NO_2^-

Answers

1. $(NH_4)_3PO_4$, ammonium phosphate
2. $Co(NO_2)_3$, cobalt(III) nitrite

Food and Drink App: Sodium in Your Food

The element sodium, at least in its ionic form as Na^+, is a necessary nutrient for humans to live. In fact, the human body is approximately 0.15% sodium, with the average person having one-twentieth to one-tenth of a kilogram in their body at any given time, mostly in fluids outside cells and in other bodily fluids.

Sodium is also present in our diet. The common table salt we use on our foods is an ionic sodium compound. Many processed foods also contain significant amounts of sodium added to them as a variety of ionic compounds. Why are sodium compounds used so much? Usually sodium compounds are inexpensive, but, more importantly, most ionic sodium compounds dissolve easily. This allows processed food manufacturers to add sodium-containing substances to food mixtures and know that the compound will dissolve and distribute evenly throughout the food. Simple ionic compounds such as sodium nitrite ($NaNO_2$) are added to cured meats, such as bacon and deli-style meats, while a compound called sodium benzoate is added to many packaged foods as a preservative. Table 5.3 is a partial list of some sodium additives used in food. Some of them you may recognize after reading this chapter. Others you may not recognize, but they are all ionic sodium compounds with some negatively charged ion also present.

TABLE 5.3 Some Sodium Compounds Added to Food

Sodium Compound	Use in Food
Sodium acetate	preservative, acidity regulator
Sodium adipate	food acid
Sodium alginate	thickener, vegetable gum, stabilizer, gelling agent, emulsifier
Sodium aluminum phosphate	acidity regulator, emulsifier
Sodium aluminosilicate	anticaking agent
Sodium ascorbate	antioxidant
Sodium benzoate	preservative
Sodium bicarbonate	mineral salt
Sodium bisulfite	preservative, antioxidant
Sodium carbonate	mineral salt
Sodium carboxymethylcellulose	emulsifier
Sodium citrates	food acid
Sodium dehydroacetate	preservative
Sodium erythorbate	antioxidant
Sodium erythorbin	antioxidant
Sodium ethyl para-hydroxybenzoate	preservative
Sodium ferrocyanide	anticaking agent
Sodium formate	preservative
Sodium fumarate	food acid
Sodium gluconate	stabilizer
Sodium hydrogen acetate	preservative, acidity regulator
Sodium hydroxide	mineral salt
Sodium lactate	food acid
Sodium malate	food acid
Sodium metabisulfite	preservative, antioxidant, bleaching agent
Sodium methyl para-hydroxybenzoate	preservative
Sodium nitrate	preservative, color fixative
Sodium nitrite	preservative, color fixative
Sodium orthophenyl phenol	preservative
Sodium propionate	preservative
Sodium propyl para-hydroxybenzoate	preservative
Sodium sorbate	preservative
Sodium stearoyl lactylate	emulsifier
Sodium succinates	acidity regulator, flavor enhancer
Sodium salts of fatty acids	emulsifier, stabilizer, anticaking agent
Sodium sulfate	mineral salt, preservative, antioxidant
Sodium sulfite	preservative, antioxidant

Sodium Compound	Use in Food
Sodium tartrate	food acid
Sodium tetraborate	preservative

The use of so many sodium compounds in prepared and processed foods has alarmed some physicians and nutritionists. They argue that the average person consumes too much sodium from his or her diet. The average person needs only about 500 mg of sodium every day; most people consume more than this—up to 10 times as much. Some studies have implicated increased sodium intake with high blood pressure; newer studies suggest that the link is questionable. However, there has been a push to reduce the amount of sodium most people ingest every day: avoid processed and manufactured foods, read labels on packaged foods (which include an indication of the sodium content), don't oversalt foods, and use other herbs and spices besides salt in cooking.

Food labels include the amount of sodium per serving. This particular label shows that there are 75 mg of sodium in one serving of this particular food item.

Nutrition Facts

Serving Size 8 oz (227 g/8 oz)
Servings Per Container About 3

Amount Per Serving

Calories 180   Calories from Fat 60

	% Daily Value*
Total Fat 6g	10%
Saturated Fat 1g	5%
Trans Fat 0g	
Cholesterol 5mg	2%
Sodium 75mg	3%
Total Carbohydrate 26g	9%
Dietary Fiber 5g	19%
Sugars 11g	
Protein 8g	

Vitamin A 60%	•	Vitamin C 70%
Calcium 8%	•	Iron 10%

* Percent Daily Values are based on a 2,000 calorie diet. Your daily values may be higher or lower depending on your calorie needs.

	Calories	2,000	2,500
Total Fat	Less than	65g	80g
Sat Fat	Less than	20g	25g
Cholesterol	Less than	300mg	300mg
Sodium	Less than	2,400mg	2,400mg
Total Carbohydrate		300g	375g
Dietary Fiber		25g	30g

Calories per gram:
Fat 9 • Carbohydrate 4 • Protein 4

Key Takeaways

- Ions form when atoms lose or gain electrons.
- Ionic compounds have positive ions and negative ions.
- Ionic formulas balance the total positive and negative charges.
- Ionic compounds have a simple system of naming.
- Groups of atoms, called polyatomic ions, can have an overall charge and make ionic compounds.

Exercises

1. Explain how cations form.
2. Explain how anions form.
3. Give the charge each atom takes when it forms an ion. If more than one charge is possible, list both.

    a. K

    b. O

    c. Co

4. Give the charge each atom takes when it forms an ion. If more than one charge is possible, list both.

    a. Ca

    b. I

    c. Fe

5. Give the charge each atom takes when it forms an ion. If more than one charge is possible, list both.

    a. Ag

    b. Au

    c. Br

6. Give the charge each atom takes when it forms an ion. If more than one charge is possible, list both.

    a. S

    b. Na

    c. H

7. Name the ions from Exercise 3.
8. Name the ions from Exercise 4.
9. Name the ions from Exercise 5.
10. Name the ions from Exercise 6.
11. Give the formula and name for each ionic compound formed between the two listed ions.

    a. Mg^{2+} and Cl^-

    b. Fe^{2+} and O^{2-}

    c. Fe^{3+} and O^{2-}

12. Give the formula and name for each ionic compound formed between the two listed ions.

    a. K^+ and S^{2-}

    b. Ag^+ and Br^-

    c. Sr^{2+} and N^{3-}

13. Give the formula and name for each ionic compound formed between the two listed ions.

    a. Cu^{2+} and F^-

    b. Ca^{2+} and O^{2-}

    c. K^+ and P^{3-}

14. Give the formula and name for each ionic compound formed between the two listed ions.

    a. Na^+ and N^{3-}

    b. Co^{2+} and I^-

    c. Au^{3+} and S^{2-}

15. Give the formula and name for each ionic compound formed between the two listed ions.

    a. K^+ and SO_4^{2-}

b. NH_4^+ and S^{2-}

c. NH_4^+ and PO_4^{3-}

16. Give the formula and name for each ionic compound formed between the two listed ions.

   a. Ca^{2+} and NO_3^-

   b. Ca^{2+} and NO_2^-

   c. Sc^{3+} and $C_2H_3O_2^-$

17. Give the formula and name for each ionic compound formed between the two listed ions.

   a. Pb^{4+} and SO_4^{2-}

   b. Na^+ and I_3^-

   c. Li^+ and $Cr_2O_7^{2-}$

18. Give the formula and name for each ionic compound formed between the two listed ions.

   a. NH_4^+ and N^{3-}

   b. Mg^{2+} and CO_3^{2-}

   c. Al^{3+} and OH^-

19. Give the formula and name for each ionic compound formed between the two listed ions.

   a. Ag^+ and SO_3^{2-}

   b. Na^+ and HCO_3^-

   c. Fe^{3+} and ClO_3^-

20. Give the formula and name for each ionic compound formed between the two listed ions.

   a. Rb^+ and O_2^{2-}

   b. Au^{3+} and HSO_4^-

   c. Sr^{2+} and NO_2^-

Answers

1. Cations form by losing electrons.
2. Anions form when atoms gain additional electrons.
3. a. 1+
   b. 2–
   c. 2+, 3+
4. a. 2+
   b. 1–
   c. 2+, 3+
5. a. 1+
   b. 1+, 3+
   c. 1–
6. a. 2–
   b. 1+
   c. 1+, 1–
7. a. the potassium ion
   b. the oxide ion
   c. the cobalt(II) and cobalt(III) ions, respectively
8. a. calcium ion

b. iodide ion

c. iron(II) and iron(III) ions, respectively

9. a. the silver ion

b. the gold(I) and gold(III) ions, respectively

c. the bromide ion

10. a. the sulfide ion

b. the sodium ion

c. the hydrogen and hydride ions, respectively

11. a. magnesium chloride, $MgCl_2$

b. iron(II) oxide, FeO

c. iron(III) oxide, Fe_2O_3

12. a. potassium sulfide, K_2S

b. silver bromide, $AgBr$

c. strontium nitride, Sr_3N_2

13. a. copper(II) fluoride, CuF_2

b. calcium oxide, CaO

c. potassium phosphide, K_3P

14. a. sodium nitride, Na_3N

b. cobalt(II) iodide, CoI_2

c. gold(III) sulfide, Ag_2S_3

15. a. potassium sulfate, K_2SO_4

b. ammonium sulfide, $(NH_4)_2S$

c. ammonium phosphate, $(NH_4)_3PO_4$

16. a. calcium nitrate, $Ca(NO_3)_2$

b. calcium nitrite, $Ca(NO_2)_2$

c. scandium acetate, $Sc(C_2H_3O_2)_3$

17. a. lead(IV) sulfate, $Pb(SO_4)_2$

b. sodium triiodide, NaI_3

c. lithium dichromate, $Li_2Cr_2O_7$

18. a. ammonium nitride, $(NH_4)_3N$

b. magnesium carbonate, $MgCO_3$

c. aluminum hydroxide, $Al(OH)_3$

19. a. silver sulfite, Ag_2SO_3

b. sodium hydrogen carbonate, $NaHCO_3$

c. iron(III) chlorate, $Fe(ClO_3)_3$

20. a. rubidium peroxide, Rb_2O_2

b. gold(III) hydrogen sulfate, $Au(HSO_4)_3$

c. strontium nitrite, $Sr(NO_2)_2$

5.2 Lewis Electron Dot Diagrams

Learning Objective

1. Draw a Lewis electron dot diagram for an atom or a monatomic ion.

In almost all cases, chemical bonds are formed by interactions of valence electrons in atoms. To facilitate our understanding of how valence electrons interact, a simple way of representing those valence electrons would be useful.

A **Lewis electron dot diagram** (or electron dot diagram or a Lewis diagram or a Lewis structure) is a representation of the valence electrons of an atom that uses dots around the symbol of the element. The number of dots equals the number of valence electrons in the atom. These dots are arranged to the right and left and above and below the symbol, with no more than two dots on a side. (It does not matter what order the positions are used.) For example, the Lewis electron dot diagram for hydrogen is simply

> **Lewis electron dot diagram**
>
> A representation of the valence electrons of an atom that uses dots around the symbol of the element.

$$H \cdot$$

Because the side is not important, the Lewis electron dot diagram could also be drawn as follows:

$$\overset{\cdot}{H} \quad \text{or} \quad \cdot H \quad \text{or} \quad \underset{\cdot}{H}$$

The electron dot diagram for helium, with two valence electrons, is as follows:

$$He \!:\!$$

By putting the two electrons together on the same side, we emphasize the fact that these two electrons are both in the 1s subshell; this is the common convention we will adopt, although there will be exceptions later. The next atom, lithium, has an electron configuration of $1s^2 2s^1$, so it has only one electron in its valence shell. Its electron dot diagram resembles that of hydrogen, except the symbol for lithium is used:

$$Li \cdot$$

Beryllium has two valence electrons in its 2s shell, so its electron dot diagram is like that of helium:

$$Be \!:\!$$

The next atom is boron. Its valence electron shell is $2s^2 2p^1$, so it has three valence electrons. The third electron will go on another side of the symbol:

$$\overset{\Large\cdot}{B}:$$

Again, it does not matter on which sides of the symbol the electron dots are positioned.

For carbon, there are four valence electrons, two in the 2s subshell and two in the 2p subshell. As usual, we will draw two dots together on one side, to represent the 2s electrons. However, conventionally, we draw the dots for the two p electrons on different sides. As such, the electron dot diagram for carbon is as follows:

$$\overset{\Large\cdot}{\cdot C}:$$

With N, which has three p electrons, we put a single dot on each of the three remaining sides:

$$\overset{\Large\cdot}{\underset{\Large\cdot}{\cdot N}}:$$

For oxygen, which has four p electrons, we now have to start doubling up on the dots on one other side of the symbol. When doubling up electrons, make sure that a side has no more than two electrons.

$$\overset{\Large\cdot}{\underset{\Large\cdot\cdot}{\cdot O}}:$$

Fluorine and neon have seven and eight dots, respectively:

$$\overset{\Large\cdot\cdot}{\underset{\Large\cdot}{:F}}:\qquad\overset{\Large\cdot\cdot}{\underset{\Large\cdot\cdot}{:Ne}}:$$

With the next element, sodium, the process starts over with a single electron because sodium has a single electron in its highest-numbered shell, the $n = 3$ shell. By going through the periodic table, we see that the Lewis electron dot diagrams of atoms will never have more than eight dots around the atomic symbol.

Example 5

What is the Lewis electron dot diagram for each element?

1. aluminum
2. selenium

Solution

1. The valence electron configuration for aluminum is $3s^2 3p^1$. So it would have three dots around the symbol for aluminum, two of them paired to represent the 3s electrons:

$$\overset{\Large\cdot}{Al}:$$

2. The valence electron configuration for selenium is $4s^2 4p^4$. In the highest-numbered shell, the $n = 4$ shell, there are six electrons. Its electron dot diagram is as follows:

$$\overset{\Large\cdot}{\underset{\Large\cdot\cdot}{\cdot Se}}:$$

Test Yourself

What is the Lewis electron dot diagram for each element?

1. phosphorus
2. argon

Answer

$$\cdot \overset{\displaystyle \cdot}{\underset{\displaystyle \cdot}{P}} \colon \quad \text{and} \quad \colon \overset{\displaystyle \cdot \cdot}{\underset{\displaystyle \cdot \cdot}{Ar}} \colon$$

For atoms with partially filled d or f subshells, these electrons are typically omitted from Lewis electron dot diagrams. For example, the electron dot diagram for iron (valence shell configuration $4s^2 3d^6$) is as follows:

$$\text{Fe} \colon$$

Elements in the same column of the periodic table have similar Lewis electron dot diagrams because they have the same valence shell electron configuration. Thus the electron dot diagrams for the first column of elements are as follows:

$$H \cdot \quad Li \cdot \quad Na \cdot \quad K \cdot \quad Rb \cdot \quad Cs \cdot$$

Monatomic ions are atoms that have either lost (for cations) or gained (for anions) electrons. Electron dot diagrams for ions are the same as for atoms, except that some electrons have been removed for cations, while some electrons have been added for anions. Thus in comparing the electron configurations and electron dot diagrams for the Na atom and the Na^+ ion, we note that the Na atom has a single valence electron in its Lewis diagram, while the Na^+ ion has lost that one valence electron:

Lewis dot diagram:	$Na \cdot$	Na^+
Electron configuration:	[Ne] $3s^1$	[Ne]

Technically, the valence shell of the Na^+ ion is now the $n = 2$ shell, which has eight electrons in it. So why do we not put eight dots around Na^+? Conventionally, when we show electron dot diagrams for ions, we show the original valence shell of the atom, which in this case is the $n = 3$ shell and empty in the Na^+ ion.

In making cations, electrons are first lost from the *highest numbered shell*, not necessarily the last subshell filled. For example, in going from the neutral Fe atom to the Fe^{2+} ion, the Fe atom loses its two $4s$ electrons first, not its $3d$ electrons, despite the fact that the $3d$ subshell is the last subshell being filled. Thus we have

Lewis dot diagram:	Fe$\colon$	Fe^{2+}
Electron configuration:	[Ar] $4s^2 3d^6$	[Ar] $3d^6$

Anions have extra electrons when compared to the original atom. Here is a comparison of the Cl atom with the Cl⁻ ion:

Lewis dot diagram:	:C̈l·	:C̈l:⁻
Electron configuration:	[Ne] $3s^2 3p^5$	[Ne] $3s^2 3p^6$

Example 6

What is the Lewis electron dot diagram for each ion?

1. Ca^{2+}
2. O^{2-}

Solution

1. Having lost its two original valence electrons, the Lewis electron dot diagram is just Ca^{2+} :

2. The O^{2-} ion has gained two electrons in its valence shell, so its Lewis electron dot diagram is as follows:

$$:\ddot{O}:^{2-}$$

Test Yourself

The valence electron configuration of thallium, whose symbol is Tl, is $6s^2 5d^{10} 6p^1$. What is the Lewis electron dot diagram for the Tl^+ ion?

Answer

$$Tl:^+$$

Key Takeaways

- Lewis electron dot diagrams use dots to represent valence electrons around an atomic symbol.
- Lewis electron dot diagrams for ions have less (for cations) or more (for anions) dots than the corresponding atom.

Exercises

1. Explain why the first two dots in a Lewis electron dot diagram are drawn on the same side of the atomic symbol.
2. Is it necessary for the first dot around an atomic symbol to go on a particular side of the atomic symbol?
3. What column of the periodic table has Lewis electron dot diagrams with two electrons?
4. What column of the periodic table has Lewis electron dot diagrams that have six electrons in them?
5. Draw the Lewis electron dot diagram for each element.

a. strontium

b. silicon

6. Draw the Lewis electron dot diagram for each element.

   a. krypton

   b. sulfur

7. Draw the Lewis electron dot diagram for each element.

   a. titanium

   b. phosphorus

8. Draw the Lewis electron dot diagram for each element.

   a. bromine

   b. gallium

9. Draw the Lewis electron dot diagram for each ion.

   a. Mg^{2+}

   b. S^{2-}

10. Draw the Lewis electron dot diagram for each ion.

    a. In^+

    b. Br^-

11. Draw the Lewis electron dot diagram for each ion.

    a. Fe^{2+}

    b. N^{3-}

12. Draw the Lewis electron dot diagram for each ion.

    a. H^+

    b. H^-

Answers

1. The first two electrons in a valence shell are *s* electrons, which are paired.

3. the second column of the periodic table

5.

   a.

   Sr:

   b.

   ·Si:

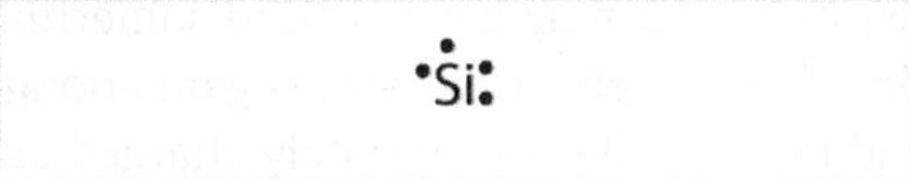

7.

a.

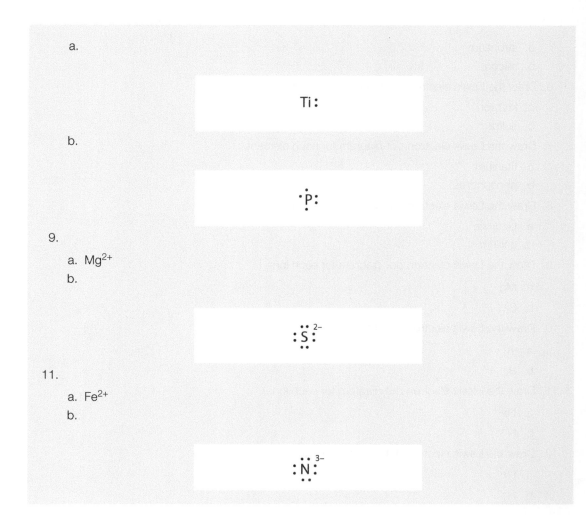

Ti :

b.

· P̈ :

9.

    a. Mg^{2+}
    b.

: S̈ : $^{2-}$

11.

    a. Fe^{2+}
    b.

: N̈ : $^{3-}$

5.3 Electron Transfer: Ionic Bonds

Learning Objectives

1. State the octet rule.
2. Define *ionic bond*.
3. Demonstrate electron transfer between atoms to form ionic bonds.

octet rule

The trend that atoms like to have eight electrons in their valence shell.

In Section 2, we saw how ions are formed by losing electrons to make cations or by gaining electrons to form anions. The astute reader may have noticed something: Many of the ions that form have eight electrons in their valence shell. Either atoms gain enough electrons to have eight electrons in the valence shell and become the appropriately charged anion, or they lose the electrons in their original valence shell; the *lower* shell, now the valence shell, has eight electrons in it, so the atom becomes positively charged. For whatever reason, having eight electrons in a valence shell is a particularly energetically stable arrangement of electrons. The trend that atoms like to have eight electrons in their valence shell is called the **octet rule**. When atoms form compounds, the octet rule is not always satisfied for all atoms at all times, but it is a very good rule of thumb for understanding the kinds of bonding arrangements that atoms can make.

It is not impossible to violate the octet rule. Consider sodium: in its elemental form, it has one valence electron and is stable. It is rather reactive, however, and does not require a lot of energy to remove that electron to make the Na^+ ion. We *could* remove another electron by adding even more energy to the ion, to make the Na^{2+} ion. However, that requires much more energy than is normally available in chemical reactions, so sodium stops at a 1+ charge after losing a single electron. It turns out that the Na^+ ion has a complete octet in its new valence shell, the $n = 2$ shell, which satisfies the octet rule. The octet rule is a result of trends in energies and is useful in explaining why atoms form the ions that they do.

Now consider an Na atom in the presence of a Cl atom. The two atoms have these Lewis electron dot diagrams and electron configurations:

$$Na\bullet \qquad \bullet\overset{\displaystyle\cdot\cdot}{\underset{\displaystyle\cdot\cdot}{Cl}}:$$

$$[Ne]\,3s^1 \qquad [Ne]\,3s^2\,3p^5$$

For the Na atom to obtain an octet, it must lose an electron; for the Cl atom to gain an octet, it must gain an electron. An electron transfers from the Na atom to the Cl atom:

$$Na\bullet \curvearrowright :\overset{\displaystyle\cdot\cdot}{\underset{\displaystyle\cdot\cdot}{Cl}}:$$

resulting in two ions—the Na^+ ion and the Cl^- ion:

$$Na^+ \qquad :\overset{\displaystyle\cdot\cdot}{\underset{\displaystyle\cdot\cdot}{Cl}}:^-$$

$$[Ne] \qquad [Ne]3s^23p^6$$

Both species now have complete octets, and the electron shells are energetically stable. From basic physics, we know that opposite charges attract. This is what happens to the Na^+ and Cl^- ions:

$$Na^+ \;+\; :\overset{\displaystyle\cdot\cdot}{\underset{\displaystyle\cdot\cdot}{Cl}}: \;\longrightarrow\; Na^+Cl^- \;\text{ or }\; NaCl$$

where we have written the final formula (the formula for sodium chloride) as per the convention for ionic compounds, without listing the charges explicitly. The attraction between oppositely charged ions is called an **ionic bond**, and it is one of the main types of chemical bonds in chemistry. Ionic bonds are caused by electrons *transferring* from one atom to another.

In electron transfer, the number of electrons lost must equal the number of electrons gained. We saw this in the formation of NaCl. A similar process occurs between Mg atoms and O atoms, except in this case two electrons are transferred:

The two ions each have octets as their valence shells, and the two oppositely charged particles attract, making an ionic bond:

$$Mg^{2+} \quad + \quad :\!\overset{..}{\underset{..}{O}}\!:^{2-} \qquad\qquad Mg^{2+}O^{2-} \quad or \quad MgO$$

Remember, in the final formula for the ionic compound, we do not write the charges on the ions.

What about when an Na atom interacts with an O atom? The O atom needs two electrons to complete its valence octet, but the Na atom supplies only one electron:

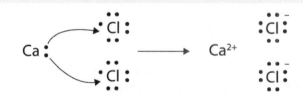

The O atom still does not have an octet of electrons. What we need is a second Na atom to donate a second electron to the O atom:

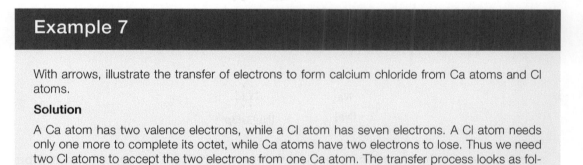

These three ions attract each other to give an overall neutral-charged ionic compound, which we write as Na_2O. The need for the number of electrons lost being equal to the number of electrons gained explains why ionic compounds have the ratio of cations to anions that they do. This is required by the law of conservation of matter as well.

Example 7

With arrows, illustrate the transfer of electrons to form calcium chloride from Ca atoms and Cl atoms.

Solution

A Ca atom has two valence electrons, while a Cl atom has seven electrons. A Cl atom needs only one more to complete its octet, while Ca atoms have two electrons to lose. Thus we need two Cl atoms to accept the two electrons from one Ca atom. The transfer process looks as follows:

The oppositely charged ions attract each other to make $CaCl_2$.

Test Yourself

With arrows, illustrate the transfer of electrons to form potassium sulfide from K atoms and S atoms.

Answer

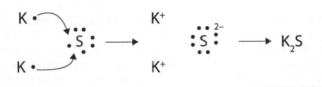

The strength of ionic bonding depends on two major characteristics: the magnitude of the charges and the size of the ion. The greater the magnitude of the charge, the stronger the ionic bond. The smaller the ion, the stronger the ionic bond (because a smaller ion size allows the ions to get closer together). The measured strength of ionic bonding is called the **lattice energy**. Some lattice energies are given in Table 5.4.

lattice energy

The measured strength of ionic bonding.

TABLE 5.4 Lattice Energies of Some Ionic Compounds

Compound	Lattice Energy (kJ/mol)
LiF	1,036
LiCl	853
NaCl	786
NaBr	747
MgF_2	2,957
Na_2O	2,481
MgO	3,791

Chemistry Is Everywhere: Salt

The element sodium (part [a] in the accompanying figure) is a very reactive metal; given the opportunity, it will react with the sweat on your hands and form sodium hydroxide, which is a very corrosive substance. The element chlorine (part [b] in the accompanying figure) is a pale yellow, corrosive gas that should not be inhaled due to its poisonous nature. Bring these two hazardous substances together, however, and they react to make the ionic compound sodium chloride (part [c] in the accompanying figure), known simply as salt.

FIGURE 5.2 Sodium + Chlorine = Sodium Chloride
(a) Sodium is a very reactive metal. (b) Chlorine is a pale yellow, noxious gas. (c) Together, sodium and chlorine make sodium chloride—salt—which is necessary for our survival.

Source: Photo on the left courtesy of Greenhorn1, http://commons.wikimedia.org/wiki/File:Sodium.jpg. Photo in the center courtesy of Benjah-bmm27, http://commons.wikimedia.org/wiki/File:Chlorine-sample.jpg. Photo on the right © Thinkstock.

Salt is necessary for life. Na^+ ions are one of the main ions in the human body and are necessary to regulate the fluid balance in the body. Cl^- ions are necessary for proper nerve function and respiration. Both of these ions are supplied by salt. The taste of salt is one of the fundamental tastes; salt is probably the most ancient flavoring known, and one of the few rocks we eat.

The health effects of too much salt are still under debate, although a 2010 report by the US Department of Agriculture concluded that "excessive sodium intake...raises blood pressure, a well-accepted and extraordinarily common risk factor for stroke, coronary heart disease, and kidney disease."[1]http://www.cnpp.usda.gov/DGAs2010-DGACReport.htm. It is clear that most people ingest more salt than their bodies need, and most nutritionists recommend curbing salt intake. Curiously, people who suffer from low salt (called *hyponatria*) do so not because they ingest too little salt but because they drink too much water. Endurance athletes and others involved in extended strenuous exercise need to watch their water intake so their body's salt content is not diluted to dangerous levels.

Key Takeaways

- The tendency to form species that have eight electrons in the valence shell is called the octet rule.
- The attraction of oppositely charged ions caused by electron transfer is called an ionic bond.
- The strength of ionic bonding depends on the magnitude of the charges and the sizes of the ions.

Exercises

1. Comment on the possible formation of the K^{2+} ion. Why is its formation unlikely?
2. Comment on the possible formation of the Cl^{2-} ion. Why is its formation unlikely?
3. How many electrons does a Ba atom have to lose to have a complete octet in its valence shell?
4. How many electrons does a Pb atom have to lose to have a complete octet in its valence shell?
5. How many electrons does an Se atom have to gain to have a complete octet in its valence shell?
6. How many electrons does an N atom have to gain to have a complete octet in its valence shell?
7. With arrows, illustrate the transfer of electrons to form potassium chloride from K atoms and Cl atoms.
8. With arrows, illustrate the transfer of electrons to form magnesium sulfide from Mg atoms and S atoms.
9. With arrows, illustrate the transfer of electrons to form scandium fluoride from Sc atoms and F atoms.
10. With arrows, illustrate the transfer of electrons to form rubidium phosphide from Rb atoms and P atoms.
11. Which ionic compound has the higher lattice energy—KI or MgO? Why?
12. Which ionic compound has the higher lattice energy—KI or LiF? Why?
13. Which ionic compound has the higher lattice energy—BaS or MgO? Why?
14. Which ionic compound has the higher lattice energy—NaCl or NaI? Why?

Answers

1. The K^{2+} ion is unlikely to form because the K^+ ion already satisfies the octet rule and is rather stable.

2. The Cl^{2-} ion is unlikely to form because the Cl^- ion already has a stable octet.

3. two

4. four

5. two

6. three

7.

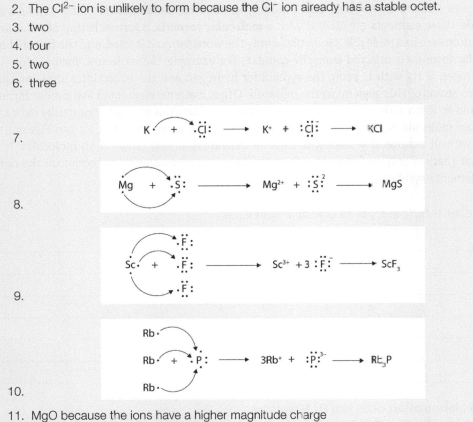

8.

9.

10.

11. MgO because the ions have a higher magnitude charge

12. LiF because the ions are smaller

13. MgO because the ions are smaller

14. NaCl because the anion is smaller

5.4 Molecules and Chemical Nomenclature

Learning Objectives

1. Define *molecule*.
2. Name simple molecules based on their formulas.
3. Determine a formula of a molecule based on its name.

There are many substances that exist as two or more atoms connected together so strongly that they behave as a single particle. These multiatom combinations are called **molecules**. A molecule is the smallest part of a substance that has the physical and chemical properties of that substance. In some respects, a molecule is similar to an atom. A molecule, however, is composed of more than one atom.

molecule

The smallest part of a substance that has the physical and chemical properties of that substance.

diatomic molecule

A molecule with only two atoms.

molecular formula

A formal listing of what and how many atoms are in a molecule.

Some elements exist naturally as molecules. For example, hydrogen and oxygen exist as two-atom molecules. Other elements also exist naturally as **diatomic molecules** (see Table 5.5). As with any molecule, these elements are labeled with a **molecular formula**, a formal listing of what and how many atoms are in a molecule. (Sometimes only the word *formula* is used, and the fact that it's the molecular formula is inferred from the context.) For example, the molecular formula for elemental hydrogen is H_2, with H being the symbol for hydrogen and the subscript 2 implying that there are two atoms of this element in the molecule. Other diatomic elements have similar formulas: O_2, N_2, and so forth. Other elements exist as molecules—for example, sulfur normally exists as an eight-atom molecule, S_8, while phosphorus exists as a four-atom molecule, P_4 (see Figure 5.3). Otherwise, we will assume that elements exist as individual atoms, rather than molecules. It is assumed that there is only one atom in a formula if there is no numerical subscript on the right side of an element's symbol.

TABLE 5.5 Elements That Exist as Diatomic Molecules

Hydrogen
Oxygen
Nitrogen
Fluorine
Chlorine
Bromine
Iodine

FIGURE 5.3 Molecular Art of S_8 and P_4 Molecules
If each green ball represents a sulfur atom, then the diagram on the left represents an S_8 molecule. The molecule on the right shows that one form of elemental phosphorus exists, as a four-atom molecule.

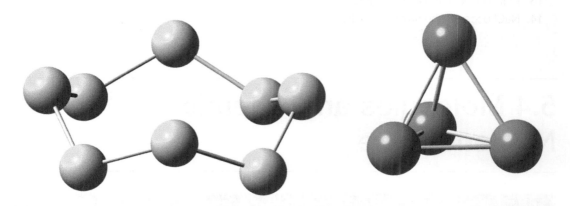

chemical bond

The connection between two atoms in a molecule.

Figure 5.3 shows two examples of how we will be representing molecules in this text. An atom is represented by a small ball or sphere, which generally indicates where the nucleus is in the molecule. A cylindrical line connecting the balls represents the connection between the atoms that make this collection of atoms a molecule. This connection is called a **chemical bond**. In Section 5, we will explore the origin of chemical bonds. You will see other examples of this "ball and cylinder" representation of molecules throughout this book.

Many compounds exist as molecules. In particular, when nonmetals connect with other nonmetals, the compound typically exists as molecules. (Compounds between a metal and a nonmetal are different and were considered in Section 1.) Furthermore, in some cases there are many different kinds of molecules that can be formed between any given elements, with all the different molecules having different chemical and physical properties. How do we tell them apart?

The answer is a very specific system of naming compounds, called **chemical nomenclature**. By following the rules of nomenclature, each and every compound has its own unique name, and each name refers to one and only one compound. Here, we will start with relatively simple molecules that have only two elements in them, the so-called *binary compounds*:

chemical
nomenclature

A very specific system for
naming compounds, in
which unique substances
get unique names.

1. Identify the elements in the molecule from its formula. This is why you need to know the names and symbols of the elements in Table 3.2.

2. Begin the name with the element name of the first element. If there is more than one atom of this element in the molecular formula, use a numerical prefix to indicate the number of atoms, as listed in Table 5.6. *Do not use the prefix mono- if there is only one atom of the first element.*

TABLE 5.6 Numerical Prefixes Used in Naming Molecular Compounds

The Number of Atoms of an Element	Prefix
1	mono-
2	di-
3	tri-
4	tetra-
5	penta-
6	hexa-
7	hepta-
8	octa-
9	nona-
10	deca-

3. Name the second element by using three pieces:

   a. a numerical prefix indicating the number of atoms of the second element, plus

   b. the stem of the element name (e.g., *ox* for oxygen, *chlor* for chlorine, etc.), plus

   c. the suffix *-ide*.

4. Combine the two words, leaving a space between them.

Let us see how these steps work for a molecule whose molecular formula is SO_2, which has one sulfur atom and two oxygen atoms—this completes step 1. According to step 2, we start with the name of the first element—sulfur. Remember, we don't use the *mono-* prefix for the first element. Now for step 3, we combine the numerical prefix *di-* (see Table 5.6) with the stem *ox-* and the suffix *-ide*, to make *dioxide*. Bringing these two words together, we have the unique name for this compound—sulfur dioxide.

Why all this trouble? There is another common compound consisting of sulfur and oxygen whose molecular formula is SO_3, so the compounds need to be distinguished. SO_3 has three oxygen atoms in it, so it is a different compound with different chemical and physical properties. The system of chemical nomenclature is designed to *give this compound its own unique name*. Its name, if you go through all the steps, is sulfur trioxide. Different compounds have different names.

In some cases, when a prefix ends in *a* or *o* and the element name begins with *o* we drop the *a* or *o* on the prefix. So we see *monoxide* or *pentoxide* rather than *monooxide* or *pentaoxide* in molecule names.

One great thing about this system is that it works both ways. From the name of a compound, you should be able to determine its molecular formula. Simply list the element symbols, with a numerical subscript if there is more than one atom of that element, in the order of the name (we do not use a subscript 1 if there is only one atom of the element present; 1 is implied). From the name *nitrogen trichloride*, you should be able to get NCl_3 as the formula for this molecule. From the name *diphosphorus pentoxide*, you should be able to get the formula P_2O_5 (note the numerical prefix on the first element, indicating there is more than one atom of phosphorus in the formula).

Example 8

Name each molecule.

1. PF_3
2. CO
3. Se_2Br_2

Solution

1. A molecule with a single phosphorus atom and three fluorine atoms is called phosphorus trifluoride.
2. A compound with one carbon atom and one oxygen atom is properly called carbon monoxide, not carbon monooxide.
3. There are two atoms of each element, selenium and bromine. According to the rules, the proper name here is diselenium dibromide.

Test Yourself

Name each molecule.

1. SF_4
2. P_2S_5

Answers

1. sulfur tetrafluoride
2. diphosphorus pentasulfide

Example 9

Give the formula for each molecule.

1. carbon tetrachloride
2. silicon dioxide
3. trisilicon tetranitride

Solution

1. The name *carbon tetrachloride* implies one carbon atom and four chlorine atoms, so the formula is CCl_4.
2. The name *silicon dioxide* implies one silicon atom and two oxygen atoms, so the formula is SiO_2.
3. We have a name that has numerical prefixes on both elements. *Tri-* means three, and *tetra-* means four, so the formula of this compound is Si_3N_4.

Test Yourself

Give the formula for each molecule.

1. disulfur difluoride
2. iodine pentabromide

Answers

1. S_2F_2
2. IBr_5

Some simple molecules have common names that we use as part of the formal system of chemical nomenclature. For example, H_2O is given the name *water*, not *dihydrogen monoxide*. NH_3 is called *ammonia*, while CH_4 is called *methane*. We will occasionally see other molecules that have common names; we will point them out as they occur.

We understand that atoms have mass. It is easy to extend the concept to the mass of molecules. The **molecular mass** is the sum of the masses of the atoms in a molecule. This may seem like a trivial extension of the concept, but it is important to correctly count the number of each type of atom in the molecular formula. Also, although each atom in a molecule is a particular isotope, we use the weighted average, or atomic mass, for each atom in the molecule.

> **molecular mass**
>
> The sum of the masses of the atoms in a molecule.

For example, if we were to determine the molecular mass of dinitrogen trioxide, N_2O_3, we would need to add the atomic mass of nitrogen two times with the atomic mass of oxygen three times:

2 N masses = 3 x 14.007	= 28.014	
3 O masses = 3 x 15.999 u	= 47.997 u	
Total	= 76.011 u	= the molecular mass of N_2O_3

We would not be far off if we limited our numbers to one or even two decimal places.

Example 10

What is the molecular mass of each substance?

1. NBr_3
2. C_2H_6

Solution

1. Add one atomic mass of nitrogen and three atomic masses of bromine:

1 N mass	= 14.007 u
3 Br masses = 3 × 79.904 u	= <u>239.712 u</u>
Total	= 253.719 u = the molecular mass of NBr_3

2. Add two atomic masses of carbon and six atomic masses of hydrogen:

2 C masses = 2 × 12.011 u	= 24.022 u
6 H masses = 6 × 1.008 u	= <u>6.048 u</u>
Total	= 30.070 u = the molecular mass of C_2H_6

The compound C_2H_6 also has a common name—ethane.

Test Yourself

What is the molecular mass of each substance?

1. SO_2
2. PF_3

Answers

1. 64.063 u
2. 87.968 u

Key Takeaways

- Molecules are groups of atoms that behave as a single unit.
- Some elements exist as molecules: hydrogen, oxygen, sulfur, and so forth.
- There are rules that can express a unique name for any given molecule, and a unique formula for any given name.
- Molecular masses can be determined by adding the masses of all the atoms in the molecule.

Chemistry Is Everywhere: Sulfur Hexafluoride

On March 20, 1995, the Japanese terrorist group Aum Shinrikyo (Sanskrit for "Supreme Truth") released some sarin gas in the Tokyo subway system; twelve people were killed, and thousands were injured (part (a) in the accompanying figure). Sarin (molecular formula $C_4H_{10}FPO_2$) is a nerve toxin that was first synthesized in 1938. It is regarded as one of the most deadly toxins known, estimated to be about 500 times more potent than cyanide. Scientists and engineers who study the spread of chemical weapons such as sarin (yes, there are such scientists) would like to have a less dangerous chemical, indeed one that is nontoxic, so they are not at risk themselves.

Sulfur hexafluoride is used as a model compound for sarin. SF_6 (a molecular model of which is shown in part (b) in the accompanying figure) has a similar molecular mass (about 146 u) as sarin (about 140 u), so it has similar physical properties in the vapor phase. Sulfur hexafluoride is also very easy to detect accurately, even at low levels, and it is not a normal part of the atmosphere, so there is little potential for contamination from natural sources. Consequently, SF_6 is also used as an aerial tracer for ventilation systems in buildings. It is nontoxic and very chemically inert, so workers do not have to take special precautions other than watching for asphyxiation.

FIGURE 5.4 Sarin and Sulfur Hexafluoride
(a) Properly protected workers clear out the Tokyo subway after the nerve toxin sarin was released. (b) A molecular model of SF_6. (c) A high-voltage electrical switchgear assembly that would be filled with SF_6 as a spark suppressant.

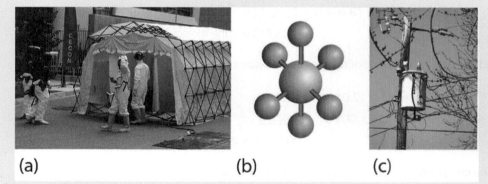

(a)   (b)   (c)

Source: © Thinkstock

Sulfur hexafluoride also has another interesting use: a spark suppressant in high-voltage electrical equipment. High-pressure SF_6 gas is used in place of older oils that may have contaminants that are environmentally unfriendly (part (c) in the accompanying figure).

Exercises

1. Which of these formulas represent molecules? State how many atoms are in each molecule.
   a. Fe
   b. PCl_3

   c. P_4

   d. Ar

2. Which of these formulas represent molecules? State how many atoms are in each molecule.

   a. I_2

   b. He

   c. H_2O

   d. Al

3. What is the difference between CO and Co?

4. What is the difference between H_2O and H_2O_2 (hydrogen peroxide)?

5. Give the proper formula for each diatomic element.

6. In 1986, when Halley's comet last passed the earth, astronomers detected the presence of S_2 in their telescopes. Why is sulfur not considered a diatomic element?

7. What is the stem of fluorine used in molecule names? CF_4 is one example.

8. What is the stem of selenium used in molecule names? $SiSe_2$ is an example.

9. Give the proper name for each molecule.

   a. PF_3

   b. $TeCl_2$

   c. N_2O_3

10. Give the proper name for each molecule.

   a. NO

   b. CS_2

   c. As_2O_3

11. Give the proper name for each molecule.

   a. XeF_2

   b. O_2F_2

   c. SF_6

12. Give the proper name for each molecule.

   a. P_4O_{10}

   b. B_2O_3

   c. P_2S_3

13. Give the proper name for each molecule.

   a. N_2O

   b. N_2O_4

   c. N_2O_5

14. Give the proper name for each molecule.

   a. SeO_2

   b. Cl_2O

   c. XeF_6

15. Give the proper formula for each name.

   a. dinitrogen pentoxide

   b. tetraboron tricarbide

   c. phosphorus pentachloride

16. Give the proper formula for each name.

   a. nitrogen triiodide

   b. diarsenic trisulfide

   c. iodine trichloride

17. Give the proper formula for each name.

   a. dioxygen dichloride

   b. dinitrogen trisulfide

   c. xenon tetrafluoride

18. Give the proper formula for each name.

   a. chlorine dioxide

   b. selenium dibromide

   c. dinitrogen trioxide

19. Give the proper formula for each name.

   a. iodine trifluoride

   b. xenon trioxide

   c. disulfur decafluoride

20. Give the proper formula for each name.

   a. germanium dioxide

   b. carbon disulfide

   c. diselenium dibromide

21. Determine the mass of each substance.

   a. F_2

   b. CO

   c. CO_2

22. Determine the mass of each substance.

   a. KrF_4

   b. PF_5

23. Determine the mass of each substance.

   a. B_2O_3

   b. S_2Cl_2

24. Determine the mass of each substance.

   a. IBr_3

   b. N_2O_5

   c. CCl_4

25. Determine the mass of each substance.

   a. GeO_2

   b. IF_3

   c. XeF_6

26. Determine the mass of each substance.

   a. NO

   b. N_2O_4

   c. CH_3Cl

27. What is the difference between SO_3 and SO_3^{2-}?

28. What is the difference between NO_2 and NO_2^-?

Answers

1. a. not a molecule

    b. a molecule; four atoms total

    c. a molecule; four atoms total

    d. not a molecule

2. a. molecule; two atoms

    b. not a molecule

    c. molecule; three atoms

    d. not a molecule

3. CO is a compound of carbon and oxygen; Co is the element cobalt.

4. The first molecule has one oxygen atom, while the second molecule has two oxygen atoms. The first molecule is water, while the second molecule is hydrogen peroxide.

5. H_2, O_2, N_2, F_2, Cl_2, Br_2, I_2

6. S_2 is not a stable form of elemental sulfur.

7. *fluor-*

8. *selen-*

9. a. phosphorus trifluoride

    b. tellurium dichloride

    c. dinitrogen trioxide

10. a. nitrogen monoxide

    b. carbon disulfide

    c. diarsenic trioxide

11. a. xenon difluoride

    b. dioxygen difluoride

    c. sulfur hexafluoride

12. a. tetraphosphorus decoxide

    b. diboron trioxide

    c. diphosphorus trisulfide

13. a. dinitrogen monoxide

    b. dinitrogen tetroxide

    c. dinitrogen pentoxide

14. a. selenium dioxide

    b. dichlorine monoxide

    c. xenon hexafluoride

15. a. N_2O_5

    b. B_4C_3

    c. PCl_5

16. a. NI_3

    b. As_2S_3

    c. ICl_3

17. a. O_2Cl_2

    b. N_2S_3

    c. XeF_4

18. a. ClO_2

    b. $SeBr_2$

    c. N_2O_3

19. a. IF$_3$
    b. XeO$_3$
    c. S$_2$F$_{10}$
20. a. GeO$_2$
    b. CS$_2$
    c. Se$_2$Br$_2$
21. a. 37.996 u
    a. 28.010 u
    b. 44.009 u
22. a. 157.79 u
    a. 125.964 u
23. a. 69.617 u
    a. 135.02 u
24. a. 366.612 u
    a. 108.009 u
    b. 153.811 u
25. a. 183.894 u
    a. 104.628 u
    b. 245.278 u
26. a. 50.485 u
    a. 92.006 u
    b. 30.005 u
27. One is a molecular compound and one is the sulfite ion.
28. One is a molecular compound and one is the nitrite ion.

5.5 Covalent Bonds

Learning Objectives

1. Define *covalent bond*.
2. Illustrate covalent bond formation with Lewis electron dot diagrams.

Ionic bonding typically occurs when it is easy for one atom to lose one or more electrons and another atom to gain one or more electrons. However, some atoms won't give up or gain electrons easily. Yet they still participate in compound formation. How?

covalent bond

A chemical bond formed by two atoms sharing electrons.

There is another mechanism for obtaining a complete valence shell: *sharing* electrons. When electrons are shared between two atoms, they make a bond called a **covalent bond**.

Let us illustrate a covalent bond by using H atoms, with the understanding that H atoms need only two electrons to fill the 1s subshell. Each H atom starts with a single electron in its valence shell:

H·   ·H

The two H atoms can share their electrons:

H:H

We can use circles to show that each H atom has two electrons around the nucleus, completely filling each atom's valence shell:

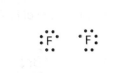

2 electrons   2 electrons
on this H   on this H

Because each H atom has a filled valence shell, this bond is stable, and we have made a diatomic hydrogen molecule. (This explains why hydrogen is one of the diatomic elements.) For simplicity's sake, it is not unusual to represent the covalent bond with a dash, instead of with two dots:

H–H

Because two atoms are sharing one pair of electrons, this covalent bond is called a **single bond**.

As another example, consider fluorine. F atoms have seven electrons in their valence shell:

:F·   ·F:

These two atoms can do the same thing that the H atoms did; they share their unpaired electrons to make a covalent bond.

:F:F:

Note that each F atom has a complete octet around it now:

:F:F:

8 electrons   8 electrons
on this F   on this F

We can also write this using a dash to represent the shared electron pair:

:F—F:

bonding electron pair

A pair of electrons that makes a covalent bond.

lone electron pairs

A pair of electrons that does not make a covalent bond.

There are two different types of electrons in the fluorine molecule. The **bonding electron pair** makes the covalent bond. Each F atom has three other pairs of electrons that do not participate in the bonding; they are called **lone electron pairs**. Each F atom has one bonding pair and three lone pairs of electrons.

Covalent bonds can be made between different elements as well. One example is HF. Each atom starts out with an odd number of electrons in its valence shell:

$$H\cdot \qquad \cdot \overset{\cdot\cdot}{\underset{\cdot\cdot}{F}}\colon$$

The two atoms can share their unpaired electrons to make a covalent bond:

$$H\colon\overset{\cdot\cdot}{\underset{\cdot\cdot}{F}}\colon \quad \text{or} \quad H-\overset{\cdot\cdot}{\underset{\cdot\cdot}{F}}\colon$$

We note that the H atom has a full valence shell with two electrons, while the F atom has a complete octet of electrons.

Example 11

Use Lewis electron dot diagrams to illustrate the covalent bond formation in HBr.

Solution

HBr is very similar to HF, except that it has Br instead of F. The atoms are as follows:

$$H\cdot \qquad \cdot \overset{\cdot\cdot}{\underset{\cdot\cdot}{Br}}\colon$$

The two atoms can share their unpaired electron:

$$H\colon\overset{\cdot\cdot}{\underset{\cdot\cdot}{Br}}\colon \quad \text{or} \quad H-\overset{\cdot\cdot}{\underset{\cdot\cdot}{Br}}\colon$$

Test Yourself

Use Lewis electron dot diagrams to illustrate the covalent bond formation in Cl_2.

Answer

$$\colon\overset{\cdot\cdot}{\underset{\cdot\cdot}{Cl}}-\overset{\cdot\cdot}{\underset{\cdot\cdot}{Cl}}\colon$$

More than two atoms can participate in covalent bonding, although any given covalent bond will be between two atoms only. Consider H and O atoms:

$$H\cdot \qquad \cdot \overset{\cdot\cdot}{\underset{\cdot}{O}}\colon$$

The H and O atoms can share an electron to form a covalent bond:

$$H\colon\overset{\cdot\cdot}{\underset{\cdot}{O}}\colon$$

The H atom has a complete valence shell. However, the O atom has only seven electrons around it, which is not a complete octet. We fix this by including a second H atom, whose single electron will make a second covalent bond with the O atom:

Now the O atom has a complete octet around it, and each H atom has two electrons, filling its valence shell. What we have is a molecule of water: H_2O.

Example 12

Use a Lewis electron dot diagram to show the covalent bonding in NH_3.

Solution

The N atom has the following Lewis electron dot diagram:

$$\cdot \ddot{N} \cdot$$

It has three unpaired electrons, each of which can make a covalent bond by sharing electrons with an H atom. The electron dot diagram of NH_3 is as follows:

$$H : \overset{\displaystyle H}{\underset{\displaystyle \cdot\cdot}{N}} : H$$

Test Yourself

Use a Lewis electron dot diagram to show the covalent bonding in PCl_3.

Answer

$$\begin{array}{c} :\ddot{Cl}: \\ :\ddot{Cl}:\ddot{P}:\ddot{Cl}: \end{array}$$

There is a simple set of steps for determining the Lewis electron dot diagram of a simple molecule. First, you must identify the central atom and the surrounding atoms. The **central atom** is the atom in the center of the molecule, while the **surrounding atoms** are the atoms making bonds to the central atom. The central atom is usually written first in the formula of the compound (H_2O is the notable exception). After the central and surrounding atoms have been identified, follow these steps:

1. Count the total number of valence electrons. Add extra if the species has negative charges and remove one for every positive charge on the species.

2. Write the central atom and surround it with the surrounding atoms.

3. Put a pair of electrons between the central atom and each surrounding atom.

4. Complete the octets around the surrounding atoms (except for H).

5. Put remaining electrons, if any, around the central atom.

6. Check that every atom has a full valence shell.

central atom

The atom in the center of a molecule.

surrounding atom

An atom that makes covalent bonds to the central atom(s).

Let us try these steps to determine the electron dot diagram for BF_4^-. The B atom is the central atom, and the F atoms are the surrounding atoms. There is a negative sign on the species, so we have an extra electron to consider.

1. **Count the total number of electrons.** B has 3, each F has 7, and there is one extra electron: 3 + 7 + 7 + 7 + 1 = 32.

2. **Write the central atom surrounded by surrounding atoms.**

3. **Put a pair of electrons between the central atom and each surrounding atom.** This uses up eight electrons, so we have 32 – 8 = 24 electrons left.

4. **Complete the octets around the surrounding atoms (except for H).** This uses up 24 more electrons, leaving 24 – 24 = 0 electrons left.

5. **Put remaining electrons, if any, around the central atom.** There are no additional electrons to add to the central atom.

6. **Check.** The B atom has eight electrons around it, as does each F atom. Each atom has a complete octet. This is a good Lewis electron dot diagram for BF_4^-.

Sometimes, however, these steps don't work. If we were to follow these steps for the compound formaldehyde (CH_2O), we would get the following:

The H and O atoms have the proper number of electrons, but the C atom has only six electrons around it, not the eight electrons for an octet. How do we fix this?

We fix this by recognizing that two atoms can share more than one pair of electrons. In the case of CH_2O, the O and C atoms share two pairs of electrons, with the following Lewis electron dot diagram as a result:

:O:
::
H:C:H

By circling the electrons around each atom, we can now see that the O and C atoms have octets, while each H atom has two electrons:

Each valence shell is full, so this is an acceptable Lewis electron dot diagram. If we were to use lines to represent the bonds, we would use two lines between the C and O atoms:

$$
\begin{array}{c}
\ddot{\text{:O:}} \\
\parallel \\
\text{H}-\text{C}-\text{H}
\end{array}
$$

The bond between the C and O atoms is a **double bond** and represents two bonding pairs of electrons between the atoms. If using the rules for drawing Lewis electron dot diagrams don't work as written, a double bond may be required.

double bond

A covalent bond composed of two pairs of bonding electrons.

Example 13

What is the proper Lewis electron dot diagram for CO_2?

Solution

The central atom is a C atom, with O atoms as surrounding atoms. We have a total of $4 + 6 + 6 = 16$ valence electrons. Following the rules for Lewis electron dot diagrams for compounds gives us

$$\ddot{\text{:O:}}\text{C}\ddot{\text{:O:}}$$

The O atoms have complete octets around them, but the C atom has only four electrons around it. The way to solve this dilemma is to make a double bond between carbon and *each* O atom:

$$\ddot{\text{O}}::\text{C}::\ddot{\text{O}}$$

Each O atom still has eight electrons around it, but now the C atom also has a complete octet. This is an acceptable Lewis electron dot diagram for CO_2.

Test Yourself

What is the proper Lewis electron dot diagram for carbonyl sulfide (COS)?

Answer

$$\ddot{\text{S}}::\text{C}::\ddot{\text{O}}$$

It is also possible to have a **triple bond**, in which there are three pairs of electrons between two atoms. Good examples of this are elemental nitrogen (N_2) and acetylene (C_2H_2):

triple bond

A covalent bond composed of three pairs of bonding electrons.

$$:\text{N}:::\text{N}: \quad \text{or} \quad :\text{N}\equiv\text{N}: \qquad\qquad \text{H}:\text{C}:::\text{C}:\text{H} \quad \text{or} \quad \text{H}:\text{C}\equiv\text{C}:\text{H}$$

Acetylene is an interesting example of a molecule with two central atoms, which are both C atoms.

Polyatomic ions are bonded together with covalent bonds. Because they are ions, however, they participate in ionic bonding with other ions. So both major types of bonding can occur at the same time.

Food and Drink App: Vitamins and Minerals

Vitamins are nutrients that our bodies need in small amounts but cannot synthesize; therefore, they must be obtained from the diet. The word *vitamin* comes from "vital amine" because it was once thought that all these compounds had an amine group (NH_2) in them. This is not actually true, but the name stuck anyway.

All vitamins are covalently bonded molecules. Most of them are commonly named with a letter, although all of them also have formal chemical names. Thus, vitamin A is also called retinol, vitamin C is called ascorbic acid, and vitamin E is called tocopherol. There is no single vitamin B; there is a group of substances called the *B complex vitamins* that are all water soluble and participate in cell metabolism. If a diet is lacking in a vitamin, diseases such as scurvy or rickets develop. Luckily, all vitamins are available as supplements, so any dietary deficiency in a vitamin can be easily corrected.

A mineral is any chemical element other than carbon, hydrogen, oxygen, or nitrogen that is needed by the body. Minerals that the body needs in quantity include sodium, potassium, magnesium, calcium, phosphorus, sulfur, and chlorine. Essential minerals that the body needs in tiny quantities (so-called *trace elements*) include manganese, iron, cobalt, nickel, copper, zinc, molybdenum, selenium, and iodine. Minerals are also obtained from the diet. Interestingly, most minerals are consumed in ionic form, rather than as elements or from covalent molecules. Like vitamins, most minerals are available in pill form, so any deficiency can be compensated for by taking supplements.

Every entry down through pantothenic acid is a vitamin, and everything from calcium and below is a mineral.

Key Takeaways

- Covalent bonds are formed when atoms share electrons.
- Lewis electron dot diagrams can be drawn to illustrate covalent bond formation.
- Double bonds or triple bonds between atoms may be necessary to properly illustrate the bonding in some molecules.

Exercises

1. How many electrons will be in the valence shell of H atoms when it makes a covalent bond?

2. How many electrons will be in the valence shell of non-H atoms when they make covalent bonds?

3. What is the Lewis electron dot diagram of I_2? Circle the electrons around each atom to verify that each valence shell is filled.

4. What is the Lewis electron dot diagram of H_2S? Circle the electrons around each atom to verify that each valence shell is filled.

5. What is the Lewis electron dot diagram of NCl_3? Circle the electrons around each atom to verify that each valence shell is filled.

6. What is the Lewis electron dot diagram of SiF_4? Circle the electrons around each atom to verify that each valence shell is filled.

7. Draw the Lewis electron dot diagram for each substance.

   a. SF_2

   b. BH_4^-

8. Draw the Lewis electron dot diagram for each substance.

   a. PI_3

   b. OH^-

9. Draw the Lewis electron dot diagram for each substance.

   a. GeH_4

   b. ClF

10. Draw the Lewis electron dot diagram for each substance.

    a. AsF_3

    b. NH_4^+

11. Draw the Lewis electron dot diagram for each substance. Double or triple bonds may be needed.

    a. SiO_2

    b. C_2H_4 (assume two central atoms)

12. Draw the Lewis electron dot diagram for each substance. Double or triple bonds may be needed.

    a. CN^-

    b. C_2Cl_2 (assume two central atoms)

13. Draw the Lewis electron dot diagram for each substance. Double or triple bonds may be needed.

    a. CS_2

    b. NH_2CONH_2 (assume that the N and C atoms are the central atoms)

14. Draw the Lewis electron dot diagram for each substance. Double or triple bonds may be needed.

a. POCl

b. HCOOH (assume that the C atom and one O atom are the central atoms)

Answers

1. two
2. usually eight

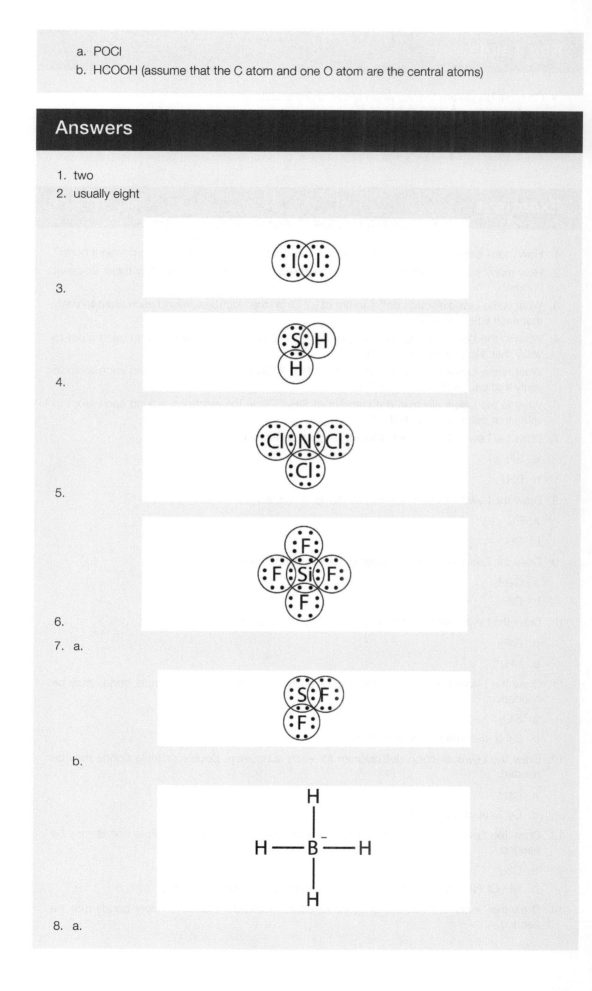

3.

4.

5.

6.

7. a.

b.

8. a.

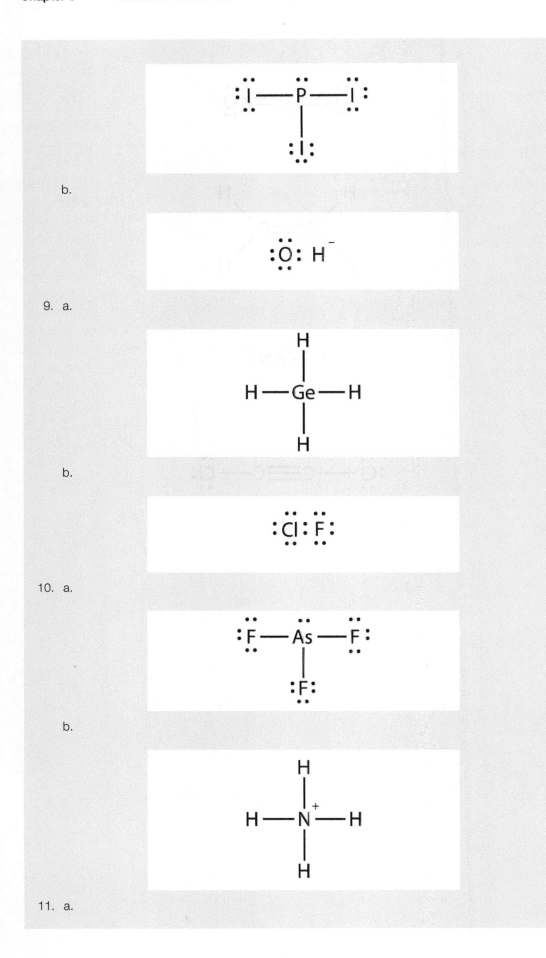

b.

9. a.

b.

10. a.

b.

11. a.

b.

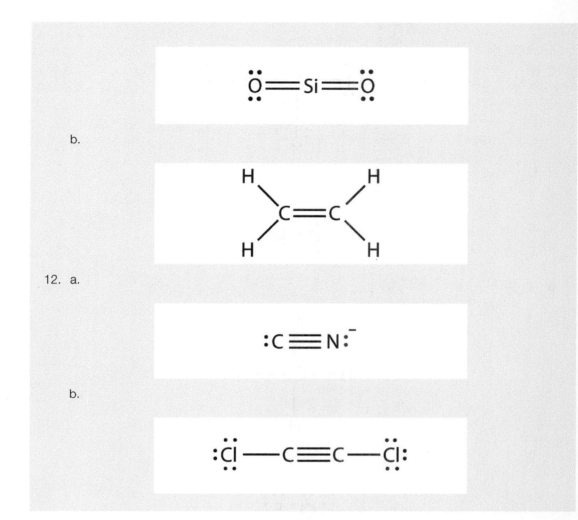

12. a.

b.

13. a.

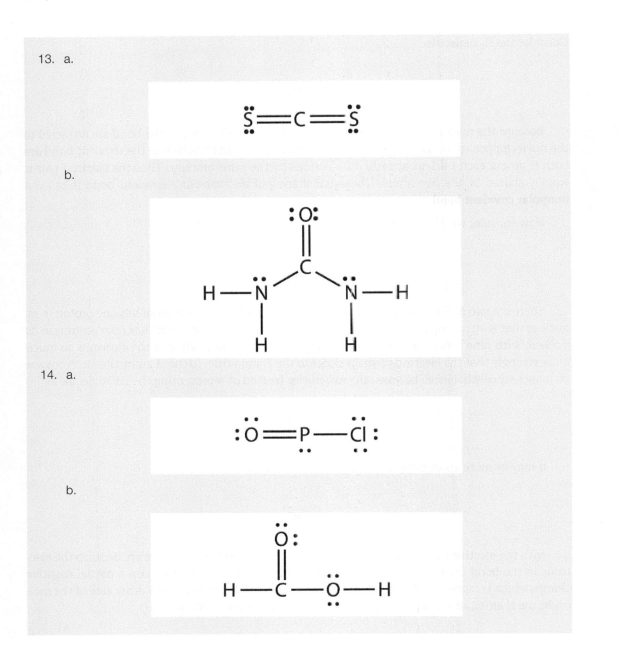

b.

14. a.

b.

5.6 Other Aspects of Covalent Bonds

Learning Objectives

1. Describe a nonpolar bond and a polar bond.
2. Use electronegativity to determine whether a bond between two elements will be nonpolar covalent, polar covalent, or ionic.
3. Describe the bond energy of a covalent bond.

Consider the H_2 molecule:

$$H \!:\! H$$

nonpolar covalent bond

The equal sharing of electrons in a covalent bond.

Because the nuclei of each H atom contain protons, the electrons in the bond are attracted to the nuclei (opposite charges attract). But because the two atoms involved in the covalent bond are both H atoms, each nucleus attracts the electrons by the same amount. Thus the electron pair is equally shared by the two atoms. The equal sharing of electrons in a covalent bond is called a **nonpolar covalent bond**.

Now consider the HF molecule:

$$H \!:\! \ddot{\underset{\cdot\cdot}{F}} \!:$$

There are two different atoms involved in the covalent bond. The H atom has one proton in its nucleus that is attracting the bonding pair of electrons. However, the F atom has nine protons in its nucleus, with nine times the attraction of the H atom. The F atom attracts the electrons so much more strongly that the electrons remain closer to the F atom than to the H atom; the electrons are no longer equally balanced between the two nuclei. Instead of representing the HF molecule as

$$H - \ddot{\underset{\cdot\cdot}{F}} \!:$$

it may be more appropriate to draw the covalent bond as

$$H \blacktriangleleft \ddot{\underset{\cdot\cdot}{F}} \!:$$

with the electrons in the bond being nearer to the F atom than the H atom. Because the electrons in the bond are nearer to the F atom, this side of the molecule takes on a partial negative charge, which is represented by δ– (δ is the lowercase Greek letter delta). The other side of the molecule, the H atom, adopts a partial positive charge, which is represented by δ+:

$$\overset{\delta+ \quad \delta-}{H - \ddot{\underset{\cdot\cdot}{F}} \!:}$$

polar covalent bond

The unequal sharing of electrons in a covalent bond.

A covalent bond between different atoms that attract the shared electrons by different amounts and cause an imbalance of electron distribution is called a **polar covalent bond**.

Technically, any covalent bond between two different elements is polar. However, the degree of polarity is important. A covalent bond between two different elements may be so slightly imbalanced that the bond is, essentially, nonpolar. A bond may be so polar that an electron actually transfers from one atom to another, forming a true ionic bond. How do we judge the degree of polarity?

electronegativity

A qualitative scale for judging how much atoms of any element attract electrons.

Scientists have devised a scale called **electronegativity**, a scale for judging how much atoms of any element attract electrons. Electronegativity is a unitless number; the higher the number, the more an atom attracts electrons. A common scale for electronegativity is shown in Figure 5.5.

FIGURE 5.5 Electronegativities of the Elements
Electronegativities are used to determine the polarity of covalent bonds.

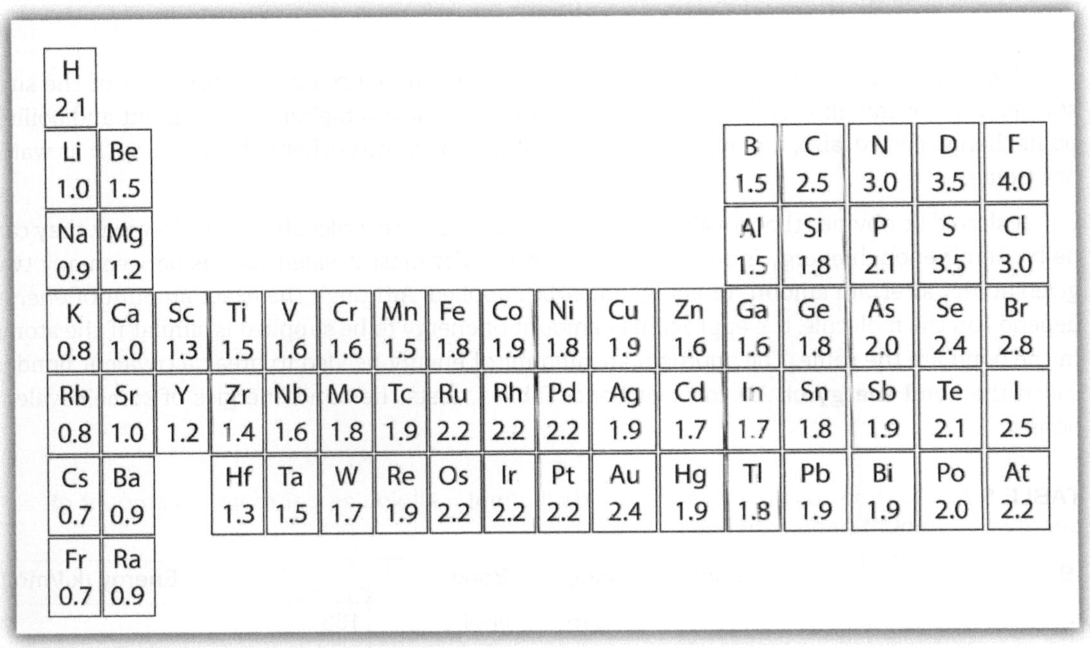

H 2.1																	
Li 1.0	Be 1.5											B 1.5	C 2.5	N 3.0	D 3.5	F 4.0
Na 0.9	Mg 1.2											Al 1.5	Si 1.8	P 2.1	S 3.5	Cl 3.0
K 0.8	Ca 1.0	Sc 1.3	Ti 1.5	V 1.6	Cr 1.6	Mn 1.5	Fe 1.8	Co 1.9	Ni 1.8	Cu 1.9	Zn 1.6	Ga 1.6	Ge 1.8	As 2.0	Se 2.4	Br 2.8
Rb 0.8	Sr 1.0	Y 1.2	Zr 1.4	Nb 1.6	Mo 1.8	Tc 1.9	Ru 2.2	Rh 2.2	Pd 2.2	Ag 1.9	Cd 1.7	In 1.7	Sn 1.8	Sb 1.9	Te 2.1	I 2.5
Cs 0.7	Ba 0.9		Hf 1.3	Ta 1.5	W 1.7	Re 1.9	Os 2.2	Ir 2.2	Pt 2.2	Au 2.4	Hg 1.9	Tl 1.8	Pb 1.9	Bi 1.9	Po 2.0	At 2.2
Fr 0.7	Ra 0.9															

The polarity of a covalent bond can be judged by determining the *difference* of the electronegativities of the two atoms involved in the covalent bond, as summarized in the following table:

Electronegativity Difference	Bond Type
0	nonpolar covalent
0–0.4	slightly polar covalent
0.4–1.9	definitely polar covalent
>1.9	likely ionic

Example 14

What is the polarity of each bond?

1. C–H
2. O–H

Solution

Using Figure 5.5, we can calculate the difference of the electronegativities of the atoms involved in the bond.

1. For the C–H bond, the difference in the electronegativities is 2.5 – 2.1 = 0.4. Thus we predict that this bond will be slightly polar covalent.

2. For the O–H bond, the difference in electronegativities is 3.5 – 2.1 = 1.4, so we predict that this bond will be definitely polar covalent.

Test Yourself

What is the polarity of each bond?

1. Rb–F
2. P–Cl

Answers

1. likely ionic
2. polar covalent

The polarity of a covalent bond can have significant influence on the properties of the substance. If the overall molecule is polar, the substance may have a higher melting point and boiling point than expected; also, it may or may not be soluble in various other substances, such as water or hexane.

bond energy

The approximate amount of energy needed to bread a covalent bond.

It should be obvious that covalent bonds are stable because molecules exist. However, they can be broken if enough energy is supplied to a molecule. For most covalent bonds between any two given atoms, a certain amount of energy must be supplied. Although the exact amount of energy depends on the molecule, the approximate amount of energy to be supplied is similar if the atoms in the bond are the same. The approximate amount of energy needed to break a covalent bond is called the **bond energy** of the covalent bond. Table 5.7 lists the bond energies of some covalent bonds.

TABLE 5.7 Bond Energies of Covalent Bonds (kJ/mol = kilojoules per mole, an amount of energy per amount of molecules)

Bond	Energy (kJ/mol)	Bond	Energy (kJ/mol)
C–C	348	N–N	163
C=C	611	N=N	418
C≡C	837	N≡N	946
C–O	351	N–H	389
C=O	799	O–O	146
C–Cl	328	O=O	498
C–H	414	O–H	463
F–F	159	S–H	339
H–Cl	431	S=O	523
H–F	569	Si–H	293
H–H	436	Si–O	368

A few trends are obvious from Table 5.7. For bonds that involve the same two elements, a double bond is stronger than a single bond, and a triple bond is stronger than a double bond. The energies of multiple bonds are not exact multiples of the single bond energy; for carbon-carbon bonds, the energy increases somewhat less than double or triple the C–C bond energy, while for nitrogen-nitrogen bonds the bond energy increases at a rate greater than the multiple of the N–N single bond energy. The bond energies in Table 5.7 are average values; the exact value of the covalent bond energy will vary slightly among molecules with these bonds but should be close to these values.

To be broken, covalent bonds always require energy; that is, covalent bond breaking always requires putting energy into the bond. Thus the energy change for this process is positive:

$$\text{Molecule}\!-\!\text{O}\!-\!\text{H} \rightarrow \text{Molecule}\!-\!\text{O} + \text{H} \qquad \text{energy change} = 463 \text{ kJ into the bond}$$

However, when making a covalent bond, energy is always given off. The energy change for this process is negative because the molecules loses energy:

$$\text{Molecule}\!-\!\text{S} + \text{H} \rightarrow \text{Molecule}\!-\!\text{S}\!-\!\text{H} \qquad \text{energy change} = 339 \text{ kJ out of the molecule}$$

Bond energies can be used to estimate the energy change of a chemical reaction. When bonds are broken in the reactants, the energy change for this process is positive because energy must be added to the molecule. When bonds are formed in the products, the energy change for this process is negative because energy is coming out of the molecule. We combine the positive energy change with the negative energy change to estimate the overall energy change of the reaction. For example, in

$$2H_2 + O_2 \rightarrow 2H_2O$$

we can draw Lewis electron dot diagrams for each substance to see what bonds are broken and what bonds are formed:

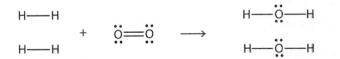

We are breaking two H–H bonds and one O–O double bond and forming four O–H single bonds. The energy required for breaking the bonds is as follows:

2 H–H bonds: 2(+436 kJ/mol)

1 O=O bond: +498 kJ/mol

Total: +1,370 kJ/mol

The energy given off when the four O–H bonds are made is as follows:

4 O–H bonds: 4(−463 kJ/mol)

Total: −1,852 kJ/mol

Combining these two numbers:

	+1,370 kJ/mol + (−1,852 kJ/mol)
Net Change:	−482 kJ/mol ≈ energy change of reaction

The actual energy change is −572 kJ/mol; we are off by about 16%—although not ideal, a 16% difference is reasonable because we used estimated, not exact, bond energies.

Example 15

Estimate the energy change of this reaction. Use the data in Table 5.7.

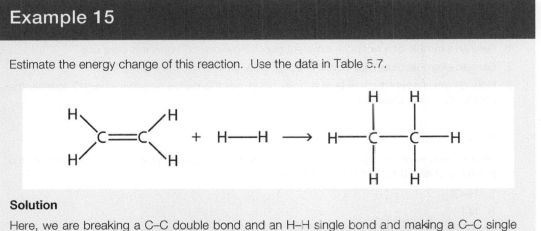

Solution

Here, we are breaking a C–C double bond and an H–H single bond and making a C–C single bond and two C–H single bonds. Bond breaking is energy added (and therefore positive in value), while bond making is energy given off (and therefore negative in value). For the bond breaking:

1 C=C	+611 kJ/mol
1 H–H	+436 kJ/mol
Total	+1,047 kJ/mol

For the bond making:

1 C–C	−348 kJ/mol
2 C–H	2(−414 kJ/mol)
Total	−1,176 kJ/mol

Overall, the energy change is +1,047 + (−1,176) = −129 kJ/mol.

Test Yourself

Estimate the energy change of this reaction. Use the data in Table 5.7.

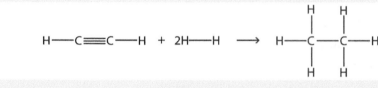

Answer

−295 kJ/mol

Key Takeaways

- Covalent bonds can be nonpolar or polar, depending on the electronegativities of the atoms involved.
- Covalent bonds can be broken if energy is added to a molecule.
- The formation of covalent bonds is accompanied by energy given off.
- Covalent bond energies can be used to estimate the enthalpy changes of chemical reactions.

Exercises

1. Give an example of a nonpolar covalent bond. How do you know it is nonpolar?

2. Give an example of a polar covalent bond. How do you know it is polar?

3. How do you know which side of a polar bond has the partial negative charge? Identify the negatively charged side of each polar bond.

   a. H–Cl

   b. H–S

4. How do you know which side of a polar bond has the partial positive charge? Identify the positively charged side of each polar bond.

   a. H–Cl

   b. N–F

5. Label the bond between the given atoms as nonpolar covalent, slightly polar covalent, definitely polar covalent, or likely ionic.

   a. H and C

  b. C and F

  c. K and F

6. Label the bond between the given atoms as nonpolar covalent, slightly polar covalent, definitely polar covalent, or likely ionic.

   a. S and Cl

   b. P and O

   c. Cs and O

7. Which covalent bond is stronger—a C–C bond or a C–H bond?

8. Which covalent bond is stronger—an O–O double bond or an N–N double bond?

9. Estimate the energy change for this reaction. Start by drawing the Lewis electron dot diagrams for each substance.

10. Estimate the energy change for this reaction. Start by drawing the Lewis electron dot diagrams for each substance.

11. Estimate the energy change for this reaction. Start by drawing the Lewis electron dot diagrams for each substance.

12. Estimate the energy change for this reaction. Start by drawing the Lewis electron dot diagrams for each substance.

Answers

1. H–H; it is nonpolar because the two atoms have the same electronegativities (answers will vary).

2. H–F; it is polar because the two atoms have different electronegativities (answers will vary).

3. a. Cl side

   b. S side

4. a. H side

   b. N side

5. a. slightly polar covalent

   b. definitely polar covalent

   c. likely ionic

6. a. slightly polar covalent

   b. definitely polar covalent

   c. likely ionic

7. C–H bond

8. O=O

9. –80 kJ

10. –266 kJ

11. –798 kJ

12. –1,286 kJ

5.7 Violations of the Octet Rule

Learning Objective

1. Recognize the three major types of violations of the octet rule.

As important and useful as the octet rule is in chemical bonding, there are some well-known violations. This does not mean that the octet rule is useless—quite the contrary. As with many rules, there are exceptions.

odd-electron molecule

A molecule with an odd number of electrons in the valence shell of an atom.

Odd-electron molecules represent the first violation to the octet rule. Although they are few, some stable compounds have an odd number of electrons in their valence shells. With an odd number of electrons, at least one atom in the molecule will have to violate the octet rule. Examples of stable odd-electron molecules are NO, NO_2, and ClO_2. The Lewis electron dot diagram for NO is as follows:

$$\cdot \ddot{N} :: \ddot{O}$$

Although the O atom has an octet of electrons, the N atom has only seven electrons in its valence shell. Although NO is a stable compound, it is very chemically reactive, as are most other odd-electron compounds.

electron-deficient molecule

A molecule with less than eight electrons in the valence shell of an atom.

Electron-deficient molecules represent the second violation to the octet rule. These stable compounds have less than eight electrons around an atom in the molecule. The most common examples are the covalent compounds of beryllium and boron. For example, beryllium can form two covalent bonds, resulting in only four electrons in its valence shell:

$$:\ddot{Cl} \text{---} Be \text{---} \ddot{Cl}:$$

Boron commonly makes only three covalent bonds, resulting in only six valence electrons around the B atom. A well-known example is BF_3:

expanded valence shell molecule

A molecule with more than eight electrons in the valence shell of an atom.

The third violation to the octet rule is found in those compounds with more than eight electrons assigned to their valence shell. These are called **expanded valence shell molecules**. Such compounds are formed only by central atoms in the third row of the periodic table or beyond that have empty d orbitals in their valence shells that can participate in covalent bonding. One such compound is PF_5. The only reasonable Lewis electron dot diagram for this compound has the P atom making five covalent bonds:

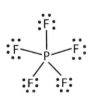

Formally, the P atom has 10 electrons in its valence shell.

Example 16

Identify each violation to the octet rule by drawing a Lewis electron dot diagram.

1. ClO
2. SF_6

Solution

1. With one Cl atom and one O atom, this molecule has $6 + 7 = 13$ valence electrons, so it is an odd-electron molecule. A Lewis electron dot diagram for this molecule is as follows:

2. In SF_6, the central S atom makes six covalent bonds to the six surrounding F atoms, so it is an expanded valence shell molecule. Its Lewis electron dot diagram is as follows:

Test Yourself

Identify the violation to the octet rule in XeF_2 by drawing a Lewis electron dot diagram.

Answer

The Xe atom has an expanded valence shell with more than eight electrons around it.

Key Takeaway

- There are three types of violations to the octet rule: odd-electron molecules, electron-deficient molecules, and expanded valence shell molecules.

Exercises

1. Why can an odd-electron molecule not satisfy the octet rule?
2. Why can an atom in the second row of the periodic table not form expanded valence shell molecules?

3. Draw an acceptable Lewis electron dot diagram for these molecules that violate the octet rule.

   a. NO_2

   b. XeF_4

4. Draw an acceptable Lewis electron dot diagram for these molecules that violate the octet rule.

   a. BCl_3

   b. ClO_2

5. Draw an acceptable Lewis electron dot diagram for these molecules that violate the octet rule.

   a. POF_3

   b. ClF_3

6. Draw an acceptable Lewis electron dot diagram for these molecules that violate the octet rule.

   a. SF_4

   b. BeH_2

Answers

1. There is no way all electrons can be paired if there are an odd number of them.

2. Second-row elements do not have a d subshell.

3. a.

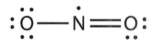

   b.

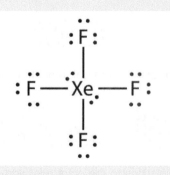

4. a.

b.

5. a.

b.

6. a.

b.

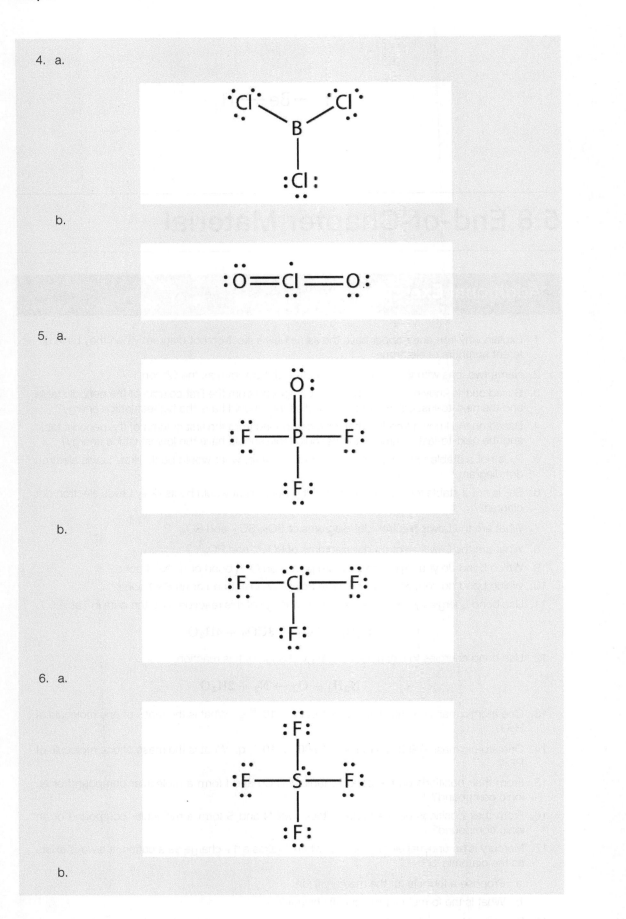

$$H \text{---} Be \text{---} H$$

5.8 End-of-Chapter Material

Additional Exercises

1. Explain why iron and copper have the same Lewis electron dot diagram when they have different numbers of electrons.

2. Name two ions with the same Lewis electron dot diagram as the Cl^- ion.

3. Based on the known trends, what ionic compound from the first column of the periodic table and the next-to-last column of the periodic table should have the highest lattice energy?

4. Based on the known trends, what ionic compound from the first column of the periodic table and the next-to-last column of the periodic table should have the lowest lattice energy?

5. P_2 is not a stable form of phosphorus, but if it were, what would be its likely Lewis electron dot diagram?

6. Se_2 is not a stable form of selenium, but if it were, what would be its likely Lewis electron dot diagram?

7. What are the Lewis electron dot diagrams of SO_2, SO_3, and SO_4^{2-}?

8. What are the Lewis electron dot diagrams of PO_3^{3-} and PO_4^{3-}?

9. Which bond do you expect to be more polar—an O–H bond or an N–H bond?

10. Which bond do you expect to be more polar—an O–F bond or an S–O bond?

11. Use bond energies to estimate the energy change of this reaction. Use the data in Table 5.7.

$$C_3H_8 + 5O_2 \rightarrow 3CO_2 + 4H_2O$$

12. Use bond energies to estimate the energy change of this reaction.

$$N_2H_4 + O_2 \rightarrow N_2 + 2H_2O$$

13. One atomic mass unit has a mass of 1.6605×10^{-24} g. What is the mass of one molecule of H_2O?

14. One atomic mass unit has a mass of 1.6605×10^{-24} g. What is the mass of one molecule of PF_5?

15. From their positions on the periodic table, will Cu and I form a molecular compound or an ionic compound?

16. From their positions on the periodic table, will N and S form a molecular compound or an ionic compound?

17. Mercury is an unusual element in that when it takes a 1+ charge as a cation, it always exists as the diatomic ion.

    a. Propose a formula for the mercury(I) ion.

    b. What is the formula for mercury(I) chloride?

18. Propose a formula for hydrogen peroxide, a substance used as a bleaching agent.

19. The uranyl cation has the formula UO_2^{2+}. Propose formulas and names for the ionic compounds between the uranyl cation and F^-, SO_4^{2-}, and PO_4^{3-}.

20. The permanganate ion has the formula MnO_4^-. Propose formulas and names for the ionic compounds between the permanganate ion and K^+, Ca^{2+}, and Fe^{3+}.

Answers

1. Iron has *d* electrons that typically are not shown on Lewis electron dot diagrams.

3. LiF

5. It would be like N_2:

:P≡≡P:

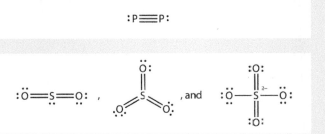

7.

9. an O–H bond

11. –2,000 kJ

13. 2.992×10^{-24} g

15. ionic

17. a. Hg_2^{2+}

    b. Hg_2Cl_2

19. UO_2F_2, uranyl fluoride; UO_2SO_4, uranyl sulfate; $(UO_2)_3(PO_4)_2$, uranyl phosphate

Endnotes

1. US Department of Agriculture Committee for Nutrition Policy and Promotion, "Report of the Dietary Guidelines Advisory Committee on the Dietary Guidelines for Americans," accessed January 5, 2010,

CHAPTER 6
The Shape of Molecules

Opening Essay

The human body is one large chemical factory. Even today, scientists are spending their entire careers trying to unravel the chemistry that occurs in our cells and organs. Even the function of the brain is based on chemistry.

One important class of compounds found in the body is proteins, which perform a large range of essential chemical processes. Some of these processes can be very slow—so slow that the body might die if the process didn't have some kind of help.

Help exists in the form of *enzymes*, which are special proteins that speed up certain chemical processes. Exactly how enzymes work is an intense field of study. One proposed method is called the lock-and-key model, in which the enzyme has just the right shape to interact with another protein, just like a key just fits into a lock to open it.

The lock-and-key model of enzyme function proposes that the enzyme has just the right shape (drawing (a)) to fit into another molecule (drawing (b)), just like a key fits into a lock.

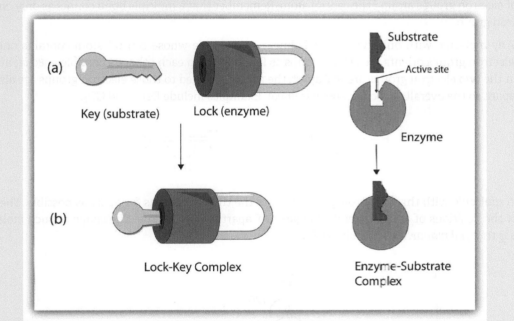

What this demonstrates is that the shape of a molecule can have an impact on its properties. Although it is difficult to know in advance what the shape of a very large molecule will be, for smaller molecules it is relatively straightforward.

6.1 Molecular Shapes

Molecules have shapes. There is an abundance of experimental evidence to that effect—from their physical properties to their chemical reactivity. Small molecules—molecules with a single central atom—have shapes that can be easily predicted.

The basic idea in molecular shapes is called **valence shell electron pair repulsion (VSEPR)**. It basically says that electron pairs, being composed of negatively charged particles, repel each other to get as far away from each other as possible. VSEPR makes a distinction between *electron group geometry*, which expresses how electron groups (bonds and nonbonding electron pairs) are arranged, and *molecular geometry*, which expresses how the atoms in a molecule are arranged. However, the two geometries are related.

There are two types of **electron groups**: any type of bond—single, double, or triple—and lone electron pairs. When applying VSEPR to simple molecules, the first thing to do is to count the number of electron groups around the central atom. Remember that a multiple bond counts as only *one* electron group.

Any molecule with only two atoms is linear. A molecule whose central atom contains only two electron groups orients those two groups as far apart from each other as possible—180° apart. When the two electron groups are 180° apart, the atoms attached to those electron groups are also 180° apart, so the overall molecular shape is linear. Examples include BeH_2 and CO_2:

A molecule with three electron groups orients the three groups as far apart as possible. They adopt the positions of an equilateral triangle—120° apart and in a plane. The shape of such molecules is *trigonal planar*. An example is BF_3:

Some substances have a trigonal planar electron group distribution but have atoms bonded to only two of the three electron groups. An example is GeF_2:

From an electron group geometry perspective, GeF_2 has a trigonal planar shape, but its real shape is dictated by the positions of the atoms. This shape is called *bent* or *angular*.

---

valence shell electron pair repulsion (VSEPR)

The general concept that estimates the shape of a simple molecule.

electron group

A covalent bond of any type or a lone electron pair.

A molecule with four electron groups about the central atom orients the four groups in the direction of a tetrahedron, as shown in Figure 6.1. If there are four atoms attached to these electron groups, then the molecular shape is also *tetrahedral*. Methane (CH_4) is an example.

FIGURE 6.1 Tetrahedral Geometry
Four electron groups orient themselves in the shape of a tetrahedron.

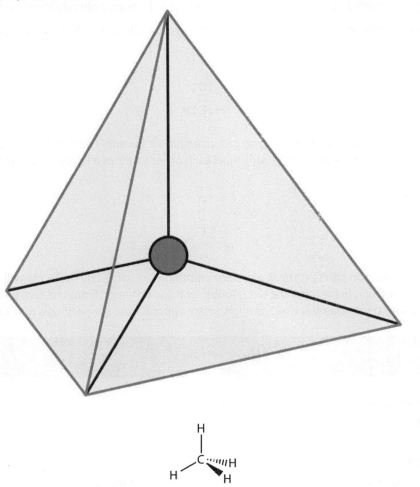

This diagram of CH_4 illustrates the standard convention of displaying a three-dimensional molecule on a two-dimensional surface. The straight lines are in the plane of the page, the solid wedged line is coming out of the plane toward the reader, and the dashed wedged line is going out of the plane away from the reader.

NH_3 is an example of a molecule whose central atom has four electron groups but only three of them are bonded to surrounding atoms.

Although the electron groups are oriented in the shape of a tetrahedron, from a molecular geometry perspective, the shape of NH_3 is *trigonal pyramidal*.

H_2O is an example of a molecule whose central atom has four electron groups but only two of them are bonded to surrounding atoms.

Although the electron groups are oriented in the shape of a tetrahedron, the shape of the molecule is *bent* or *angular*. A molecule with four electron groups about the central atom but only one electron group bonded to another atom is linear because there are only two atoms in the molecule.

Double or triple bonds count as a single electron group. CH_2O has the following Lewis electron dot diagram:

The central C atom has three electron groups around it because the double bond counts as one electron group. The three electron groups repel each other to adopt a trigonal planar shape:

(The lone electron pairs on the O atom are omitted for clarity.) The molecule will not be a perfect equilateral triangle because the C–O double bond is different from the two C–H bonds, but both planar and triangular describe the appropriate approximate shape of this molecule.

Example 1

What is the approximate shape of each molecule?

1. PCl_3
2. NOF

Solution

The first step is to draw the Lewis electron dot diagram of the molecule.

1. For PCl_3, the electron dot diagram is as follows:

The lone electron pairs on the Cl atoms are omitted for clarity. The P atom has four electron groups with three of them bonded to surrounding atoms, so the molecular shape is trigonal pyramidal.

2. The electron dot diagram for NOF is as follows:

The N atom has three electron groups on it, two of which are bonded to other atoms. The molecular shape is bent.

Test Yourself

What is the approximate molecular shape of CH_2Cl_2?

Answer

Tetrahedral

Chemistry is Everywhere: Crystals and Gemstones

We have established that molecules have shapes. One ramification of molecular shapes is when a lot of molecules, ions, or combinations of them come together in the solid phase. If it is carefully done, all of the species will be lined up in some regular order in all three dimensions. We have a **crystal**.

The ability to make a crystal of a compound, whether it be ionic or covalent, is directly related to how complicated its shape is. Simple ionic compounds make crystals very easily—for example, consider the salt (NaCl) in your kitchen, all composed of tiny cubes of sodium chloride crystals. More complicated shapes are more difficult to turn into crystals. Biological molecules are especially challenging to crystallize. Although crystals were detected in blood samples as early as the mid-1850s, the first reported intentional crystallization of a protein occurred in 1926 with the crystallization of urease, a protein with a molecular mass of about 500,000 u. Although protein crystallization is difficult, today it is a standard technique used to study proteins.

Some crystals are durable, beautiful, and relatively rare. Many of these serve as **gemstones**, which are substances that are cut and polished to maximize their beauty. The chemical species that make gemstones vary tremendously: The gemstone sphalerite is simply crystalline zinc sulfide (ZnS), while amber is fossilized tree resin that is composed of long, twisty molecules not unlike plastic.

Emeralds are one of the most prized gemstones. From the Gail Ball Collection, pictured are green Muzo emeralds (left) and very rare red beryl (right).

Source: Photo courtesy of Melissa Lessick, IMG Jewelers, Inc.

One interesting gemstone is emerald, which is a mineral in the beryl family having a molecular formula of $Be_3Al_2(SiO_3)_6$. The normal green color of most emeralds is due to impurities of chromium, although sometimes vanadium is also present. One very rare form of emerald has manganese impurities instead of chromium, giving the crystal a red color. Red beryl, as it is known, is found in only three or four places in the world and would be much more valuable if it were more well-known!

Table 6.1 summarizes the shapes of molecules based on their number of electron groups and surrounding atoms.

TABLE 6.1 Summary of Molecular Shapes

Number of Electron Groups on Central Atom	Number of Surrounding Atoms	Molecular Shape
any	1	linear
2	2	linear
3	3	trigonal planar
3	2	bent
4	4	tetrahedral

Number of Electron Groups on Central Atom	Number of Surrounding Atoms	Molecular Shape
4	3	trigonal pyramidal
4	2	bent

Key Takeaway

- The approximate shape of a molecule can be predicted from the number of electron groups and the number of surrounding atoms.

Exercises

1. What is the basic premise behind VSEPR?
2. What is the difference between the electron group geometry and the molecular geometry?
3. Identify the electron group geometry and the molecular geometry of each molecule.

    a. H_2S

    b. $POCl_3$

4. Identify the electron group geometry and the molecular geometry of each molecule.

    a. CS_2

    b. H_2S

5. Identify the electron group geometry and the molecular geometry of each molecule.

    a. HCN

    b. CCl_4

6. Identify the electron group geometry and the molecular geometry of each molecule.

    a. BI_3

    b. PH_3

7. What is the geometry of each species?

    a. CN^-

    b. PO_4^{3-}

8. What is the geometry of each species?

    a. PO_3^{3-}

    b. NO_3^-

9. What is the geometry of each species?

    a. COF_2

    b. C_2Cl_2 (both C atoms are central atoms and are bonded to each other)

10. What is the geometry of each species?

    a. CO_3^{2-}

    b. N_2H_4 (both N atoms are central atoms and are bonded to each other)

Answers

1. Electron pairs repel each other.

2. Electron group geometry is the placement of the electrons of the central atom in space, whereas molecular geometry is the placement of nuclei about the central atom in space.

3. a. electron group geometry: tetrahedral; molecular geometry: bent
   b. electron group geometry: tetrahedral; molecular geometry: tetrahedral

4. a. electron group geometry: linear; molecular geometry: linear
   b. electron group geometry: tetrahedral; molecular geometry: bent

5. a. electron group geometry: linear; molecular geometry: linear
   b. electron group geometry: tetrahedral; molecular geometry: tetrahedral

6. a. electron group geometry: trigonal planar; molecular geometry: trigonal planar
   b. electron group geometry: tetrahedral; molecular geometry: trigonal pyramidal

7. a. linear
   b. tetrahedral

8. a. trigonal pyramidal
   b. trigonal planar

9. a. trigonal planar
   b. linear and linear about each central atom

10. a. trigonal planar
    b. trigonal pyramidal about each central atom

6.2 Polarity of Molecules

Learning Objectives

1. Predict the polarity of a simple molecule based on its shape.

When the shape of a simple molecule is known, several useful properties of the molecule can be deduced. One of the most useful properties is the polarity of the molecule.

Recall in Chapter 5 Section 6, we introduced the idea of the polarity of a covalent bond between two different atoms. For example, in the molecule hydrogen fluoride:

$$H - \ddot{\underset{\cdot\cdot}{F}}:$$

We argued that the atoms don't share the electrons in the covalent bond equally, so it may be better to represent the bond as a wedge, favoring the more electronegative fluorine atom:

$$H \blacktriangleleft \ddot{\underset{\cdot\cdot}{F}}:$$

Finally, because electrons have a negative charge, we argued that the fluorine atom has a partial negative charge, while the hydrogen atom has a partial positive charge:

$$\overset{\delta+}{H}—\overset{\delta-}{\ddot{\underset{..}{F}}}:$$

We referred to the covalent bond as a *polar covalent bond*. In this case, though, there is only one covalent bond in the molecule, so in addition to saying that the bond is polar, we can also claim—correctly—that the *molecule itself* is polar.

A **polar molecule** is a molecule that has an imbalance of electron charge so that there is an overall polarity of the molecule as a whole. If all of the electron charge is balanced around the molecule, then it is considered a **nonpolar molecule**. To determine if a molecule is polar, the shape of the molecule must be considered, not just the atoms in the molecule.

For example, in the diatomic fluorine molecule

$$:\ddot{\underset{..}{F}}—\ddot{\underset{..}{F}}:$$

the same atom appears on either side of the covalent bond. Although we know that fluorine is the most electronegative element, the fact that there is a fluorine atom on either side of the bond means that they are attracting the electrons in the bond equally, so overall the molecule is nonpolar.

Carbon dioxide is a linear triatomic (three-atom) molecule, composed of two C=O bonds 180° apart from each other:

180°

Oxygen is the second-most electronegative element, so it attracts the electrons in the covalent bonds more than the carbon atom does. Each bond is polar:

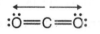
:Ö=C=Ö:

The arrows show that each C=O bond is polar. However, because the two bonds are pointing 180° apart from each other, their polarities cancel each other out and *the overall molecule is nonpolar*. It's like having a tug-of-war game with both teams pulling the same amount—they cancel each other out.

Water is also a triatomic molecule, but it has a different shape (bent) than carbon dioxide does (linear):

Each O-H bond is polar, as shown by the arrows pointing toward the oxygen atom, which is more electronegative. However, because the two O-H bonds aren't 180° apart, they don't cancel each other out and *the overall molecule is polar*.

polar molecule

A molecule that has an imbalance of electron charge overall.

nonpolar molecule

A molecule without an imbalance of electron charge around it.

Other shapes can have bonds whose polarities cancel out, but they're a bit harder to see. Molecules that are trigonal planar and tetrahedral are also nonpolar because their bonds all cancel each other:

In BF_3, the three polar B-F bonds cancel each other out, so overall the molecule is nonpolar. In CCl_4, the four polar C-Cl bonds cancel each other out, so carbon tetrachloride is also nonpolar.

The idea of canceling dipole moments for certain shapes only works if the opposing bonds (whether in two, three, or four directions) are exactly the same—they must have the same central atom and surrounding atoms. Otherwise, the polar bonds don't cancel each other out exactly because of differing electronegativities. For example, in carbonyl sulfide

the bonds are 180° apart from each other and they are polar, but the C=O bond is more polar than the C=S bond, so they do not cancel out exactly. Therefore, carbonyl sulfide is polar.

Example 2

Indicate whether each molecule of polar. You may have to draw its electron dot diagram first.

1. H_2S
2. CH_3Cl
3. CS_2

Solution

1. H_2S is bent, like H_2O. Therefore, it is polar.
2. CH_3Cl has an overall tetrahedral shape, but one of the bonds, the C-Cl bond, is different from the other three C-H bonds. Therefore, the polarity of the bonds do not perfectly cancel out and the molecule is polar.
3. CS_2 is linear, like CO_2. The two C=S bonds are polar, but are 180° apart and their polarities cancel. Therefore, the molecule is nonpolar.

Test Yourself

Is BCl_3 polar or nonpolar?

Answer

nonpolar

Why is knowing about polarity important? One key issue in chemistry is how different atoms and molecules interact with each other, a topic that will be used in several chapters in this book. One useful rule of thumb regarding molecular interactions is "like interacts with like." This is a simple way of remembering that polar molecules can interact strongly with other polar molecules, while nonpolar molecules can interact strongly with other nonpolar molecules. But polar molecules and nonpolar molecules—they do *not* want to interact very strongly. A lot can be explained using this very simple rule of thumb.

Polarity also impacts how molecules of one substance interact with each other. In the presentation of solids, liquids, and gases, the polarity of a molecule can have a major impact on which phase is present under certain conditions.

Food and Drink App: Taste and Smell

Tasting and smelling are an important part of eating and drinking. It may not surprise you to learn that the senses of taste and smell are based on chemistry.

The human tongue contains 100,000 - 500,000 taste buds that are sensitive to certain chemicals that accompany flavors: sodium ions and hydrogen ions for salty and sour, more complicated molecules for sweet, bitter, and savory. Other animals have either a different number of taste buds, making them more or less sensitive to certain flavors, or different types of taste buds, allowing them to taste (or not taste) different flavors. For example, birds do not have any sensitivity for capsaicin, the chemical responsible for the hotness of chili peppers, so chili-based products for warding off mammalian wildlife in your backyard are useless against birds.

The most currently-accepted theory behind the sense of smell (more properly called *olfaction*) is that molecules of a certain shape convey a certain smell. Research in the early 1990s identified certain proteins in olfactory sensors (the nose's equivalent of taste buds) that were known to interact only with molecules having specific shapes. If molecules had the right shape to fit with the protein, a signal would be sent to the brain to register a certain type of smell. Food technologists and perfumeries use these ideas to invent new scents for their products. So, shape makes the smell!

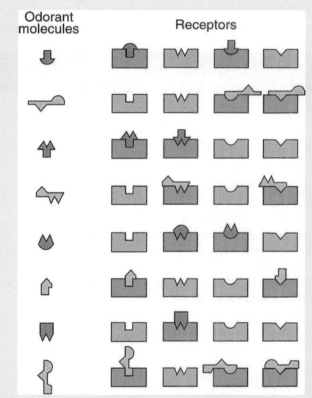

Source: Adapted from http://wiki.bethanycrane.com/olfactorysystem.

You may not believe it, but the sense of smell is probably more important than the sense of taste when enjoying food and drink. A simple experiment to support this is to pinch your nose shut, close your eyes, and have a trusted friend give you a piece of apple or onion without telling you which. If you are like most people, you won't be able to tell the difference!

Key Takeaway

- Molecules can be polar or nonpolar depending on the polarity and directions of their covalent bonds.

Exercises

1. Explain how a molecule can have polar bonds but be a nonpolar molecule overall.
2. Can a molecule with nonpolar bonds ever be polar?
3. Determine if these molecules are polar or nonpolar. You may have to draw the electron dot diagrams first.
   a. HOF
   b. CF_4
   c. BBr_3
4. Determine if these molecules are polar or nonpolar. You may have to draw the electron dot diagrams first.
   a. PCl_3
   b. $COCl_2$ (the C is the central atom and the others are surrounding atoms)
   c. SiH_4

Answers

1. The polar bonds can be oriented in such a way that their polarities cancel, yielding a nonpolar molecule.

3. a. polar
   b. nonpolar
   c. nonpolar

6.3 End-of-Chapter Material

Additional Exercises

1. Would there be any difference in the VSEPR model if electrons were positively charged and nuclei were negatively charged?
2. What are the two things that are considered electron groups?
3. Complete this table with the proper molecular shapes.

Number of electron groups	Number of surrounding atoms	Molecular shape
2	2	

3	2	
4	3	

4. Complete this table with the proper molecular shapes.

Number of electron groups	Number of surrounding atoms	Molecular shape
3	3	
4	2	
4	4	

5. Indicate whether each species listed is polar or nonpolar.

   a. CBr_4

   b. NF_3

   c. BeH_2

6. Indicate whether each species listed is polar or nonpolar.

   a. PH_3

   b. SF_4

   c. NH_2NH_2 (hydrazine; treat each nitrogen as if it were a central atom)

7. Can a neutral atom be polar? Explain why or why not.

8. Can an ion be polar? Explain why or why not.

Answers

1. No, because positively-charged electron groups would also repel each other.

3. linear; bent; trigonal pyramidal

5. a. nonpolar

    b. polar

    c. nonpolar

7. No; there is no separation of positive and negative charge.

CHAPTER 7
Solids and Liquids

Opening Essay

There is an urban legend that glass is an extremely thick liquid rather than a solid, even at room temperature. Proponents claim that old windows are thicker at the bottom than at the top, suggesting that the glass flowed down over time. Unfortunately, the proponents of this idea have no credible evidence that this is true, as old windows were likely not subject to the stricter manufacturing standards that exist today. Also, when mounting a piece of glass that has an obviously variable thickness, it makes structural sense to put the thicker part at the bottom, where it will support the object better.

Liquids flow when a small force is placed on them, even if only very slowly. Solids, however, may deform under a small force, but they return to their original shape when the force is relaxed. This is how glass behaves: it goes back to its original shape (unless it breaks under the applied force). Observers also point out that telescopes with glass lenses to focus light still do so even decades after manufacture—a circumstance that would not be so if the lens were liquid and flowed.

Glass is a solid at room temperature. Don't let anyone tell you otherwise!

Is this woman cleaning a solid or a liquid? Contrary to some claims, glass is a solid, not a very thick liquid.

Source: © Thinkstock

The phase of a substance is one fundamental description of that substance. Most of us are familiar with the solid, liquid, and gas phases. Phases have an important impact on chemistry, so it's useful to understand how they behave. Here, we consider some properties of liquids and solids. As a review, Table 7.1 lists some general properties of the three phases of matter, some of which we will discuss in more detail in the coming material.

TABLE 7.1 Properties of the Three Phases of Matter

Phase	Shape	Density	Compressibility
Gas	fills entire container	low	high
Liquid	fills a container from bottom to top	high	low
Solid	rigid	high	low

7.1 Intermolecular Forces

Learning Objective

1. Relate phase to intermolecular forces.

Why does a substance have the phase it does? The preferred phase of a substance at a given set of conditions is a balance between the energy of the particles and intermolecular forces (or intermolecular interactions) between the particles. If the forces between particles are strong enough, the substance is a liquid or, if stronger, a solid. If the forces between particles are weak and sufficient energy is present, the particles separate from each other, so the gas phase is the preferred phase. The energy of the particles is mostly determined by temperature, so temperature is the main variable that determines what phase is stable at any given point.

dispersion force

An intermolecular force caused by the instantaneous position of an electron in a molecule.

What forces define intermolecular interactions? There are several. A force present in all substances with electrons is the **dispersion force** (sometimes called the *London dispersion force*, after the physicist Fritz London, who first described this force in the early 1900s). This interaction is caused by the instantaneous position of an electron in a molecule, which temporarily makes that point of the molecule negatively charged and the rest of the molecule positively charged. In an instant, the electron is now somewhere else, but the fleeting imbalance of electric charge in the molecule allows molecules to interact with each other. As you might expect, the greater the number of electrons in a species, the stronger the dispersion force; this partially explains why smaller molecules are gases and larger molecules are liquids and solids at the same temperature. (Mass is a factor as well.)

dipole-dipole interactions

An intermolecular force caused by molecules with a permanent dipole.

Molecules with a permanent dipole moment experience **dipole-dipole interactions**, which are generally stronger than dispersion forces if all other things are equal. The oppositely charged ends of a polar molecule, which have partial charges on them, attract each other (Figure 7.1). Thus a polar molecule such CH_2Cl_2 has a significantly higher boiling point (313 K, or 40°C) than a nonpolar molecule like CF_4 (145 K, or –128°C), even though it has a slightly lower molar mass (85 u vs. 88 u).

FIGURE 7.1 Dipole-Dipole Interactions
Oppositely charged ends of polar molecules attract each other.

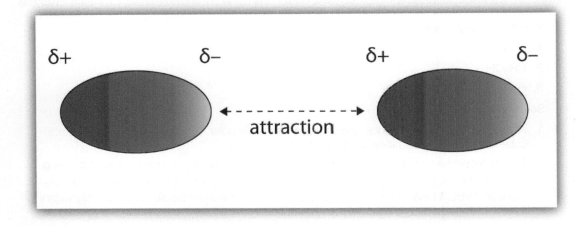

An unusually strong form of dipole-dipole interaction is called **hydrogen bonding**. Hydrogen bonding is found in molecules with an H atom bonded to an N atom, an O atom, or an F atom. Such covalent bonds are very polar, and the dipole-dipole interaction between these bonds in two or more molecules is strong enough to create a new category of intermolecular force. Hydrogen bonding is the reason water has unusual properties. For such a small molecule (its molar mass is only 18 u), H_2O has relatively high melting and boiling points. Its boiling point is 373 K (100°C), while the boiling point of a similar molecule, H_2S, is 233 K (-60°C). This is because H_2O molecules experience hydrogen bonding, while H_2S molecules do not. This strong attraction between H_2O molecules requires additional energy to separate the molecules in the condensed phase, so its boiling point is higher than would be expected. Hydrogen bonding is also responsible for water's ability as a solvent, its high heat capacity, and its ability to expand when freezing; the molecules line up in such a way that there is extra space between the molecules, increasing its volume in the solid state (Figure 7.2).

hydrogen bonding

The very strong interaction between molecules due to H atoms being bonded to N, O, or F atoms.

FIGURE 7.2 Hydrogen Bonding
When water solidifies, hydrogen bonding between the molecules forces the molecules to line up in a way that creates empty space between the molecules, increasing the overall volume of the solid. This is why ice is less dense than liquid water.

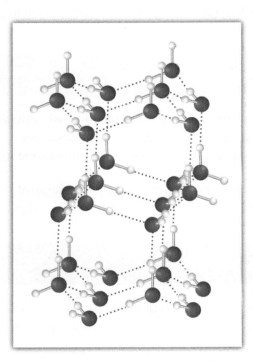

Example 1

Identify the most significant intermolecular force in each substance.

1. C_3H_8
2. CH_3OH
3. H_2S

Solution

1. Although C–H bonds are polar, they are only minimally polar. The most significant intermolecular force for this substance would be dispersion forces.
2. This molecule has an H atom bonded to an O atom, so it will experience hydrogen bonding.
3. Although this molecule does not experience hydrogen bonding, the Lewis electron dot diagram and VSEPR indicate that it is bent, so it has a permanent dipole. The most significant force in this substance is dipole-dipole interaction.

Test Yourself

Identify the most significant intermolecular force in each substance.

1. HF
2. HCl

Answers

1. hydrogen bonding
2. dipole-dipole interactions

The preferred phase a substance adopts can change with temperature. At low temperatures, most substances are solids (only helium is predicted to be a liquid at absolute zero). As the temperature increases, those substances with very weak intermolecular forces become gases directly (in a process called *sublimation*, which will be discussed in Section 2). Substances with weak interactions can become liquids as the temperature increases. As the temperature increases even more, the individual particles will have so much energy that the intermolecular forces are overcome, so the particles separate from each other, and the substance becomes a gas (assuming that their chemical bonds are not so weak that the compound decomposes from the high temperature). Although is it difficult to predict the temperature ranges for which solid, liquid, or gas is the preferred phase for any random substance, all substances progress from solid to liquid to gas in that order as temperature increases.

Key Takeaways

- All substances experience dispersion forces between their particles.
- Substances that are polar experience dipole-dipole interactions.
- Substances with covalent bonds between an H atom and N, O, or F atoms experience hydrogen bonding.
- The preferred phase of a substance depends on the strength of the intermolecular force and the energy of the particles.

Exercises

1. What type of intermolecular force do all substances have?
2. What is necessary for a molecule to experience dipole-dipole interactions?

3. What is necessary for a molecule to experience hydrogen bonding?

4. How does varying the temperature change the preferred phase of a substance?

5. Identify the strongest intermolecular force present in each substance.

   a. He

   b. $CHCl_3$

   c. HOF

6. Identify the strongest intermolecular force present in each substance.

   a. CH_3OH

   b. $(CH_3)_2CO$

   c. N_2

7. Identify the strongest intermolecular force present in each substance.

   a. HBr

   b. $C_6H_5NH_2$

   c. CH_4

8. Identify the strongest intermolecular force present in each substance.

   a. $C_{10}H_{22}$

   b. HF

   c. glucose, whose structure is:

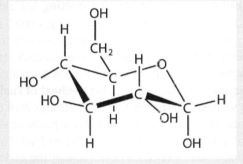

Answers

1. dispersion force

2. The molecule must have a permanent dipole moment.

3. An H atom must be bonded to an N, O, or F atom.

4. The higher the temperature, the more energy a substance has and the more able it is to break the intermolecular interactions between its molecules.

5. a. dispersion forces

   b. dipole-dipole interactions

   c. hydrogen bonding

6. a. hydrogen bonding

   b. dipole-dipole interactions

   c. dispersion forces

7. a. dipole-dipole interactions

   b. hydrogen bonding

   c. dispersion forces

8. a. dispersion forces

b. hydrogen bonding
c. hydrogen bonding

7.2 Phase Transitions: Melting, Boiling, and Subliming

Learning Objectives

1. Describe what happens during a phase change.
2. Calculate the energy change needed for a phase change.

Substances can change phase—often because of a temperature change. At low temperatures, most substances are solid; as the temperature increases, they become liquid; at higher temperatures still, they become gaseous.

The process of a solid becoming a liquid is called **melting** (an older term that you may see sometimes is *fusion*). The opposite process, a liquid becoming a solid, is called **solidification**. For any pure substance, the temperature at which melting occurs—known as the **melting point**—is a characteristic of that substance. It requires energy for a solid to melt into a liquid (we will consider energy in more detail in Chapter 13). Every pure substance has a certain amount of energy it needs to change from a solid to a liquid. This amount is called the **heat of fusion** of the substance, represented as ΔH_{fus}. Some ΔH_{fus} values are listed in Table 7.2; it is assumed that these values are at the melting point of the substance. Note that the unit of ΔH_{fus} is joules of energy per gram, so we need to know the mass of material to know how much energy is involved. The ΔH_{fus} is always tabulated as a positive number. However, it can be used for both the melting and the solidification processes as long as you keep in mind that melting is always increasing the energy (so ΔH will be positive), while solidification is always removing energy (so ΔH will be negative).

melting

The process of a solid becoming a liquid. An older term that you may see sometimes is fusion.

solidification

The process of a liquid becoming a solid.

melting point

The characteristic temperature at which a solid becomes a liquid.

heat of fusion

The amount of energy needed to change from a solid to a liquid or from a liquid to a solid.

TABLE 7.2 Heats of Fusion for Various Substances

Substance (Melting Point)	ΔH_{fus} (J/g)
Water, H_2O (0°C)	333.5
Aluminum, Al (660°C)	396.6
Benzene, C_6H_6 (5.5°C)	127.4
Ethanol, C_2H_5OH (−114.3°C)	108.9
Mercury, Hg (−38.8°C)	11.4

Example 2

What is the energy change when 45.7 g of H_2O melt at 0°C?

Solution

The ΔH_{fus} of H_2O is 333.5 J/g. We can use ΔH_{fus} as a conversion factor from mass to energy. Because the substance is melting, the process is adding energy, so the energy change will be positive.

$$45.7 \text{ g } H_2O \times \frac{333.5 \text{ J}}{g} = 15.3 \text{ kJ}$$

Without a sign, the number is assumed to be positive.

Test Yourself

What is the energy change when 108 g of C_6H_6 freeze at 5.5°C?

Answer

−13.8 kJ

During melting, energy goes exclusively to changing the phase of a substance; it does not go into changing the temperature of a substance. Hence melting is an **isothermal** process because a substance stays at the same temperature. Only when all of a substance is melted does any additional energy go to changing its temperature.

What happens when a solid becomes a liquid? In a solid, individual particles are stuck in place because the intermolecular forces cannot be overcome by the energy of the particles. When more energy is supplied (e.g., by raising the temperature), there comes a point at which the particles have enough energy to move around but not enough energy to separate. This is the liquid phase: particles are still in contact but are able to move around each other. This explains why liquids can assume the shape of their containers: the particles move around and, under the influence of gravity, fill the lowest volume possible (unless the liquid is in a zero-gravity environment—see Figure 7.3).

isothermal

A process that does not change the temperature.

FIGURE 7.3 Liquids and Gravity

(a) A liquid fills the bottom of its container as it is drawn downward by gravity and the particles slide over each other. (b) A liquid floats in a zero-gravity environment. The particles still slide over each other because they are in the liquid phase, but now there is no gravity to pull them down.

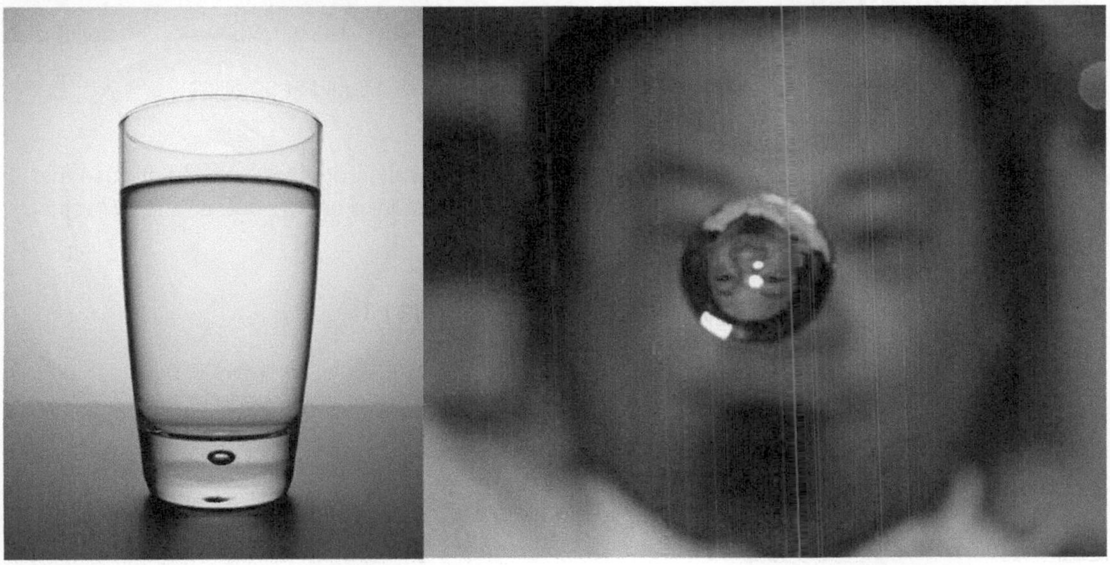

(a)   (b)

Source: Photo on the left © Thinkstock. Photo on the right courtesy of NASA, http://www.nasa.gov/mission_pages/station/multimedia/Exp10_image_009.html.

boiling (vaporization)

The process of a liquid becoming a gas.

condensation

The process of a gas becoming a liquid.

boiling point

The characteristic temperature at which a liquid becomes a gas.

normal boiling point

The characteristic temperature at which a liquid becomes a gas when the surrounding pressure is exactly 1 atm.

heat of vaporization

The amount of energy required to convert a liquid to a gas.

The phase change between a liquid and a gas has some similarities to the phase change between a solid and a liquid. At a certain temperature, the particles in a liquid have enough energy to become a gas. The process of a liquid becoming a gas is called **boiling (or vaporization)**, while the process of a gas becoming a liquid is called **condensation**. However, unlike the solid/liquid conversion process, the liquid/gas conversion process is noticeably affected by the surrounding pressure on the liquid because gases are strongly affected by pressure. This means that the temperature at which a liquid becomes a gas, the **boiling point**, can change with surrounding pressure. Therefore, we define the **normal boiling point** as the temperature at which a liquid changes to a gas when the surrounding pressure is exactly 1 atmosphere, or the average air pressure at sea level.

Like the solid/liquid phase change, the liquid/gas phase change involves energy. The amount of energy required to convert a liquid to a gas is called the **heat of vaporization**, represented as ΔH_{vap}. Some ΔH_{vap} values are listed in Table 7.3; it is assumed that these values are for the normal boiling point temperature of the substance, which is also given in the table. The unit for ΔH_{vap} is also joules per gram, so we need to know the mass of material to know how much energy is involved. The ΔH_{vap} is also always tabulated as a positive number. It can be used for both the boiling and the condensation processes as long as you keep in mind that boiling is always increasing the energy (so ΔH will be positive), while condensation is always removing energy (so ΔH will be negative).

TABLE 7.3 Heats of Vaporization for Various Substances

Substance (Normal Boiling Point)	ΔH_{vap} (J/g)
Water, H_2O (100°C)	2257
Bromine, Br_2 (59.5°C)	96.4
Benzene, C_6H_6 (80.1°C)	394.3
Ethanol, C_2H_5OH (78.3°C)	838.0
Mercury, Hg (357°C)	295.3

Example 3

What is the energy change when 66.7 g of $Br_2(g)$ condense to a liquid at 59.5°C?

Solution

The ΔH_{vap} of Br_2 is 96.4 J/g. Even though this is a condensation process, we can still use the numerical value of ΔH_{vap} as long as we realize that we must take energy out, so the ΔH value will be negative. We can use ΔH_{vap} as a conversion factor.

$$66.7 \; \cancel{g \, Br_2} \times \frac{96.4 J}{\cancel{g}} = 6.43 \; kJ$$

Because we must remove energy, the actual value of the change will be negative: $\Delta H = -6.43$ kJ.

Test Yourself

What is the energy change when 822 g of $C_2H_5OH(\ell)$ boil at its normal boiling point of 78.3°C?

Answer

689 kJ

As with melting, the energy in boiling goes exclusively to changing the phase of a substance; it does not go into changing the temperature of a substance. So boiling is also an isothermal process. Only when all of a substance has boiled does any additional energy go to changing its temperature.

What happens when a liquid becomes a gas? We have already established that a liquid is composed of particles in contact with each other. When a liquid becomes a gas, the particles separate from each other, with each particle going its own way in space. This is how gases tend to fill their containers. Indeed, in the gas phase most of the volume is empty space; only about 1/1,000th of the volume is actually taken up by matter (Figure 7.4). It is this property of gases that explains why they can be compressed, a fact that is considered in Chapter 11.

FIGURE 7.4 Liquids and Gases
In (a), the particles are a liquid; the particles are in contact but are also able to move around each other. In (b), the particles are a gas, and most of the volume is actually empty space.

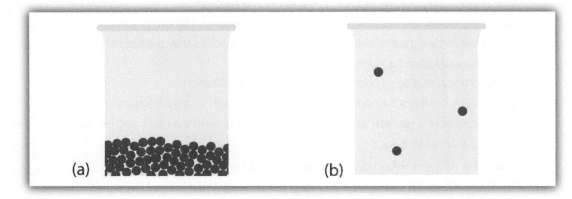

Under some circumstances, the solid phase can transition directly to the gas phase without going through a liquid phase, and a gas can directly become a solid. The solid-to-gas change is called **sublimation**, while the reverse process is called **deposition**. Sublimation is isothermal, like the other phase changes. There is a measurable energy change during sublimation; this energy change is called the **heat of sublimation**, represented as ΔH_{sub}. The relationship between the ΔH_{sub} and the other energy changes is as follows:

$$\Delta H_{sub} = \Delta H_{fus} + \Delta H_{vap}$$

As such, ΔH_{sub} is not always tabulated because it can be simply calculated from ΔH_{fus} and ΔH_{vap}.

There are several common examples of sublimation. A well-known product—dry ice—is actually solid CO_2. Dry ice is dry because it sublimes, with the solid bypassing the liquid phase and going straight to the gas phase. The sublimation occurs at temperature of −77°C, so it must be handled with caution. If you have ever noticed that ice cubes in a freezer tend to get smaller over time, it is because the solid water is very slowly subliming. "Freezer burn" isn't actually a burn; it occurs when certain foods, such as meats, slowly lose solid water content because of sublimation. The food is still good but looks unappetizing. Reducing the temperature of a freezer will slow the sublimation of solid water. Tightly wrapping food also leaves little volume for the water to sublime into, minimizing freezer burn.

sublimation
The process of a solid becoming a gas.

deposition
The process of a gas becoming a solid.

heat of sublimation
The amount of energy needed to change from a solid to a gas or from a gas to a solid.

Key Takeaways

- Phase changes can occur between any two phases of matter.
- All phase changes occur with a simultaneous change in energy.
- All phase changes are isothermal.

Exercises

1. What is the difference between *melting* and *solidification*?
2. What is the difference between *boiling* and *condensation*?
3. Describe the molecular changes when a solid becomes a liquid.
4. Describe the molecular changes when a liquid becomes a gas.
5. What is the energy change when 78.0 g of Hg melt at −38.8°C?
6. What is the energy change when 30.8 g of Al solidify at 660°C?
7. What is the energy change when 111 g of Br_2 boil at 59.5°C?
8. What is the energy change when 98.6 g of H_2O condense at 100°C?
9. Each of the following statements is incorrect. Rewrite them so they are correct.

   a. Temperature changes during a phase change.

   b. The process of a liquid becoming a gas is called sublimation.

10. Each of the following statements is incorrect. Rewrite them so they are correct.

   a. The volume of a gas contains only about 10% matter, with the rest being empty space.

   b. ΔH_{sub} is equal to ΔH_{vap}.

11. What is the ΔH_{sub} of H_2O? (Hint: see Table 7.2 and Table 7.3.)
12. The ΔH_{sub} of I_2 is 238.2 J/g, while its ΔH_{vap} is 164.3 J/g. What is the ΔH_{fus} of I_2?

Answers

1. Melting is the phase change from a solid to a liquid, whereas solidification is the phase change from a liquid to a solid.
2. Boiling is the phase change from a liquid to a gas, whereas condensation is the phase change from a gas to a liquid.
3. The molecules have enough energy to move about each other but not enough to completely separate from each other.
4. The energy of the individual molecules is large enough to separate the molecules from each other.
5. 890 J
6. −12.2 kJ
7. 10.7 kJ
8. −223 kJ
9. a. Temperature does not change during a phase change.

   b. The process of a liquid becoming a gas is called boiling; the process of a solid becoming a gas is called sublimation.

10. a. The volume of a gas contains only about 0.1% matter, with the rest being empty space.

   b. ΔH_{sub} is equal to ΔH_{fus} plus ΔH_{vap}.

11. 2591 J/g
12. 73.9 J/g

7.3 Properties of Liquids

Learning Objectives

1. Define the vapor pressure of liquids.
2. Explain the origin of both surface tension and capillary action.

There are some properties that all liquids have. The liquid that we are most familiar with is probably water, and it has these properties. Other liquids have them as well, which is something to keep in mind.

All liquids have a certain portion of their particles having enough energy to enter the gas phase, and if these particles are at the surface of the liquid, they do so (Figure 7.5). The formation of a gas from a liquid at temperatures below the boiling point is called **evaporation**. At these temperatures, the material in the gas phase is called **vapor**, rather than gas; the term *gas* is reserved for when the gas phase is the stable phase.

evaporation

The formation of a gas phase from a liquid at temperatures below the boiling point.

vapor

Material in the gas phase due to evaporation.

FIGURE 7.5 Evaporation
Some particles of a liquid have enough energy to escape the liquid phase to become a vapor.

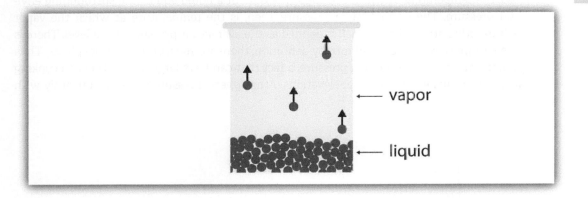

If the available volume is large enough, eventually all the liquid will become vapor. But if the available volume is not enough, eventually some of the vapor particles will reenter the liquid phase (Figure 7.6). At some point, the number of particles entering the vapor phase will equal the number of particles leaving the vapor phase, so there is no net change in the amount of vapor in the system. We say that the system is *at equilibrium*. The partial pressure of the vapor at equilibrium is called the *vapor pressure of the liquid*.

FIGURE 7.6 Equilibrium

At some point, the number of particles entering the vapor phase will be balanced by the number of particles returning to the liquid. This point is called equilibrium.

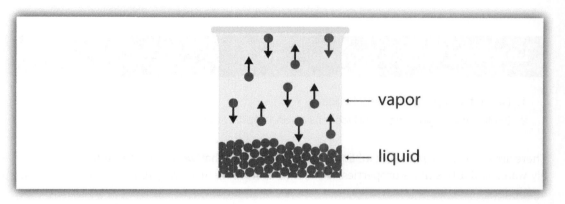

It is important to note that the liquid *has not stopped evaporating*. The reverse process—condensation—is occurring as fast as evaporation is, so there is no net change in the amount of vapor in the system. The term **dynamic equilibrium** represents a situation in which a process still occurs, but the opposite process also occurs at the same rate so that there is no net change in the system.

The vapor pressure for a substance is dependent on the temperature of the substance; as the temperature increases, so does the vapor pressure. Figure 7.7 is a plot of vapor pressure versus temperature for several liquids. Having defined vapor pressure, we can also redefine the *boiling point* of a liquid: the temperature at which the vapor pressure of a liquid equals the surrounding environmental pressure. The normal vapor pressure, then, is the temperature at which the vapor pressure is exactly 1 atmosphere, which is defined as the average air pressure at sea level. There is also a smaller unit of pressure called *torr*; by definition, there are 760 torr in an atmosphere. Thus boiling points vary with surrounding pressure, a fact that can have large implications on cooking foods at lower- or higher-than-normal elevations. Atmospheric pressure varies significantly with altitude.

FIGURE 7.7 Plots of Vapor Pressure versus Temperature for Several Liquids
The vapor pressure of a liquid depends on the identity of the liquid and the temperature, as this plot shows.

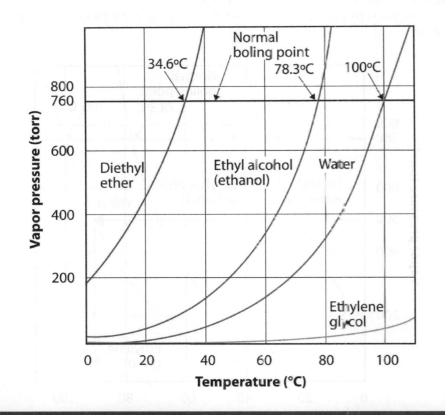

Example 4

Use Figure 7.7 to estimate the boiling point of water at 500 torr, which is the approximate atmospheric pressure at the top of Mount Everest.

Solution

See the accompanying figure. Five hundred torr is between 400 and 600, so we extend a line from that point on the y-axis across to the curve for water and then drop it down to the x-axis to read the associated temperature. It looks like the point on the water vapor pressure curve corresponds to a temperature of about 90°C, so we conclude that the boiling point of water at 500 torr is 90°C.

FIGURE 7.8 Using Figure 7.7 **to Answer Example 4**
By reading the graph properly, you can estimate the boiling point of a liquid at different temperatures.

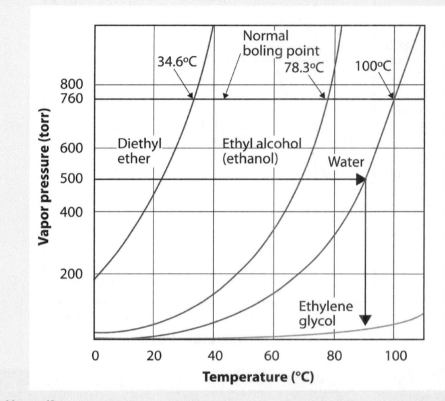

Test Yourself

Use Figure 7.7 to estimate the boiling point of ethanol at 400 torr.

Answer

about 65°C

The vapor pressure curve for water is not exactly zero at the melting point—0°C. Even ice has a vapor pressure; that is why it sublimes over time. However, the vapor pressures of solids are typically much lower than that of liquids. At –1°C, the vapor pressure of ice is 4.2 torr. At a freezer temperature of 0°F (–17°C), the vapor pressure of ice is still 1.0 torr; so-called deep freezers can get down to –23°C, where the vapor pressure of ice is only 0.6 torr.

surface tension

An effect caused by an imbalance of forces on the atoms at the surface of a liquid.

All liquids share some other properties as well. **Surface tension** is an effect caused by an imbalance of forces on the atoms at the surface of a liquid, as shown in Figure 7.9. The blue particle in the bulk of the liquid experiences intermolecular forces from all around, as illustrated by the arrows. However, the yellow particle on the surface does not experience any forces above it because there are no particles above it. This leads to an imbalance of forces that we call surface tension.

FIGURE 7.9 Surface Tension
Surface tension comes from the fact that particles at the surface of a liquid do not experience interactions from all directions, leading to an imbalance of forces on the surface.

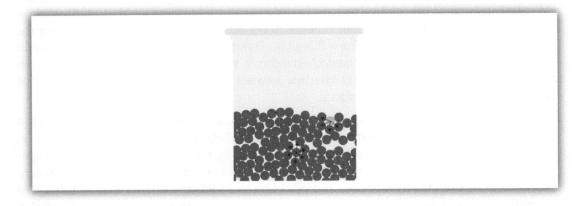

Surface tension is responsible for several well-known behaviors of liquids, including water. Liquids with high surface tension tend to bead up when present in small amounts (Figure 7.10). Surface tension causes liquids to form spheres in free fall or zero gravity (see Figure 7.3: the "floating" water isn't in the shape of a sphere by accident; it is the result of surface tension). Surface tension is also responsible for the fact that small insects can "walk" on water. Because of surface tension, it takes energy to break the surface of a liquid, and if an object (such as an insect) is light enough, there is not enough force due to gravity for the object to break through the surface, so the object stays on top of the water (Figure 7.11). Carefully done, this phenomenon can also be illustrated with a thin razor blade or a paper clip.

FIGURE 7.10 Effects of Surface Tension
Water on the surface of this apple beads up due to the effect of surface tension.

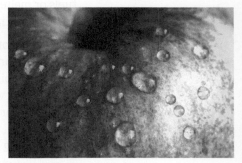

Source: © Thinkstock

FIGURE 7.11 Walking on Water
Small insects can actually walk on top of water because of surface tension effects.

Source: © Thinkstock

adhesion

The tendency of a substance to interact with other substances because of intermolecular forces.

cohesion

The tendency of a substance to interact with itself.

capillary action

The behavior of a liquid in narrow surfaces due to differences in adhesion and cohesion.

meniscus

The curved surface a liquid makes as it approaches a solid barrier.

The fact that small droplets of water bead up on surfaces does not mean that water—or any other liquid—does not interact with other substances. Sometimes the attraction can be very strong. **Adhesion** is the tendency of a substance to interact with other substances because of intermolecular forces, while **cohesion** is the tendency of a substance to interact with itself. If cohesive forces within a liquid are stronger than adhesive forces between a liquid and another substance, then the liquid tends to keep to itself; it will bead up. However, if adhesive forces between a liquid and another substance are stronger than cohesive forces, then the liquid will spread out over the other substance, trying to maximize the interface between the other substance and the liquid. We say that the liquid *wets* the other substance.

Adhesion and cohesion are important for other phenomena as well. In particular, if adhesive forces are strong, then when a liquid is introduced to a small-diameter tube of another substance, the liquid moves up or down in the tube, as if ignoring gravity. Because tiny tubes are called capillaries, this phenomenon is called **capillary action**. For example, one type of capillary action—*capillary rise*—is seen when water or water-based liquids rise up in thin glass tubes (like the capillaries sometimes used in blood tests), forming an upwardly curved surface called a **meniscus**. Capillary action is also responsible for the "wicking" effect that towels and sponges use to dry wet objects; the matting of fibers forms tiny capillaries that have good adhesion with water. Cotton is a good material for this; polyester and other synthetic fabrics do not display similar capillary action, which is why you seldom find rayon bath towels. A similar effect is observed with liquid fuels or melted wax and their wicks. Capillary action is thought to be at least partially responsible for transporting water from the roots to the tops of trees, even tall ones.

On the other hand, some liquids have stronger cohesive forces than adhesive forces. In this case, in the presence of a capillary, the liquid is forced down from its surface; this is an example of a type of capillary action called *capillary depression*. In this case, the meniscus curves downward. Mercury has very strong cohesive forces; when a capillary is placed in a pool of mercury, the surface of the mercury liquid is depressed (Figure 7.12).

FIGURE 7.12 Capillary Action

(a) Capillary rise is seen when adhesion is strong, such as with water in a thin glass tube. (b) Capillary depression is seen when cohesive forces are stronger than adhesive forces, such as with mercury and thin glass tubes.

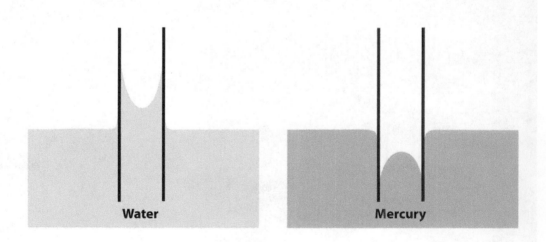

Water   Mercury

Chemistry Is Everywhere: Waxing a Car

Responsible car owners are encouraged to wax their cars regularly. In addition to making the car look nicer, it also helps protect the surface, especially if the surface is metal. Why?

The answer has to do with cohesion and adhesion (and, to a lesser extent, rust). Water is an important factor in the rusting of iron, sometimes used extensively in outer car bodies. Keeping water away from the metal is one way to minimize rusting. A coat of paint helps with this. However, dirty or scratched paint can attract water, and adhesive forces will allow the water to wet the surface, maximizing its contact with the metal and promoting rust.

Wax is composed of long hydrocarbon molecules that do not interact well with water. (Hydrocarbons are compounds with C and H atoms; for more information on hydrocarbons, see Chapter 17.) That is, a thin layer of wax will not be wetted by water. A freshly waxed car has low adhesive forces with water, so water beads up on the surface, as a consequence of its cohesion and surface tension. This minimizes the contact between water and metal, thus minimizing rust.

Droplets of water on a freshly waxed car do not wet the car well because of low adhesion between water and the waxed surface. This helps protect the car from rust.

Source: © Thinkstock

Key Takeaways

- All liquids evaporate.
- If volume is limited, evaporation eventually reaches a dynamic equilibrium, and a constant vapor pressure is maintained.
- All liquids experience surface tension, an imbalance of forces at the surface of the liquid.
- All liquids experience capillary action, demonstrating either capillary rise or capillary depression in the presence of other substances.

Exercises

1. What is the difference between evaporation and boiling?
2. What is the difference between a gas and vapor?
3. Define *normal boiling point* in terms of vapor pressure.
4. Is the boiling point higher or lower at higher environmental pressures? Explain your answer.
5. Referring to Figure 7.7, if the pressure is 400 torr, which liquid boils at the lowest temperature?
6. Referring to Figure 7.7, if the pressure is 100 torr, which liquid boils at the highest temperature?
7. Referring to Figure 7.7, estimate the boiling point of ethanol at 200 torr.
8. Referring to Figure 7.7, at approximately what pressure is the boiling point of water 40°C?
9. Explain how surface tension works.
10. From what you know of intermolecular forces, which substance do you think might have a higher surface tension—ethyl alcohol or mercury? Why?

11. Under what conditions would a liquid demonstrate a capillary rise?
12. Under what conditions would a liquid demonstrate a capillary depression?

Answers

1. Evaporation occurs when a liquid becomes a gas at temperatures below that liquid's boiling point, whereas boiling is the conversion of a liquid to a gas at the liquid's boiling point.
2. A gas is a stable phase at temperatures greater than the boiling point of a liquid, whereas vapor is a term used for the gas that comes from the liquid phase of a substance.
3. the temperature at which the vapor pressure of a liquid is 760 torr
4. higher because it takes a higher temperature for the vapor pressure to reach the surrounding pressure
5. diethyl ether
6. ethylene glycol
7. 48°C
8. 50 torr
9. Surface tension is an imbalance of attractive forces between liquid molecules at the surface of a liquid.
10. mercury because it has stronger dispersion forces
11. Adhesion must be greater than cohesion.
12. Cohesion must be stronger than adhesion.

7.4 Solids

Learning Objectives

1. Describe the general properties of a solid.
2. Describe the six different types of solids.

A solid is like a liquid in that particles are in contact with each other. Solids are unlike liquids in that the intermolecular forces are strong enough to hold the particles in place. At low enough temperatures, all substances are solids (helium is the lone exception), but the temperature at which the solid state becomes the stable phase varies widely among substances, from 20 K (-253°C) for hydrogen to over 3,900 K (3,600°C) for carbon.

The solid phase has several characteristics. First, solids maintain their shape. They do not fill their entire containers like gases do, and they do not adopt the shape of their containers like liquids do. They cannot be easily compressed like gases can, and they have relatively high densities.

Solids may also demonstrate a variety of properties. For example, many metals can be beaten into thin sheets or drawn into wires, while compounds such as NaCl will shatter if they are struck. Some metals, such as sodium and potassium, are rather soft, while others, such as diamond, are very hard and can easily scratch other substances. Appearances differ as well: most metals are shiny and silvery, but sulfur (a nonmetal) is yellow, and ionic compounds can take on a rainbow of colors. Solid metals conduct electricity and heat, while ionic solids do not. Many solids are opaque, but some are transparent. Some dissolve in water, but some do not. Figure 7.13 shows two solids that exemplify the similar and dissimilar properties of solids.

FIGURE 7.13 Properties of Solids
(a) Sodium metal is silvery, soft, and opaque and conducts electricity and heat well. (b) NaCl is transparent, hard, and colorless and does not conduct electricity or heat well in the solid state. These two substances illustrate the range of properties that solids can have.

(a)   (b)

Source: Photo on left courtesy of Images of Elements, http://images-of-elements.com/sodium.php. Photo on right courtesy of Choba Poncho, http://commons.wikimedia.org/wiki/File:Sodiumchloride_crystal_01.jpg.

Solids can have a wide variety of physical properties because there are different types of solids. Here we will review the different types of solids and the bonding that gives them their properties.

First, we must distinguish between two general types of solids. An **amorphous solid** is a solid with no long-term structure or repetition. Examples include glass and many plastics, both of which are composed of long chains of molecules with no order from one molecule to the next. A **crystalline solid** is a solid that has a regular, repeating three-dimensional structure. A crystal of NaCl (see Figure 7.13) is one example: at the atomic level, NaCl is composed of a regular three-dimensional array of Na^+ ions and Cl^- ions.

There is only one type of amorphous solid. However, there are several different types of crystalline solids, depending on the identity of the units that compose the crystal.

An **ionic solid** is a crystalline solid composed of ions (even if the ions are polyatomic). NaCl is an example of an ionic solid (Figure 7.14). The Na^+ ions and Cl^- ions alternate in three dimensions, repeating a pattern that goes on throughout the sample. The ions are held together by the attraction of opposite charges—a very strong force. Hence most ionic solids have relatively high melting points; for example, the melting point of NaCl is 801°C. Ionic solids are typically very brittle. To break them, the very strong ionic attractions need to be broken; a displacement of only about 1×10^{-10} m will move ions next to ions of the same charge, which results in repulsion. Ionic solids do not conduct electricity in their solid state; however, in the liquid state and when dissolved in some solvent, they do conduct electricity. This fact originally promoted the idea that some substances exist as ionic particles.

amorphous solid

A solid with no long-term structure or repetition.

crystalline solid

A solid with a regular, repeating three-dimensional structure.

ionic solid

A crystalline solid composed of ions.

FIGURE 7.14 An Ionic Solid
NaCl is a solid composed of a three-dimensional array of alternating Na⁺ ions (green) and Cl⁻ ions (purple) held together by the attraction of opposite charges.

molecular solid

A crystalline solid whose components are covalently bonded molecules.

A **molecular solid** is a crystalline solid whose components are covalently bonded molecules. Many molecular substances, especially when carefully solidified from the liquid state, form solids in which the molecules line up in a regular fashion similar to an ionic crystal, but they are composed of molecules instead of ions. Because the intermolecular forces between molecules are typically less strong than in ionic solids, molecular solids typically melt at lower temperatures and are softer than ionic solids. Ice is an example of a molecular solid. In the solid state, the molecules line up in a regular pattern (Figure 7.15). Some very large molecules, such as biological molecules, will form crystals only if they are very carefully solidified from the liquid state or, more usually, from a dissolved state; otherwise, they will form amorphous solids.

FIGURE 7.15 Molecular Solids

Water molecules line up in a regular pattern to form molecular solids. The dotted lines show how the polar O–H covalent bonds in one molecule engage in hydrogen bonding with other molecules. The O atoms are red, and the H atoms are white.

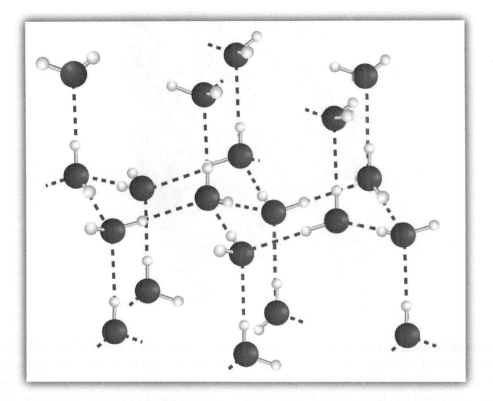

Some solids are composed of atoms of one or more elements that are covalently bonded together in a seemingly never-ending fashion. Such solids are called **covalent network solids**. Each piece of the substance is essentially one huge molecule, as the covalent bonding in the crystal extends throughout the entire crystal. The two most commonly known covalent network solids are carbon in its diamond form and silicon dioxide (SiO_2). Figure 7.16 shows the bonding in a covalent network solid. Generally, covalent network solids are poor conductors of electricity, although their ability to conduct heat is variable: diamond is one of the most thermally conductive substances known, while SiO_2 is about 100 times less thermally conductive. Most covalent network solids are very hard, as exemplified by diamond, which is the hardest known substance. Covalent network solids have high melting points by virtue of their network of covalent bonds, all of which would have to be broken for them to transform into a liquid. Indeed, covalent network solids are among the highest-melting substances known: the melting point of diamond is over 3,500°C, while the melting point of SiO_2 is around 1,650°C. These characteristics are explained by the network of covalent bonds throughout the sample.

covalent network solid

A crystalline solid composed of atoms of one or more elements that are covalently bonded together in a seemingly never-ending fashion.

FIGURE 7.16 Covalent Network Solids
Diamond is a covalent network solid, with each C atom making four covalent bonds to four other C atoms. A diamond is essentially one huge molecule.

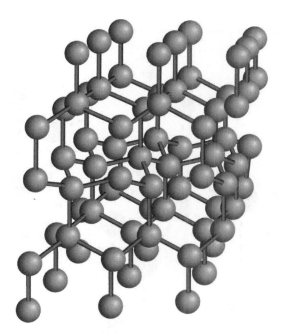

metallic solid

A solid with the characteristic properties of a metal.

A **metallic solid** is a solid with the characteristic properties of a metal: shiny and silvery in color and a good conductor of heat and electricity. A metallic solid can also be hammered into sheets and pulled into wires. A metallic solid exhibits metallic bonding, a type of intermolecular interaction caused by the sharing of the *s* valence electrons by all atoms in the sample. It is the sharing of these valence electrons that explains the ability of metals to conduct electricity and heat well. It is also relatively easy for metals to lose these valence electrons, which explains why metallic elements usually form cations when they make compounds.

Example 5

Predict the type of crystal exhibited by each solid.

1. MgO
2. Ag
3. CO_2

Solution

1. A combination of a metal and a nonmetal makes an ionic compound, so MgO would exist as ionic crystals in the solid state.
2. Silver is a metal, so it would exist as a metallic solid in the solid state.
3. CO_2 is a covalently bonded molecular compound. In the solid state, it would form molecular crystals. (You can actually see the crystals in dry ice with the naked eye.)

Test Yourself

Predict the type of crystal exhibited by each solid.

1. I_2
2. $Ca(NO_3)_2$

Answers

1. molecular crystals
2. ionic crystals

Food and Drink App: The Rocks We Eat

The foods and beverages we eat and drink all have different phases: solid, liquid, and gas. (How do we ingest gases? Carbonated beverages have gas, which sometimes cause a person to belch.) However, among the solids we eat, three in particular are or are produced from, rocks. Yes, rocks!

The first one is NaCl, or common salt. Salt is the only solid that we ingest that is actually mined as a rock (hence the term *rock salt*; it really is a rock). Salt provides both Na^+ ions and Cl^- ions, both of which are necessary for good health. Salt preserves food, a function that was much more important before the days of modern food preparation and storage. The fact that saltiness is one of the major tastes the tongue can detect suggests a strong evolutionary link between ingesting salt and survival. There is some concern today that there is too much salt in the diet; it is estimated that the average person consumes at least three times as much salt daily than is necessary for proper bodily function.

The other two rocks we eat are related: sodium bicarbonate ($NaHCO_3$) and sodium carbonate (Na_2CO_3). However, we do not mine these substances directly from the ground; we mine trona, whose chemical formula is $Na_3H(CO_3)_2$. This substance is dissolved in water and treated with CO_2 gas to make either Na_2CO_3 or $NaHCO_3$. Another process, called the Solvay process, is also used to make Na_2CO_3. In the Solvay process, NH_3 and CO_2 are added to solutions of NaCl to make $NaHCO_3$ and NH_4Cl; the $NaHCO_3$ precipitates and is heated to produce Na_2CO_3. Either way, we get these two products from the ground (i.e., rocks).

$NaHCO_3$ is also known as baking soda, which is used in many baked goods. Na_2CO_3 is used in foods to regulate the acid balance. It is also used in laundry (where it is called washing soda) to interact with other ions in water that tend to reduce detergent efficiency.

Salt mining can be at the surface or below ground. Here salt is mined from surface deposits. Part of the processing facility can be seen in the background.

Source: © Thinkstock

Key Takeaways

- Solids can be divided into amorphous solids and crystalline solids.
- Crystalline solids can be ionic, molecular, covalent network, or metallic.

Exercises

1. What is the difference between a crystalline solid and an amorphous solid?
2. What two properties do solids have in common? What two properties of solids can vary?
3. Explain how the bonding in an ionic solid explains some of the properties of these solids.
4. Explain how the bonding in a molecular solid explains some of the properties of these solids.

5. Explain how the bonding in a covalent network solid explains some of the properties of these solids.

6. Explain how the bonding in a metallic solid explains some of the properties of these solids.

7. Which type(s) of solid has/have high melting points?

8. Which type(s) of solid conduct(s) electricity in their solid state? In their liquid state?

9. Which type of solid(s) is/are considered relatively soft?

10. Which type of solid(s) is/are considered very hard?

11. Predict the type of solid exhibited by each substance.
    a. Hg
    b. PH_3
    c. CaF_2

12. Predict the type of solid exhibited by each substance.
    a. $(CH_2)_n$ (polyethylene, a form of plastic)
    b. PCl_3
    c. NH_4Cl

13. Predict the type of solid exhibited by each substance.
    a. SO_3
    b. Br_2
    c. Na_2SO_3

14. Predict the type of solid exhibited by each substance.
    a. BN (boron nitride, a diamond-like compound)
    b. B_2O_3
    c. $NaBF_4$

15. Predict the type of solid exhibited by each substance.
    a. H_2S
    b. Si
    c. CsF

16. Predict the type of solid exhibited by each substance.
    a. Co
    b. CO
    c. $CaCO_3$

Answers

1. At the atomic level, a crystalline solid has a regular arrangement of atoms, whereas an amorphous solid has a random arrangement of atoms.

2. definite shape and volume; hardness and melting point

3. The oppositely charged ions are very strongly held together, so ionic crystals have high melting points. Ionic crystals are also brittle because any distortion of the crystal moves same-charged ions closer to each other, so they repel.

4. The interactions between molecules are typically weak, so molecular solids have low melting points and are rather soft.

5. The covalent network solid is essentially one molecule, making it very hard and giving it a very high melting point.

6. Because electrons cover the entire metal, metals conduct electricity and heat well.

7. ionic solids, covalent network solids

8. metallic; metallic and ionic

9. molecular solids

10. covalent network solids

11. a. metallic
    b. molecular solid
    c. ionic crystal

12. a. amorphous solid
    b. molecular solid
    c. ionic crystal

13. a. molecular solid
    b. molecular solid
    c. ionic crystal

14. a. covalent network solid
    b. molecular solid
    c. ionic crystal

15. a. molecular solid
    b. molecular solid
    c. ionic crystal

16. a. metallic solid
    b. molecular solid
    c. ionic crystal

7.5 End-of-Chapter Material

Additional Exercises

1. All other things being equal, rank the intermolecular forces in order of increasing strength.

2. Which subatomic particles (protons, neutrons, electrons) are most responsible for intermolecular forces? Explain your answer.

3. Can a molecule experience more than one intermolecular force at the same time? Why or why not?

4. Of the properties boiling point, structure of the solid phase, and molar mass, which are influenced by hydrogen bonding? Explain your answer.

5. How many grams of solid water can be melted with 1.55 kJ of energy?

6. How many grams of Hg can be vaporized using 29,330 J of energy?

7. Another way to minimize freezer burn is to wrap food tightly before freezing. Why would this minimize freezer burn?

8. The ΔH_{sub} of naphthalene ($C_{10}H_8$) is 566.4 J/g. What energy, in kJ, is needed to sublime 100.0 g of $C_{10}H_8$?

9. Which do you think would have a higher surface tension—liquid neon or liquid krypton? Explain your answer.

10. Under what condition would a liquid not show either capillary rise or capillary depression?

Answers

1. dispersion forces < dipole-dipole interactions < hydrogen bonding < ionic bonding
2. electrons because their distribution in a molecule determines intermolecular forces
3. Yes, but one intermolecular force usually dominates.
4. boiling point because it depends on how strong the intermolecular forces are
5. 4.64 g
6. 99.33 g
7. Water in the vapor phase has no space to evaporate into.
8. 56.2 kJ
9. liquid krypton because it would have stronger dispersion forces
10. if cohesion and adhesion forces are balanced

CHAPTER 8
Chemical Reactions and Equations

Opening Essay

The now-retired space shuttle—and any other rocket-based system—used chemical reactions to propel itself into space and maneuver itself when it got into orbit. The rockets that lifted the orbiter were of two different types. The three main engines were powered by reacting liquid hydrogen with liquid oxygen to generate water. Then there were the two solid rocket boosters, which used a solid fuel mixture that contains mainly ammonium perchlorate and powdered aluminum. The chemical reaction between these substances produces aluminum oxide, water, nitrogen gas, and hydrogen chloride. Although the solid rocket boosters each had a significantly lower mass than the liquid oxygen and liquid hydrogen tanks, they provided over 80% of the lift needed to put the shuttle into orbit—all because of chemical reactions.

Source: © Thinkstock

Chemistry is largely about chemical changes. Indeed, if there were no chemical changes, chemistry as such would not exist! Chemical changes are a fundamental part of chemistry. Because chemical changes are so central, it may be no surprise that chemistry has developed some special ways of presenting them.

8.1 The Chemical Equation

Learning Objectives

1. Define *chemical equation*.
2. Identify the parts of a chemical equation.

A chemical reaction expresses a chemical change. For example, one chemical property of hydrogen is that it will react with oxygen to make water. We can write that as follows:

hydrogen reacts with oxygen to make water

We can represent this chemical change more succinctly as

hydrogen + oxygen → water

where the + sign means that the two substances interact chemically with each other and the → symbol implies that a chemical reaction takes place. But substances can also be represented by chemical formulas. Remembering that hydrogen and oxygen both exist as diatomic molecules, we can rewrite our chemical change as:

$$H_2 + O_2 \rightarrow H_2O$$

chemical equation

A concise way of representing a chemical reaction.

reactant

An initial substance in a chemical equation.

product

A final substance in a chemical equation.

This is an example of a **chemical equation**, which is a concise way of representing a chemical reaction. The initial substances are called **reactants**, and the final substances are called **products**.

Unfortunately, it is also an *incomplete* chemical equation. The law of conservation of matter says that matter cannot be created or destroyed. In chemical equations, the number of atoms of each element in the reactants must be the same as the number of atoms of each element in the products. If we count the number of hydrogen atoms in the reactants and products, we find two hydrogen atoms. But if we count the number of oxygen atoms in the reactants and products, we find that there are two oxygen atoms in the reactants but only one oxygen atom in the products.

What can we do? Can we change the subscripts in the formula for water so that it has two oxygen atoms in it? No; you *cannot* change the formulas of individual substances because the chemical formula for a given substance is characteristic of that substance. What you *can* do, however, is change the number of molecules that react or are produced. We do this one element at a time, going from one side of the reaction to the other, changing the number of molecules of a substance until all elements have the same number of atoms on each side.

To accommodate the two oxygen atoms as reactants, let us assume that we have two water molecules as products:

$$H_2 + O_2 \rightarrow 2H_2O$$

coefficient

A number in a chemical equation indicating more than one molecule of the substance.

The 2 in front of the formula for water is called a **coefficient**. Now there are the same number of oxygen atoms in the reactants as there are in the product. But in satisfying the need for the same number of oxygen atoms on both sides of the reaction, we have also changed the number of hydrogen atoms on the product side, so the number of hydrogen atoms is no longer equal. No problem—simply go back to the reactant side of the equation and add a coefficient in front of the H_2. The coefficient that works is 2:

$$2H_2 + O_2 \rightarrow 2H_2O$$

There are now four hydrogen atoms in the reactants and four atoms of hydrogen in the product. There are two oxygen atoms in the reactants and two atoms of oxygen in the product. The law of conservation of matter has been satisfied. When the reactants and products of a chemical equation have the same number of atoms of all elements present, we say that an equation is **balanced**. All proper chemical equations are balanced. If a substance does not have a coefficient written in front of it, it is assumed to be 1. Also, it is conventional to use all whole numbers when balancing chemical equations. This sometimes makes us do a bit more "back and forth" work when balancing a chemical equation.

> **balanced**
>
> A condition when the reactants and products of a chemical equation have the same number of atoms of all elements present.

Example 1

Write and balance the chemical equation for each given chemical reaction.

1. Hydrogen and chlorine react to make HCl.
2. Ethane, C_2H_6, reacts with oxygen to make carbon dioxide and water.

Solution

1. Let us start by simply writing a chemical equation in terms of the formulas of the substances, remembering that both elemental hydrogen and chlorine are diatomic:

$$H_2 + Cl_2 \rightarrow HCl$$

There are two hydrogen atoms and two chlorine atoms in the reactants and one of each atom in the product. We can fix this by including the coefficient 2 on the product side:

$$H_2 + Cl_2 \rightarrow 2HCl$$

Now there are two hydrogen atoms and two chlorine atoms on both sides of the chemical equation, so it is balanced.

2. Start by writing the chemical equation in terms of the substances involved:

$$C_2H_6 + O_2 \rightarrow CO_2 + H_2O$$

We have two carbon atoms on the left, so we need two carbon dioxide molecules on the product side, so that each side has two carbon atoms; carbon atoms are now balanced. We have six hydrogen atoms in the reactants, so we need six hydrogen atoms in the products. We can get this by having three water molecules:

$$C_2H_6 + O_2 \rightarrow 2CO_2 + 3H_2O$$

Now we have seven oxygen atoms in the products (four from the CO_2 and three from the H_2O). That means we need seven oxygen atoms in the reactants. However, because oxygen is a diatomic molecule, we can only get an even number of oxygen atoms at a time. We can achieve this by multiplying the other coefficients by 2:

$$2C_2H_6 + O_2 \rightarrow 4CO_2 + 6H_2O$$

By multiplying everything else by 2, we don't unbalance the other elements, and we now get an even number of oxygen atoms in the product—14. We can get 14 oxygen atoms on the reactant side by having 7 oxygen molecules:

$$2C_2H_6 + 7O_2 \rightarrow 4CO_2 + 6H_2O$$

As a check, recount everything to determine that each side has the same number of atoms of each element. This chemical equation is now balanced.

Test Yourself

Write and balance the chemical equation that represents nitrogen and hydrogen reacting to produce ammonia, NH_3.

Answer

$N_2 + 3H_2 \rightarrow 2NH_3$

Many chemical equations also include phase labels for the substances: (s) for solid, (l) for liquid, (g) for gas, and (aq) for aqueous (i.e., dissolved in water). Special conditions, such as temperature, may also be listed above the arrow. For example,

$$2NaHCO_3(s) \xrightarrow{200\,^{\circ}C} Na_2CO_3(s) + CO_2(g) + H_2O(\ell)$$

Chemical equations can also be used to represent a phase change. In such cases, it is crucial to use phase labels on the substances. For example, the chemical equation for the melting of ice to make water is:

$$H_2O(s) \rightarrow H_2O(\ell)$$

No chemical change is taking place; instead, a physical change is occurring.

Key Takeaways

- A chemical equation is a concise description of a chemical reaction.
- Proper chemical equations are balanced.

Exercises

1. From the statement "nitrogen and hydrogen react to produce ammonia," identify the reactants and the products.
2. From the statement "sodium metal reacts with water to produce sodium hydroxide and hydrogen," identify the reactants and the products.
3. From the statement "magnesium hydroxide reacts with nitric acid to produce magnesium nitrate and water," identify the reactants and the products.
4. From the statement "propane reacts with oxygen to produce carbon dioxide and water," identify the reactants and the products.
5. Write and balance the chemical equation described by Exercise 1.
6. Write and balance the chemical equation described by Exercise 2.
7. Write and balance the chemical equation described by Exercise 3.
8. Write and balance the chemical equation described by Exercise 4. The formula for propane is C_3H_8.
9. Balance: ___$NaClO_3$ → ___$NaCl$ + ___O_2
10. Balance: ___N_2 + ___H_2 → ___N_2H_4
11. Balance: ___Al + ___O_2 → ___Al_2O_3
12. Balance: ___C_2H_4 + ___O_2 → ___CO_2 + ___H_2O
13. How would you write the balanced chemical equation in Exercise 10 if all substances were gases?
14. How would you write the balanced chemical equation in Exercise 12 if all the substances except water were gases and water itself were a liquid?
15. Write the chemical equation for the melting of elemental sodium.
16. Write the chemical equation for the solidification of benzene (C_6H_6).
17. Write the chemical equation for the sublimation of CO_2.
18. Write the chemical equation for the boiling of propanol (C_3H_7OH).

Answers

1. reactants: nitrogen and hydrogen; product: ammonia
2. reactants: sodium and water; products: sodium hydroxide and hydrogen

3. reactants: magnesium hydroxide and nitric acid; products: magnesium nitrate and water

4. reactants: propane and oxygen; products: carbon dioxide and water

5. $N_2 + 3H_2 \rightarrow 2NH_3$

6. $2Na + 2H_2O \rightarrow 2NaOH + H_2$

7. $Mg(OH)_2 + 2HNO_3 \rightarrow Mg(NO_3)_2 + 2H_2O$

8. $C_3H_8 + 5O_2 \rightarrow 3CO_2 + 4H_2O$

9. $2NaClO_3 \rightarrow 2NaCl + 3O_2$

10. $N_2 + 2H_2 \rightarrow N_2H_4$

11. $4Al + 3O_2 \rightarrow 2Al_2O_3$

12. $C_2H_4 + 3O_2 \rightarrow 2CO_2 + 2H_2O$

13. $N_2(g) + 3H_2(g) \rightarrow 2NH_3(g)$

14. $C_2H_4(g) + 3O_2(g) \rightarrow 2CO_2(g) + 2H_2O(\ell)$

15. $Na(s) \rightarrow Na(\ell)$

16. $C_6H_6(\ell) \rightarrow C_6H_6(s)$

17. $CO_2(s) \rightarrow CO_2(g)$

18. $C_3H_7OH(\ell) \rightarrow C_3H_7OH(g)$

8.2 Types of Chemical Reactions: Single- and Double-Displacement Reactions

Learning Objectives

1. Recognize chemical reactions as single-displacement reactions and double-displacement reactions.
2. Use the periodic table, an activity series, or solubility rules to predict whether single-displacement reactions or double-displacement reactions will occur.

Previously, we presented chemical reactions as a topic but have not discussed how the products of a chemical reaction can be predicted. Here we will begin our study of certain types of chemical reactions that allow us to predict what the products of the reaction will be.

A **single-displacement reaction** is a chemical reaction in which one element is substituted for another element in a compound, generating a new element and a new compound as products. For example,

$$2HCl(aq) + Zn(s) \rightarrow ZnCl_2(aq) + H_2(g)$$

is an example of a single-displacement reaction. The hydrogen atoms in HCl are replaced by Zn atoms, and in the process a new element—hydrogen—is formed. Another example of a single-displacement reaction is:

$$2NaCl(aq) + F_2(g) \rightarrow 2NaF(s) + Cl_2(g)$$

single-displacement reaction

A chemical reaction in which one element is substituted for another element in a compound.

Here the negatively charged ion changes from chloride to fluoride. A typical characteristic of a single-displacement reaction is that there is one element as a reactant and another element as a product.

Not all proposed single-displacement reactions will occur between two given reactants. This is most easily demonstrated with fluorine, chlorine, bromine, and iodine. Collectively, these elements are called the *halogens* and are in the next-to-last column on the periodic table (see Figure 8.1). The elements on top of the column will replace the elements below them on the periodic table but not the other way around. Thus, the reaction represented by

$$CaI_2(s) + Cl_2(g) \rightarrow CaCl_2(s) + I_2(s)$$

will occur, but the reaction

$$CaF_2(s) + Br_2(\ell) \rightarrow CaBr_2(s) + F_2(g)$$

will not because bromine is below fluorine on the periodic table. This is just one of many ways the periodic table helps us understand chemistry.

FIGURE 8.1 Halogens on the Periodic Table
The halogens are the elements in the next-to-last column on the periodic table.

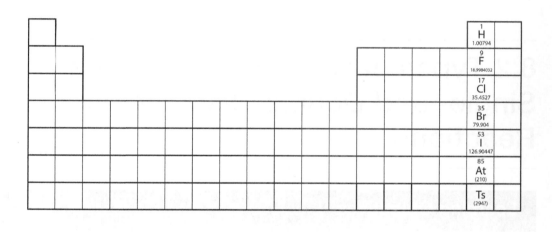

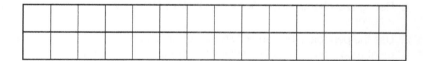

Example 2

Will a single-displacement reaction occur? If so, identify the products.

1. $MgCl_2 + I_2 \rightarrow$?
2. $CaBr_2 + F_2 \rightarrow$?

Solution

1. Because iodine is below chlorine on the periodic table, a single-displacement reaction will not occur.
2. Because fluorine is above bromine on the periodic table, a single-displacement reaction will occur, and the products of the reaction will be CaF_2 and Br_2.

Test Yourself

Will a single-displacement reaction occur? If so, identify the products.

$FeI_2 + Cl_2 \rightarrow ?$

Answer

Yes; $FeCl_2$ and I_2

Chemical reactivity trends are easy to predict when replacing anions in simple ionic compounds—simply use their relative positions on the periodic table. However, when replacing the cations, the trends are not as straightforward. This is partly because there are so many elements that can form cations; an element in one column on the periodic table may replace another element nearby, or it may not. A list called the **activity series** does the same thing the periodic table does for halogens: it lists the elements that will replace elements below them in single-displacement reactions. A simple activity series is shown below.

activity series

A list of elements that will replace elements below them in single-displacement reactions.

Activity Series for Cation Displacement in Single-Displacement Reactions

- Li
- K
- Ba
- Sr
- Ca
- Na
- Mg
- Al
- Mn
- Zn
- Cr
- Fe
- Ni
- Sn
- Pb
- H_2
- Cu
- Hg
- Ag
- Pd
- Pt
- Au

Using the activity series is similar to using the positions of the halogens on the periodic table. An element on top will replace an element below it in compounds undergoing a single-displacement reaction. Elements will not replace elements above them in compounds.

Example 3

Use the activity series to predict the products, if any, of each equation.

1. $FeCl_2 + Zn \rightarrow$?
2. $HNO_3 + Au \rightarrow$?

Solution

1. Because zinc is above iron in the activity series, it will replace iron in the compound. The products of this single-displacement reaction are $ZnCl_2$ and Fe.
2. Gold is below hydrogen in the activity series. As such, it will not replace hydrogen in a compound with the nitrate ion. No reaction is predicted.

Test Yourself

Use the activity series to predict the products, if any, of this equation.

$AlPO_4 + Mg \rightarrow$?

Answer

$Mg_3(PO_4)_2$ and Al

double-displacement reaction

A chemical reaction in which parts of two ionic compounds are exchanged.

A **double-displacement reaction** occurs when parts of two ionic compounds are exchanged, making two new compounds. A characteristic of a double-displacement equation is that there are two compounds as reactants and two different compounds as products. An example is:

$$CuCl_2\,(aq) + 2AgNO_3\,(aq) \rightarrow Cu(NO_3)_2\,(aq) + 2AgCl(s)$$

There are two equivalent ways of considering a double-displacement equation: either the cations are swapped, or the anions are swapped. (You cannot swap both; you would end up with the same substances you started with.) Either perspective should allow you to predict the proper products, as long as you pair a cation with an anion and not a cation with a cation or an anion with an anion.

Example 4

Predict the products of this double-displacement equation: $BaCl_2 + Na_2SO_4 \rightarrow$?

Solution

Thinking about the reaction as either switching the cations or switching the anions, we would expect the products to be $BaSO_4$ and NaCl.

Test Yourself

Predict the products of this double-displacement equation: $KBr + AgNO_3 \rightarrow$?

Answer

KNO_3 and AgBr

precipitation reaction

A chemical reaction in which two ionic compounds are dissolved in water and form a new ionic compound that does not dissolve.

precipitate

A solid that falls out of solution in a precipitation reaction.

Predicting whether a double-displacement reaction occurs is somewhat more difficult than predicting a single-displacement reaction. However, there is one type of double-displacement reaction that we can predict: the precipitation reaction. A **precipitation reaction** occurs when two ionic compounds are dissolved in water and form a new ionic compound that does not dissolve; this new compound falls out of solution as a solid **precipitate**. The formation of a solid precipitate is the driving force that makes the reaction proceed.

To judge whether double-displacement reactions will occur, we need to know what kinds of ionic compounds form precipitates. For this, we use **solubility rules**, which are general statements that predict which ionic compounds dissolve (are soluble) and which do not (are not soluble or insoluble). Table 8.1 lists some general solubility rules. We need to consider each ionic compound (both the reactants and the possible products) in light of the solubility rules in Table 8.1. If a compound is soluble, we use the (aq) label with it, indicating it dissolves. If a compound is not soluble, we use the (s) label with it and assume that it will precipitate out of solution. If everything is soluble, then no reaction will be expected.

solubility rules

General statements that predict which ionic compounds dissolve and which do not.

TABLE 8.1 Some Useful Solubility Rules

These compounds generally dissolve in water (are soluble):	Exceptions:
All compounds of Li^+, Na^+, K^+, Rb^+, Cs^+, and NH_4^+	None
All compounds of NO_3^- and $C_2H_3O_2^-$	None
Compounds of Cl^-, Br^-, I^-	Ag^+, Hg_2^{2+}, Pb^{2+}
Compounds of SO_4^{2}	Hg_2^{2+}, Pb^{2+}, Sr^{2+}, Ba^{2+}
These compounds generally do not dissolve in water (are insoluble):	**Exceptions:**
Compounds of CO_3^{2-} and PO_4^{3-}	Compounds of Li^+, Na^-, K^+, Rb^+, Cs^+, and NH_4^+
Compounds of OH^-	Compounds of Li^-, Na^+, K^+, Rb^+, Cs^+, NH_4^+, Sr^{2+}, and Ba^{2-}

For example, consider the possible double-displacement reaction between Na_2SO_4 and $SrCl_2$. The solubility rules say that all ionic sodium compounds are soluble and all ionic chloride compounds are soluble except for Ag^+, Hg_2^{2+}, and Pb^{2+}, which are not being considered here. Therefore, Na_2SO_4 and $SrCl_2$ are both soluble. The possible double-displacement reaction products are NaCl and $SrSO_4$. Are these soluble? NaCl is (by the same rule we just quoted), but what about $SrSO_4$? Compounds of the sulfate ion are generally soluble, but Sr^{2+} is an exception: we expect it to be insoluble—a precipitate. Therefore, we expect a reaction to occur, and the balanced chemical equation would be

$$Na_2SO_4(aq) + SrCl_2(aq) \rightarrow 2NaCl(aq) + SrSO_4(s)$$

You would expect to see a visual change corresponding to $SrSO_4$ precipitating out of solution (Figure 8.2).

FIGURE 8.2 Double-Displacement Reactions

Some double-displacement reactions are obvious because you can see a solid precipitate coming out of solution.

Source: Photo courtesy of Choij, http://commons.wikimedia.org/wiki/File:Copper_solution.jpg.

Example 5

Will a double-displacement reaction occur? If so, identify the products.

1. $Ca(NO_3)_2 + KBr \rightarrow$?
2. $NaOH + FeCl_2 \rightarrow$?

Solution

1. According to the solubility rules, both $Ca(NO_3)_2$ and KBr are soluble. Now we consider what the double-displacement products would be by switching the cations (or the anions)—namely, $CaBr_2$ and KNO_3. However, the solubility rules predict that these two substances would also be soluble, so no precipitate would form. Thus, we predict no reaction in this case.

2. According to the solubility rules, both NaOH and $FeCl_2$ are expected to be soluble. If we assume that a double-displacement reaction may occur, we need to consider the possible products, which would be NaCl and $Fe(OH)_2$. NaCl is soluble, but, according to the solubility rules, $Fe(OH)_2$ is not. Therefore, a reaction would occur, and $Fe(OH)_2(s)$ would precipitate out of solution. The balanced chemical equation is

$$2NaOH(aq) + FeCl_2(aq) \rightarrow 2NaCl(aq) + Fe(OH)_2(s)$$

Test Yourself

Will a double-displacement equation occur? If so, identify the products.

$Sr(NO_3)_2 + KCl \rightarrow$?

Answer

No reaction; both possible products are soluble.

Key Takeaways

- A single-displacement reaction replaces one element for another in a compound.
- The periodic table or an activity series can help predict whether single-displacement reactions occur.
- A double-displacement reaction exchanges the cations (or the anions) of two ionic compounds.
- A precipitation reaction is a double-displacement reaction in which one product is a solid precipitate.
- Solubility rules are used to predict whether some double-displacement reactions will occur.

Exercises

1. What are the general characteristics that help you recognize single-displacement reactions?
2. What are the general characteristics that help you recognize double-displacement reactions?
3. Assuming that each single-displacement reaction occurs, predict the products and write each balanced chemical equation.

    a. $Zn + Fe(NO_3)_2 \rightarrow$?

    b. $F_2 + FeI_3 \rightarrow$?

4. Assuming that each single-displacement reaction occurs, predict the products and write each balanced chemical equation.

    a. $Li + MgSO_4 \rightarrow$?

    b. $NaBr + Cl_2 \rightarrow$?

5. Assuming that each single-displacement reaction occurs, predict the products and write each balanced chemical equation.

    a. $Sn + H_2SO_4 \rightarrow$?

    b. $Al + NiBr_2 \rightarrow$?

6. Assuming that each single-displacement reaction occurs, predict the products and write each balanced chemical equation.

    a. $Mg + HCl \rightarrow$?

    b. $HI + Br_2 \rightarrow$?

7. Use the periodic table or the activity series to predict if each single-displacement reaction will occur and, if so, write a balanced chemical equation.

    a. $FeCl_2 + Br_2 \rightarrow$?

    b. $Fe(NO_3)_3 + Al \rightarrow$?

8. Use the periodic table or the activity series to predict if each single-displacement reaction will occur and, if so, write a balanced chemical equation.

    a. $Zn + Fe_3(PO_4)_2 \rightarrow$?

    b. $Ag + HNO_3 \rightarrow$?

9. Use the periodic table or the activity series to predict if each single-displacement reaction will occur and, if so, write a balanced chemical equation.

    a. $NaI + Cl_2 \rightarrow$?

    b. $AgCl + Au \rightarrow$?

10. Use the periodic table or the activity series to predict if each single-displacement reaction will occur and, if so, write a balanced chemical equation.

    a. $Pt + H_3PO_4 \rightarrow$?

    b. $Li + H_2O \rightarrow$? (Hint: treat H_2O as if it were composed of H^+ and OH^- ions.)

11. Assuming that each double-displacement reaction occurs, predict the products and write each balanced chemical equation.

    a. $Zn(NO_3)_2 + NaOH \rightarrow$?

    b. $HCl + Na_2S \rightarrow$?

12. Assuming that each double-displacement reaction occurs, predict the products and write each balanced chemical equation.

    a. $Ca(C_2H_3O_2)_2 + HNO_3 \rightarrow$?

    b. $Na_2CO_3 + Sr(NO_2)_2 \rightarrow$?

13. Assuming that each double-displacement reaction occurs, predict the products and write each balanced chemical equation.

    a. $Pb(NO_3)_2 + KBr \rightarrow$?

    b. $K_2O + MgCO_3 \rightarrow$?

14. Assuming that each double-displacement reaction occurs, predict the products and write each balanced chemical equation.

    a. $Sn(OH)_2 + FeBr_3 \rightarrow$?

    b. $CsNO_3 + KCl \rightarrow$?

15. Use the solubility rules to predict if each double-displacement reaction will occur and, if so, write a balanced chemical equation.

    a. $Pb(NO_3)_2 + KBr \rightarrow$?

    b. $K_2O + Na_2CO_3 \rightarrow$?

16. Use the solubility rules to predict if each double-displacement reaction will occur and, if so, write a balanced chemical equation.

    a. $Na_2CO_3 + Sr(NO_2)_2 \rightarrow$?

    b. $(NH_4)_2SO_4 + Ba(NO_3)_2 \rightarrow$?

17. Use the solubility rules to predict if each double-displacement reaction will occur and, if so, write a balanced chemical equation.

    a. $K_3PO_4 + SrCl_2 \rightarrow$?

    b. $NaOH + MgCl_2 \rightarrow$?

18. Use the solubility rules to predict if each double-displacement reaction will occur and, if so, write a balanced chemical equation.

    a. $KC_2H_3O_2 + Li_2CO_3 \rightarrow$?

    b. $KOH + AgNO_3 \rightarrow$?

Answers

1. One element replaces another element in a compound.

3. a. $Zn + Fe(NO_3)_2 \rightarrow Zn(NO_3)_2 + Fe$

    b. $3F_2 + 2FeI_3 \rightarrow 3I_2 + 2FeF_3$

5. a. $Sn + H_2SO_4 \rightarrow SnSO_4 + H_2$

    b. $2Al + 3NiBr_2 \rightarrow 2AlBr_3 + 3Ni$

7. a. No reaction occurs.

9. b. $Fe(NO_3)_3 + Al \rightarrow Al(NO_3)_3 + Fe$

      a. $2NaI + Cl_2 \rightarrow 2NaCl + I_2$

      b. No reaction occurs.

11.   a. $Zn(NO_3)_2 + 2NaOH \rightarrow Zn(OH)_2 + 2NaNO_3$

      b. $2HCl + Na_2S \rightarrow 2NaCl + H_2S$

13.   a. $Pb(NO_3)_2 + 2KBr \rightarrow PbBr_2 + 2KNO_3$

      b. $K_2O + MgCO_3 \rightarrow K_2CO_3 + MgO$

15.   a. $Pb(NO_3)_2 + 2KBr \rightarrow PbBr_2(s) + 2KNO_3$

      b. No reaction occurs.

17.   a. $2K_3PO_4 + 3SrCl_2 \rightarrow Sr_3(PO_4)_2(s) + 6KCl$

      b. $2NaOH + MgCl_2 \rightarrow 2NaCl + Mg(OH)_2(s)$

8.3 Ionic Equations: A Closer Look

Learning Objectives

1. Write ionic equations for chemical reactions between ionic compounds.
2. Write net ionic equations for chemical reactions between ionic compounds.

For single-replacement and double-replacement reactions, many of the reactions included ionic compounds: compounds between metals and nonmetals or compounds that contained recognizable polyatomic ions. Now we take a closer look at reactions that include ionic compounds.

One important aspect about ionic compounds that differs from molecular compounds has to do with dissolving in a liquid, such as water. When molecular compounds, such as sugar, dissolve in water, the individual molecules drift apart from each other. When ionic compounds dissolve, *the ions physically separate from each other*. We can use a chemical equation to represent this process—for example, with NaCl:

$$NaCl(s) \xrightarrow{\text{H}_2\text{O}} Na^+(aq) + Cl^-(aq)$$

When NaCl dissolves in water, the ions separate and go their own way in solution; the ions are now written with their respective charges, and the (aq) phase label emphasizes that they are dissolved (Figure 8.3). This process is called **dissociation**; we say that the ions *dissociate*.

dissociation

The process of an ionic compound separating into ions when it dissolves.

FIGURE 8.3 Ionic Solutions
When an ionic compound dissociates in water, water molecules (the red-and-white molecules) surround each ion (a blue or green sphere) and separate it from the rest of the solid. Each ion goes its own way in solution.

All ionic compounds that dissolve behave this way. (This behavior was first suggested by the Swedish chemist Svante August Arrhenius [1859–1927] as part of his PhD dissertation in 1884. Interestingly, his PhD examination team had a hard time believing that ionic compounds would behave like this, so they gave Arrhenius a barely passing grade. Later, this work was cited when Arrhenius was awarded the Nobel Prize in Chemistry.) Keep in mind that when the ions separate, *all* the ions separate. Thus, when $CaCl_2$ dissolves, the one Ca^{2+} ion and the two Cl^- ions separate from each other:

$$CaCl_2(s) \xrightarrow{H_2O} Ca^{2+}(aq) + Cl^-(aq) + Cl^-(aq)$$

or

$$CaCl_2(s) \xrightarrow{H_2O} Ca^{2+}(aq) + 2Cl^-(aq)$$

That is, the two chloride ions go off on their own. They do not remain as Cl_2 (that would be elemental chlorine; these are chloride ions); they do not stick together to make Cl_2^- or Cl_2^{2-}. They become dissociated ions in their own right. Polyatomic ions also retain their overall identity when they are dissolved.

Example 6

Write the chemical equation that represents the dissociation of each ionic compound.

1. KBr
2. Na_2SO_4

Solution

1. $KBr(s) \rightarrow K^+(aq) + Br^-(aq)$
2. Not only do the two sodium ions go their own way, but the sulfate ion stays together as the sulfate ion. The dissolving equation is $Na_2SO_4(s) \rightarrow 2Na^+(aq) + SO_4^{2-}(aq)$

Test Yourself

Write the chemical equation that represents the dissociation of $(NH_4)_2S$.

Answer

$(NH_4)_2S(s) \rightarrow 2NH_4^+(aq) + S^{2-}(aq)$

When chemicals in solution react, the proper way of writing the chemical formulas of the dissolved ionic compounds is in terms of the dissociated ions, not the complete ionic formula. A **complete ionic equation** is a chemical equation in which the dissolved ionic compounds are written as separated ions. Solubility rules are very useful in determining which ionic compounds are dissolved and which are not. For example, when $NaCl(aq)$ reacts with $AgNO_3(aq)$ in a double-replacement reaction to precipitate $AgCl(s)$ and form $NaNO_3(aq)$, the complete ionic equation includes NaCl, $AgNO_3$, and $NaNO_3$ written as separated ions:

$$Na^+(aq) + Cl^-(aq) + Ag^+(aq) + NO_3^-(aq) \rightarrow AgCl(s) + Na^+(aq) + NO_3^-(aq)$$

This is more representative of what is occurring in the solution.

> **complete ionic equation**
>
> A chemical equation in which the dissolved ionic compounds are written as separated ions.

Example 7

Write the complete ionic equation for each chemical reaction.

1. $KBr(aq) + AgC_2H_3O_2(aq) \rightarrow KC_2H_3O_2(aq) + AgBr(s)$
2. $MgSO_4(aq) + Ba(NO_3)_2(aq) \rightarrow Mg(NO_3)_2(aq) + BaSO_4(s)$

Solution

For any ionic compound that is aqueous, we will write the compound as separated ions.

1. The complete ionic equation is

$$K^+(aq) + Br^-(aq) + Ag^+(aq) + C_2H_3O_2^-(aq)$$
$$\rightarrow K^+(aq) + C_2H_3O_2^-(aq) + AgBr(s)$$

2. The complete ionic equation is

$$Mg^{2+}(aq) + SO_4^{2-}(aq) + Ba^{2+}(aq) + 2NO_3^-(aq)$$
$$\rightarrow Mg^{2+}(aq) + 2NO_3^-(aq) + BaSO_4(s)$$

Test Yourself

Write the complete ionic equation for

$$CaCl_2(aq) + Pb(NO_3)_2(aq) \rightarrow Ca(NO_3)_2(aq) + PbCl_2(s)$$

Answer

$Ca^{2+}(aq) + 2Cl^-(aq) + Pb^{2+}(aq) + 2NO_3^-(aq) \rightarrow Ca^{2+}(aq) - 2NO_3^-(aq) + PbCl_2(s)$

You may notice that in a complete ionic equation, some ions do not change their chemical form; they stay exactly the same on the reactant and product sides of the equation. For example, in

$$Na^+(aq) + Cl^-(aq) + Ag^+(aq) + NO_3^-(aq) \rightarrow AgCl(s) + Na^+(aq) + NO_3^-(aq)$$

spectator ion

An ion that does nothing in the overall course of a chemical reaction.

the $Ag^+(aq)$ and $Cl^-(aq)$ ions become $AgCl(s)$, but the $Na^+(aq)$ ions and the $NO_3^-(aq)$ ions stay as $Na^+(aq)$ ions and $NO_3^-(aq)$ ions. These two ions are examples of **spectator ions**, ions that do nothing in the overall course of a chemical reaction. They are present, but they do not participate in the overall chemistry. It is common to cancel spectator ions (something also done with algebraic quantities) on the opposite sides of a chemical equation:

$$\cancel{Na^+(aq)} + Cl^-(aq) + Ag^+(aq) + \cancel{NO_3^-(aq)} \rightarrow AgCl(s) + \cancel{Na^+(aq)} + \cancel{NO_3^-(aq)}$$

net ionic equation

A chemical equation with the spectator ions removed.

What remains when the spectator ions are removed is called the **net ionic equation**, which represents the actual chemical change occurring between the ionic compounds:

$$Cl^-(aq) + Ag^+(aq) \rightarrow AgCl(s)$$

It is important to reiterate that the spectator ions are still present in solution, but they don't experience any net chemical change, so they are not written in a net ionic equation.

Example 8

Write the net ionic equation for each chemical reaction.

1. $K^+(aq) + Br^-(aq) + Ag^+(aq) + C_2H_3O_2^-(aq) \rightarrow K^+(aq) + C_2H_3O_2^-(aq) + AgBr(s)$
2. $Mg^{2+}(aq) + SO_4^{2-}(aq) + Ba^{2+}(aq) + 2NO_3^-(aq) \rightarrow Mg^{2+}(aq) + 2NO_3^-(aq) + BaSO_4(s)$

Solution

1. In the first equation, the $K^+(aq)$ and $C_2H_3O_2^-(aq)$ ions are spectator ions, so they are canceled:

$$\cancel{K^+(aq)} + Br^-(aq) + Ag^+(aq) + \cancel{C_2H_3O_2^-(aq)}$$
$$\rightarrow \cancel{K^+(aq)} + \cancel{C_2H_3O_2^-(aq)} + AgBr(s)$$

The net ionic equation is

$$Br^-(aq) + Ag^+(aq) \rightarrow AgBr(s)$$

2. In the second equation, the $Mg^{2+}(aq)$ and $NO_3^-(aq)$ ions are spectator ions, so they are canceled:

$$\cancel{Mg^{2+}(aq)} + SO_4^{2-}(aq) + Ba^{2+}(aq) + \cancel{2NO_3^-(aq)}$$
$$\rightarrow \cancel{Mg^{2+}(aq)} + \cancel{2NO_3^-(aq)} + BaSO_4(s)$$

The net ionic equation is

$$SO_4^{2-}(aq) + Ba^{2+}(aq) \rightarrow BaSO_4(s)$$

Test Yourself

Write the net ionic equation for

$$CaCl_2(aq) + Pb(NO_3)_2(aq) \rightarrow Ca(NO_3)_2(aq) + PbCl_2(s)$$

Answer

$Pb^{2+}(aq) + 2Cl^-(aq) \rightarrow PbCl_2(s)$

Chemistry Is Everywhere: Soluble and Insoluble Ionic Compounds

The concept of solubility versus insolubility in ionic compounds is a matter of degree. Some ionic compounds are very soluble, some are only moderately soluble, and some are soluble so little that they are considered insoluble. For most ionic compounds, there is also a limit to the amount of compound can be dissolved in a sample of water. For example, you can dissolve a maximum of 36.0 g of NaCl in 100 g of water at room temperature, but you can dissolve only 0.00019 g of AgCl in 100 g of water. We consider NaCl soluble but AgCl insoluble.

One place where solubility is important is in the tank-type water heater found in many homes in the United States. Domestic water frequently contains small amounts of dissolved ionic compounds, including calcium carbonate ($CaCO_3$). However, $CaCO_3$ has the relatively unusual property of being less soluble in hot water than in cold water. So as the water heater operates by heating water, $CaCO_3$ can precipitate if there is enough of it in the water. This precipitate, called *limescale*, can also contain magnesium compounds, hydrogen carbonate compounds, and phosphate compounds. The problem is that too much limescale can impede the function of a water heater, requiring more energy to heat water to a specific temperature or even blocking water pipes into or out of the water heater, causing dysfunction.

Most homes in the United States have a tank-type water heater like this one.

Source: © Thinkstock

Another place where solubility versus insolubility is an issue is the Grand Canyon. We usually think of rock as insoluble. But it is actually ever so slightly soluble. This means that over a period of about two billion years, the Colorado River carved rock from the surface by slowly dissolving it, eventually generating a spectacular series of gorges and canyons. And all because of solubility!

The Grand Canyon was formed by water running through rock for billions of years, very slowly dissolving it. Note the Colorado River is still present in the lower part of the photo.

Source: © Thinkstock

Key Takeaways

- Ionic compounds that dissolve separate into individual ions.
- Complete ionic equations show dissolved ionic solids as separated ions.
- Net ionic equations show only the ions and other substances that change in a chemical reaction.

Exercises

1. Write a chemical equation that represents $NaBr(s)$ dissociating in water.

2. Write a chemical equation that represents $SrCl_2(s)$ dissociating in water.

3. Write a chemical equation that represents $(NH_4)_3PO_4(s)$ dissociating in water.

4. Write a chemical equation that represents $Fe(C_2H_3O_2)_3(s)$ dissociating in water.

5. Write the complete ionic equation for the reaction of $FeCl_2(aq)$ and $AgNO_3(aq)$. You may have to consult the solubility rules.

6. Write the complete ionic equation for the reaction of $BaCl_2(aq)$ and $Na_2SO_4(aq)$. You may have to consult the solubility rules.

7. Write the complete ionic equation for the reaction of $KCl(aq)$ and $NaC_2H_3O_2(aq)$. You may have to consult the solubility rules.

8. Write the complete ionic equation for the reaction of $Fe_2(SO_4)_3(aq)$ and $Sr(NO_3)_2(aq)$. You may have to consult the solubility rules.

9. Write the net ionic equation for the reaction of $FeCl_2(aq)$ and $AgNO_3(aq)$. You may have to consult the solubility rules.

10. Write the net ionic equation for the reaction of $BaCl_2$(aq) and Na_2SO_4(aq). You may have to consult the solubility rules.

11. Write the net ionic equation for the reaction of KCl(aq) and $NaC_2H_3O_2$(aq). You may have to consult the solubility rules.

12. Write the net ionic equation for the reaction of $Fe_2(SO_4)_3$(aq) and $Sr(NO_3)_2$(aq). You may have to consult the solubility rules.

13. Identify the spectator ions in Exercises 9 and 10.

14. Identify the spectator ions in Exercises 11 and 12.

Answers

1. $NaBr(s) \xrightarrow{\text{H}_2\text{O}} Na^+(aq) + Br^-(aq)$

2. $SrCl_2(s) \xrightarrow{\text{H}_2\text{O}} Sr^{2+}(aq) + 2Cl^-(aq)$

3. $(NH_4)_3PO_4(s) \xrightarrow{\text{H}_2\text{O}} 3NH_4^+(aq) + PO_4^{3-}(aq)$

4. $Fe(C_2H_3O_2)_3(s) \xrightarrow{\text{H}_2\text{O}} Fe^{3+}(aq) + 3C_2H_3O_2^-(aq)$

5. $Fe^{2+}(aq) + 2Cl^-(aq) + 2Ag^+(aq) + 2NO_3^-(aq) \rightarrow Fe^{2+}(aq) + 2NO_3^-(aq) + 2AgCl(s)$

6. $Ba^{2+}(aq) + 2Cl^-(aq) + 2Na^+(aq) + SO_4^{2-}(aq) \rightarrow BaSO_4(s) + 2Na^+(aq) + 2Cl^-(aq)$

7. $K^+(aq) + Cl^-(aq) + Na^+(aq) + C_2H_3O_2^-(aq) \rightarrow Na^+(aq) + Cl^-(aq) + K^+(aq) + C_2H_3O_2^-(aq)$

8. $2Fe^{3+}(aq) + 3SO_4^{2-}(aq) + 3Sr^{2+}(aq) + 6NO_3^-(aq) \rightarrow 3SrSO_4(s) + 2Fe^{3+}(aq) + 6NO_3^-(aq)$

9. $2Cl^-(aq) + 2Ag^+(aq) \rightarrow 2AgCl(s)$

10. $Ba^{2+}(aq) + SO_4^{2-}(aq) \rightarrow BaSO_4(s)$

11. There is no overall reaction.

12. $3SO_4^{2-}(aq) + 3Sr^{2+}(aq) \rightarrow 3SrSO_4(s)$

13. In Exercise 9, $Fe^{2+}(aq)$ and $NO_3^-(aq)$ are spectator ions; in Exercise 10, $Na^+(aq)$ and $Cl^-(aq)$ are spectator ions.

14. In Exercise 11, every ion is a spectator ion; in Exercise 12, $Fe^{3+}(aq)$ and $NO_3^-(aq)$ are spectator ions.

8.4 Composition, Decomposition, and Combustion Reactions

Learning Objectives

1. Recognize composition, decomposition, and combustion reactions.

2. Predict the products of a combustion reaction.

Three classifications of chemical reactions will be reviewed in this section. Predicting the products in some of them may be difficult, but the reactions are still easy to recognize.

composition reaction

A chemical reaction in which a single substance is produced from multiple reactants.

A **composition reaction** (sometimes also called a *combination reaction* or a *synthesis reaction*) produces a single substance from multiple reactants. A single substance as a product is the key characteristic of the composition reaction. There may be a coefficient other than one for the substance, but if the reaction has only a single substance as a product, it can be called a composition reaction. In the reaction

$$2H_2(g) + O_2(g) \rightarrow 2H_2O(\ell)$$

water is produced from hydrogen and oxygen. Although there are two molecules of water being produced, there is only one substance—water—as a product. So this is a composition reaction.

decomposition reaction

A chemical reaction in which a single substance becomes more than one substance.

A **decomposition reaction** starts from a single substance and produces more than one substance; that is, it decomposes. One substance as a reactant and more than one substance as the products is the key characteristic of a decomposition reaction. For example, in the decomposition of sodium hydrogen carbonate (also known as sodium bicarbonate),

$$2NaHCO_3(s) \rightarrow Na_2CO_3(s) + CO_2(g) + H_2O(\ell)$$

sodium carbonate, carbon dioxide, and water are produced from the sodium hydrogen carbonate.

Composition and decomposition reactions are difficult to predict; however, they should be easy to recognize.

Example 9

Identify each equation as a composition reaction, a decomposition reaction, or neither.

1. $Fe_2O_3 + 3SO_3 \rightarrow Fe_2(SO_4)_3$
2. $NaCl + AgNO_3 \rightarrow AgCl + NaNO_3$
3. $(NH_4)_2Cr_2O_7 \rightarrow Cr_2O_3 + 4H_2O + N_2$

Solution

1. In this equation, two substances combine to make a single substance. This is a composition reaction.
2. Two different substances react to make two new substances. This does not fit the definition of either a composition reaction or a decomposition reaction, so it is neither. In fact, you may recognize this as a double-replacement reaction.
3. A single substance reacts to make multiple substances. This is a decomposition reaction.

Test Yourself

Identify the equation as a composition reaction, a decomposition reaction, or neither.

$$C_3H_8 \rightarrow C_3H_4 + 2H_2$$

Answer

decomposition

combustion reaction

A chemical reaction in which a reactant combines with oxygen to produce oxides of all other elements as products.

A **combustion reaction** occurs when a reactant combines with oxygen, many times from the atmosphere, to produce oxides of all other elements as products; any nitrogen in the reactant is converted to elemental nitrogen, N_2. Many reactants, called *fuels*, contain only carbon and hydrogen atoms, reacting with oxygen to produce CO_2 and H_2O. For example, the balanced chemical equation for the combustion of methane, CH_4, is as follows:

$$CH_4 + 2O_2 \rightarrow CO_2 + 2H_2O$$

Kerosene can be approximated with the formula $C_{12}H_{26}$, and its balanced combustion reaction is:

$$2C_{12}H_{26} + 37O_2 \rightarrow 24CO_2 + 26H_2O$$

Sometimes fuels contain oxygen atoms, which must be counted when balancing the chemical equation. One common fuel is ethanol, C_2H_5OH, whose combustion equation is:

$$C_2H_5OH + 3O_2 \rightarrow 2CO_2 + 3H_2O$$

If nitrogen is present in the original fuel, it is converted to N_2, not to a nitrogen-oxygen compound. Thus, for the combustion of the fuel dinitroethylene, whose formula is $C_2H_2N_2O_4$, we have:

$$2C_2H_2N_2O_4 + O_2 \rightarrow 4CO_2 + 2H_2O + 2N_2$$

Example 10

Complete and balance each combustion equation.

1. the combustion of propane, C_3H_8
2. the combustion of ammonia, NH_3

Solution

1. The products of the reaction are CO_2 and H_2O, so our unbalanced equation is:

$$C_3H_8 + O_2 \rightarrow CO_2 + H_2O$$

Balancing (and you may have to go back and forth a few times to balance this), we get:

$$C_3H_8 + 5O_2 \rightarrow 3CO_2 + 4H_2O$$

2. The nitrogen atoms in ammonia will react to make N_2, while the hydrogen atoms will react with O_2 to make H_2O:

$$NH_3 + O_2 \rightarrow N_2 + H_2O$$

To balance this equation without fractions (which is the convention), we get:

$$4NH_3 + 3O_2 \rightarrow 2N_2 + 6H_2O$$

Test Yourself

Complete and balance the combustion equation for cyclopropanol, C_3H_6O.

Answer

$C_3H_6O + 4O_2 \rightarrow 3CO_2 + 3H_2O$

Propane is a fuel used to provide heat for some homes. Propane is stored in large tanks like that shown here.

Source: © Thinkstock

Food and Drink App: Browning Reactions

The microwave oven has become a staple in home kitchens—and, to the dismay of some diners, the restaurant kitchen as well. Although microwaves can heat food quickly, there are some foods that you just don't cook in a microwave, like bread or meat or French fries. Why not?

Because of chemistry: You don't get Maillard reactions.

Maillard (pronounced MY-YARD) reactions are also known as *browning reactions*. Named after French chemist Louis-Camille Maillard, who studied them in the early 1900s, they are chemical reactions between amino acids from proteins and certain sugars from starch. The reactions, which start occurring at a temperature of about 140°C (285°F), make a complex combination of brown products which happen to have very appealing tastes and aromas. Because different amino acids and sugars yield different tastes and aromas, food technologists study them as sources of flavor additives for processed food.

Why don't microwaves cause browning reactions? Because microwaves work on water, warming it up so the hot water cooks the food. That's one reason why dried foods won't cook in a microwave, or why containers or plates don't get hot: They don't have any water. But water can only get to 100°C (212°F) before boiling away. You can try to microwave longer, but food will get no hotter than this until it dries up into a culinary hockey puck. In short: The microwave just doesn't get the food hot enough for browning reactions to occur. You certainly *can* cook these foods in a microwave, but they won't be as appealing.

The grill lines on this steak are from Maillard reactions, giving the meat color and flavor.

Source: © Shutterstock, Inc.

Another cooking method is *sous vide* (French for "under vacuum"), in which food is sealed in an evacuated plastic bag and immersed in hot water that is kept at the proper final temperature. It does an excellent job of cooking food, especially meat, without overcooking. However, once again the cooking method doesn't get hot enough for Maillard reactions. The solution? Take a few minutes at the end of the cooking process to sear the food in a pan on the stove, or on a grill. *Bon appetit!*

Key Takeaways

- A composition reaction produces a single substance from multiple reactants.
- A decomposition reaction produces multiple products from a single reactant.
- Combustion reactions are the combination of some compound with oxygen to make oxides of the other elements as products (although nitrogen atoms react to make N_2).

Exercises

1. Which is a composition reaction and which is not?

   a. $NaCl + AgNO_3 \rightarrow AgCl + NaNO_3$

   b. $CaO + CO_2 \rightarrow CaCO_3$

2. Which is a composition reaction and which is not?

   a. $H_2 + Cl_2 \rightarrow 2HCl$

   b. $2HBr + Cl_2 \rightarrow 2HCl + Br_2$

3. Which is a composition reaction and which is not?

   a. $2SO_2 + O_2 \rightarrow 2SO_3$

   b. $6C + 3H_2 \rightarrow C_6H_6$

4. Which is a composition reaction and which is not?

   a. $4Na + 2C + 3O_2 \rightarrow 2Na_2CO_3$

   b. $Na_2CO_3 \rightarrow Na_2O + CO_2$

5. Which is a decomposition reaction and which is not?

   a. $HCl + NaOH \rightarrow NaCl + H_2O$

   b. $CaCO_3 \rightarrow CaO + CO_2$

6. Which is a decomposition reaction and which is not?

   a. $3O_2 \rightarrow 2O_3$

   b. $2KClO_3 \rightarrow 2KCl + 3O_2$

7. Which is a decomposition reaction and which is not?

   a. $Na_2O + CO_2 \rightarrow Na_2CO_3$

   b. $H_2SO_3 \rightarrow H_2O + SO_2$

8. Which is a decomposition reaction and which is not?

   a. $2C_7H_5N_3O_6 \rightarrow 3N_2 + 5H_2O + 7CO + 7C$

   b. $C_6H_{12}O_6 + 6O_2 \rightarrow 6CO_2 + 6H_2O$

9. Which is a combustion reaction and which is not?

   a. $C_6H_{12}O_6 + 6O_2 \rightarrow 6CO_2 + 6H_2O$

   b. $2Fe_2S_3 + 9O_2 \rightarrow 2Fe_2O_3 + 6SO_2$

10. Which is a combustion reaction and which is not?

    a. $CH_4 + 2F_2 \rightarrow CF_4 + 2H_2$

    b. $2H_2 + O_2 \rightarrow 2H_2O$

11. Which is a combustion reaction and which is not?

    a. $P_4 + 5O_2 \rightarrow 2P_2O_5$

    b. $2Al_2S_3 + 9O_2 \rightarrow 2Al_2O_3 + 6SO_2$

12. Which is a combustion reaction and which is not?

    a. $C_2H_4 + O_2 \rightarrow C_2H_4O_2$

    b. $C_2H_4 + Cl_2 \rightarrow C_2H_4Cl_2$

13. Is it possible for a composition reaction to also be a combustion reaction? Give an example to support your case.

14. Is it possible for a decomposition reaction to also be a combustion reaction? Give an example to support your case.

15. Complete and balance each combustion equation.

    a. $C_4H_9OH + O_2 \rightarrow ?$

    b. $CH_3NO_2 + O_2 \rightarrow ?$

16. Complete and balance each combustion equation.

    a. $B_2H_6 + O_2 \rightarrow ?$ (The oxide of boron formed is B_2O_3.)

    b. $Al_2S_3 + O_2 \rightarrow ?$ (The oxide of sulfur formed is SO_2.)

    c. $Al_2S_3 + O_2 \rightarrow ?$ (The oxide of sulfur formed is SO_3.)

Answers

1. a. not composition
   b. composition
2. a. composition
   b. not composition
3. a. composition
   b. composition
4. a. composition
   b. not composition
5. a. not decomposition
   b. decomposition
6. a. not decomposition
   b. decomposition
7. a. not decomposition
   b. decomposition
8. a. decomposition
   b. not decomposition
9. a. combustion
   b. combustion
10. a. not combustion
    b. combustion
11. a. combustion
    b. combustion
12. a. combustion
    b. not combustion
13. Yes; $2H_2 + O_2 \rightarrow 2H_2O$ (answers will vary)
14. No, it is not possible.
15. a. $C_4H_9OH + 6O_2 \rightarrow 4CO_2 + 5H_2O$
    b. $4CH_3NO_2 + 3O_2 \rightarrow 4CO_2 + 6H_2O + 2N_2$
16. a. $B_2H_6 + 3O_2 \rightarrow B_2O_3 + 3H_2O$
    b. $2Al_2S_3 + 9O_2 \rightarrow 2Al_2O_3 + 6SO_2$
    c. $Al_2S_3 + 6O_2 \rightarrow Al_2O_3 + 3SO_3$

8.5 End-of-Chapter Material

Additional Exercises

1. Chemical equations can also be used to represent physical processes. Write a chemical reaction for the boiling of water, including the proper phase labels.

2. Chemical equations can also be used to represent physical processes. Write a chemical reaction for the freezing of water, including the proper phase labels.

3. Explain why

$$4Na(s) + 2Cl_2(g) \rightarrow 4NaCl(s)$$

should not be considered a proper chemical equation.

4. Explain why

$$H_2(g) + 1/2O_2(g) \rightarrow H_2O(\ell)$$

should not be considered a proper chemical equation.

5. Does the chemical reaction represented by

$$3Zn(s) + 2Al(NO_3)_3(aq) \rightarrow 3Zn(NO_3)_2(aq) + 2Al(s)$$

proceed as written? Why or why not?

6. Does the chemical reaction represented by

$$2Au(s) + 2HNO_3(aq) \rightarrow 2AuNO_3(aq) + H_2(g)$$

proceed as written? Gold is a relatively useful metal for certain applications, such as jewelry and electronics. Does your answer suggest why this is so?

7. Explain what is wrong with this double-replacement reaction.

$$NaCl(aq) + KBr(aq) \rightarrow NaK(aq) + ClBr(aq)$$

8. Predict the products of and balance this double-replacement reaction.

$$AgSO_4(aq) + SrCl_2(aq) \rightarrow ?$$

9. Write the complete and net ionic equations for this double-replacement reaction.

$$BaCl_2(aq) + Ag_2SO_4(aq) \rightarrow ?$$

10. Write the complete and net ionic equations for this double-replacement reaction.

$$Ag_2SO_4(aq) + SrCl_2(aq) \rightarrow ?$$

11. Identify the spectator ions in this reaction. What is the net ionic equation?

$$NaCl(aq) + KBr(aq) \rightarrow NaBr(aq) + KCl(aq)$$

12. Complete this reaction and identify the spectator ions. What is the net ionic equation?

$$3H_2SO_4(aq) + 2Al(OH)_3(s) \rightarrow ?$$

Answers

1. $H_2O(\ell) \rightarrow H_2O(g)$
2. $H_2O(\ell) \rightarrow H_2O(s)$
3. The coefficients are not in their lowest whole-number ratio.
4. The coefficients are not all whole numbers.
5. No; zinc is lower in the activity series than aluminum.
6. No; gold is below hydrogen in the activity series, so it does not replace hydrogen.
7. In the products, the cation is pairing with the cation, and the anion is pairing with the anion.

8. $Ag_2SO_4(aq) + SrCl_2(aq) \rightarrow 2AgCl(s) + SrSO_4(s)$

9. Complete ionic equation: $Ba^{2+}(aq) + 2Cl^-(aq) + 2Ag^+(aq) + SO_4^{2-}(aq) \rightarrow BaSO_4(s) + 2AgCl(s)$

   Net ionic equation: The net ionic equation is the same as the complete ionic equation.

10. Complete ionic equation: $2Ag^+(aq) + SO_4^{2-}(aq) + Sr^{2+}(aq) + 2Cl^-(aq) \rightarrow 2AgCl(s) + SrSO_4(s)$

    Net ionic equation: The net ionic equation is the same as the complete ionic equation.

11. Each ion is a spectator ion; there is no overall net ionic equation.

12. $SO_4^{2-}(aq)$ is the only spectator ion. Net ionic equation: $6H^+(aq) + 2Al(OH)_3(s) \rightarrow 3H_2O(\ell) + 2Al^{3+}(aq)$

CHAPTER 9
Stoichiometry and the Mole

Opening Essay

At Contrived State University in Anytown, Ohio, a new building was dedicated in March 2010 to house the College of Education. The 100,000-square-foot building has enough office space to accommodate 86 full-time faculty members and 167 full-time staff.

In a fit of monetary excess, the university administration offered to buy new furniture (desks and chairs) and computer workstations for all faculty and staff members moving into the new building. However, to save on long-term energy and materials costs, the university offered to buy only 1 laser printer per 10 employees, with the plan to network the printers together.

How many laser printers did the administration have to buy? It is rather simple to show that 26 laser printers are needed for all the employees. However, what if a chemist were calculating quantities for a chemical reaction? Interestingly enough, similar calculations can be performed for chemicals as well as laser printers.

In filling a new office building with furniture and equipment, managers do calculations similar to those performed by scientists doing chemical reactions.

Source: Photo courtesy of Benjamin Benschneider, Cleveland State University.

We have already established that quantities are important in science, especially in chemistry. It is important to make accurate measurements of a variety of quantities when performing experiments. However, it is also important to be able to relate one measured quantity to another, unmeasured quantity. In this chapter, we will consider how we manipulate quantities to relate them to each other.

9.1 Stoichiometry

Consider a classic recipe for pound cake: 1 pound of eggs, 1 pound of butter, 1 pound of flour, and 1 pound of sugar. (That's why it's called "pound cake.") If you have 4 pounds of butter, how many pounds of sugar, flour, and eggs do you need? You would need 4 pounds each of sugar, flour, and eggs.

Now suppose you have 1.00 g H_2. If the chemical equation is

$$2H_2(g) + O_2(g) \rightarrow 2H_2O(\ell)$$

then what mass of oxygen do you need to make water?

stoichiometry

The relating of one chemical substance to another using a balanced chemical reaction.

Curiously, this chemical reaction question is very similar to the pound cake question. Both of them involve relating a quantity of one substance to a quantity of another substance or substances. The relating of one chemical substance to another using a balanced chemical reaction is called **stoichiometry**. Using stoichiometry is a fundamental skill in chemistry; it greatly broadens your ability to predict what will occur and, more importantly, how much is produced.

Let us consider a more complicated example. A recipe for pancakes calls for 2 cups (c) of pancake mix, 1 egg, and 1/2 c of milk. We can write this in the form of a chemical equation:

$$2 \text{ c mix} + 1 \text{ egg} + 1/2 \text{ c milk} \rightarrow 1 \text{ batch of pancakes}$$

If you have 9 c of pancake mix, how many eggs and how much milk do you need? It might take a little bit of work, but eventually you will find you need 4½ eggs and 2¼ c milk.

How can we formalize this? We can make a conversion factor using our original recipe and use that conversion factor to convert from a quantity of one substance to a quantity of another substance, similar to the way we constructed a conversion factor between feet and yards in Chapter 2. Because one recipe's worth of pancakes requires 2 c of pancake mix, 1 egg, and 1/2 c of milk, we actually have the following mathematical relationships that relate these quantities:

$$2 \text{ c pancake mix} \Leftrightarrow 1 \text{ egg} \Leftrightarrow 1/2 \text{ c milk}$$

where $\Leftrightarrow$ is the mathematical symbol for "is equivalent to." This does not mean that 2 c of pancake mix equal 1 egg. However, *as far as this recipe is concerned*, these are the equivalent quantities needed for a single recipe of pancakes. So, any possible quantities of two or more ingredients must have the same numerical ratio as the ratios in the equivalence.

We can deal with these equivalences in the same way we deal with equalities in unit conversions: we can make conversion factors that essentially equal 1. For example, to determine how many eggs we need for 9 c of pancake mix, we construct the conversion factor

$$\frac{1 \text{ egg}}{2 \text{ c pancake mix}}$$

This conversion factor is, in a strange way, equivalent to 1 because the recipe relates the two quantities. Starting with our initial quantity and multiplying by our conversion factor:

$$9 \text{ c pancake mix} \times \frac{1 \text{ egg}}{2 \text{ c pancake mix}} = 4.5 \text{ eggs}$$

Note how the units *cups pancake mix* canceled, leaving us with units of *eggs*. This is the formal, mathematical way of getting our amounts to mix with 9 c of pancake mix. We can use a similar conversion factor for the amount of milk:

$$9 \text{ c pancake mix} \times \frac{1/2 \text{ c milk}}{2 \text{ c pancake mix}} = 2.25 \text{ c milk}$$

Again, units cancel, and new units are introduced.

A balanced chemical equation is nothing more than *a recipe for a chemical reaction*. The difference is that a balanced chemical equation is written in terms of atoms and molecules, not cups, pounds, and eggs.

For example, consider the following chemical equation:

$$2H_2(g) + O_2(g) \rightarrow 2H_2O(\ell)$$

We can interpret this as, literally, "two hydrogen molecules react with one oxygen molecule to make two water molecules." That interpretation leads us directly to some equivalences, just as our pancake recipe did:

$$2H_2 \text{ molecules} \Leftrightarrow 1O_2 \text{ molecule} \Leftrightarrow 2H_2O \text{ molecules}$$

(Remember that the "1" is understood for the number of oxygen molecules in the chemical equation. Here, we are writing "1" explicitly.) These equivalences allow us to construct conversion factors

$$\frac{2 \text{ molecules } H_2}{1 \text{ molecule } O_2} \quad \frac{2 \text{ molecules } H_2}{2 \text{ molecules } H_2O} \quad \frac{1 \text{ molecule } O_2}{2 \text{ molecules } H_2O}$$

and so forth. These conversions can be used to relate quantities of one substance to quantities of another. For example, suppose we need to know how many molecules of oxygen are needed to react with 16 molecules of H_2. As we did with converting units, we start with our given quantity and use the appropriate conversion factor:

$$16 \text{ molecules } H_2 \times \frac{1 \text{ molecule } O_2}{2 \text{ molecules } H_2} = 8 \text{ molecules } O_2$$

Note how the unit *molecules H_2* cancels algebraically, just as any unit does in a conversion like this. The conversion factor came directly from the coefficients in the balanced chemical equation. This is another reason why a properly balanced chemical equation is important.

Example 1

How many molecules of SO_3 are needed to react with 144 molecules of Fe_2O_3 given this balanced chemical equation?

$$Fe_2O_3 + 3SO_3(g) \rightarrow Fe_2(SO_4)_3(s)$$

Solution

We use the balanced chemical equation to construct a conversion factor between Fe_2O_3 and SO_3. The number of molecules of Fe_2O_3 goes on the bottom of our conversion factor so it cancels with our given amount, and the molecules of SO_3 go on the top. Thus, the appropriate conversion factor is:

$$\frac{3 \text{ molecules } SO_3}{1 \text{ molecule } Fe_2O_3}$$

Starting with our given amount and applying the conversion factor, the result is:

$$144 \ \cancel{\text{molecules } Fe_2O_3} \times \frac{3 \text{ molecules } SO_3}{1 \ \cancel{\text{molecule } Fe_2O_3}} = 432 \text{ molecules } SO_3$$

We need 432 molecules of SO_3 to react with 144 molecules of Fe_2O_3.

Test Yourself

How many molecules of H_2 are needed to react with 29 molecules of N_2 to make ammonia if the balanced chemical equation is $N_2 + 3H_2 \rightarrow 2NH_3$?

Answer

87 molecules

Chemical equations also allow us to make conversions regarding the number of atoms in a chemical reaction because a chemical formula lists the number of atoms of each element in a compound. The formula H_2O indicates that there are two hydrogen atoms and one oxygen atom in each molecule, and these relationships can be used to make conversion factors:

$$\frac{2 \text{ atoms } H}{1 \text{ molecule } H_2O} \qquad \frac{1 \text{ molecule } H_2O}{1 \text{ atom } O}$$

Conversion factors like this can also be used in stoichiometry calculations.

Example 2

How many molecules of NH_3 can you make if you have 228 atoms of H_2?

Solution

From the formula, we know that one molecule of NH_3 has three H atoms. Use that fact as a conversion factor:

$$228 \ \cancel{\text{atoms } H} \times \frac{1 \text{ molecule } NH_3}{3 \ \cancel{\text{atoms } H}} = 76 \text{ molecules } NH_3$$

Test Yourself

How many molecules of $Fe_2(SO_4)_3$ can you make from 777 atoms of S?

Answer

259 molecules

Key Takeaway

- Quantities of substances can be related to each other using balanced chemical equations.

Exercises

1. Think back to the pound cake recipe. What possible conversion factors can you construct relating the components of the recipe?

2. Think back to the pancake recipe. What possible conversion factors can you construct relating the components of the recipe?

3. What are all the conversion factors that can be constructed from the balanced chemical reaction $2H_2(g) + O_2(g) \rightarrow 2H_2O(\ell)$?

4. What are all the conversion factors that can be constructed from the balanced chemical reaction $N_2(g) + 3H_2(g) \rightarrow 2NH_3(g)$?

5. Given the chemical equation

$$Na(s) + H_2O(\ell) \rightarrow NaOH(aq) + H_2(g)$$

   a. Balance the equation.
   b. How many molecules of H_2 are produced when 332 atoms of Na react?

6. Given the chemical equation

$$S(s) + O_2(g) \rightarrow SO_3(g)$$

   a. Balance the equation.
   b. How many molecules of O_2 are needed when 38 atoms of S react?

7. For the balanced chemical equation

$$6H^+(aq) + 2MnO_4^-(aq) + 5H_2O_2(\ell) \rightarrow 2Mn^{2+}(aq) + 5O_2(g) + 8H_2O(\ell)$$

   how many molecules of H_2O are produced when 75 molecules of H_2O_2 react?

8. For the balanced chemical reaction

$$2C_6H_6(\ell) + 15O_2(g) \rightarrow 12CO_2(g) + 6H_2O(\ell)$$

   how many molecules of CO_2 are produced when 56 molecules of C_6H_6 react?

9. Given the balanced chemical equation

$$Fe_2O_3(s) + 3SO_3(g) \rightarrow Fe_2(SO_4)_3$$

   how many molecules of $Fe_2(SO_4)_3$ are produced if 321 atoms of S are reacted?

10. For the balanced chemical equation

$$CuO(s) + H_2S(g) \rightarrow CuS + H_2O(\ell)$$

   how many molecules of CuS are formed if 9,044 atoms of H react?

11. For the balanced chemical equation

$$Fe_2O_3(s) + 3SO_3(g) \rightarrow Fe_2(SO_4)_3$$

   suppose we need to make 145,000 molecules of $Fe_2(SO_4)_3$. How many molecules of SO_3 do we need?

12. One way to make sulfur hexafluoride is to react thioformaldehyde, CH_2S, with elemental fluorine:

$$CH_2S + 6F_2 \rightarrow CF_4 + 2HF + SF_6$$

   If 45,750 molecules of SF_6 are needed, how many molecules of F_2 are required?

13. Construct the three independent conversion factors possible for these two reactions:

a. $2H_2 + O_2 \rightarrow 2H_2O$

b. $H_2 + O_2 \rightarrow H_2O_2$

Why are the ratios between H_2 and O_2 different?

The conversion factors are different because the stoichiometries of the balanced chemical reactions are different.

14. Construct the three independent conversion factors possible for these two reactions:

a. $2Na + Cl_2 \rightarrow 2NaCl$

b. $4Na + 2Cl_2 \rightarrow 4NaCl$

What similarities, if any, exist in the conversion factors from these two reactions?

Answers

1. $\dfrac{1 \text{ pound butter}}{1 \text{ pound flour}}$ or $\dfrac{1 \text{ pound sugar}}{1 \text{ pound eggs}}$ are two conversion factors that can be constructed from the pound cake recipe. Other conversion factors are also possible.

2. $\dfrac{2 \text{ c mix}}{1/2 \text{ c milk}}$, $\dfrac{1 \text{ egg}}{1/2 \text{ c milk}}$, and $\dfrac{1/2 \text{ c milk}}{1 \text{ batch pancakes}}$ are three conversions factors that can be constructed. Other conversion factors are also possible.

3. $\dfrac{2 \text{ molecules } H_2}{1 \text{ molecule } O_2}$, $\dfrac{1 \text{ molecule } O_2}{2 \text{ molecules } H_2O}$, $\dfrac{2 \text{ molecules } H_2}{2 \text{ molecules } H_2O}$, and their reciprocals are the conversion factors that can be constructed.

4. $\dfrac{1 \text{ molecule } N_2}{3 \text{ molecules } H_2}$, $\dfrac{1 \text{ molecule } N_2}{2 \text{ molecules } NH_3}$, $\dfrac{3 \text{ molecules } H_2}{2 \text{ molecules } NH_3}$, and their reciprocals are the conversion factors that can be constructed.

5. a. $2Na(s) + 2H_2O(\ell) \rightarrow 2NaOH(aq) + H_2(g)$

   b. 166 molecules

6. a. $2S(s) + 3O_2(g) \rightarrow 2SO_3(g)$

   b. 57 molecules

7. 120 molecules

8. 336 molecules

9. 107 molecules

10. 4,522 molecules

11. 435,000 molecules

12. 274,500 molecules

13. a. $\dfrac{2 \text{ molecules } H_2}{1 \text{ molecule } O_2}$, $\dfrac{1 \text{ molecule } O_2}{2 \text{ molecules } H_2O}$, and $\dfrac{2 \text{ molecules } H_2}{2 \text{ molecules } H_2O}$

    b. $\dfrac{1 \text{ molecule } H_2}{1 \text{ molecule } O_2}$, $\dfrac{1 \text{ molecule } O_2}{1 \text{ molecule } H_2O_2}$, and $\dfrac{1 \text{ molecule } H_2}{1 \text{ molecule } H_2O_2}$

14. a. $\dfrac{2 \text{ molecules Na}}{1 \text{ molecule } Cl_2}$, $\dfrac{2 \text{ molecules Na}}{2 \text{ molecules NaCl}}$, and $\dfrac{1 \text{ molecule } Cl_2}{2 \text{ molecules NaCl}}$

    b. $\dfrac{4 \text{ molecules Na}}{2 \text{ molecule } Cl_2}$, $\dfrac{4 \text{ molecules Na}}{4 \text{ molecules NaCl}}$, and $\dfrac{2 \text{ molecule } Cl_2}{4 \text{ molecules NaCl}}$

9.2 The Mole

Learning Objectives

1. Describe the unit *mole*.
2. Relate the mole quantity of substance to its mass.

So far, we have been talking about chemical substances in terms of individual atoms and molecules. Yet we don't typically deal with substances an atom or a molecule at a time; we work with millions, billions, and trillions of atoms and molecules at a time. What we need is a way to deal with macroscopic, rather than microscopic, amounts of matter. We need a unit of amount that relates quantities of substances on a scale that we can interact with.

Chemistry uses a unit called mole. A **mole** (mol) is a number of things equal to the number of atoms in exactly 12 g of carbon-12. Experimental measurements have determined that this number is very large:

$$1 \text{ mol} = 6.02214179 \times 10^{23} \text{ things}$$

Understand that a mole means a number of things, just like a dozen means a certain number of things—twelve, in the case of a dozen. But a mole is a much larger number of things. These things can be atoms, or molecules, or eggs; however, in chemistry, we usually use the mole to refer to the amounts of atoms or molecules. Although the number of things in a mole is known to eight decimal places, it is usually fine to use only two or three decimal places in calculations. The numerical value of things in a mole is often called *Avogadro's number* (N_A), which is also known as the *Avogadro constant*, after Amadeo Avogadro, an Italian chemist who first proposed its importance.

mole

The number of things equal to the number of atoms in exactly 12 g of carbon-12; equals 6.022×10^{23} things.

Example 3

How many molecules are present in 2.76 mol of H_2O? How many atoms is this?

Solution

The definition of a mole is an equality that can be used to construct a conversion factor. Also, because we know that there are three atoms in each molecule of H_2O, we can also determine the number of atoms in the sample.

$$2.76 \text{ mol } H_2O \times \frac{6.022 \times 10^{23} \text{ molecules } H_2O}{\text{mol } H_2O} = 1.66 \times 10^{24} \text{ molecules } H_2O$$

To determine the total number of atoms, we have

$$1.66 \times 10^{24} \text{ molecules } H_2O \times \frac{3 \text{ atoms}}{1 \text{ molecule}} = 4.99 \times 10^{24} \text{ atoms}$$

Test Yourself

How many molecules are present in 4.61×10^{-2} mol of O_2?

Answer

2.78×10^{22} molecules

How big is a mole? It is very large. Suppose you had a mole of dollar bills that need to be counted. If everyone on Earth (about 7 billion people) counted one bill per second, it would take about 2.7 million years to count all the bills. A mole of sand would fill a cube about 32 km on a side. A mole of pennies stacked on top of each other would have about the same diameter as our galaxy, the Milky Way. A mole is a lot of things—but atoms and molecules are very tiny. One mole of carbon atoms would make a cube that is 1.74 cm on a side, small enough to carry in your pocket.

Why is the mole unit so important? It represents the link between the microscopic and the macroscopic, especially in terms of mass. *A mole of a substance has the same mass in grams as one unit (atom or molecules) has in atomic mass units.* The mole unit allows us to express amounts of atoms and molecules in visible amounts that we can understand.

For example, we already know that, by definition, a mole of carbon has a mass of exactly 12 g. This means that exactly 12 g of C has 6.022×10^{23} atoms:

$$12 \text{ g C} = 6.022 \times 10^{23} \text{ atoms C}$$

We can use this equality as a conversion factor between the number of atoms of carbon and the number of grams of carbon. How many grams are there, say, in 1.50×10^{25} atoms of carbon? This is a one-step conversion:

$$1.50 \times 10^{25} \text{ atoms C} \times \frac{12.0000... \text{ g C}}{6.022 \times 10^{23} \text{ atoms C}} = 299 \text{ g C}$$

molar mass
The mass of 1 mol of a substance in grams.

But it also goes beyond carbon. Previously we defined atomic and molecular masses as the number of atomic mass units per atom or molecule. Now we can do so in terms of grams. The atomic mass of an element is the number of grams in 1 mol of atoms of that element, while the molecular mass of a compound is the number of grams in 1 mol of molecules of that compound. Sometimes these masses are called **molar masses** to emphasize the fact that they are the mass for 1 mol of things. (The term *molar* is the adjective form of mole and has nothing to do with teeth.)

Here are some examples. The mass of a hydrogen atom is 1.0079 u; the mass of 1 mol of hydrogen atoms is 1.0079 g. Elemental hydrogen exists as a diatomic molecule, H_2. One molecule has a mass of 1.0079 + 1.0079 = 2.0158 u, while 1 mol H_2 has a mass of 2.0158 g. A molecule of H_2O has a mass of about 18.02 u; 1 mol H_2O has a mass of 18.02 g. A single unit of NaCl has a mass of 58.45 u; NaCl has a molar mass of 58.45 g. In each of these moles of substances, there are 6.022×10^{23} units: 6.022×10^{23} atoms of H, 6.022×10^{23} molecules of H_2 and H_2O, 6.022×10^{23} units of NaCl ionic units. These relationships give us plenty of opportunities to construct conversion factors for simple calculations.

Example 4

What is the molar mass of $C_6H_{12}O_6$?

Solution

To determine the molar mass, we simply add the atomic masses of the atoms in the molecular formula but express the total in grams per mole, not atomic mass units. The masses of the atoms can be taken from the periodic table or the list of elements in Appendix A:

6 C = 6 × 12.011	= 72.066
12 H = 12 × 1.0079	= 12.0948
6 O = 6 × 15.999	= 95.994
TOTAL	= 180.155 g/mol

Per convention, the unit *grams per mole* is written as a fraction.

Test Yourself

What is the molar mass of $AgNO_3$?

Answer

169.87 g/mol

    Knowing the molar mass of a substance, we can calculate the number of moles in a certain mass of a substance and vice versa, as these examples illustrate. The molar mass is used as the conversion factor.

Example 5

What is the mass of 3.56 mol of $HgCl_2$? The molar mass of $HgCl_2$ is 271.49 g/mol.

Solution

Use the molar mass as a conversion factor between moles and grams. Because we want to cancel the mole unit and introduce the gram unit, we can use the molar mass as given:

$$3.56 \ \cancel{\text{mol } HgCl_2} \times \frac{271.49 \text{ g } HgCl_2}{\cancel{\text{mol } HgCl_2}} = 967 \text{ g } HgCl_2$$

Test Yourself

What is the mass of 33.7 mol of H_2O?

Answer

607 g

Example 6

How many moles of H_2O are present in 240.0 g of water (about the mass of a cup of water)?

Solution

Use the molar mass of H_2O as a conversion factor from mass to moles. The molar mass of water is (1.0079 + 1.0079 + 15.999) = 18.015 g/mol. However, because we want to cancel the gram unit and introduce moles, we need to take the reciprocal of this quantity, or 1 mol/18.015 g:

$$240.0 \ \cancel{\text{g } H_2O} \times \frac{1 \text{ mol } H_2O}{18.015 \ \cancel{\text{g } H_2O}} = 13.32 \text{ mol } H_2O$$

Test Yourself

How many moles are present in 35.6 g of H_2SO_4 (molar mass = 98.08 g/mol)?

Answer

0.363 mol

    Other conversion factors can be combined with the definition of mole—density, for example.

Example 7

The density of ethanol is 0.789 g/mL. How many moles are in 100.0 mL of ethanol? The molar mass of ethanol is 46.08 g/mol.

Solution

Here, we use density to convert from volume to mass and then use the molar mass to determine the number of moles.

$$100.0 \; \cancel{mL} \; \text{ethanol} \times \frac{0.789 \; \cancel{g}}{\cancel{mL}} \times \frac{1 \; \text{mol}}{46.08 \; \cancel{g}} = 1.71 \; \text{mol ethanol}$$

Test Yourself

If the density of benzene, C_6H_6, is 0.879 g/mL, how many moles are present in 17.9 mL of benzene?

Answer

0.202 mol

Key Takeaways

- The mole is a key unit in chemistry.
- The molar mass of a substance, in grams, is numerically equal to one atom's or molecule's mass in atomic mass units.

Exercises

1. How many atoms are present in 4.55 mol of Fe?
2. How many atoms are present in 0.0665 mol of K?
3. How many molecules are present in 2.509 mol of H_2S?
4. How many molecules are present in 0.336 mol of acetylene (C_2H_2)?
5. How many moles are present in 3.55×10^{24} Pb atoms?
6. How many moles are present in 2.09×10^{22} Ti atoms?
7. How many moles are present in 1.00×10^{23} PF_3 molecules?
8. How many moles are present in 5.52×10^{25} penicillin molecules?
9. Determine the molar mass of each substance.

   a. Si
   b. SiH_4
   c. K_2O

10. Determine the molar mass of each substance.

    a. Cl_2
    b. $SeCl_2$
    c. $Ca(C_2H_3O_2)_2$

11. Determine the molar mass of each substance.

    a. Al
    b. Al_2O_3
    c. $CoCl_3$

12. Determine the molar mass of each substance.

    a. O_3
    b. NaI
    c. $C_{12}H_{22}O_{11}$

13. What is the mass of 4.44 mol of Rb?

14. What is the mass of 0.311 mol of Xe?

15. What is the mass of 12.34 mol of $Al_2(SO_4)_3$?

16. What is the mass of 0.0656 mol of $PbCl_2$?

17. How many moles are present in 45.6 g of CO?

18. How many moles are present in 0.00339 g of LiF?

19. How many moles are present in 1.223 g of SF_6?

20. How many moles are present in 48.8 g of $BaCO_3$?

21. How many moles are present in 54.8 mL of mercury if the density of mercury is 13.6 g/mL?

22. How many moles are present in 56.83 mL of O_2 if the density of O_2 is 0.00133 g/mL?

Answers

1. 2.74×10^{24} atoms

2. 4.00×10^{22} atoms

3. 1.511×10^{24} molecules

4. 2.02×10^{23} molecules

5. 5.90 mol

6. 0.0347 mol

7. 0.166 mol

8. 91.7 mol

9. a. 28.086 g

   b. 32.118 g

   c. 94.195 g

10. a. 70.906 g

    b. 149.87 g

    c. 158.166 g

11. a. 26.981 g

    b. 101.959 g

    c. 165.292 g

12. a. 47.997 g

    b. 149.894 g

    c. 342.297 g

13. 379 g

14. 40.8 g

15. 4,222 g

16. 18.2 g

17. 1.63 mol

18. 0.000131 mol

19. 0.008374 mol

20. 0.247 mol

21. 3.72 mol

22. 0.00236 mol

9.3 The Mole in Chemical Reactions

Learning Objectives

1. Balance a chemical equation in terms of moles.
2. Use the balanced equation to construct conversion factors in terms of moles.
3. Calculate moles of one substance from moles of another substance using a balanced chemical equation.

Consider this balanced chemical equation:

$$2H_2 + O_2 \rightarrow 2H_2O$$

We interpret this as "two molecules of hydrogen react with one molecule of oxygen to make two molecules of water." The chemical equation is balanced as long as the coefficients are in the ratio 2:1:2. For instance, this chemical equation is also balanced:

$$100H_2 + 50O_2 \rightarrow 100H_2O$$

This equation is not conventional—because convention says that we use the lowest ratio of coefficients—but it is balanced. So is this chemical equation:

$$5,000H_2 + 2,500O_2 \rightarrow 5,000H_2O$$

Again, this is not conventional, but it is still balanced. Suppose we use a much larger number:

$$12.044 \times 10^{23}\ H_2 + 6.022 \times 10^{23}\ O_2 \rightarrow 12.044 \times 10^{23}\ H_2O$$

These coefficients are also in the ratio of 2:1:2. But these numbers are related to the number of things in a mole: the first and last numbers are two times Avogadro's number, while the second number is Avogadro's number. That means that the first and last numbers represent 2 mol, while the middle number is just 1 mol. Well, why not just use the number of moles in balancing the chemical equation?

$$2H_2 + O_2 \rightarrow 2H_2O$$

is the same balanced chemical equation we started with! What this means is that chemical equations are not just balanced in terms of molecules; *they are also balanced in terms of moles.* We can just as easily read this chemical equation as "two moles of hydrogen react with one mole of oxygen to make two moles of water." All balanced chemical reactions are balanced in terms of moles.

Example 8

Interpret this balanced chemical equation in terms of moles.

$$P_4 + 5O_2 \rightarrow P_4O_{10}$$

Solution

The coefficients represent the number of moles that react, not just molecules. We would speak of this equation as "one mole of molecular phosphorus reacts with five moles of elemental oxygen to make one mole of tetraphosphorus decoxide."

Test Yourself

Interpret this balanced chemical equation in terms of moles.

$$N_2 + 3H_2 \rightarrow 2NH_3$$

Answer

One mole of elemental nitrogen reacts with three moles of elemental hydrogen to produce two moles of ammonia.

In Chapter 8 Section 1, we stated that a chemical equation is simply a recipe for a chemical reaction. As such, chemical equations also give us equivalences—equivalences between the reactants and the products. However, now we understand that *these equivalences are expressed in terms of moles*. Consider the chemical equation:

$$2H_2 + O_2 \rightarrow 2H_2O$$

This chemical reaction gives us the following equivalences:

$$2 \text{ mol H}_2 \Leftrightarrow 1 \text{ mol O}_2 \Leftrightarrow 2 \text{ mol H}_2O$$

Any two of these quantities can be used to construct a conversion factor that lets us relate the number of moles of one substance to an equivalent number of moles of another substance. If, for example, we want to know how many moles of oxygen will react with 17.6 mol of hydrogen, we construct a conversion factor between 2 mol of H_2 and 1 mol of O_2 and use it to convert from moles of one substance to moles of another:

$$17.6 \ \cancel{\text{mol H}_2} \times \frac{1 \text{ mol O}_2}{2 \ \cancel{\text{mol H}_2}} = 8.80 \text{ mol O}_2$$

Note how the mol H_2 unit cancels, and mol O_2 is the new unit introduced. This is an example of a **mole-mole calculation**, when you start with moles of one substance and convert to moles of another substance by using the balanced chemical equation. The example may seem simple because the numbers are small, but numbers won't always be so simple!

mole-mole calculation

A stoichiometry calculation when one starts with moles of one substance and convert to moles of another substance using the balanced chemical equation.

Example 9

For the balanced chemical equation

$$2C_4H_{10}(g) + 13O_2 \rightarrow 8CO_2(g) + 10H_2O(\ell)$$

if 154 mol of O_2 are reacted, how many moles of CO_2 are produced?

Solution

We are relating an amount of oxygen to an amount of carbon dioxide, so we need the equivalence between these two substances. According to the balanced chemical equation, the equivalence is:

$$13 \text{ mol O}_2 \Leftrightarrow 8 \text{ mol CO}_2$$

We can use this equivalence to construct the proper conversion factor. We start with what we are given and apply the conversion factor:

$$154 \ \cancel{\text{mol O}_2} \times \frac{8 \text{ mol CO}_2}{13 \ \cancel{\text{mol O}_2}} = 94.8 \text{ mol CO}_2$$

The mol O_2 unit is in the denominator of the conversion factor, so it cancels. Both the 8 and the 13 are exact numbers, so they don't contribute to the number of significant figures in the final answer.

Test Yourself

Using the above equation, how many moles of H_2O are produced when 154 mol of O_2 react?

Answer

118 mol

It is important to reiterate that balanced chemical equations are balanced in terms of *moles*. Not grams, kilograms, or liters—but moles. Any stoichiometry problem will likely need to work through the mole unit at some point, especially if you are working with a balanced chemical reaction.

Key Takeaways

- Balanced chemical reactions are balanced in terms of moles.
- A balanced chemical reaction gives equivalences in moles that allow stoichiometry calculations to be performed.

Exercises

1. Express in mole terms what this chemical equation means.

$$CH_4 + 2O_2 \rightarrow CO_2 + 2H_2O$$

2. Express in mole terms what this chemical equation means.

$$Na_2CO_3 + 2HCl \rightarrow 2NaCl + H_2O + CO_2$$

3. How many molecules of each substance are involved in the equation in Exercise 1 if it is interpreted in terms of moles?

4. How many molecules of each substance are involved in the equation in Exercise 2 if it is interpreted in terms of moles?

5. For the chemical equation

$$2C_2H_6 + 7O_2 \rightarrow 4CO_2 + 6H_2O$$

what equivalences can you write in terms of moles? Use the ⇔ sign.

6. For the chemical equation

$$2Al + 3Cl_2 \rightarrow 2AlCl_3$$

what equivalences can you write in terms of moles? Use the ⇔ sign.

7. Write the balanced chemical reaction for the combustion of C_5H_{12} (the products are CO_2 and H_2O) and determine how many moles of H_2O are formed when 5.8 mol of O_2 are reacted.

8. Write the balanced chemical reaction for the formation of $Fe_2(SO_4)_3$ from Fe_2O_3 and SO_3 and determine how many moles of $Fe_2(SO_4)_3$ are formed when 12.7 mol of SO_3 are reacted.

9. For the balanced chemical equation

$$3Cu(s) + 2NO_3^-(aq) + 8H^+(aq) \rightarrow 3Cu^{2+}(aq) + 4H_2O(\ell) + 2NO(g)$$

how many moles of Cu^{2+} are formed when 55.7 mol of H^+ are reacted?

10. For the balanced chemical equation

$$Al(s) + 3Ag^+(aq) \rightarrow Al^{3+}(aq) + 3Ag(s)$$

    how many moles of Ag are produced when 0.661 mol of Al are reacted?

11. For the balanced chemical reaction

$$4NH_3(g) + 5O_2(g) \rightarrow 4NO(g) + 6H_2O(\ell)$$

    how many moles of H_2O are produced when 0.669 mol of NH_3 react?

12. For the balanced chemical reaction

$$4NaOH(aq) + 2S(s) + 3O_2(g) \rightarrow 2Na_2SO_4(aq) + 2H_2O(\ell)$$

    how many moles of Na_2SO_4 are formed when 1.22 mol of O_2 react?

13. For the balanced chemical reaction

$$4KO_2(s) + 2CO_2(g) \rightarrow 2K_2CO_3(s) + 3C_2(g)$$

    determine the number of moles of both products formed when 6.88 mol of KO_2 react.

14. For the balanced chemical reaction

$$2AlCl_3 + 3H_2O(\ell) \rightarrow Al_2O_3 + 6HCl(g)$$

    determine the number of moles of both products formed when 0.0552 mol of $AlCl_3$ react.

Answers

1. One mole of CH_4 reacts with 2 mol of O_2 to make 1 mol of CO_2 and 2 mol of H_2O.

2. One mole of Na_2CO_3 reacts with 2 mol of HCl to make 2 mol of NaCl, 1 mol of H_2O, and 1 mol of CO_2.

3. 6.022×10^{23} molecules of CH_4, 1.2044×10^{24} molecules of O_2, 6.022×10^{23} molecules of CO_2, and 1.2044×10^{24} molecules of H_2O

4. 6.022×10^{23} molecules of Na_2CO_3 react with 1.2044×10^{24} molecules of HCl to make 1.2044×10^{24} molecules of NaCl, 6.022×10^{23} molecules of H_2O, and 6.022×10^{23} molecules of CO_2

5. 2 mol of $C_2H_6 \Leftrightarrow$ 7 mol of $O_2 \Leftrightarrow$ 4 mol of $CO_2 \Leftrightarrow$ 6 mol of H_2O

6. 2 mol of $Al \Leftrightarrow$ 3 mol of $Cl_2 \Leftrightarrow$ 2 mol of $AlCl_3$

7. $C_5H_{12} + 8O_2 \rightarrow 5CO_2 + 6H_2O$; 4.4 mol

8. $Fe_2O_3 + 3SO_3 \rightarrow Fe_2(SO_4)_3$; 4.23 mol

9. 20.9 mol

10. 1.98 mol

11. 1.00 mol

12. 0.813 mol

13. 3.44 mol of K_2CO_3; 5.16 mol of O_2

14. 0.0276 mol of Al_2O_3; 0.166 mol of HCl

9.4 Mole-Mass and Mass-Mass Calculations

Learning Objectives

1. From a given number of moles of a substance, calculate the mass of another substance involved using the balanced chemical equation.
2. From a given mass of a substance, calculate the moles of another substance involved using the balanced chemical equation.
3. From a given mass of a substance, calculate the mass of another substance involved using the balanced chemical equation.

mole-mass calculation

A calculation in which you start with a given number of moles of a substance and calculate the mass of another substance involved in the chemical equation, or vice versa.

Mole-mole calculations are not the only type of calculations that can be performed using balanced chemical equations. Recall that the molar mass can be determined from a chemical formula and used as a conversion factor. We can add that conversion factor as another step in a calculation to make a **mole-mass calculation**, where we start with a given number of moles of a substance and calculate the mass of another substance involved in the chemical equation, or vice versa.

For example, suppose we have the balanced chemical equation:

$$2Al + 3Cl_2 \rightarrow 2AlCl_3$$

Suppose we know we have 123.2 g of Cl_2. How can we determine how many moles of $AlCl_3$ we will get when the reaction is complete? First and foremost, *chemical equations are not balanced in terms of grams; they are balanced in terms of moles.* So to use the balanced chemical equation to relate an amount of Cl_2 to an amount of $AlCl_3$, we need to convert the given amount of Cl_2 into moles. We know how to do this by simply using the molar mass of Cl_2 as a conversion factor. The molar mass of Cl_2 (which we get from the atomic mass of Cl from the periodic table) is 70.90 g/mol. We must invert this fraction so that the units cancel properly:

$$123.2 \ \text{g } Cl_2 \times \frac{1 \ \text{mol } Cl_2}{70.90 \ \text{g } Cl_2} = 1.738 \ \text{mol } Cl_2$$

Now that we have the quantity in moles, we can use the balanced chemical equation to construct a conversion factor that relates the number of moles of Cl_2 to the number of moles of $AlCl_3$. The numbers in the conversion factor come from the coefficients in the balanced chemical equation:

$$\frac{2 \ \text{mol } AlCl_3}{3 \ \text{mol } Cl_2}$$

Using this conversion factor with the molar quantity we calculated above, we get:

$$1.738 \ \text{mol } Cl_2 \times \frac{2 \ \text{mol } AlCl_3}{3 \ \text{mol } Cl_2} = 1.159 \ \text{mol } AlCl_3$$

Therefore, we will get 1.159 mol of $AlCl_3$ if we react 123.2 g of Cl_2.

In this last example, we did the calculation in two steps. However, it is mathematically equivalent to perform the two calculations sequentially on one line:

$$123.2 \ \cancel{\text{g Cl}_2} \times \frac{1 \ \cancel{\text{mol Cl}_2}}{70.90 \ \cancel{\text{g Cl}_2}} \times \frac{2 \ \text{mol AlCl}_3}{3 \ \cancel{\text{mol Cl}_2}} = 1.159 \ \text{mol AlCl}_3$$

The units still cancel appropriately, and we get the same numerical answer in the end. Sometimes the answer may be slightly different from doing it one step at a time because of rounding of the intermediate answers, but the final answers should be effectively the same.

Example 10

How many moles of HCl will be produced when 249 g of $AlCl_3$ are reacted according to this chemical equation?

$$2AlCl_3 + 3H_2O \rightarrow Al_2O_3 + 6HCl$$

Solution

We will do this in two steps: convert the mass of $AlCl_3$ to moles and then use the balanced chemical equation to find the number of moles of HCl formed. The molar mass of $AlCl_3$ is 133.33 g/mol, which we have to invert to get the appropriate conversion factor:

$$249 \ \cancel{\text{g AlCl}_3} \times \frac{1 \ \text{mol AlCl}_3}{133.33 \ \cancel{\text{g AlCl}_3}} = 1.87 \ \text{mol AlCl}_3$$

Now we can use this quantity to determine the number of moles of HCl that will form. From the balanced chemical equation, we construct a conversion factor between the number of moles of $AlCl_3$ and the number of moles of HCl:

$$\frac{6 \ \text{mol HCl}}{2 \ \text{mol AlCl}_3}$$

Applying this conversion factor to the quantity of $AlCl_3$, we get:

$$1.87 \ \cancel{\text{mol AlCl}_3} \times \frac{6 \ \text{mol HCl}}{2 \ \cancel{\text{mol AlCl}_3}} = 5.61 \ \text{mol HCl}$$

Alternatively, we could have done this in one line:

$$249 \ \cancel{\text{g AlCl}_3} \times \frac{1 \ \cancel{\text{mol AlCl}_3}}{133.33 \ \cancel{\text{g AlCl}_3}} \times \frac{6 \ \text{mol HCl}}{2 \ \cancel{\text{mol AlCl}_3}} = 5.60 \ \text{mol HCl}$$

The last digit in our final answer is slightly different because of rounding differences, but the answer is essentially the same.

Test Yourself

How many moles of Al_2O_3 will be produced when 23.9 g of H_2O are reacted according to this chemical equation?

$$2AlCl_3 + 3H_2O \rightarrow Al_2O_3 + 6HCl$$

Answer

0.443 mol

A variation of the mole-mass calculation is to start with an amount in moles and then determine an amount of another substance in grams. The steps are the same but are performed in reverse order.

Example 11

How many grams of NH_3 will be produced when 33.9 mol of H_2 are reacted according to this chemical equation?

$$N_2 + 3H_2 \rightarrow 2NH_3$$

Solution

The conversions are the same, but they are applied in a different order. Start by using the balanced chemical equation to convert to moles of another substance and then use its molar mass to determine the mass of the final substance. In two steps, we have:

$$33.9 \; \cancel{mol \, H_2} \times \frac{2 \; mol \; NH_3}{3 \; \cancel{mol \, H_2}} = 22.6 \; mol \; NH_3$$

Now, using the molar mass of NH_3, which is 17.03 g/mol, we get:

$$22.6 \; \cancel{mol \, NH_3} \times \frac{17.03 \; g \; NH_3}{1 \; \cancel{mol \, NH_3}} = 385 \; g \; NH_3$$

Test Yourself

How many grams of N_2 are needed to produce 2.17 mol of NH_3 when reacted according to this chemical equation?

$$N_2 + 3H_2 \rightarrow 2NH_3$$

Answer

30.4 g (Note: Here we go from a product to a reactant, showing that mole-mass problems can begin and end with any substance in the chemical equation.)

---

mass-mass calculation

A calculation in which you start with a given mass of a substance and calculate the mass of another substance involved in the chemical equation.

It should be a trivial task now to extend the calculations to **mass-mass calculations**, in which we start with a mass of some substance and end with the mass of another substance in the chemical reaction. For this type of calculation, the molar masses of two different substances must be used—be sure to keep track of which is which. Again, however, it is important to emphasize that before the balanced chemical reaction is used, the mass quantity must first be converted to moles. Then the coefficients of the balanced chemical reaction can be used to convert to moles of another substance, which can then be converted to a mass.

For example, let us determine the number of grams of SO_3 that can be produced by the reaction of 45.3 g of SO_2 with O_2:

$$2SO_2(g) + O_2(g) \rightarrow 2SO_3(g)$$

First, we convert the given amount, 45.3 g of SO_2, to moles of SO_2 using its molar mass (64.06 g/mol):

$$45.3 \; \cancel{g \, SO_2} \times \frac{1 \; mol \; SO_2}{64.06 \; \cancel{g \, SO_2}} = 0.707 \; mol \; SO_2$$

Second, we use the balanced chemical reaction to convert from moles of SO_2 to moles of SO_3:

$$0.707 \; \cancel{mol \, SO_2} \times \frac{2 \; mol \; SO_3}{2 \; \cancel{mol \, SO_2}} = 0.707 \; mol \; SO_3$$

Finally, we use the molar mass of SO_3 (80.06 g/mol) to convert to the mass of SO_3:

$$0.707 \ \cancel{mol \ SO_3} \times \frac{80.06 \ g \ SO_3}{1 \ \cancel{mol \ SO_3}} = 56.6 \ g \ SO_3$$

We can also perform all three steps sequentially, writing them on one line as:

$$45.3 \ \cancel{g \ SO_2} \times \frac{1 \ \cancel{mol \ SO_2}}{64.06 \ \cancel{g \ SO_2}} \times \frac{2 \ \cancel{mol \ SO_3}}{2 \ \cancel{mol \ SO_2}} \times \frac{80.06 \ g \ SO_3}{1 \ \cancel{mol \ SO_3}} = 56.6 \ g \ SO_3$$

We get the same answer. Note how the initial and all the intermediate units cancel, leaving grams of SO_3, which is what we are looking for, as our final answer.

Example 12

What mass of Mg will be produced when 86.4 g of K are reacted?

$$MgCl_2 + 2K \rightarrow Mg + 2KCl$$

Solution

We will simply follow the steps:

$$mass \ K \rightarrow mol \ K \rightarrow mol \ Mg \rightarrow mass \ Mg$$

In addition to the balanced chemical equation, we need the molar masses of K (39.09 g/mol) and Mg (24.31 g/mol). In one line,

$$86.4 \ \cancel{g \ K} \times \frac{1 \ \cancel{mol \ K}}{39.09 \ \cancel{g \ K}} \times \frac{1 \ \cancel{mol \ Mg}}{2 \ \cancel{mol \ K}} \times \frac{24.31 \ g \ Mg}{1 \ \cancel{mol \ Mg}} = 26.87 \ g \ Mg$$

Test Yourself

What mass of H_2 will be produced when 122 g of Zn are reacted?

$$Zn + 2HCl \rightarrow ZnCl_2 + H_2$$

Answer

3.77 g

Key Takeaways

- Mole quantities of one substance can be related to mass quantities using a balanced chemical equation.
- Mass quantities of one substance can be related to mass quantities using a balanced chemical equation.
- In all cases, quantities of a substance must be converted to moles before the balanced chemical equation can be used to convert to moles of another substance.

Exercises

1. What mass of CO_2 is produced by the combustion of 1.00 mol of CH_4?

$$CH_4(g) + 2O_2(g) \rightarrow CO_2(g) + 2H_2O(\ell)$$

2. What mass of H_2O is produced by the combustion of 1.00 mol of CH_4?

$$CH_4(g) + 2O_2(g) \rightarrow CO_2(g) + 2H_2O(\ell)$$

3. What mass of HgO is required to produce 0.692 mol of O_2?

$$2HgO(s) \rightarrow 2Hg(\ell) + O_2(g)$$

4. What mass of $NaHCO_3$ is needed to produce 2.659 mol of CO_2?

$$2NaHCO_3(s) \rightarrow Na_2CO_3(s) + H_2O(\ell) + CO_2(g)$$

5. How many moles of Al can be produced from 10.87 g of Ag?

$$Al(NO_3)_3(s) + 3Ag \rightarrow Al + 3AgNO_3$$

6. How many moles of HCl can be produced from 0.226 g of $SOCl_2$?

$$SOCl_2(\ell) + H_2O(\ell) \rightarrow SO_2(g) + 2HCl(g)$$

7. How many moles of O_2 are needed to prepare 1.00 g of $Ca(NO_3)_2$?

$$Ca(s) + N_2(g) + 3O_2(g) \rightarrow Ca(NO_3)_2(s)$$

8. How many moles of C_2H_5OH are needed to generate 106.7 g of H_2O?

$$C_2H_5OH(\ell) + 3O_2(g) \rightarrow 2CO_2(g) + 3H_2O(\ell)$$

9. What mass of O_2 can be generated by the decomposition of 100.0 g of $NaClO_3$?

$$2NaClO_3 \rightarrow 2NaCl(s) + 3O_2(g)$$

10. What mass of Li_2O is needed to react with 1,060 g of CO_2?

$$Li_2O(aq) + CO_2(g) \rightarrow Li_2CO_3(aq)$$

11. What mass of Fe_2O_3 must be reacted to generate 324 g of Al_2O_3?

$$Fe_2O_3(s) + 2Al(s) \rightarrow 2Fe(s) + Al_2O_3(s)$$

12. What mass of Fe is generated when 100.0 g of Al are reacted?

$$Fe_2O_3(s) + 2Al(s) \rightarrow 2Fe(s) + Al_2O_3(s)$$

13. What mass of MnO_2 is produced when 445 g of H_2O are reacted?

$$H_2O(\ell) + 2MnO_4^-(aq) + Br^-(aq) \rightarrow BrO_3^-(aq) + 2MnO_2(s) + 2OH^-(aq)$$

14. What mass of $PbSO_4$ is produced when 29.6 g of H_2SO_4 are reacted?

$$Pb(s) + PbO_2(s) + 2H_2SO_4(aq) \rightarrow 2PbSO_4(s) + 2H_2O(\ell)$$

15. If 83.9 g of ZnO are formed, what mass of Mn_2O_3 is formed with it?

$$Zn(s) + 2MnO_2(s) \rightarrow ZnO(s) + Mn_2O_3(s)$$

16. If 14.7 g of NO_2 are reacted, what mass of H_2O is reacted with it?

$$3NO_2(g) + H_2O(\ell) \rightarrow 2HNO_3(aq) + NO(g)$$

17. If 88.4 g of CH_2S are reacted, what mass of HF is produced?

$$CH_2S + 6F_2 \rightarrow CF_4 + 2HF + SF_6$$

18. If 100.0 g of Cl_2 are needed, what mass of NaOCl must be reacted?

$$NaOCl + HCl \rightarrow NaOH + Cl_2$$

Answers

1. 44.0 g
2. 36.0 g
3. 3.00×10^2 g
4. 447 g
5. 0.0336 mol
6. 0.00380 mol
7. 0.0183 mol
8. 1.97 mol
9. 45.1 g
10. 7.20×10^2 g
11. 507 g
12. 207 g
13. 4.30×10^3 g
14. 91.5 g
15. 163 g
16. 1.92 g
17. 76.7 g
18. 105.0 g

9.5 Yields

Learning Objective

1. Define and determine theoretical yields, actual yields, and percent yields.

In all the previous calculations we have performed involving balanced chemical equations, we made two assumptions: (1) the reaction goes exactly as written, and (2) the reaction proceeds completely. In reality, such things as side reactions occur that make some chemical reactions rather messy. For example, in the actual combustion of some carbon-containing compounds, such as methane, some CO is produced as well as CO_2. However, we will continue to ignore side reactions, unless otherwise noted.

theoretical yield

An amount that is theoretically produced as calculated using the balanced chemical reaction.

actual yield

The amount that is actually produced in a chemical reaction.

percent yield

Actual yield divided by theoretical yield times 100% to give a percentage between 0% and 100%.

The second assumption, that the reaction proceeds completely, is more troublesome. Many chemical reactions do not proceed to completion as written, for a variety of reasons (some of which we will consider in Chapter 14). When we calculate an amount of product assuming that all the reactant reacts, we calculate the **theoretical yield**, an amount that is theoretically produced as calculated using the balanced chemical reaction.

In many cases, however, this is not what really happens. In many cases, less—sometimes much less—of a product is made during the course of a chemical reaction. The amount that is actually produced in a reaction is called the **actual yield**. By definition, the actual yield is less than or equal to the theoretical yield. If it is not, then an error has been made.

Both theoretical yields and actual yields are expressed in units of moles or grams. It is also common to see something called a percent yield. The **percent yield** is a comparison between the actual yield and the theoretical yield and is defined as:

$$\text{percent yield} = \frac{\text{actual yield}}{\text{theoretical yield}} \times 100\%$$

It does not matter whether the actual and theoretical yields are expressed in moles or grams, as long as they are expressed in the same units. However, the percent yield always has units of percent. Proper percent yields are between 0% and 100%—again, if percent yield is greater than 100%, an error has been made.

Example 13

A worker reacts 30.5 g of Zn with nitric acid and evaporates the remaining water to obtain 65.2 g of $Zn(NO_3)_2$. What are the theoretical yield, the actual yield, and the percent yield?

$$Zn + 2HNO_3 \rightarrow Zn(NO_3)_2 + H_2$$

Solution

A mass-mass calculation can be performed to determine the theoretical yield. We need the molar masses of Zn (65.39 g/mol) and $Zn(NO_3)_2$ (189.41 g/mol). In three steps, the mass-mass calculation is

$$30.5 \ \text{g Zn} \times \frac{1 \ \text{mol Zn}}{65.39 \ \text{g Zn}} \times \frac{1 \ \text{mol Zn(NO}_3)_2}{1 \ \text{mol Zn}}$$

$$\times \frac{189.41 \ \text{g Zn(NO}_3)_2}{1 \ \text{mol Zn(NO}_3)_2} = 88.3 \ \text{g Zn(NO}_3)_2$$

Thus, the theoretical yield is 88.3 g of $Zn(NO_3)_2$. The actual yield is the amount that was actually made, which was 65.2 g of $Zn(NO_3)_2$. To calculate the percent yield, we take the actual yield and divide it by the theoretical yield and multiply by 100:

$$\frac{65.2 \ \text{g Zn(NO}_3)_2}{88.3 \ \text{Zn(NO}_3)_2} \times 100\% = 73.8\%$$

The worker achieved almost three-fourths of the possible yield.

Test Yourself

A synthesis produced 2.05 g of NH_3 from 16.5 g of N_2. What is the theoretical yield and the percent yield?

$$N_2 + 3H_2 \rightarrow 2NH_3$$

Answer

theoretical yield = 20.1 g; percent yield = 10.2%

Chemistry Is Everywhere: Actual Yields in Drug Synthesis and Purification

Many drugs are the product of several steps of chemical synthesis. Each step typically occurs with less than 100% yield, so the overall percent yield might be very small. The general rule is that the overall percent yield is the product of the percent yields of the individual synthesis steps. For a drug synthesis that has many steps, the overall percent yield can be very tiny, which is one factor in the huge cost of some drugs. For example, if a 10-step synthesis has a percent yield of 90% for each step, the overall yield for the entire synthesis is only 35%. Many scientists work every day trying to improve percent yields of the steps in the synthesis to decrease costs, improve profits, and minimize waste.

Even purifications of complex molecules into drug-quality purity are subject to percent yields. Consider the purification of impure albuterol. Albuterol ($C_{13}H_{21}NC_2$; accompanying figure) is an inhaled drug used to treat asthma, bronchitis, and other obstructive pulmonary diseases. It is synthesized from norepinephrine, a naturally occurring hormone and neurotransmitter. Its initial synthesis makes very impure albuterol that is purified in five chemical steps. The details of the steps do not concern us; only the percent yields do:

impure albuterol → intermediate A	percent yield = 70%
intermediate A → intermediate B	percent yield = 100%
intermediate B → intermediate C	percent yield = 40%
intermediate C → intermediate D	percent yield = 72%
intermediate D → purified albuterol	percent yield = 35%
overall percent yield = 70% × 100% × 40% × 72% × 35% = 7.5%	

That is, only about *one-fourteenth* of the original material was turned into the purified drug. This gives you one reason why some drugs are so expensive; a lot of material is lost in making a high-purity pharmaceutical.

A child using an albuterol inhaler, the container of albuterol medication, and a molecular model of the albuterol molecule.

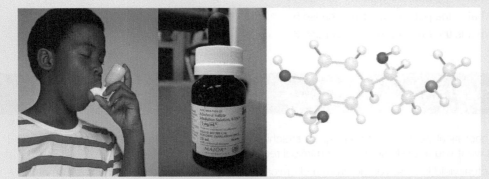

Source: Photo on far left © Thinkstock. Photo in center courtesy of Intropin, http://commons.wikimedia.org/wiki/File:Albuterol_Sulfate_(1).JPG.

Key Takeaways

- Theoretical yield is the amount of product you calculate using the balanced chemical reaction.
- Actual yield is what you actually get in a chemical reaction.
- Percent yield is a comparison of the actual yield with the theoretical yield.

Exercises

1. What is the difference between the theoretical yield and the actual yield?
2. What is the difference between the actual yield and the percent yield?
3. A worker isolates 2.675 g of SiF_4 after reacting 2.339 g of SiO_2 with HF. What are the theoretical yield and the actual yield?

$$SiO_2(s) + 4HF(g) \rightarrow SiF_4(g) + 2H_2O(\ell)$$

4. A worker synthesizes aspirin, $C_9H_8O_4$, according to this chemical equation. If 12.66 g of $C_7H_6O_3$ are reacted and 12.03 g of aspirin are isolated, what are the theoretical yield and the actual yield?

$$C_7H_6O_3 + C_4H_6O_3 \rightarrow C_9H_8O_4 + HC_2H_3O_2$$

5. A chemist decomposes 1.006 g of $NaHCO_3$ and obtains 0.0334 g of Na_2CO_3. What are the theoretical yield and the actual yield?

$$2NaHCO_3(s) \rightarrow Na_2CO_3(s) + H_2O(\ell) + CO_2(g)$$

6. A chemist combusts a 3.009 g sample of C_5H_{12} and obtains 3.774 g of H_2O. What are the theoretical yield and the actual yield?

$$C_5H_{12}(\ell) + 8O_2(g) \rightarrow 5CO_2 + 6H_2O(\ell)$$

7. What is the percent yield in Exercise 3?
8. What is the percent yield in Exercise 4?
9. What is the percent yield in Exercise 5?
10. What is the percent yield in Exercise 6?

Answers

1. Theoretical yield is what you expect stoichiometrically from a chemical reaction; actual yield is what you actually get from a chemical reaction.
2. Actual yield is what you get from a chemical reaction; percent yield is a comparison of theoretical yield and actual yield.
3. theoretical yield = 4.052 g; actual yield = 2.675 g
4. theoretical yield = 16.51 g; actual yield = 12.03 g
5. theoretical yield = 0.635 g; actual yield = 0.0334 g
6. theoretical yield = 4.509 g; actual yield = 3.774 g
7. 66.02%
8. 72.86%

9.6 Limiting Reagents

Learning Objectives

1. Identify a limiting reagent from a set of reactants.
2. Calculate how much product will be produced from the limiting reagent.
3. Calculate how much reactant(s) remains when the reaction is complete.

One additional assumption we have made about chemical reactions—in addition to the assumption that reactions proceed all the way to completion—is that all the reactants are present in the proper quantities to react to products. This is not always the case.

Consider Figure 9.1. Here we are taking hydrogen atoms and oxygen atoms (left) to make water molecules (right). However, there are not enough oxygen atoms to use up all the hydrogen atoms. We run out of oxygen atoms and cannot make any more water molecules, so the process stops when we run out of oxygen atoms.

FIGURE 9.1 Making Water
In this scenario for making water molecules, we run out of O atoms before we use up all the H atoms. Similar situations exist for many chemical reactions when one reactant runs out before the other.

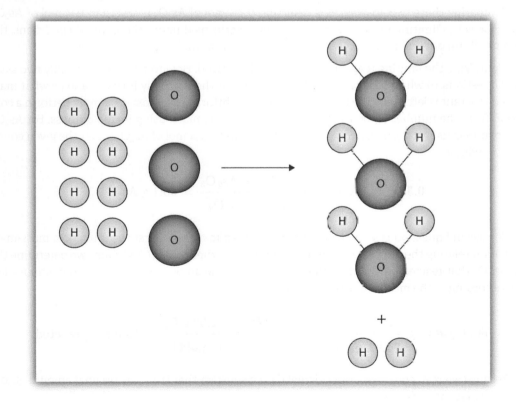

limiting reagent

The reactant that runs out first.

A similar situation exists for many chemical reactions: you usually run out of one reactant before all of the other reactant has reacted. The reactant you run out of is called the **limiting reagent**; the other reactant or reactants are considered to be *in excess*. A crucial skill in evaluating the conditions of a chemical process is to determine which reactant is the limiting reagent and which is in excess.

The key to recognizing which reactant is the limiting reagent is based on a mole-mass or mass-mass calculation: whichever reactant gives the *lesser* amount of product is the limiting reagent. What we need to do is determine an amount of one product (either moles or mass) assuming all of each reactant reacts. Whichever reactant gives the least amount of that particular product is the limiting reagent. It does not matter which product we use, as long as we use the same one each time. It does not matter whether we determine the number of moles or grams of that product; however, we will see shortly that knowing the final mass of product can be useful.

For example, consider this reaction:

$$4As(s) + 3O_2(g) \rightarrow 2As_2O_3(s)$$

Suppose we start a reaction with 50.0 g of As and 50.0 g of O_2. Which one is the limiting reagent? We need to perform two mole-mass calculations, each assuming that each reactant reacts completely. Then we compare the amount of the product produced by each and determine which is less.

The calculations are as follows:

$$50.0 \text{ g As} \times \frac{1 \text{ mol As}}{74.92 \text{ g As}} \times \frac{2 \text{ mol As}_2O_3}{4 \text{ mol As}} = 0.334 \text{ mol As}_2O_3$$

$$50.0 \text{ g O}_2 \times \frac{1 \text{ mol O}_2}{32.00 \text{ g O}_2} \times \frac{2 \text{ mol As}_2O_3}{3 \text{ mol O}_2} = 1.04 \text{ mol As}_2O_3$$

Comparing these two answers, it is clear that 0.334 mol of As_2O_3 is less than 1.04 mol of As_2O_3, so arsenic is the limiting reagent. If this reaction is performed under these initial conditions, the arsenic will run out before the oxygen runs out. We say that the oxygen is "in excess."

Identifying the limiting reagent, then, is straightforward. However, there are usually two associated questions: (1) what mass of product (or products) is then actually formed? and (2) what mass of what reactant is left over? The first question is straightforward to answer: simply perform a conversion from the number of moles of product formed to its mass, using its molar mass. For As_2O_3, the molar mass is 197.84 g/mol; knowing that we will form 0.334 mol of As_2O_3 under the given conditions, we will get

$$0.334 \text{ mol As}_2O_3 \times \frac{197.84 \text{ g As}_2O_3}{1 \text{ mol As}_2O_3} = 66.1 \text{ g As}_2O_3$$

The second question is somewhat more convoluted to answer. First, we must do a mass-mass calculation relating the limiting reagent (here, As) to the other reagent (O_2). Once we determine the mass of O_2 that reacted, we subtract that from the original amount to determine the amount left over. According to the mass-mass calculation,

$$50.0 \text{ g As} \times \frac{1 \text{ mol As}}{74.92 \text{ g As}} \times \frac{3 \text{ mol O}_2}{4 \text{ mol As}} \times \frac{32.00 \text{ g O}_2}{1 \text{ mol O}_2} = 16.0 \text{ g O}_2 \text{ reacted}$$

Because we reacted 16.0 g of our original O_2, we subtract that from the original amount, 50.0 g, to get the mass of O_2 remaining:

$$50.0 \text{ g O}_2 - 16.0 \text{ g O}_2 \text{ reacted} = 34.0 \text{ g O}_2 \text{ left over}$$

You must remember to perform this final subtraction to determine the amount remaining; a common error is to report the 16.0 g as the amount remaining.

Example 14

A 5.00 g quantity of Rb is combined with 3.44 g of $MgCl_2$ according to this chemical reaction:

$$2Rb + MgCl_2 \rightarrow Mg + 2RbCl$$

What mass of Mg is formed, and what mass of what reactant is left over?

Solution

Because the question asks what mass of magnesium is formed, we can perform two mass-mass calculations and determine which amount is less.

$$5.00 \text{ g Rb} \times \frac{1 \text{ mol Rb}}{85.47 \text{ g Rb}} \times \frac{1 \text{ mol Mg}}{2 \text{ mol Rb}} \times \frac{24.31 \text{ g Mg}}{1 \text{ mol Mg}} = 0.711 \text{ g Mg}$$

$$3.44 \text{ g MgCl}_2 \times \frac{1 \text{ mol MgCl}_2}{95.21 \text{ g MgCl}_2} \times \frac{1 \text{ mol Mg}}{1 \text{ mol MgCl}_2} \times \frac{24.31 \text{ g Mg}}{1 \text{ mol Mg}} = 0.878 \text{ g Mg}$$

The 0.711 g of Mg is the lesser quantity, so the associated reactant—5.00 g of Rb—is the limiting reagent. To determine how much of the other reactant is left, we have to do one more mass-mass calculation to determine what mass of $MgCl_2$ reacted with the 5.00 g of Rb and then subtract the amount reacted from the original amount.

$$5.00 \text{ g Rb} \times \frac{1 \text{ mol Rb}}{85.47 \text{ g Rb}} \times \frac{1 \text{ mol MgCl}_2}{2 \text{ mol Rb}}$$

$$\times \frac{95.21 \text{ g Mg}}{1 \text{ mol MgCl}_2} = 2.78 \text{ g MgCl}_2 \text{ reacted}$$

Because we started with 3.44 g of $MgCl_2$, we have:

$$3.44 \text{ g MgCl}_2 - 2.78 \text{ g MgCl}_2 \text{ reacted} = 0.66 \text{ g MgCl}_2 \text{ left}$$

Test Yourself

Given the initial amounts listed, what is the limiting reagent, and what is the mass of the leftover reagent?

$$\underset{22.7 \text{ g}}{MgO(s)} + \underset{17.9 \text{ g}}{H_2S(g)} \rightarrow MgS(s) + H_2O(\ell)$$

Answer

H_2S is the limiting reagent; 1.5 g of MgO are left over.

Key Takeaways

- The limiting reagent is that reactant that produces the least amount of product.
- Mass-mass calculations can determine how much product is produced and how much of the other reactants remain.

Exercises

1. The box below shows a group of nitrogen and hydrogen molecules that will react to produce ammonia, NH_3. What is the limiting reagent?

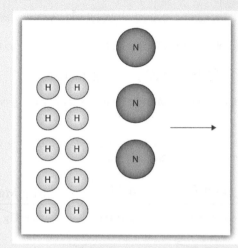

2. The box below shows a group of hydrogen and oxygen molecules that will react to produce water, H_2O. What is the limiting reagent?

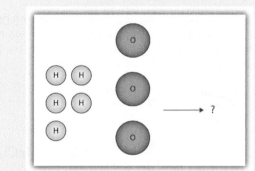

3. Given the statement "20.0 g of methane is burned in excess oxygen," is it obvious which reactant is the limiting reagent?

4. Given the statement "the metal is heated in the presence of excess hydrogen," is it obvious which substance is the limiting reagent despite not specifying any quantity of reactant?

5. Acetylene (C_2H_2) is formed by reacting 7.08 g of C and 4.92 g of H_2.

$$2C(s) + H_2(g) \rightarrow C_2H_2(g)$$

What is the limiting reagent? How much of the other reactant is in excess?

6. Ethane (C_2H_6) is formed by reacting 7.08 g of C and 4.92 g of H_2.

$$2C(s) + 3H_2(g) \rightarrow C_2H_6(g)$$

What is the limiting reagent? How much of the other reactant is in excess?

7. Given the initial amounts listed, what is the limiting reagent, and how much of the other reactant is in excess?

$$\underset{35.6\text{ g}}{P_4O_6(s)} + \underset{4.77\text{ g}}{6H_2O(\ell)} \rightarrow 4H_3PO_4$$

8. Given the initial amounts listed, what is the limiting reagent, and how much of the other reactant is in excess?

$$3NO_2(g) + H_2O(\ell) \rightarrow 2HNO_3(aq) + NO(g)$$
$$\underset{377\ g}{} \quad \underset{244\ g}{}$$

9. To form the precipitate $PbCl_2$, 2.88 g of NaCl and 7.21 g of $Pb(NO_3)_2$ are mixed in solution. How much precipitate is formed? How much of which reactant is in excess?

10. In a neutralization reaction, 18.06 g of KOH are reacted with 13.43 g of HNO_3. What mass of H_2O is produced, and what mass of which reactant is in excess?

Answers

1. Nitrogen is the limiting reagent.
2. Hydrogen is the limiting reagent.
3. Yes; methane is the limiting reagent.
4. The metal is the limiting reagent.
5. C is the limiting reagent; 4.33 g of H_2 are left over.
6. C is the limiting reagent; 3.14 g of H_2 are left over.
7. H_2O is the limiting reagent; 25.9 g of P_4O_6 are left over.
8. NO_2 is the limiting reagent; 195 g of H_2O are left over.
9. 6.06 g of $PbCl_2$ are formed; 0.33 g of NaCl is left over.
10. 3.84 g of H_2O are made; 6.10 g of KOH are left over.

9.7 End-of-Chapter Material

Additional Exercises

1. How many molecules of O_2 will react with 6.022×10^{23} molecules of H_2 to make water? The reaction is $2H_2(g) + O_2(g) \rightarrow 2H_2O(\ell)$.

2. How many molecules of H_2 will react with 6.022×10^{23} molecules of N_2 to make ammonia? The reaction is $N_2(g) + 3H_2(g) \rightarrow 2NH_3(g)$.

3. How many moles are present in 6.411 kg of CO_2? How many molecules is this?

4. How many moles are present in 2.998 mg of SCl_4? How many molecules is this?

5. What is the mass in milligrams of 7.22×10^{20} molecules of CO_2?

6. What is the mass in kilograms of 3.408×10^{25} molecules of SiS_2?

7. What is the mass in grams of 1 molecule of H_2O?

8. What is the mass in grams of 1 atom of Al?

9. What is the volume of 3.44 mol of Ga if the density of Ga is 6.08 g/mL?

10. What is the volume of 0.662 mol of He if the density of He is 0.1785 g/L?

11. For the chemical reaction

$$2C_4H_{10}(g) + 13O_2(g) \rightarrow 8CO_2(g) + 10H_2O(\ell)$$

assume that 13.4 g of C_4H_{10} reacts completely to products. The density of CO_2 is 1.96 g/L. What volume in liters of CO_2 is produced?

12. For the chemical reaction

$$2GaCl_3(s) + 3H_2(g) \rightarrow 2Ga(\ell) + 6HCl(g)$$

if 223 g of GaCl₃ reacts completely to products and the density of Ga is 6.08 g/mL, what volume in milliliters of Ga is produced?

13. Calculate the mass of each product when 100.0 g of CuCl react according to the reaction:

$$2CuCl(aq) \rightarrow CuCl_2(aq) + Cu(s)$$

What do you notice about the sum of the masses of the products? What concept is being illustrated here?

14. Calculate the mass of each product when 500.0 g of SnCl₂ react according to the reaction:

$$2SnCl_2(aq) \rightarrow SnCl_4(aq) + Sn(s)$$

What do you notice about the sum of the masses of the products? What concept is being illustrated here?

15. What mass of CO_2 is produced from the combustion of 1 gal of gasoline? The chemical formula of gasoline can be approximated as C_8H_{18}. Assume that there are 2,801 g of gasoline per gallon.

16. What mass of H_2O is produced from the combustion of 1 gal of gasoline? The chemical formula of gasoline can be approximated as C_8H_{18}. Assume that there are 2,801 g of gasoline per gallon.

17. A chemical reaction has a theoretical yield of 19.98 g and a percent yield of 88.40%. What is the actual yield?

18. A chemical reaction has an actual yield of 19.98 g and a percent yield of 88.40%. What is the theoretical yield?

19. Given the initial amounts listed, what is the limiting reagent, and how much of the other reactants are in excess?

$$\underset{35.0 \text{ g}}{P_4} + \underset{12.7 \text{ g}}{3NaOH} + \underset{9.33 \text{ g}}{3H_2O} \rightarrow 2Na_2HPO_4 + PH_3$$

20. Given the initial amounts listed, what is the limiting reagent, and how much of the other reactants are in excess?

$$\underset{46.3 \text{ g}}{2NaCrO_2} + \underset{88.2 \text{ g}}{3NaBrO_4} + \underset{32.5 \text{ g}}{2NaOH} \rightarrow 3NaBrO_3 + 2Na_2CrO_4 + H_2O$$

21. Verify that it does not matter which product you use to predict the limiting reagent by using both products in this combustion reaction to determine the limiting reagent and the amount of the reactant in excess. Initial amounts of each reactant are given.

$$\underset{26.3 \text{ g}}{C_3H_8} + \underset{21.8 \text{ g}}{5O_2} \rightarrow 3CO_2(g) + 4H_2O(\ell)$$

22. Just in case you suspect Exercise 21 is rigged, do it for another chemical reaction and verify that it does not matter which product you use to predict the limiting reagent by using both products in this combustion reaction to determine the limiting reagent and the amount of the reactant in excess. Initial amounts of each reactant are given.

$$\underset{35.0 \text{ g}}{2P_4} + \underset{12.7 \text{ g}}{6NaOH} + \underset{9.33 \text{ g}}{6H_2O} \rightarrow 3Na_2HPO_4 + 5PH_3$$

Answers

1. 1.2044×10^{24} molecules

2. 1.8066×10^{24} molecules

3. 145.7 mol; 8.77×10^{25} molecules

4. 1.724×10^{-5} mol; 1.038×10^{19} molecules

5. 52.8 mg

6. 5.219 kg

7. 2.99×10^{-23} g

8. 4.480×10^{-23} g

9. 39.4 mL

10. 14.8 L

11. 20.7 L

12. 14.5 mL

13. 67.91 g of $CuCl_2$; 32.09 g of Cu. The two masses add to 100.0 g, the initial amount of starting material, demonstrating the law of conservation of matter.

14. 343.5 g of $SnCl_4$; 156.5 g of Sn. The two masses add to 500.0 g, the initial amount of starting material, demonstrating the law of conservation of matter.

15. 8,632 g

16. 3,967 g

17. 17.66 g

18. 22.60 g

19. The limiting reagent is NaOH; 21.9 g of P_4 and 3.61 g of H_2O are left over.

20. The limiting reagent is $NaBrO_4$; 8.61 g of $NaClO_2$ and 18.4 g of NaOH are left over.

21. Both products predict that O_2 is the limiting reagent; 20.3 g of C_3H_8 are left over.

22. In both cases, NaOH is the limiting reagent; 21.9 g of P_4 and 3.61 g of H_2O are left over.

CHAPTER 10
Oxidation and Reduction

Opening Essay

Most of us are familiar with rusty iron: metal that has a dark red-brown scale that falls off an object, ultimately weakening it. Although we usually attribute rusting exclusively to iron, this process occurs with many materials. The more formal term for rusting is *corrosion*.

These support beams on a bridge are obviously rusted. If the rusting becomes too bad, it will compromise the integrity of the bridge, requiring replacement.

Source: © Thinkstock

Corrosion is defined as the disintegration of a material due to chemical reactions with other substances in the environment. In many cases, oxygen in the air causes the disintegration. Corrosion is not uniformly destructive. Although the corrosion of iron is generally considered bad, the corrosion of aluminum and copper forms a protective barrier on the surface of the metal, protecting it from further reaction with the environment.

Having said that, it has been estimated that as much as 5% of expenditures in the United States apply to fixing problems caused by corrosion. The replacement of structures built with iron, steel, aluminum, and concrete must be performed regularly to keep these structures safe. As an example of what might happen, consider the story of the Silver Bridge on US Interstate 35, connecting West Virginia and Ohio. On December 15, 1967, the 39-year-old bridge collapsed, killing 46 people. The ultimate cause of the collapse was determined to be corrosion of a suspension chain on the Ohio side of the bridge.

Corrosion is an example of the type of chemical reaction discussed in this chapter. Although we usually think of corrosion as bad, the reaction it typifies can actually be put to good use.

One important type of chemical reaction is the oxidation-reduction reaction, also known as the redox reaction.

10.1 Oxidation-Reduction Reactions

Learning Objectives

1. Define *oxidation* and *reduction*.
2. Assign oxidation numbers to atoms in simple compounds.
3. Recognize a reaction as an oxidation-reduction reaction.

Consider this chemical reaction:

$$Mg(s) + Cl_2(g) \rightarrow MgCl_2(s)$$

The reactants are two electrically neutral elements; they have the same number of electrons as protons. The product, however, is ionic; it is composed of Mg^{2+} and Cl^- ions. Somehow, the individual Mg atoms lose two electrons to make the Mg^{2+} ion, while the Cl atoms gain an electron to become Cl^- ions. This reaction involves the *transfer of electrons* between atoms.

oxidation

The loss of one or more electrons by an atom; an increase in oxidation number.

reduction

The gain of one or more electrons by an atom; a decrease in oxidation number.

oxidation-reduction (redox) reaction

A chemical reaction that involves the transfer of electrons.

oxidation number

A number assigned to an atom that helps keep track of the number of electrons on the atom.

The process of losing and gaining electrons occurs simultaneously. However, mentally we can separate the two processes. **Oxidation** is defined as the loss of one or more electrons by an atom. **Reduction** is defined as the gain of one or more electrons by an atom. So oxidation and reduction always occur together; it is only mentally that we can separate them. Chemical reactions that involve the transfer of electrons are called **oxidation-reduction (or redox) reactions**.

Redox reactions require that we keep track of the electrons assigned to each atom in a chemical reaction. How do we do that? We use **oxidation numbers** to keep track of electrons in atoms. Oxidation numbers are assigned to atoms based on four rules. Oxidation numbers are not necessarily equal to the charge on the atom (although sometimes they can be); we must keep the concepts of charge and oxidation numbers separate.

The rules for assigning oxidation numbers to atoms are as follows:

1. Atoms in their elemental state are assigned an oxidation number of 0.
2. Atoms in monatomic (i.e., one-atom) ions are assigned an oxidation number equal to their charge. Oxidation numbers are usually written with the sign first, then the magnitude, to differentiate them from charges.
3. In compounds, fluorine is assigned a –1 oxidation number; oxygen is usually assigned a –2 oxidation number [except in peroxide compounds (where it is –1) and in binary compounds with fluorine (where it is positive)]; and hydrogen is usually assigned a +1 oxidation number [except when it exists as the hydride ion (H^-), in which case rule 2 prevails].
4. In compounds, all other atoms are assigned an oxidation number so that the sum of the oxidation numbers on all the atoms in the species equals the charge on the species (which is zero if the species is neutral).

Here are some examples for practice. In H_2, both H atoms have an oxidation number of 0 by rule 1. In $MgCl_2$, magnesium has an oxidation number of +2, while chlorine has an oxidation number of –1 by rule 2. In H_2O, the H atoms each have an oxidation number of +1, while the O atom has an oxidation number of –2, even though hydrogen and oxygen do not exist as ions in this compound (rule 3). In contrast, by rule 3, each H atom in hydrogen peroxide (H_2O_2) has an oxidation number of +1, while each O atom has an oxidation number of –1. We can use rule 4 to determine oxidation numbers for the atoms in SO_2. Each O atom has an oxidation number of –2; for the sum of the oxidation numbers to equal the charge on the species (which is zero, because it's a neutral molecule), the S atom is assigned an oxidation number of +4. Does this mean that the sulfur atom has a 4+ charge on it? No, it means only that the S atom is assigned a +4 oxidation number by our rules of apportioning electrons among the atoms in a compound.

Example 1

Assign oxidation numbers to the atoms in each substance.

1. Cl_2
2. GeO_2
3. $Ca(NO_3)_2$

Solution

1. Cl_2 is the elemental form of chlorine. Rule 1 states each atom has an oxidation number of 0.

2. By rule 3, oxygen is normally assigned an oxidation number of –2. For the sum of the oxidation numbers to equal the charge on the species (zero) the Ge atom is assigned an oxidation number of +4.

3. $Ca(NO_3)_2$ can be separated into two parts: the Ca^{2+} ion and the NO_3^- ion. Considering these separately, the Ca^{2+} ion has an oxidation number of +2 by rule 2. Now consider the NO_3^- ion. Oxygen is assigned an oxidation number of –2, and there are three of them. According to rule 4, the sum of the oxidation numbers on all atoms must equal the charge on the species, so we have the simple algebraic equation

$$x + 3(-2) = -1$$

where x is the oxidation number of the N atom and the –1 represents the charge on the species. Evaluating for x,

$$x + (-6) = -1$$

$$x = +5$$

Thus the oxidation number on the N atom in the NO_3^- ion is +5.

Test Yourself

Assign oxidation numbers to the atoms in H_3PO_4.

Answer

H: +1; O: –2; P: +5

All redox reactions occur with a simultaneous change in the oxidation numbers of some atoms. At least two elements must change their oxidation numbers. When an oxidation number of an atom is increased in the course of a redox reaction, that atom is being *oxidized*. When an oxidation number of an atom is decreased in the course of a redox reaction, that atom is being *reduced*. Thus oxidation and reduction can also be defined in terms of increasing or decreasing oxidation numbers, respectively.

Example 2

Identify what is being oxidized and reduced in this redox reaction

$$2Na + Br_2(g) \rightarrow 2NaBr$$

Solution

Both reactants are the elemental forms of their atoms, so the Na and Br atoms have oxidation numbers of 0. In the ionic product, the Na^+ ions have an oxidation number of +1, while the Br^- ions have an oxidation number of –1.

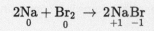

$$2\text{Na} + \text{Br}_2 \rightarrow 2\text{NaBr}$$
$$\phantom{2\text{Na}}\!\!\!0 \phantom{+ \text{Br}}\!\!\!0 \phantom{\rightarrow 2\text{Na}}\!\!\!+1 \;\; -1$$

Sodium is increasing its oxidation number from 0 to +1, so it is being oxidized; bromine is decreasing its oxidation number from 0 to –1, so it is being reduced:

Because oxidation numbers are changing, this is a redox reaction. The total number of electrons being lost by sodium (two, one lost from each Na atom) is gained by bromine (two, one gained for each Br atom).

Test Yourself

Identify what is being oxidized and reduced in this redox reaction.

$$\text{C} + \text{O}_2 \rightarrow \text{CO}_2$$

Answer

C is being oxidized from 0 to +4; O is being reduced from 0 to –2.

Oxidation reactions can become quite complex, as attested by the following redox reaction:

$$6\text{H}^+(\text{aq}) + 2\underset{+7}{\text{MnO}_4^-}(\text{aq}) + 5\underset{-1}{\text{H}_2\text{O}_2}(\ell) \rightarrow 2\underset{+2}{\text{Mn}^{2+}}(\text{aq}) + 5\underset{0}{\text{O}_2}(\text{g}) + 8\text{H}_2\text{O}(\ell)$$

To demonstrate that this is a redox reaction, the oxidation numbers of the species being oxidized and reduced are listed; can you determine what is being oxidized and what is being reduced? This is also an example of a net ionic reaction; spectator ions that do not change oxidation numbers are not displayed in the equation. Eventually, we will need to learn techniques for writing correct (i.e., balanced) redox reactions.

Food and Drink App: Fortifying Food with Iron

Iron is an essential mineral in our diet; iron-containing compounds like the heme protein in hemoglobin could not function without it. Most biological iron has the form of the Fe^{2+} ion; iron with other oxidation numbers is almost inconsequential in human biology (although the body does contain an enzyme to reduce Fe^{3+} to Fe^{2+}, so Fe^{3+} must have some biological significance, albeit minor). To ensure that we ingest enough iron, many foods are enriched with iron. Although Fe^{2+} compounds are the most logical substances to use, some foods—bread and breakfast cereals are the most well-known examples—use "reduced iron" as an ingredient. Reduced iron is simply iron metal; iron is added as a fine metallic powder. The metallic iron is oxidized to Fe^{2+} in the digestive system and then absorbed by the body, but the question remains: Why are we ingesting metallic iron? Why not just use Fe^{2+} salts as an additive?

Many prepared foods list reduced iron in their ingredients list.

Ingredients

Flour (Contains: Wheat Flour, Malted Barley Flour, Niacin,

Reduced Iron, Thiamine Mononitrate, Riboflavin, Folic Acid)

Water, Sourdough (6.4%) (Contains: Water, Flour [Wheat Flour,

Malted Barley Flour, Niacin, Reduced Iron, Thiamine

Mononitrate, Riboflavin, Folic Acid], Yeast). Salt, Wheat Germ,

Semolina (Contains: Durum Wheat Semolina, Niacin, Ferrous,

Sulphate, Thiamine Mononitrate, Riboflavin, Folic Acid).

Although it is difficult to establish conclusive reasons, a search of scientific and medical literature suggests a few reasons. One reason is that fine iron filings do not affect the taste of the product. The size of the iron powder (several dozen micrometers) is not noticeable when chewing iron-supplemented foods, and the tongue does not detect any changes in flavor that can be detected when using Fe^{2+} salts. Fe^{2+} compounds can affect other properties of foodstuffs during preparation and cooking, like dough pliability, yeast growth, and color. Finally, of the common iron substances that might be used, metallic iron is the least expensive. These factors appear to be among the reasons why metallic iron is the supplement of choice in some foods.

Key Takeaways

- Oxidation-reduction (redox) reactions involve the transfer of electrons from one atom to another.
- Oxidation numbers are used to keep track of electrons in atoms.
- There are rules for assigning oxidation numbers to atoms.
- Oxidation is an increase in oxidation number (loss of electrons); reduction is a decrease in oxidation number (gain of electrons).

Exercises

1. Is this reaction a redox reaction? Explain your answer.

$$2K(s) + Br_2(\ell) \rightarrow 2KBr(s)$$

2. Is this reaction a redox reaction? Explain your answer.

$$2NaCl(aq) + Pb(NO_3)_2(aq) \rightarrow 2NaNO_3(aq) + PbCl_2(s)$$

3. Which substance loses electrons and which substance gains electrons in this reaction?

$$2Mg(s) + O_2(g) \rightarrow 2MgO$$

4. Which substance loses electrons and which substance gains electrons in this reaction?

$$16Fe(s) + 3S_8(s) \rightarrow 8Fe_2S_3(s)$$

5. Which substance is oxidized and which substance is reduced in this reaction?

$$2\text{Li}(s) + \text{O}_2(g) \rightarrow \text{Li}_2\text{O}_2(s)$$

6. Which substance is oxidized and which substance is reduced in this reaction?

$$2\text{Fe}(s) + 3\text{I}_2(s) \rightarrow 2\text{FeI}_3(s)$$

7. What are two different definitions of oxidation?

8. What are two different definitions of reduction?

9. Assign oxidation numbers to the atoms in each substance.

   a. P_4

   b. SO_3

   c. SO_3^{2-}

   d. $Ca_3(PO_3)_2$

10. Assign oxidation numbers to the atoms in each substance.

    a. PCl_5

    b. $(NH_4)_2Se$

    c. Ag

    d. Li_2O_2

11. Assign oxidation numbers to the atoms in each substance.

    a. NO

    b. NO_2

    c. $CrCl_2$

    d. $CrCl_3$

12. Assign oxidation numbers to the atoms in each substance.

    a. NaH

    b. N_2O_3

    c. NO_2^-

    d. $CuNO_3$

13. Assign oxidation numbers to the atoms in each substance.

    a. CH_2O

    b. NH_3

    c. Rb_2SO_4

    d. $Zn(C_2H_3O_2)_2$

14. Assign oxidation numbers to the atoms in each substance.

    a. C_6H_6

    b. $B(OH)_3$

    c. Li_2S

    d. Au

15. Identify what is being oxidized and reduced in this redox reaction by assigning oxidation numbers to the atoms.

$$2\text{NO} + \text{Cl}_2 \rightarrow 2\text{NOCl}$$

16. Identify what is being oxidized and reduced in this redox reaction by assigning oxidation numbers to the atoms.

$$\text{Sr} + \text{SO}_3 \rightarrow \text{SrSO}_3$$

17. Identify what is being oxidized and reduced in this redox reaction by assigning oxidation numbers to the atoms.

$$2KrF_2 + 2H_2O \rightarrow 2Kr + 4HF + O_2$$

18. Identify what is being oxidized and reduced in this redox reaction by assigning oxidation numbers to the atoms.

$$SO_3 + SCl_2 \rightarrow SOCl_2 + SO_2$$

19. Identify what is being oxidized and reduced in this redox reaction by assigning oxidation numbers to the atoms.

$$2Rb + MgCl_2 \rightarrow 2RbCl + Mg$$

20. Identify what is being oxidized and reduced in this redox reaction by assigning oxidation numbers to the atoms.

$$2C_8H_{18} + 25O_2 \rightarrow 16CO_2 + 18H_2O$$

Answers

1. Yes, because oxidation numbers are changing.
2. No, because oxidation numbers are not changing.
3. lose: Mg; gain: O
4. lose: Fe; gain: S
5. oxidized: Li; reduced: O
6. oxidized: Fe; reduced: I
7. increase in oxidation number; loss of electrons
8. decrease in oxidation number, gain of electrons
9. a. P: 0
   b. S: +6; O: –2
   c. S: +4; O: –2
   d. Ca: +2; P: +3; O: –2
10. a. P: +5; Cl: –1
    b. N: –3; H: +1; Se: –2
    c. Ag: 0
    d. Li: +1; O: –1
11. a. N: +2; O: –2
    b. N: +4; O: –2
    c. Cr: +2; Cl: –1
    d. Cr: +3; Cl: –1
12. a. Na: +1; H: –1
    b. N: +3; O: –2
    c. N: +3; O: –2
    d. Cu: +1; N: +5; O: –2
13. a. C: 0; H: +1; O: –2
    b. N: –3; H: +1
    c. Rb: +1; S: +6; O: –2
    d. Zn: +2; C: 0; H: +1; O: –2
14. a. C: –1; H: +1
    b. B: +3; O: –2; H: +1

c. Li: +1; S: –2
d. Au: 0

15. oxidized: N; reduced: Cl
16. oxidized: Sr; reduced: S
17. oxidized: O; reduced: Kr
18. oxidized: S in SCl$_2$; reduced: S in SO$_3$
19. oxidized: Rb; reduced: Mg
20. oxidized: C; reduced: O

10.2 Balancing Redox Reactions

Learning Objectives

1. Learn to balance simple redox reactions by inspection.
2. Learn to balance complex redox reactions by the half reaction method.
3. Use the solvent, or parts of it, as a reactant or a product in balancing a redox reaction.

Balancing simple redox reactions can be a straightforward matter of going back and forth between products and reactants. For example, in the redox reaction of Na and Cl$_2$

$$Na + Cl_2 \rightarrow NaCl$$

it should be immediately clear that the Cl atoms are not balanced. We can fix this by putting the coefficient 2 in front of the product:

$$Na + Cl_2 \rightarrow 2NaCl$$

However, now the sodium is unbalanced. This can be fixed by including the coefficient 2 in front of the Na reactant:

$$2Na + Cl_2 \rightarrow 2NaCl$$

This reaction is now balanced. That was fairly straightforward; we say that we are able to balance the reaction *by inspection*. Many simple redox reactions can be balanced by inspection.

Example 3

Balance this redox reaction by inspection.

$$SO_2 + O_2 \rightarrow SO_3$$

Solution

There is one S atom on both sides of the equation, so the sulfur is balanced. However, the reactant side has four O atoms while the product side has three. Clearly we need more O atoms on the product side, so let us start by including the coefficient 2 on the SO$_3$:

$$SO_2 + O_2 \rightarrow 2SO_3$$

This now gives us six O atoms on the product side, and it also imbalances the S atoms. We can balance both the elements by adding coefficient 2 on the SO_2 on the reactant side:

$$2SO_2 + O_2 \rightarrow 2SO_3$$

This gives us two S atoms on both sides and a total of six O atoms on both sides of the chemical equation. This redox reaction is now balanced.

Test Yourself

Balance this redox reaction by inspection.

$$Al + O_2 \rightarrow Al_2O_3$$

Answer

$4Al + 3O_2 \rightarrow 2Al_2O_3$

The first thing you should do when encountering an unbalanced redox reaction is to try to balance it by inspection.

Some redox reactions are not easily balanced by inspection. Consider this redox reaction:

$$Al + Ag^+ \rightarrow Al^{3+} + Ag$$

At first glance, this equation seems balanced: there is one Ag atom on both sides and one Al atom on both sides. However, if you look at the total charge on each side, there is a charge imbalance: the reactant side has a total charge of 1+, while the product side has a total charge of 3+. Something is amiss with this chemical equation; despite the equal number of atoms on each side, it is not balanced.

A fundamental point about redox reactions that has not arisen previously is that *the total number of electrons being lost must equal the total number of electrons being gained* for a redox reaction to be balanced. This is not the case for the aluminum and silver reaction: the Al atom loses three electrons to become the Al^{3+} ion, while the Ag^+ ion gains only one electron to become elemental silver.

To balance this, we will write each oxidation and reduction reaction separately, listing the number of electrons explicitly in each. Individually, the oxidation and reduction reactions are called **half reactions**. We will then take multiples of each reaction until the number of electrons on each side cancels completely and combine the half reactions into an overall reaction, which should then be balanced. This method of balancing redox reactions is called the **half reaction method**. (There are other ways of balancing redox reactions, but this is the only one that will be used in this text. The reason for this will be seen in Section 3.)

The oxidation half reaction involves aluminum, which is being oxidized:

$$Al \rightarrow Al^{3+}$$

This half reaction is not completely balanced because the overall charges on each side are not equal. When an Al atom is oxidized to Al^{3+}, it loses three electrons. We can write these electrons explicitly as products:

$$Al \rightarrow Al^{3+} + 3e^-$$

Now this half reaction is balanced—in terms of both atoms and charges.

The reduction half reaction involves silver:

$$Ag^+ \rightarrow Ag$$

The overall charge is not balanced on both sides. But we can fix this by adding one electron to the reactant side because the Ag^+ ion must accept one electron to become the neutral Ag atom:

half reaction

The individual oxidation or reduction reaction of a redox reaction.

half reaction method

The method of balancing redox reactions by writing and balancing the individual half reactions.

$$Ag^+ + e^- \rightarrow Ag$$

This half reaction is now also balanced.

When combining the two half reactions into a balanced chemical equation, the key is that *the total number of electrons must cancel*, so the number of electrons lost by atoms are equal to the number of electrons gained by other atoms. This may require we multiply one or both half reaction(s) by an integer to make the number of electrons on each side equal. With three electrons as products and one as reactant, the least common multiple of these two numbers is three: we can use a single aluminum reaction but must take three times the silver reaction:

$$Al \rightarrow Al^{3+} + 3e^-$$

$$3 \times [Ag^+ + e^- \rightarrow Ag]$$

The 3 on the second reaction is distributed to all species in the reaction:

$$Al \rightarrow Al^{3+} + 3e^-$$

$$3Ag^+ + 3e^- \rightarrow 3Ag$$

Now the two half reactions can be combined just like two algebraic equations, with the arrow serving as the equals sign. The same species on opposite sides of the arrow can be canceled:

$$Al + 3Ag^+ + \cancel{3e^-} \rightarrow Al^{3+} + 3Ag + \cancel{3e^-}$$

The net balanced redox reaction is as follows:

$$Al + 3Ag^+ \rightarrow Al^{3+} + 3Ag$$

There is still only one Al atom on each side of the chemical equation, but there are now three Ag atoms, and the total charge on each side of the equation is the same (3+ for both sides). This redox reaction is balanced. It took more effort to use the half reaction method than by inspection, but the correct balanced redox reaction was obtained.

Example 4

Balance this redox reaction by using the half reaction method.

$$Fe^{2+} + Cr \rightarrow Fe + Cr^{3+}$$

Solution

We start by writing the two half reactions. Chromium is being oxidized, and iron is being reduced:

$$Cr \rightarrow Cr^{3+} \qquad \text{oxidation}$$

$$Fe^{2+} \rightarrow Fe \qquad \text{reduction}$$

Then we include the appropriate number of electrons on the proper side to balance the charges for each reaction:

$$Cr \rightarrow Cr^{3+} + 3e^-$$

$$Fe^{2+} + 2e^- \rightarrow Fe$$

The first reaction involves three electrons, while the second reaction involves two electrons. The least common multiple of these two numbers is six, so to get six electrons in each reaction we need to double the first reaction and triple the second one:

$$2 \times \left[Cr \rightarrow Cr^{3+} + 3e^- \right] = 2Cr \rightarrow 2Cr^{3-} + 6e^-$$

$$3 \times \left[Fe^{2+} + 2e^- \rightarrow Fe \right] = 3Fe^{2+} + 6e^- \rightarrow 3Fe$$

We can combine the two final reactions, noting that the electrons cancel:

$$2Cr + 3Fe^{2+} + \cancel{6e^-} \rightarrow 2Cr^{3+} + 3Fe + \cancel{6e^-}$$

The overall, balanced redox reaction is:

$$2Cr + 3Fe^{2+} \rightarrow 2Cr^{3+} + 3Fe$$

Test Yourself

Balance this redox reaction by using the half reaction method.

$$O^{2-} + F_2 \rightarrow O_2 + F^-$$

Answer

$2O^{2-} + 2F_2 \rightarrow O_2 + 4F^-$

Many redox reactions occur in aqueous solution—in water. Because of this, in many cases H_2O or a fragment of an H_2O molecule (H^+ or OH^-, in particular) can participate in the redox reaction. As such, we need to learn how to incorporate the solvent into a balanced redox equation.

Consider the following oxidation half reaction in aqueous solution, which has one Cr atom on each side:

$$Cr^{3+} \rightarrow CrO_4^-$$

Here, the Cr atom is going from the +3 to the +7 oxidation state. To do this, the Cr atom must lose four electrons. Let us start by listing the four electrons as products:

$$Cr^{3+} \rightarrow CrO_4^- + 4e^-$$

But where do the O atoms come from? They come from water molecules or a common fragment of a water molecule that contains an O atom: the OH^- ion. When we balance this half reaction, we should feel free to include either of these species in the reaction to balance the elements. Let us use H_2O to balance the O atoms; we need to include four water molecules to balance the four O atoms in the products:

$$4H_2O + Cr^{3+} \rightarrow CrO_4^- + 4e^-$$

This balances the O atoms, but now introduces hydrogen to the reaction. We can balance the H atoms by adding an H^+ ion, which is another fragment of the water molecule. We need to add eight H^+ ions to the product side:

$$4H_2O + Cr^{3+} \rightarrow CrO_4^- + 4e^- + 8H^+$$

The Cr atoms are balanced, the O atoms are balanced, and the H atoms are balanced; if we check the total charge on both sides of the chemical equation, they are the same (3+, in this case). This half reaction is now balanced, using water molecules and parts of water molecules as reactants and products.

Reduction reactions can be balanced in a similar fashion. When oxidation and reduction half reactions are individually balanced, they can be combined in the same fashion as before: by taking multiples of each half reaction as necessary to cancel all electrons. Other species, such as H^+, OH^-, and H_2O, may also have to be canceled in the final balanced reaction.

Unless otherwise noted, it does not matter if you add H_2O or OH^- as a source of O atoms, although a reaction may specify *acidic solution* or *basic solution* as a hint of what species to use or what species to avoid. For instance, OH^- ions are not very common in acidic solutions, so they should be avoided in those circumstances.

Example 5

Balance this redox reaction. Assume a basic solution.

$$MnO_2 + CrO_3^- \rightarrow Mn + CrO_4^-$$

Solution

We start by separating the oxidation and reduction processes so we can balance each half reaction separately. The oxidation reaction is as follows:

$$CrO_3^- \rightarrow CrO_4^-$$

The Cr atom is going from a +5 to a +7 oxidation state and loses two electrons in the process. We add those two electrons to the product side:

$$CrO_3^- \rightarrow CrO_4^- + 2e^-$$

Now we must balance the O atoms. Because the solution is basic, we should use OH^- rather than H_2O:

$$OH^- + CrO_3^- \rightarrow CrO_4^- + 2e^-$$

We have introduced H atoms as part of the reactants; we can balance them by adding H^+ as products:

$$OH^- + CrO_3^- \rightarrow CrO_4^- + 2e^- + H^+$$

If we check the atoms and the overall charge on both sides, we see that this reaction is balanced. However, if the reaction is occurring in a basic solution, it is unlikely that H^+ ions will be present in quantity. The way to address this is to add an additional OH^- ion to each side of the equation:

$$OH^- + OH^- + CrO_3^- \rightarrow CrO_4^- + 2e^- + H^+ + OH^-$$

The two OH^- ions on the left side can be grouped together as $2OH^-$. On the right side, the H^+ and OH^- ions can be grouped into an H_2O molecule:

$$2OH^- + CrO_3^- \rightarrow CrO_4^- + 2e^- + H_2O$$

This is a more appropriate form for a basic solution.

Now we balance the reduction reaction:

$$MnO_2 \rightarrow Mn$$

The Mn atom is going from +4 to 0 in oxidation number, which requires a gain of four electrons:

$$4e^- + MnO_2 \rightarrow Mn$$

Then we balance the O atoms and then the H atoms:

$$4e^- + MnO_2 \rightarrow Mn + 2OH^-$$

$$2H^+ + 4e^- + MnO_2 \rightarrow Mn + 2OH^-$$

We add two OH⁻ ions to each side to eliminate the H⁺ ion in the reactants; the reactant species combine to make two water molecules, and the number of OH⁻ ions in the product increases to four:

$$2H_2O + 4e^- + MnO_2 \rightarrow Mn + 4OH^-$$

This reaction is balanced for a basic solution.

Now we combine the two balanced half reactions. The oxidation reaction has two electrons, while the reduction reaction has four. The least common multiple of these two numbers is four, so we multiply the oxidation reaction by 2 so that the electrons are balanced:

$$2 \times \left[2OH^- + CrO_3^- \rightarrow CrO_4^- + 2e^- + H_2O\right]$$

$$2H_2O + 4e^- + MnO_2 \rightarrow Mn + 4OH^-$$

Combining these two equations results in the following equation:

$$4OH^- + 2CrO_3^- + 2H_2O + 4e^- + MnO_2 \rightarrow 2CrO_4^- + 4e^- + 2H_2O + Mn + 4OH^-$$

The four electrons cancel. So do the two H₂O molecules and the four OH⁻ ions. What remains is

$$2CrO_3^- + MnO_2 \rightarrow 2CrO_4^- + Mn$$

which is our final balanced redox reaction.

Test Yourself

Balance this redox reaction. Assume a basic solution.

$$Cl^- + MnO_4^- \rightarrow MnO_2 + ClO_3^-$$

Answer

$H_2O + Cl^- + 2MnO_4^- \rightarrow 2MnO_2 + ClO_3^- + 2OH^-$

Key Takeaways

- Redox reactions can be balanced by inspection or by the half reaction method.
- A solvent may participate in redox reactions; in aqueous solutions, H₂O, H⁺, and OH⁻ may be reactants or products.

Exercises

1. Balance these redox reactions by inspection.

   a. $Na + F_2 \rightarrow NaF$

   b. $Al_2O_3 + H_2 \rightarrow Al + H_2O$

2. Balance these redox reactions by inspection.

   a. $Fe_2S_3 + O_2 \rightarrow Fe_2O_3 + S$

   b. $Cu_2O + H_2 \rightarrow Cu + H_2O$

3. Balance these redox reactions by inspection.

   a. $CH_4 + O_2 \rightarrow CO_2 + H_2O$

   b. $P_2O_5 + Cl_2 \rightarrow PCl_3 + O_2$

4. Balance these redox reactions by inspection.

   a. $PbCl_2 + FeCl_3 \rightarrow PbCl_4 + FeCl_2$

   b. $SO_2 + F_2 \rightarrow SF_4 + OF_2$

5. Balance these redox reactions by the half reaction method.

   a. $Ca + H^+ \rightarrow Ca^{2+} + H_2$

   b. $Sn^{2+} \rightarrow Sn + Sn^{4+}$ (Hint: both half reactions will start with the same reactant.)

6. Balance these redox reactions by the half reaction method.

   a. $Fe^{3+} + Sn^{2+} \rightarrow Fe + Sn^{4+}$

   b. $Pb^{2+} \rightarrow Pb + Pb^{4+}$ (Hint: both half reactions will start with the same reactant.)

7. Balance these redox reactions by the half reaction method.

   a. $Na + Hg_2Cl_2 \rightarrow NaCl + Hg$

   b. $Al_2O_3 + C \rightarrow Al + CO_2$

8. Balance these redox reactions by the half reaction method.

   a. $Br^- + I_2 \rightarrow I^- + Br_2$

   b. $CrCl_3 + F_2 \rightarrow CrF_3 + Cl_2$

9. Balance these redox reactions that occur in aqueous solution. Use whatever water-derived species is necessary; there may be more than one correct balanced equation.

   a. $Cu + NO_3^- \rightarrow Cu^{2+} + NO_2$

   b. $Fe + MnO_4^- \rightarrow Fe^{3+} + Mn$

10. Balance these redox reactions that occur in aqueous solution. Use whatever water-derived species is necessary; there may be more than one correct balanced equation.

   a. $CrO_3 + Ni^{2+} \rightarrow Cr^{3+} + Ni^{3+}$

   b. $OsO_4 + C_2H_4 \rightarrow Os + CO_2$

11. Balance these redox reactions that occur in aqueous solution. Use whatever water-derived species is necessary; there may be more than one correct balanced equation.

   a. $ClO^- + Ti^{2+} \rightarrow Ti^{4+} + Cl^-$

   b. $BrO_3^- + Ag \rightarrow Ag^+ + BrO_2$

12. Balance these redox reactions that occur in aqueous solution. Use whatever water-derived species is necessary; there may be more than one correct balanced equation.

   a. $H_2O_2 + NO \rightarrow N_2O_3 + H_2O$

   b. $VO_2^+ + NO \rightarrow V^{3+} + NO_2$

13. Explain why this chemical equation is not balanced and balance it if it can be balanced.

$$Cr^{2+} + Cl_2 \rightarrow Cr^{3+} + 2Cl^-$$

14. Explain why this equation is not balanced and balance it if it can be balanced.

$$O_2 + 2H_2O + Br_2 \rightarrow 4OH^- + 2Br^-$$

Answers

1. a. $2Na + F_2 \rightarrow 2NaF$

    b. $Al_2O_3 + 3H_2 \rightarrow 2Al + 3H_2O$

3. a. $CH_4 + 2O_2 \rightarrow CO_2 + 2H_2O$

    b. $2P_2O_5 + 6Cl_2 \rightarrow 4PCl_3 + 5O_2$

5. a. $Ca + 2H^+ \rightarrow Ca^{2+} + H_2$

    b. $2Sn^{2+} \rightarrow Sn + Sn^{4+}$

7. a. $2Na + Hg_2Cl_2 \rightarrow 2NaCl + 2Hg$

    b. $2Al_2O_3 + 3C \rightarrow 4Al + 3CO_2$

9. a. $4H^+ + Cu + 2NO_3^- \rightarrow Cu^{2+} + 2NO_2 + 2H_2O$ in acidic solution; $2H_2O + Cu + 2NO_3^- \rightarrow Cu^{2+} + 2NO_2 + 4OH^-$ in basic solution

    b. $24H^+ + 3MnO_4^- + 7Fe \rightarrow 7Fe^{3+} + 3Mn + 12H_2O$ in acidic solution; $12H_2O + 3MnO_4^- + 7Fe \rightarrow 7Fe^{3+} + 3Mn + 24OH^-$ in basic solution

11. a. $2H^+ + ClO^- + Ti^{2+} \rightarrow Cl^- + H_2O + Ti^{4+}$ in acidic solution; $H_2O + ClO^- + Ti^{2+} \rightarrow Cl^- + Ti^{4+} + 2OH^-$ in basic solution

    b. $2H^+ + BrO_3^- + Ag \rightarrow BrO_2 + H_2O + Ag^+$ in acidic solution; $H_2O + BrO_3^- + Ag \rightarrow BrO_2 + Ag^+ + 2OH^-$ in basic solution

13. The charges are not properly balanced. The correct balanced equation is $2Cr^{2+} + Cl_2 \rightarrow 2Cr^{3+} + 2Cl^-$.

10.3 Applications of Redox Reactions: Voltaic Cells

Learning Objectives

1. Learn the parts of a voltaic cell.
2. Combine half reactions to determine the voltage of a voltaic cell.
3. Understand how voltaic cells are used as batteries.

Consider this redox reaction:

$$Zn + Cu^{2+} \rightarrow Zn^{2+} + Cu$$

If you were to mix zinc metal and copper ions in a container, this reaction would proceed by itself; we say that this reaction is *spontaneous*.

Suppose, however, we set up this reaction in a way depicted in Figure 10.1. Zinc and zinc ions are on one side of the system, while copper and copper ions are on the other side of the system. The two parts are connected with a wire.

FIGURE 10.1 A Redox Reaction in Which the Two Half Reactions Are Physically Separated
One application of redox reactions requires that they be physically separated.

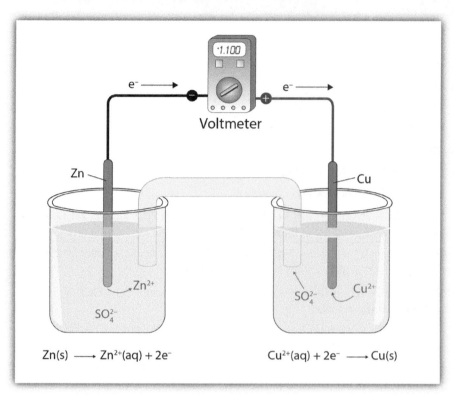

$$Zn(s) \longrightarrow Zn^{2+}(aq) + 2e^- \qquad Cu^{2+}(aq) + 2e^- \longrightarrow Cu(s)$$

voltaic (galvanic) cell

An apparatus that allows for useful electrical work to be extracted from a redox reaction.

half cell

A part of a voltaic cell that contains one half reaction.

anode

The half cell that contains the oxidation reaction.

cathode

The half cell that contains the reduction reaction.

electrode

The cathode or anode of a voltaic cell.

salt bridge

A part of a voltaic cell that contains a solution of some ionic compound whose ions migrate to either side of the voltaic cell to maintain the charge balance.

Even though the two half reactions are physically separated, a spontaneous redox reaction still occurs. However, in this case, the electrons transfer through the wire connecting the two half reactions; that is, this setup becomes a source of electricity. Useful work can be extracted from the electrons as they transfer from one side to the other—for example, a light bulb can be lit, or a motor can be operated. The apparatus as a whole, which allows useful electrical work to be extracted from a redox reaction, is called a **voltaic (galvanic) cell**.

Each individual system that contains a half reaction is called a **half cell**. The half cell that contains the oxidation reaction is called the **anode**, while the half cell that contains the reduction reaction is called the **cathode**. The cathode and anode collectively are the **electrodes** of the voltaic cell. Because electrons are coming from the anode, the anode is considered the *negative* electrode of the cell, while the cathode is considered the *positive* electrode of the cell. Finally, because electrons are moving from one half cell to the other, a charge imbalance builds up as the reaction proceeds. To counter that, a **salt bridge** is used; the salt bridge contains a solution of some ionic compound whose ions migrate to either side of the voltaic cell to maintain the charge balance.

The tendency for electrons to go from one half cell to another is called the **voltage** of the voltaic cell, represented by E. Sometimes the term *potential* is used to represent the voltage of a cell. Voltage is expressed in volts (V). The voltage of a voltaic cell is determined by the *difference* in the tendencies of the individual half cells and is characteristic of a given redox reaction when concentrations or pressures are specified (1.0 M for dissolved species and 1.0 atm for gases). Because the voltage of a redox reaction is determined by the difference of the tendencies of the individual half reactions, absolute voltages are unnecessary; only relative voltages of each half reaction are needed. The relative voltage of each half cell is represented as $E_{1/2}$ and is based on the standard that the $E_{1/2}$ for the reaction

$$H^+ + e^- \rightarrow 1/2H_2$$

is assigned to be exactly 0.000 V under standard conditions of pressure and concentration. Table 10.1 lists some relative $E_{1/2}$ values for some half reactions. Note that all half reactions are listed as reduction reactions, so these values are called the **standard reduction potentials** of each half reaction.

voltage

The tendency for electrons to go from one half cell to another.

standard reduction potential

The voltage of a reduction half reaction relative to the hydrogen half reaction.

TABLE 10.1 Standard Reduction Potentials of Half Reactions

Reduction Half Reaction	$E_{1/2}$ (V)
$F_2 + 2e^- \rightarrow 2F^-$	2.87
$Ce^{4+} + e^- \rightarrow Ce^{3+}$	1.61
$MnO_4^- + 8H^+ + 5e^- \rightarrow Mn^{2+} + 4H_2O$	1.51
$Cl_2 + 2e^- \rightarrow 2Cl^-$	1.36
$O_2 + 4H^+ + 4e^- \rightarrow 2H_2O$	1.23
$Br_2 + 2e^- \rightarrow 2Br^-$	1.06
$NO_3^- + 4H^+ + 3e^- \rightarrow NO + 2H_2O$	0.96
$Ag^+ + e^- \rightarrow Ag$	0.80
$Fe^{3+} + e^- \rightarrow Fe^{2+}$	0.77
$I_2 + 2e^- \rightarrow 2I^-$	0.54
$Cu^{2+} + 2e^- \rightarrow Cu$	0.34
$AgCl + e^- \rightarrow Ag + Cl^-$	0.222
$Sn^{4+} + 2e^- \rightarrow Sn^{2+}$	0.15
$2H^+ + 2e^- \rightarrow H_2$	0.000
$Pb^{2+} + 2e^- \rightarrow Pb$	−0.126
$Ni^{2+} + 2e^- \rightarrow Ni$	−0.25
$Cr^{3+} + e^- \rightarrow Cr^{2+}$	−0.41
$Fe^{2+} + 2e^- \rightarrow Fe$	−0.44
$Cr^{3+} + 3e^- \rightarrow Cr$	−0.74
$Zn^{2+} + 2e^- \rightarrow Zn$	−0.76
$Cr^{2+} + 2e^- \rightarrow Cr$	−0.91
$Ba^{2+} + 2e^- \rightarrow Ba$	−1.57
$Al^{3+} + 3e^- \rightarrow Al$	−1.66
$Mg^{2+} + 2e^- \rightarrow Mg$	−2.37

Reduction Half Reaction	$E_{1/2}$ (V)
$Na^+ + e^- \rightarrow Na$	−2.714
$Li^+ + e^- \rightarrow Li$	−3.045

Table 10.1 lists only reduction reactions, but a redox reaction has a reduction *and* an oxidation. To make the oxidation reaction, simply reverse the reduction reaction in Table 10.1 and change the sign on the $E_{1/2}$ value. If the reduction potential is negative, make the voltage for the oxidation positive; if the reduction potential is positive, make the voltage for the oxidation negative.

Example 6

What is the value of $E_{1/2}$ for this half reaction?

$$Ag + Cl^- \rightarrow AgCl + e^-$$

Solution

The given reaction is the reverse of this reaction:

$$AgCl + e^- \rightarrow Ag + Cl^- \qquad E_{1/2} = 0.222 \text{ V}$$

Therefore, the $E_{1/2}$ of the given reaction is −0.222 V.

Test Yourself

What is the value of $E_{1/2}$ for this half reaction?

$$Na \rightarrow Na^+ + e^-$$

Answer

2.714 V

To determine the overall voltage of a particular voltaic cell, simply combine the voltages of the oxidation and reduction half reactions. Even if you need to take a multiple of a half reaction for the electrons to cancel, do not take the multiple of the $E_{1/2}$. Use the values directly as is from Table 10.1.

Spontaneous redox reactions have positive overall voltages. If the voltage of the reaction as written is negative, it is not spontaneous in that direction. Rather, the reverse reaction is the spontaneous redox reaction.

Example 7

What is the voltage of a voltaic cell based on this reaction? Is the reaction spontaneous as written?

$$2NO_3^- + 8H^+ + 3Cu \rightarrow 2NO + 4H_2O + 3Cu^{2+}$$

Solution

The overall redox reaction is formed from these two half reactions:

$$NO_3^- + 4H^+ + 3e^- \rightarrow NO + 2H_2O \qquad E_{1/2} = 0.96 \text{ V}$$

$$Cu^{2+} + 2e^- \rightarrow Cu \qquad E_{1/2} = 0.34 \text{ V}$$

The second reaction is reversed in the overall redox reaction, so its voltage changes sign from the reduction reaction:

$$Cu \rightarrow Cu^{2+} + 2e^- \qquad E_{1/2} = -0.34 \text{ V}$$

To obtain the voltage of the voltaic cell based on the overall reaction, we simply combine the two voltages of the half reactions:

$$E = 0.96 + (-0.34) = 0.62 \text{ V}$$

Because the overall voltage is positive, the reaction is spontaneous as written.

Test Yourself

What is the voltage of a voltaic cell based on this reaction? Is the reaction spontaneous as written?

$$5Ni + 2MnO_4^- + 16H^+ \rightarrow 2Mn^{2+} + 8H_2O + 5Ni^{2+}$$

Answer

1.76 V; spontaneous

Technically, any redox reaction can be set up to make a voltaic cell. In modern society, however, only certain redox reactions are put to practical use. A portable voltaic cell that generates electricity to power devices for our convenience is called a **battery**. All batteries are based on redox reactions.

The first battery (called a "voltaic pile") was constructed by the Italian scientist Alessandro Volta in 1800 and was based on the copper/zinc reaction depicted in Figure 10.1. Unfortunately, it was messy, requiring quantities of copper and zinc salts dissolved in water. In 1866, the French scientist Georges Leclanché invented the **dry cell**, a precursor to today's modern battery. A schematic of a dry cell is shown in Figure 10.2. The zinc case and the central carbon rod serve as the anode and cathode, respectively. The other reactants are combined into a moist paste that minimizes free liquid, so the battery is less messy (hence the name *dry cell*). The actual redox reaction is complex but can be represented by the following redox reaction:

$$Zn + 2MnO_2 + 2NH_4^+ \rightarrow Zn^{2+} + Mn_2O_3 + 2NH_3 + H_2O$$

A dry cell has a voltage of about 1.56 V. While common and useful, dry cells have relatively short lifetimes and contain acidic components. They also cannot be recharged, so they are one-use only. Batteries that can be used only once are called **primary batteries**.

battery

A portable voltaic cell that generates electricity to power devices for our convenience.

dry cell

A modern battery that does not contain large amounts of aqueous solution.

primary battery

A battery that cannot be recharged.

FIGURE 10.2 Dry Cell
The Leclanché dry cell is a common type of battery.

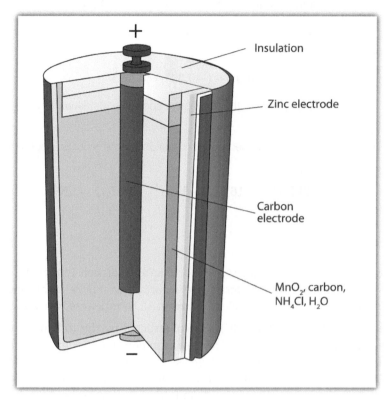

In the late 1950s, Lewis Urry of the Eveready Battery Company in Ohio invented the **alkaline battery** (still marketed today under the trade name *Energizer*). Alkaline batteries are similar to dry cells, but they use a basic moist paste rather than an acidic one. Moreover, the net amount of base does not change during the course of the redox reaction. The overall redox reaction is as follows:

$$Zn + 2MnO_2 \rightarrow ZnO + Mn_2O_3$$

Alkaline batteries have the advantage of being longer lasting and holding their voltage better—about 1.54 V—throughout their lifetime.

A common type of battery, especially with the increased popularity of personal electronic devices, is the button battery (Figure 10.3). A button battery is a small battery that can power small electronic devices; the batteries can be as small as 5 mm across. Two popular redox reactions used for button batteries are the alkaline dry-cell reaction and a silver oxide-based reaction:

$$Zn + Ag_2O \rightarrow ZnO + 2Ag$$

Some button batteries use a lithium-based redox reaction, typified by this anode reaction:

$$Li \rightarrow Li^+ + e^- \quad E_{1/2} = 3.045 \text{ V}$$

The actual redox reaction depends on the composition of the cathode and is variable depending on voltage. Lithium batteries can also be used for applications that require more energy, such as portable computers and electric vehicles. Some lithium-based batteries are rechargeable and can be used over and over again; such batteries are called **secondary batteries**.

An important secondary battery is the lead storage battery, shown in Figure 10.4. The lead storage battery is based on this redox reaction:

$$Pb + PbO_2 + 4H^+ + SO_4^{2-} \rightarrow 2PbSO_4 - 2H_2O$$

The redox reaction produces about 2 V, but it is typical to connect several individual batteries together to generate a larger voltage. The lead storage battery has the distinction that the product of both half reactions is $PbSO_4$, which as a solid accumulates on the many plates within each cell (Figure 10.4). The lead storage battery is a secondary battery, as it can be recharged and reused many times. Because it is based on lead, these batteries are rather heavy. They should also be recycled when replaced so that potentially dangerous lead does not escape into the environment. Because of their characteristics, lead storage batteries are used to start large engines in automobiles, boats, and airplanes.

FIGURE 10.3
Button Batteries
Button batteries like those seen here can be used for a variety of portable electronics, from watches and hearing aids to handheld gaming devices.

Source: © Thinkstock

FIGURE 10.4 Lead Storage Batteries
(a) A photo of a lead storage battery. (b) A schematic diagram of a lead storage battery.

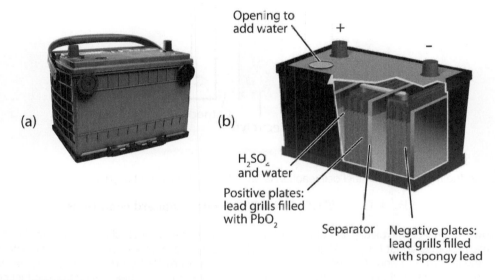

Source: Photo © Thinkstock

Chemistry Is Everywhere: Fuel Cells

A *fuel cell* is a type of battery in which reactants flow continuously into a specialized reaction chamber, and products flow out continuously while electrons are extracted from the reaction. Because all reactions in a fuel cell consist of a fuel and an oxidizer undergoing a redox reaction, an introduction of fuel cells is at home in a discussion of redox chemistry.

This fuel cell uses H_2 as the fuel and O_2 as the oxidizer.

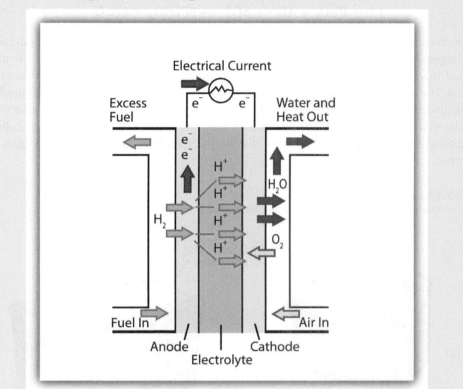

By far the most common fuel cell reaction is based on hydrogen and oxygen:

$$2H_2 + O_2 \rightarrow 2H_2O \quad E = 1.23 \text{ V under standard conditions}$$

However, fuel cells typically do not work under standard nor even optimal conditions, so they typically generate about 0.6–0.7 V. In this fuel cell, the only two products are water and electricity, so the fuel cell not only does not create pollution but also makes a by-product that in some environments is a valuable commodity (water). Other fuels can be used besides hydrogen; fuel cells have been developed that work on methane, methyl alcohol, ethyl alcohol, carbon-rich materials, and even magnesium metal.

Hydrogen-based fuel cells were and are used to provide electricity for manned space vehicles, partly because their only chemical product is water, which could be used for drinking. However, there has been a recent resurgence in interest in fuel cells because of their potential use in electric cars. Most electric cars run on conventional batteries, which can be very heavy and expensive to replace. It is thought that fuel cells, rather than conventional batteries, might be better sources of electricity for automobiles.

Several current barriers to fuel cell use in electric cars include capacity, cost, and overall energy efficiency. The 2008 Honda FCX, the first production model of a vehicle powered with a fuel cell, can hold 4.1 kg (just under 9 lb) of highly pressured H_2 gas and has a range of 450 km (280 mi). It costs about \$120,000–\$140,000 to build, making the vehicle beyond the ability of most people to own. Finally, it always requires more energy to produce elemental hydrogen as a fuel than can be extracted from hydrogen as a fuel. As such, hydrogen is described as an energy carrier (like electricity) rather than an energy source (like oil and gas). This distinction points out a fundamental argument against fuel cells as a "better" power source.

The 2008 Honda FCX was the first production car to use a fuel cell as a power source. Nonetheless, the car is in very limited service because of its need for relatively large quantities of elemental hydrogen as fuel.

Source: Photo courtesy of vernieman, http://commons.wikimedia.org/wiki/File:Honda_FCX_2006_KLIMS_front.jpg.

The limitations notwithstanding, there is a lot of interest in fuel cell research. If ways can be found to circumvent their current limitations, fuel cells may become more and more common as power sources.

Key Takeaways

- A voltaic cell produces electricity as a redox reaction occurs.
- The voltage of a voltaic cell can be determined by the reduction potentials of the half reactions.
- Voltaic cells are fashioned into batteries, which are a convenient source of electricity.

Exercises

1. Draw the voltaic cell represented by this reaction and label the cathode, the anode, the salt bridge, the oxidation half cell, the reduction half cell, the positive electrode, and the negative electrode. Use Figure 10.1 as a guide.

$$Zn + 2Ag^+ \rightarrow Zn^{2+} + 2Ag$$

2. Draw the voltaic cell represented by this reaction and label the cathode, the anode, the salt bridge, the oxidation half cell, the reduction half cell, the positive electrode, and the negative electrode. Use Figure 10.1 as a guide.

$$3Mg + 2Cr^{3+} \rightarrow 3Mg^{2+} + 2Cr$$

3. What is the voltage of this half reaction? Refer to Table 10.1

$$2F^- \rightarrow F_2 + 2e^-$$

4. What is the voltage of this half reaction? Refer to Table 10.1

$$Na \rightarrow Na^+ + e^-$$

5. What is the voltage of the voltaic cell in Exercise 1? Consult Table 10.1 for data.
6. What is the voltage of the voltaic cell in Exercise 2? Consult Table 10.1 for data.

7. Balance this redox reaction and determine its voltage. Is it spontaneous?

$$Li^+ + Al \rightarrow Li + Al^{3+}$$

8. Balance this redox reaction and determine its voltage. Is it spontaneous?

$$Pb^{2+} + Ni \rightarrow Pb + Ni^{2+}$$

9. Balance this redox reaction and determine its voltage. Is it spontaneous?

$$Cu^{2+} + Ag + Cl^- \rightarrow Cu + AgCl$$

10. Balance this redox reaction and determine its voltage. Is it spontaneous?

$$Mn^{2+} + Br_2 \rightarrow MnO_4^- + Br^-$$

11. Which reaction represents the cathode reaction in Exercise 7? The anode reaction?

12. Which reaction represents the cathode reaction in Exercise 8? The anode reaction?

13. Which reaction represents the cathode reaction in Exercise 9? The anode reaction?

14. Which reaction represents the cathode reaction in Exercise 10? The anode reaction?

15. A voltaic cell is based on this reaction:

$$Ni + 2Au^+ \rightarrow Ni^{2+} + 2Au$$

If the voltage of the cell is 0.33 V, what is the standard reduction potential of the $Au^+ + e^-$ → Au half reaction?

16. A voltaic cell is based on this reaction:

$$3Pb + 2V^{3+} \rightarrow 3Pb^{2+} + 2V$$

If the voltage of the cell is –0.72 V, what is the standard reduction potential of the $V^{3+} + 3e^-$ → V half reaction?

17. What species is being oxidized and what species is being reduced in a dry cell?

18. What species is being oxidized and what species is being reduced in an alkaline battery?

19. What species is being oxidized and what species is being reduced in a silver oxide button battery?

20. What species is being oxidized and what species is being reduced in a lead storage battery?

21. Based on the data in Table 10.1, what is the highest voltage battery you can construct?

22. Based on the data in Table 10.1, what is the lowest voltage battery you can construct? (This may be more challenging to answer than Exercise 21.)

Answers

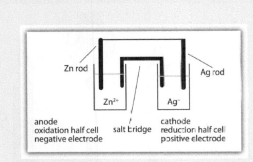

1.

3. −2.87 V

5. 1.56 V

7. $3Li^+ + Al \rightarrow 3Li + Al^{3+}$; −1.39 V; not spontaneous

9. $Cu^{2+} + 2Ag + 2Cl^- \rightarrow Cu + 2AgCl$; 0.12 V; spontaneous

11. cathode reaction: $Li^+ + e^- \rightarrow Li$; anode reaction: $A \rightarrow Al^{3+} + 3e^-$

13. cathode reaction: $Cu^{2+} + 2e^- \rightarrow Cu$; anode reaction: $Ag + Cl^- \rightarrow AgCl + e^-$

15. 0.08 V

17. oxidized: Zn; reduced: Mn

19. oxidized: Zn; reduced: Ag

21. 5.92 V from the reaction of F_2 and Li

10.4 Electrolysis

Learning Objectives

1. Describe electrolysis from a perspective of redox reactions.
2. Give examples of electrolysis applications.

Up to this point, we have considered redox reactions for processes that are spontaneous. When set up as a voltaic cell or battery, such reactions can be used as a source of electricity. However, it is possible to go in the other direction. By forcing electricity into a cell, we can make a redox reaction occur that normally would not be spontaneous. Under these circumstances, the cell is called an **electrolytic cell**, and the process that occurs in the cell is called **electrolysis** (Figure 10.5).

electrolytic cell

A cell into which electricity is forced to make a nonspontaneous reaction occur.

electrolysis

The process of making a nonspontaneous redox reaction occur by forcing electricity into a cell.

FIGURE 10.5 Electrolysis

In an electrolytic cell, electricity is forced through the cell to induce a nonspontaneous redox reaction. Here, the redox reaction $2H_2O \rightarrow 2H_2 + O_2$ is being caused by the introduction of electricity, which is supplied by the battery.

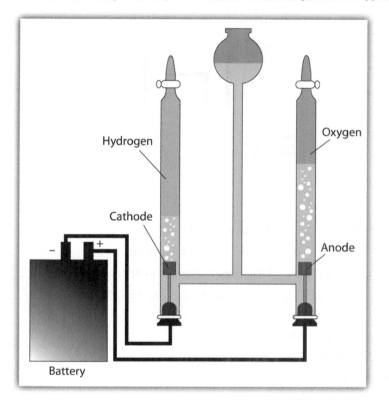

Electrolysis has many applications. For example, if NaCl is melted at about 800°C in an electrolytic cell and an electric current is passed through it, elemental sodium will appear at the cathode and elemental chlorine will appear at the anode as the following two reactions occur:

$$Na^+ + e^- \rightarrow Na$$

$$2Cl^- \rightarrow Cl_2 + 2e^-$$

Normally we expect elemental sodium and chlorine to react spontaneously to make NaCl. However, by using an input of electricity, we can force the opposite reaction to occur and generate the elements. Lithium, potassium, and magnesium can also be isolated from compounds by electrolysis.

Another element that is isolated by electrolysis is aluminum. Aluminum formerly was a difficult metal to isolate in its elemental form; in fact, the top of the Washington Monument has a 2.8 kg cap of aluminum metal, which at the time—1884—was the largest piece of elemental aluminum ever isolated. However, in 1886 the American Charles Hall and the Frenchman Paul Héroult almost simultaneously worked out an electrolytic process for isolating aluminum from bauxite, an ore of aluminum whose chemical formula is $AlO_x(OH)_{3-2x}$. The basic reactions are as follows:

$$Al^{3+} + 3e^- \rightarrow Al$$

$$2O^{2-} \rightarrow O_2 + 4e^-$$

With the development of the Hall-Héroult process, the price of aluminum dropped by a factor of over 200, and aluminum metal became common. So much elemental aluminum is produced in the United States each year that it has been estimated that the electrolysis of aluminum uses 5% of all the electricity in the country. (Recycling aluminum requires about 1/70th the energy of refining aluminum from ore, which illustrates the tremendous energy savings that recycling provides.)

Another application of electrolysis is **electroplating**, which is the deposition of a thin layer of metal on an object for protective or decorative purposes (Figure 10.6). Essentially, a metal object is connected to the cathode of an electrolytic cell and immersed in a solution of a particular metal cation. When the electrolytic cell is operated, a thin coating of the metal cation is reduced to the elemental metal on the surface of the object; the thickness of the coating can be as little as a few micrometers (10^{-6} m). Jewelry, eating utensils, electrical contacts, and car parts like bumpers are common items that are electroplated. Gold, silver, nickel, copper, and chromium are common metals used in electroplating.

electroplating

The deposition of a thin layer of metal on an object for protective or decorative purposes.

FIGURE 10.6 An Example of an Electrolytic Cell in Operation

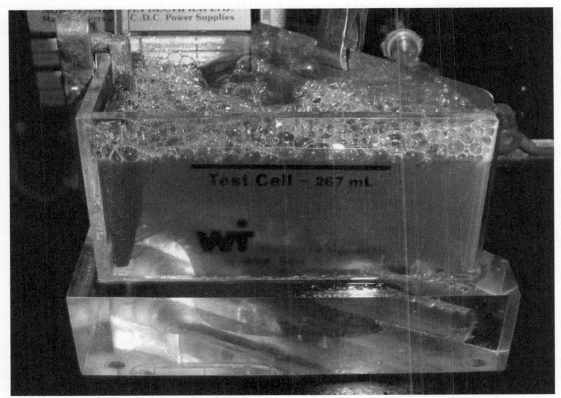

Source: Photo courtesy of Fstep, http://commons.wikimedia.org/wiki/File:Hullcell.jpg.

Key Takeaways

- Electrolysis is the forcing of a nonspontaneous redox reaction to occur by the introduction of electricity into a cell from an outside source.
- Electrolysis is used to isolate elements and electroplate objects.

Exercises

1. Define *electrolytic cell*.
2. How does the operation of an electrolytic cell differ from a voltaic cell?
3. List at least three elements that are produced by electrolysis.
4. Write the half reactions for the electrolysis of the elements listed in Exercise 3.

5. Based on Table 10.1, what voltage must be applied to an electrolytic cell to electroplate copper from Cu^{2+}?

6. Based on Table 10.1, what voltage must be applied to an electrolytic cell to electroplate aluminum from Al^{3+}?

Answers

1. an electrochemical cell in which charge is forced through and a nonspontaneous reaction occurs

2. A source of electrons is forced into the cell, rather than the cell producing electrons.

3. any three of the following: Al, K, Li, Na, Cl_2, or Mg

4. $Na^+ + e^- \rightarrow Na$; $K^+ + e^- \rightarrow K$; $Li^+ + e^- \rightarrow Li$; $Mg^{2+} + 2e^- \rightarrow Mg$, $Al^{3+} + 3e^- \rightarrow Al$; $2Cl^- \rightarrow Cl_2 + 2e^-$

5. 0.34 V

6. 1.66 V

10.5 End-of-Chapter Material

Additional Exercises

1. Oxidation was once defined as chemically adding oxygen to a substance. Use this reaction to argue that this definition is consistent with the modern definition of oxidation.

$$2Mg + O_2 \rightarrow 2MgO$$

2. Reduction was once defined as chemically adding hydrogen to a substance. Use this reaction to argue that this definition is consistent with the modern definition of reduction.

$$C_2H_2 + 2H_2 \rightarrow C_2H_6$$

3. Assign oxidation numbers to the atoms in each substance.

   a. Kr (krypton)

   b. krypton tetrafluoride (KrF_4)

   c. dioxygen difluoride (O_2F_2)

4. Assign oxidation numbers to the atoms in each substance.

   a. lithium hydride (LiH)

   b. potassium peroxide (K_2O_2)

   c. potassium fluoride (KF)

5. N atoms can have a wide range of oxidation numbers. Assign oxidation numbers for the N atom in each compound, all of which are known compounds.

   a. N_2O_5

   b. N_2O_4

   c. NO_2

   d. NO

e. N_2H_4

f. NH_3

6. Cr atoms can have a wide range of oxidation numbers. Assign oxidation numbers for the Cr atom in each compound, all of which are known compounds.

a. Na_2CrO_4

b. $Na_2Cr_2O_7$

c. CrF_5

d. $CrCl_3$

e. $CrCl_2$

7. Balance this redox reaction by inspection.

$$S_8 + O_2 \rightarrow SO_2$$

8. Balance this redox reaction by inspection.

$$C_{18}H_{38} + O_2 \rightarrow CO_2 - H_2O$$

9. Balance this redox reaction by the half reaction method by assuming an acidic solution.

$$Cr_2O_7^{2-} + Fe \rightarrow Cr^{3+} + Fe^{3+}$$

10. Balance the redox reaction in Exercise 9 by the half reaction method by assuming a basic solution.

11. The uranyl ion (UO_2^{2+}) is a fairly stable ion of uranium that requires strong reducers to reduce the oxidation number of uranium further. Balance this redox reaction using the half reaction method by assuming an acidic solution.

$$UO_2^{2+} + HN_3 \rightarrow U + N_2$$

12. Balance the redox reaction in Exercise 11 by the half reaction method by assuming a basic solution.

13. Zinc metal can be dissolved by acid, which contains H^+ ions. Demonstrate that this is consistent with the fact that this reaction has a spontaneous voltage:

$$Zn + 2H^+ \rightarrow Zn^{2+} + H_2$$

14. Copper metal cannot be dissolved by acid, which contains H^+ ions. Demonstrate that this is consistent with the fact that this reaction has a nonspontaneous voltage:

$$Cu + 2H^+ \rightarrow Cu^{2+} + H_2$$

15. A disproportionation reaction occurs when a single reactant is both oxidized and reduced. Balance and determine the voltage of this disproportionation reaction. Use the data in Table 10.1.

$$Cr^{2+} \rightarrow Cr + Cr^{3+}$$

16. A disproportionation reaction occurs when a single reactant is both oxidized and reduced. Balance and determine the voltage of this disproportionation reaction. Use the data in Table 10.1.

$$Fe^{2+} \rightarrow Fe + Fe^{3+}$$

17. What would be overall reaction for a fuel cell that uses CH_4 as the fuel?

18. What would be overall reaction for a fuel cell that uses gasoline (general formula C_8H_{18}) as the fuel?

19. When NaCl undergoes electrolysis, sodium appears at the cathode. Is the definition of cathode the same for an electrolytic cell as it is for a voltaic cell?

20. When NaCl undergoes electrolysis, chlorine appears at the anode. Is the definition of anode the same for an electrolytic cell as it is for a voltaic cell?

21. An award is being plated with pure gold before it is presented to a recipient. If the area of the award is 55.0 cm^2 and it will be plated with 3.00 μm of Au, what mass of Au will be plated on the award? The density of Au is 19.3 g/cm^3.

22. The unit of electrical charge is called the coulomb (C). It takes 96,500 coulombs of charge to reduce 27.0 g of Al from Al^{3+} to Al metal. At 1,040 cm^3, how many coulombs of charge were needed to reduce the aluminum in the cap of the Washington monument, assuming the cap is pure Al? The density of Al is 2.70 g/cm^3.

Answers

1. As oxygen is added to magnesium, it is being oxidized. In modern terms, the Mg atoms are losing electrons and being oxidized, while the electrons are going to the O atoms.

2. When hydrogen is added to C_2H_2, the oxidation number of carbon goes down, meaning it is reduced.

3. a. Kr: 0
   b. Kr: +4; F: –1
   c. O: +1; F: –1

4. a. Li: +1; H: –1
   b. K: +1; O: –1
   c. K: +1; F: –1

5. a. +5
   b. +4
   c. +4
   d. +2
   e. –2
   f. –3

6. a. +6
   b. +6
   c. +5
   d. +3
   e. +2

7. $S_8 + 8O_2 \rightarrow 8SO_2$

8. $2C_{18}H_{38} + 55O_2 \rightarrow 36CO_2 + 38H_2O$

9. $14H^+ + Cr_2O_7^{2-} + 2Fe \rightarrow 2Cr^{3+} + 7H_2O + 2Fe^{3+}$

10. $7H_2O + Cr_2O_7^{2-} + 2Fe \rightarrow 2Cr^{3+} + 2Fe^{3+} + 14OH^-$

11. $6HN_3 + UO_2^{2+} \rightarrow U + 2H_2O + 9N_2 + 2H^+$

12. $2OH^- + 6HN_3 + UO_2^{2+} \rightarrow U + 4H_2O + 9N_2$

13. The voltage of the reaction is +0.76 V, which implies a spontaneous reaction.

14. The voltage of this reaction is –0.34 V, which implies a nonspontaneous reaction.

15. $3Cr^{2+} \rightarrow Cr + 2Cr^{3+}$; –0.50 V

16. $3Fe^{2+} \rightarrow Fe + 2Fe^{3+}$ –1.21 V

17. $CH_4 + 2O_2 \rightarrow CO_2 + 2H_2O$

18. $2C_8H_{18} + 25O_2 \rightarrow 16CO_2 + 18H_2O$

19. Yes, because reduction occurs at the cathode.
20. Yes, because oxidation occurs at the anode.
21. 0.318 g
22. 1.40×10^7 C

CHAPTER 11
Gases

Opening Essay

Perhaps one of the most spectacular chemical reactions involving a gas occurred on May 6, 1937, when the German airship *Hindenburg* exploded on approach to the Naval Air Station in Lakehurst, New Jersey. The actual cause of the explosion is still unknown, but the entire volume of hydrogen gas used to float the airship, about 200,000 m^3, burned in less than a minute. Thirty-six people, including one on the ground, were killed.

The German airship *Hindenburg* (left) was one of the largest airships ever built. However, it was filled with hydrogen gas and exploded in Lakehurst, New Jersey, at the end of a transatlantic voyage in May 1937 (right).

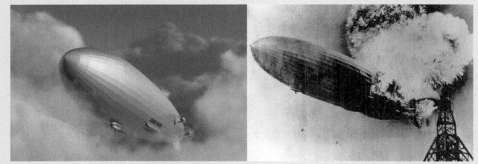

Source: Photo on left © Thinkstock. Photo on right courtesy of Gus Pasquerella, http://commons.wikimedia.org/wiki/File:Hindenburg_burning.jpg.

Hydrogen is the lightest known gas. Any balloon filled with hydrogen gas will float in air if its mass is not too great. This makes hydrogen an obvious choice for flying machines based on balloons—airships, dirigibles, and blimps. However, hydrogen also has one obvious drawback: it burns in air according to the well-known chemical equation

$$2H_2(g) + O_2(g) \rightarrow 2H_2O(\ell)$$

So although hydrogen is an obvious choice, it is also a dangerous choice.

Helium gas is also lighter than air and has 92% of the lifting power of hydrogen. Why, then, was helium not used in the *Hindenburg*? In the 1930s, helium was much more expensive. In addition, the best source of helium at the time was the United States, which banned helium exports to pre–World War II Germany. Today all airships use helium, a legacy of the *Hindenburg* disaster.

Of the three basic phases of matter—solids, liquids, and gases—only one of them has predictable physical properties: gases. In fact, the study of the properties of gases in the mid 1600s was the beginning of the development of modern chemistry from its alchemical roots. The interesting thing about some of these properties is that they are independent of the identity of the gas. That is, it doesn't matter if the gas is helium gas, oxygen gas, or sulfur vapors; some of their behavior is predictable and, as we will find, very similar. In this chapter, we will review some of the common behaviors of gases.

Let us start by reviewing some properties of gases. Gases have no definite shape or volume; they tend to fill whatever container they are in. They can compress and expand, sometimes to a great extent. Gases have extremely low densities, one-thousandth or less the density of a liquid or solid. Combinations of gases tend to mix together spontaneously; that is, they form solutions. Air, for example, is a solution of mostly nitrogen and oxygen. Any understanding of the properties of gases must be able to explain these characteristics.

11.1 Kinetic Theory of Gases

Learning Objectives

1. State the major concepts behind the kinetic theory of gases.
2. Relate the general properties of gases to the kinetic theory.

kinetic theory of gases

The fundamental model that describes the physical properties of gases.

Gases were among the first substances studied in terms of the modern scientific method, which was developed in the 1600s. It did not take long to recognize that gases all shared certain physical behaviors, suggesting that all gases could be described by one all-encompassing theory. Today, that theory is the **kinetic theory of gases**. It is based on the following statements:

1. Gases consist of tiny particles of matter that are in constant motion.

2. Gas particles are constantly colliding with each other and the walls of a container. These collisions are elastic; that is, there is no net loss of energy from the collisions.

3. Gas particles are separated by large distances, with the size of a gas particle tiny compared to the distances that separate them.

4. There are no interactive forces (i.e., attraction or repulsion) between the particles of a gas.

5. The average speed of gas particles is dependent on the temperature of the gas.

Figure 11.1 shows a representation of how we mentally picture the gas phase.

FIGURE 11.1 The Kinetic Theory of Gases
The kinetic theory of gases describes this state of matter as composed of tiny particles in constant motion with a lot of distance between the particles.

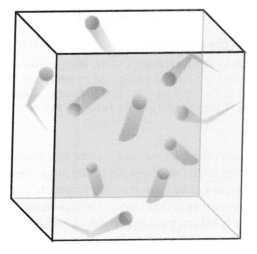

This model of gases explains some of the physical properties of gases. Because most of a gas is empty space, a gas has a low density and can expand or contract under the appropriate influence. The fact that gas particles are in constant motion means that two or more gases will always mix, as the particles from the individual gases move and collide with each other.

An **ideal gas** is a gas that exactly follows the statements of the kinetic theory. Unfortunately, *real gases* are not ideal. Many gases deviate slightly from agreeing perfectly with the kinetic theory of gases. However, most gases adhere to the statements so well that the kinetic theory of gases is well accepted by the scientific community.

ideal gas

A gas that exactly follows the statements of the kinetic theory.

Key Takeaways

- The physical behavior of gases is explained by the kinetic theory of gases.
- An ideal gas adheres exactly to the kinetic theory of gases.

Exercises

1. State the ideas behind the kinetic theory of gases.
2. The average speed of gas particles depends on what single variable?
3. Define *ideal gas*. Does an ideal gas exist?
4. What is a gas called that is not an ideal gas? Do such gases exist?

Answers

1. Gases consist of tiny particles of matter that are in constant motion. Gas particles are constantly colliding with each other and the walls of a container. These collisions are elastic; that is, there is no net loss of energy from the collisions. Gas particles are separated by large distances, with the size of a gas particle tiny compared to the distances that separate them. There are no interactive forces (i.e., attraction or repulsion) between the particles of a gas. The average speed of gas particles is dependent on the temperature of the gas.

2. temperature

3. An ideal gas is a gas that exactly follows the statements of the kinetic theory of gases. Ideal gases do not exist, but the kinetic theory allows us to model them

4. A gas that is not an ideal gas is called a real gas; all gases are real gases.

11.2 Pressure

Learning Objectives

1. Define *pressure*.
2. Learn the units of pressure and how to convert between them.

The kinetic theory of gases indicates that gas particles are always in motion and are colliding with other particles and the walls of the container holding them. Although collisions with container walls are elastic (i.e., there is no net energy gain or loss because of the collision), a gas particle does exert a force on the wall during the collision. The accumulation of all these forces distributed over

pressure

Force per unit area.

the area of the walls of the container causes something we call pressure. **Pressure** (*P*) is defined as the force of all the gas particle/wall collisions divided by the area of the wall:

$$\text{pressure} = \frac{\text{force}}{\text{area}}$$

All gases exert pressure; it is one of the fundamental measurable quantities of this phase of matter. Even our atmosphere exerts pressure—in this case, the gas is being "held in" by the earth's gravity, rather than the gas being in a container. The pressure of the atmosphere is about 14.7 pounds of force for every square inch of surface area: 14.7 lb/in^2.

Pressure has a variety of units. The SI-approved unit of pressure is the *pascal* (Pa), which is defined as 1 N/m^2 (one newton of force over an area of one square meter). However, this is usually too small in magnitude to be useful. A common unit of pressure is the **atmosphere** (atm), which was originally defined as the average atmospheric pressure at sea level.

However, "average atmospheric pressure at sea level" is difficult to pinpoint because of atmospheric pressure variations. A more reliable and common unit is **millimeters of mercury** (mmHg), which is the amount of pressure exerted by a column of mercury exactly 1 mm high. An equivalent unit is the **torr**, which equals 1 mmHg. (The torr is named after Evangelista Torricelli, a seventeenth-century Italian scientist who invented the mercury barometer.) With these definitions of pressure, the atmosphere unit is redefined: 1 atm is defined as exactly 760 mmHg, or 760 torr. We thus have the following equivalences:

$$1 \text{ atm} = 760 \text{ mmHg} = 760 \text{ torr}$$

We can use these equivalences as with any equivalences—to perform conversions from one unit to another. Relating these to the formal SI unit of pressure, 1 atm = 101,325 Pa.

atmosphere

A unit of pressure equal to the average atmospheric pressure at sea level; defined as exactly 760 mmHg.

millimeters of mercury

The amount of pressure exerted by a column of mercury exactly 1 mm high.

torr

Another name for a millimeter of mercury.

Example 1

How many atmospheres are there in 595 torr?

Solution

Using the pressure equivalences, we construct a conversion factor between torr and atmospheres: $\frac{1 \text{ atm}}{760 \text{ torr}}$. Thus,

$$595 \text{ torr} \times \frac{1 \text{ atm}}{760 \text{ torr}} = 0.783 \text{ atm}$$

Because the numbers in the conversion factor are exact, the number of significant figures in the final answer is determined by the initial value of pressure.

Test Yourself

How many atmospheres are there in 1,022 torr?

Answer

1.345 atm

Example 2

The atmosphere on Mars is largely CO_2 at a pressure of 6.01 mmHg. What is this pressure in atmospheres?

Solution

Use the pressure equivalences to construct the proper conversion factor between millimeters of mercury and atmospheres.

$$6.01 \text{ mmHg} \times \frac{1 \text{ atm}}{760 \text{ mmHg}} = 0.00791 \text{ atm} = 7.91 \times 10^{-3} \text{ atm}$$

At the end, we expressed the answer in scientific notation.

Test Yourself

Atmospheric pressure is low in the eye of a hurricane. In a 1979 hurricane in the Pacific Ocean, a pressure of 0.859 atm was reported inside the eye. What is this pressure in torr?

Answer

653 torr

Key Takeaways

- Pressure is a force exerted over an area.
- Pressure has several common units that can be converted.

Exercises

1. Define *pressure*. What causes it?
2. Define and relate three units of pressure.
3. If a force of 16.7 N is pressed against an area of 2.44 m^2, what is the pressure in pascals?
4. If a force of 2,546 N is pressed against an area of 0.0332 m^2, what is the pressure in pascals?
5. Explain why the original definition of atmosphere did not work well.
6. What units of pressure are equal to each other?
7. How many atmospheres are in 889 mmHg?
8. How many atmospheres are in 223 torr?
9. How many torr are in 2.443 atm?
10. How many millimeters of mercury are in 0.334 atm?
11. How many millimeters of mercury are in 334 torr?
12. How many torr are in 0.777 mmHg?
13. How many pascals are there in 1 torr?
14. A pressure of 0.887 atm equals how many pascals?

Answers

1. Pressure is force per unit area. It is caused by gas particles hitting the walls of its container.
2. 1 atm = 760 torr = 760 mmHg = 101,325 Pa
3. 6.84 Pa
4. 76,700 Pa
5. Because the atmospheric pressure at sea level is variable, it is not a consistent unit of pressure.
6. millimeters of mercury and torr

7. 1.17 atm
8. 0.293 atm
9. 1,857 torr
10. 254 mmHg
11. 334 mmHg
12. 0.777 torr
13. 133 Pa
14. 89,900 Pa

11.3 Gas Laws

Learning Objectives

1. Learn what is meant by the term *gas laws*.
2. Learn and apply Boyle's law.
3. Learn and apply Charles's law.

When seventeenth-century scientists began studying the physical properties of gases, they noticed some simple relationships between some of the measurable properties of the gas. Take pressure (*P*) and volume (*V*), for example. Scientists noted that for a given amount of a gas (usually expressed in units of moles [*n*]), if the temperature (*T*) of the gas was kept constant, pressure and volume were related: As one increases, the other decreases. As one decreases, the other increases. We say that pressure and volume are *inversely related*.

There is more to it, however: pressure and volume of a given amount of gas at constant temperature are *numerically* related. If you take the pressure value and multiply it by the volume value, the product is a constant for a given amount of gas at a constant temperature:

$$P \times V = \text{constant at constant } n \text{ and } T$$

If either volume or pressure changes while amount and temperature stay the same, then the other property must change so that the product of the two properties still equals that same constant. That is, if the original conditions are labeled P_1 and V_1 and the new conditions are labeled P_2 and V_2, we have

$$P_1 V_1 = \text{constant} = P_2 V_2$$

where the properties are assumed to be multiplied together. Leaving out the middle part, we have simply:

$$P_1 V_1 = P_2 V_2 \text{ at constant } n \text{ and } T$$

This equation is an example of a gas law. A **gas law** is a simple mathematical formula that allows someone to model, or predict, the behavior of a gas. This particular gas law is called **Boyle's law**, after the English scientist Robert Boyle, who first announced it in 1662. Figure 11.2 shows two representations of how Boyle's law works.

FIGURE 11.2 Boyle's Law
A piston having a certain pressure and volume (left piston) will have half the volume when its pressure is twice as much (right piston). One can also plot P versus V for a given amount of gas at a certain temperature; such a plot will look like the graph on the right.

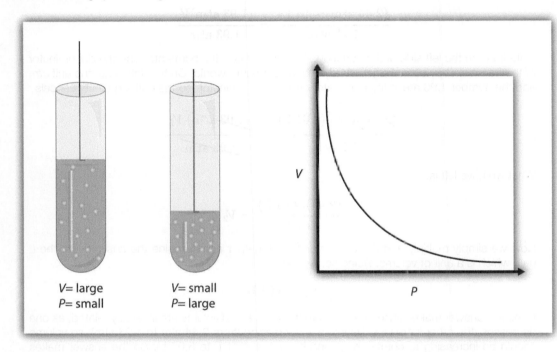

V= large
P= small

V= small
P= large

Boyle's law is an example of a second type of mathematical problem we see in chemistry—one based on a mathematical formula. Tactics for working with mathematical formulas are different from tactics for working with conversion factors. First, most of the questions you will have to answer using formulas are word-type questions, so the first step is to identify what quantities are known and assign them to variables. Second, in most formulas, some mathematical rearrangements (i.e., algebra) must be performed to solve for an unknown variable. The rule is that to find the value of the unknown variable, you must mathematically isolate the unknown variable *by itself and in the numerator* of one side of the equation. Finally, units must be consistent. For example, in Boyle's law there are two pressure variables; they must have the same unit. There are also two volume variables; they also must have the same unit. In most cases, it won't matter *what* the unit is, but the unit must be the *same* on both sides of the equation.

Example 3

A sample of gas has an initial pressure of 2.44 atm and an initial volume of 4.01 L. Its pressure changes to 1.93 atm. What is the new volume if temperature and amount are kept constant?

Solution

First, determine what quantities we are given. We are given an initial pressure and an initial volume, so let these values be P_1 and V_1:

$$P_1 = 2.44 \text{ atm and } V_1 = 4.01 \text{ L}$$

We are given another quantity, final pressure of 1.93 atm, but not a final volume. This final volume is the variable we will solve for.

$$P_2 = 1.93 \text{ atm and } V_2 = ? \text{ L}$$

Substituting these values into Boyle's law, we get

$$(2.44 \text{ atm})(4.01 \text{ L}) = (1.93 \text{ atm})V_2$$

To solve for the unknown variable, we isolate it by dividing both sides of the equation by 1.93 atm—both the number *and* the unit:

$$\frac{(2.44 \text{ atm})(4.01 \text{ L})}{1.93 \text{ atm}} = \frac{(1.93 \text{ atm})V_2}{1.93 \text{ atm}}$$

Note that, on the left side of the equation, the unit *atm* is in the numerator and the denominator of the fraction. They cancel algebraically, just as a number would. On the right side, the unit *atm* and the number 1.93 are in the numerator and the denominator, so the entire quantity cancels:

$$\frac{(2.44 \ \cancel{\text{atm}})(4.01 \text{ L})}{1.93 \ \cancel{\text{atm}}} = \frac{(\cancel{1.93 \text{ atm}})V_2}{\cancel{1.93 \text{ atm}}}$$

What we have left is:

$$\frac{(2.44)(4.01 \text{ L})}{1.93} = V_2$$

Now we simply multiply and divide the numbers together and combine the answer with the *L* unit, which is a unit of volume. Doing so, we get:

$$V_2 = 5.07 \text{ L}$$

Does this answer make sense? We know that pressure and volume are inversely related; as one decreases, the other increases. Pressure is decreasing (from 2.44 atm to 1.93 atm), so volume should be increasing to compensate, and it is (from 4.01 L to 5.07 L). So the answer makes sense based on Boyle's law.

Test Yourself

If P_1 = 334 torr, V_1 = 37.8 mL, and P_2 = 102 torr, what is V_2?

Answer

124 mL

As mentioned, you can use any units for pressure or volume, but both pressures must be expressed in the same units, and both volumes must be expressed in the same units.

Example 4

A sample of gas has an initial pressure of 722 torr and an initial volume of 88.8 mL. Its volume changes to 0.663 L. What is the new pressure?

Solution

We can still use Boyle's law to answer this, but now the two volume quantities have different units. It does not matter which unit we change, as long as we perform the conversion correctly. Let us change the 0.663 L to milliliters:

$$0.663 \ \cancel{\text{L}} \times \frac{1,000 \text{ mL}}{1 \ \cancel{\text{L}}} = 663 \text{ mL}$$

Now that both volume quantities have the same units, we can substitute into Boyle's law:

$$(722 \text{ torr})(88.8 \text{ mL}) = P_2(663 \text{ mL})$$

$$\frac{(722 \text{ torr})(88.8 \text{ mL})}{663 \text{ mL}} = P_2$$

The mL units cancel, and we multiply and divide the numbers to get

$$P_2 = 96.7 \text{ torr}$$

The volume is increasing, and the pressure is decreasing, which is as expected for Boyle's law.

Test Yourself

If $V_1 = 456$ mL, $P_1 = 308$ torr, and $P_2 = 1.55$ atm, what is V_2?

Answer

119 mL

There are other measurable characteristics of a gas. One of them is temperature (T). Perhaps one can vary the temperature of a gas sample and note what effect it has on the other properties of the gas. Early scientists did just this, discovering that if the amount of a gas and its pressure are kept constant, then changing the temperature changes the volume (V). As temperature increases, volume increases; as temperature decreases, volume decreases. We say that these two characteristics are *directly related*.

A mathematical relationship between V and T should be possible except for one thought: what temperature scale should we use? We know from Chapter 2 that science uses several possible temperature scales. Experiments show that the volume of a gas is related to its *absolute temperature in Kelvin, not its temperature in degrees Celsius*. If the temperature of a gas is expressed in kelvins, then experiments show that the *ratio* of volume to temperature is a constant:

$$\frac{V}{T} = \text{constant}$$

We can modify this equation as we modified Boyle's law: the initial conditions V_1 and T_1 have a certain value, and the value must be the same when the conditions of the gas are changed to some new conditions V_2 and T_2, as long as pressure and the amount of the gas remain constant. Thus, we have another gas law:

$$\frac{V_1}{T_1} = \frac{V_2}{T_2} \quad \text{at constant } P \text{ and } n$$

This gas law is commonly referred to as **Charles's law**, after the French scientist Jacques Charles, who performed experiments on gases in the 1780s. The tactics for using this mathematical formula are similar to those for Boyle's law. To determine an unknown quantity, use algebra to isolate the unknown variable by itself and in the numerator; the units of similar variables must be the same. But we add one more tactic: all temperatures must be expressed in the absolute temperature scale (Kelvin). As a reminder, we review the conversion between the absolute temperature scale and the Celsius temperature scale:

$$K = {}^\circ C + 273$$

where K represents the temperature in kelvins, and °C represents the temperature in degrees Celsius.

Figure 11.3 shows two representations of how Charles's law works.

Charles's law

A gas law that relates volume and temperature at constant pressure and amount.

FIGURE 11.3 Charles's Law
A piston having a certain volume and temperature (left piston) will have twice the volume when its temperature is twice as much (right piston). One can also plot V versus T for a given amount of gas at a certain pressure; such a plot will look like the graph on the right.

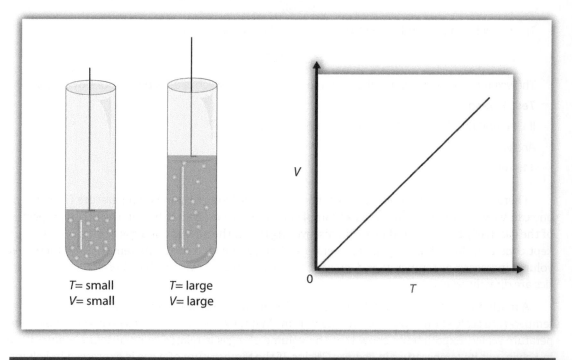

$T=$ small
$V=$ small

$T=$ large
$V=$ large

Example 5

A sample of gas has an initial volume of 34.8 mL and an initial temperature of 315 K. What is the new volume if the temperature is increased to 559 K? Assume constant pressure and amount for the gas.

Solution

First, we assign the given values to their variables. The initial volume is V_1, so $V_1 = 34.8$ mL, and the initial temperature is T_1, so $T_1 = 315$ K. The temperature is increased to 559 K, so the final temperature $T_2 = 559$ K. We note that the temperatures are already given in kelvins, so we do not need to convert the temperatures. Substituting into the expression for Charles's law yields:

$$\frac{34.8 \text{ mL}}{315 \text{ K}} = \frac{V_2}{559 \text{ K}}$$

We solve for V_2 by algebraically isolating the V_2 variable on one side of the equation. We do this by multiplying both sides of the equation by 559 K (number and unit). When we do this, the temperature unit cancels on the left side, while the entire 559 K cancels on the right side:

$$\frac{(559 \text{ \cancel{K}}) (34.8 \text{ mL})}{315 \text{ \cancel{K}}} = \frac{V_2 \ (\cancel{559 \text{ K}})}{\cancel{559 \text{ K}}}$$

The expression simplifies to:

$$\frac{(559)(34.8 \text{ mL})}{315} = V_2$$

By multiplying and dividing the numbers, we see that the only remaining unit is mL, so our final answer is:

$$V_2 = 61.8 \text{ mL}$$

Does this answer make sense? We know that as temperature increases, volume increases. Here, the temperature is increasing from 315 K to 559 K, so the volume should also increase, which it does.

Test Yourself

If $V_1 = 3.77$ L and $T_1 = 255$ K, what is V_2 if $T_2 = 123$ K?

Answer

1.82 L

It is more mathematically complicated if a final temperature must be calculated because the T variable is in the denominator of Charles's law. There are several mathematical ways to work this, but perhaps the simplest way is to take the reciprocal of Charles's law. That is, rather than write it as

$$\frac{V_1}{T_1} = \frac{V_2}{T_2}$$

write the equation as

$$\frac{T_1}{V_1} = \frac{T_2}{V_2}$$

It is still an equality and a correct form of Charles's law, but now the temperature variable is in the numerator, and the algebra required to predict a final temperature is simpler.

Example 6

A sample of a gas has an initial volume of 34.8 L and an initial temperature of –67°C. What must be the temperature of the gas for its volume to be 25.0 L?

Solution

Here, we are looking for a final temperature, so we will use the reciprocal form of Charles's law. However, the initial temperature is given in degrees Celsius, not kelvins. We must convert the initial temperature to kelvins:

$$-67°C + 273 = 206 \text{ K}$$

In using the gas law, we must use $T_1 = 206$ K as the temperature. Substituting into the reciprocal form of Charles's law, we get:

$$\frac{206 \text{ K}}{34.8 \text{ L}} = \frac{T_2}{25.0 \text{ L}}$$

Bringing the 25.0 L quantity over to the other side of the equation, we get:

$$\frac{(25.0 \, \cancel{L})(206 \text{ K})}{34.8 \, \cancel{L}} = T_2$$

The L units cancel, so our final answer is:

$$T_2 = 148 \text{ K}$$

This is equal to –125°C. As temperature decreases, volume decreases, which it does in this example.

Test Yourself

If $V_1 = 623$ mL, $T_1 = 255$°C, and $V_2 = 277$ mL, what is T_2?

Answer

235 K, or −38°C

Key Takeaways

- The behavior of gases can be modeled with gas laws.
- Boyle's law relates a gas's pressure and volume at constant temperature and amount.
- Charles's law relates a gas's volume and temperature at constant pressure and amount.
- In gas laws, temperatures must always be expressed in kelvins.

Exercises

1. Define *gas law*. What restrictions are there on the units that can be used for the physical properties?

2. What unit of temperature must be used for gas laws?

3. Boyle's law relates the _____ of a gas inversely with the _____ of that gas.

4. Charles's law relates the _____ of a gas directly with the _____ of that gas.

5. What properties must be held constant when applying Boyle's law?

6. What properties must be held constant when applying Charles's law?

7. A gas has an initial pressure of 1.445 atm and an initial volume of 1.009 L. What is its new pressure if volume is changed to 0.556 L? Assume temperature and amount are held constant.

8. A gas has an initial pressure of 633 torr and an initial volume of 87.3 mL. What is its new pressure if volume is changed to 45.0 mL? Assume temperature and amount are held constant.

9. A gas has an initial pressure of 4.33 atm and an initial volume of 5.88 L. What is its new volume if pressure is changed to 0.506 atm? Assume temperature and amount are held constant.

10. A gas has an initial pressure of 87.0 torr and an initial volume of 28.5 mL. What is its new volume if pressure is changed to 206 torr? Assume temperature and amount are held constant.

11. A gas has an initial volume of 638 mL and an initial pressure of 779 torr. What is its final volume in liters if its pressure is changed to 0.335 atm? Assume temperature and amount are held constant.

12. A gas has an initial volume of 0.966 L and an initial pressure of 3.07 atm. What is its final pressure in torr if its volume is changed to 3,450 mL? Assume temperature and amount are held constant.

13. A gas has an initial volume of 67.5 mL and an initial temperature of 315 K. What is its new volume if temperature is changed to 244 K? Assume pressure and amount are held constant.

14. A gas has an initial volume of 2.033 L and an initial temperature of 89.3 K. What is its volume if temperature is changed to 184 K? Assume pressure and amount are held constant.

15. A gas has an initial volume of 655 mL and an initial temperature of 295 K. What is its new temperature if volume is changed to 577 mL? Assume pressure and amount are held constant.

16. A gas has an initial volume of 14.98 L and an initial temperature of 238 K. What is its new temperature if volume is changed to 12.33 L? Assume pressure and amount are held constant.

17. A gas has an initial volume of 685 mL and an initial temperature of 29°C. What is its new temperature if volume is changed to 1.006 L? Assume pressure and amount are held constant.

18. A gas has an initial volume of 3.08 L and an initial temperature of –73°C. What is its new volume if temperature is changed to 104°C? Assume pressure and amount are held constant.

Answers

1. A gas law is a simple mathematical formula that allows one to predict the physical properties of a gas. The units of changing properties (volume, pressure, etc.) must be the same.

2. Absolute temperature (the Kelvin scale) must be used in gas laws.

3. pressure; volume

4. volume; temperature

5. amount of gas and temperature

6. pressure and amount of gas

7. 2.62 atm

8. 1,230 torr

9. 50.3 L

10. 12.0 mL

11. 1.95 L

12. 653 torr

13. 52.3 mL

14. 4.19 L

15. 260 K

16. 196 K

17. 444 K, or 171°C

18. 5.81 L

11.4 Other Gas Laws

Learning Objectives

1. Review other simple gas laws.
2. Learn and apply the combined gas law.

You may notice in Boyle's law and Charles's law that we actually refer to four physical properties of a gas: pressure (P), volume (V), temperature (T), and amount (in moles; n). We do this because these are the only four independent physical properties of a gas. There are other physical properties, but they are all related to one (or more) of these four properties.

Boyle's law is written in terms of two of these properties, with the other two being held constant. Charles's law is written in terms of two different properties, with the other two being held constant. It may not be surprising to learn that there are other gas laws that relate other pairs of properties—as long as the other two are held constant. Here we will mention a few.

Gay-Lussac's law relates pressure with absolute temperature. In terms of two sets of data, Gay-Lussac's law is

$$\frac{P_1}{T_1} = \frac{P_2}{T_2} \quad \text{at constant } V \text{ and } n$$

Note that it has a structure very similar to that of Charles's law, only with different variables—pressure instead of volume. *Avogadro's law* introduces the last variable for amount. The original statement of Avogadro's law states that equal volumes of different gases at the same temperature and pressure contain the same number of particles of gas. Because the number of particles is related to the number of moles (1 mol = 6.022 × 10²³ particles), Avogadro's law essentially states that equal volumes of different gases at the same temperature and pressure contain the same *amount* (moles, particles) of gas. Put mathematically into a gas law, Avogadro's law is

$$\frac{V_1}{n_1} = \frac{V_2}{n_2} \quad \text{at constant } P \text{ and } T$$

(First announced in 1811, it was Avogadro's proposal that volume is related to the number of particles that eventually led to naming the number of things in a mole as Avogadro's number.) Avogadro's law is useful because for the first time we are seeing amount, in terms of the number of moles, as a variable in a gas law.

Example 7

A 2.45 L volume of gas contains 4.5×10^{21} gas particles. How many gas particles are there in 3.87 L if the gas is at constant pressure and temperature?

Solution

We can set up Avogadro's law as follows:

$$\frac{2.45 \text{ L}}{4.5 \times 10^{21} \text{ particles}} = \frac{3.87 \text{ L}}{n_2}$$

We algebraically rearrange to solve for n_2:

$$n_2 = \frac{(3.87 \text{ L})(4.5 \times 10^{21} \text{ particles})}{2.45 \text{ L}}$$

The L units cancel, so we solve for n_2:

$$n_2 = 7.1 \times 10^{21} \text{ particles}$$

Test Yourself

A 12.8 L volume of gas contains 3.00×10^{20} gas particles. At constant temperature and pressure, what volume does 8.22×10^{18} gas particles fill?

Answer

0.351 L

The variable n in Avogadro's law can also stand for the number of moles of gas in addition to number of particles.

combined gas law

A gas law that combines pressure, volume, and temperature.

One thing we notice about all the gas laws is that, collectively, volume and pressure are always in the numerator, and temperature is always in the denominator. This suggests that we can propose a gas law that combines pressure, volume, and temperature. This gas law is known as the **combined gas law**, and its mathematical form is:

$$\frac{P_1 V_1}{T_1} = \frac{P_2 V_2}{T_2} \quad \text{at constant } n$$

This allows us to follow changes in all three major properties of a gas. Again, the usual warnings apply about how to solve for an unknown algebraically (isolate it on one side of the equation in the numerator), units (they must be the same for the two similar variables of each type), and units of temperature must be in kelvins.

Example 8

A sample of gas at an initial volume of 8.33 L, an initial pressure of 1.82 atm, and an initial temperature of 286 K simultaneously changes its temperature to 355 K and its volume to 5.72 L. What is the final pressure of the gas?

Solution

We can use the combined gas law directly; all the units are consistent with each other, and the temperatures are given in Kelvin. Substituting,

$$\frac{(1.82 \text{ atm})(8.33 \text{ L})}{286 \text{ K}} = \frac{P_2(5.72 \text{ L})}{355 \text{ K}}$$

We rearrange this to isolate the P_2 variable all by itself. When we do so, certain units cancel:

$$\frac{(1.82 \text{ atm})(8.33 \text{ L})(355 \text{ K})}{(286 \text{ K})(5.72 \text{ L})} = P_2$$

Multiplying and dividing all the numbers, we get:

$$P_2 = 3.29 \text{ atm}$$

Ultimately, the pressure increased, which would have been difficult to predict because two properties of the gas were changing.

Test Yourself

If $P_1 = 662$ torr, $V_1 = 46.7$ mL, $T_1 = 266$ K, $P_2 = 409$ torr, and $T_2 = 371$ K, what is V_2?

Answer

105 mL

As with other gas laws, if you need to determine the value of a variable in the denominator of the combined gas law, you can either cross-multiply all the terms or just take the reciprocal of the combined gas law. Remember, the variable you are solving for must be in the numerator and all by itself on one side of the equation.

Key Takeaways

- There are other gas laws that relate any two physical properties of a gas.
- The combined gas law relates pressure, volume, and temperature of a gas.

Exercises

1. State Gay-Lussac's law.
2. State Avogadro's law.

3. Use Gay-Lussac's law to determine the final pressure of a gas whose initial pressure is 602 torr, initial temperature is 356 K, and final temperature is 277 K. Assume volume and amount are held constant.

4. Use Gay-Lussac's law to determine the final temperature of a gas whose initial pressure is 1.88 atm, initial temperature is 76.3 K, and final pressure is 6.29 atm. Assume volume and amount are held constant.

5. If 3.45×10^{22} atoms of Ar have a volume of 1.55 L at a certain temperature and pressure, what volume do 6.00×10^{23} atoms of Ar have at the same temperature and pressure?

6. If 5.55×10^{22} atoms of He occupy a volume of 2.06 L at 0°C at 1.00 atm pressure, what volume do 2.08×10^{23} atoms of He occupy under the same conditions?

7. Use Avogadro's law to determine the final volume of a gas whose initial volume is 6.72 L, initial amount is 3.88 mol, and final amount is 6.10 mol. Assume pressure and temperature are held constant.

8. Use Avogadro's law to determine the final amount of a gas whose initial volume is 885 mL, initial amount is 0.552 mol, and final volume is 1,477 mL. Assume pressure and temperature are held constant.

9. Use the combined gas law to complete this table. Assume that the amount remains constant in all cases.

$V_1 =$	$P_1 =$	$T_1 =$	$V_2 =$	$P_2 =$	$T_2 =$
56.9 mL	334 torr	266 K		722 torr	334 K
0.976 L	2.33 atm	443 K	1.223 L		355 K
3.66 L	889 torr	23°C	2.19 L	739 torr	

10. Use the combined gas law to complete this table. Assume that the amount remains constant in all cases.

$V_1 =$	$P_1 =$	$T_1 =$	$V_2 =$	$P_2 =$	$T_2 =$
56.7 mL	1.07 atm	–34°C		998 torr	375 K
3.49 L	338 torr	45°C	1,236 mL		392 K
2.09 mL	776 torr	45°C	0.461 mL	0.668 atm	

11. A gas starts at the conditions 78.9 mL, 3.008 atm, and 56°C. Its conditions change to 35.6 mL and 2.55 atm. What is its final temperature?

12. The initial conditions of a sample of gas are 319 K, 3.087 L, and 591 torr. What is its final pressure if volume is changed to 2.222 L and temperature is changed to 299 K?

13. A gas starts with initial pressure of 7.11 atm, initial temperature of 66°C, and initial volume of 90.7 mL. If its conditions change to 33°C and 14.33 atm, what is its final volume?

14. A sample of gas doubles its pressure and doubles its absolute temperature. By what amount does the volume change?

Answers

1. The pressure of a gas is proportional to its absolute temperature.

3. 468 torr

5. 27.0 L

7. 10.6 L

9.

$V_1 =$	$P_1 =$	$T_1 =$	$V_2 =$	$P_2 =$	$T_2 =$
56.9 mL	334 torr	266 K	33.1 mL	722 torr	334 K
0.976 L	2.33 atm	443 K	1.223 L	1.49 atm	355 K
3.66 L	889 torr	23°C	2.19 L	739 torr	147 K, or −126°C

11. 126 K, or −147°C

13. 40.6 mL

11.5 The Ideal Gas Law and Some Applications

Learning Objectives

1. Learn the ideal gas law.
2. Apply the ideal gas law to any set of conditions of a gas.
3. Apply the ideal gas law to molar volumes, density, and stoichiometry problems.

So far, the gas laws we have considered have all required that the gas change its conditions; then we predict a resulting change in one of its properties. Are there any gas laws that relate the physical properties of a gas at any given time?

Consider a further extension of the combined gas law to include n. By analogy to Avogadro's law, n is positioned in the denominator of the fraction, opposite the volume. So:

$$\frac{PV}{nT} = \text{constant}$$

Because pressure, volume, temperature, and amount are the only four independent physical properties of a gas, the constant in the above equation is truly a constant; indeed, because we do not need to specify the identity of a gas to apply the gas laws, this constant is the same for all gases. We define this constant with the symbol R, so the previous equation is written as

$$\frac{PV}{nT} = R$$

which is usually rearranged as

$$PV = nRT$$

ideal gas law

A gas law that relates all four independent physical properties of a gas under any conditions.

This equation is called the **ideal gas law**. It relates the four independent properties of a gas at any time. The constant R is called the ideal gas law constant. Its value depends on the units used to express pressure and volume. Table 11.1 lists the numerical values of R.

TABLE 11.1 Values of the Ideal Gas Law Constant R

Numerical Value	Units
0.08205	$\dfrac{\text{L·atm}}{\text{mol·K}}$
62.36	$\dfrac{\text{L·torr}}{\text{mol·K}} = \dfrac{\text{L·mmHg}}{\text{mol·K}}$
8.314	$\dfrac{\text{J}}{\text{mol·K}}$

The ideal gas law is used like any other gas law, with attention paid to the unit and making sure that temperature is expressed in Kelvin. However, *the ideal gas law does not require a change in the conditions of a gas sample*. The ideal gas law implies that if you know any three of the physical properties of a gas, you can calculate the fourth property.

Example 9

A 4.22 mol sample of Ar has a pressure of 1.21 atm and a temperature of 34°C. What is its volume?

Solution

The first step is to convert temperature to kelvins:

$$34 + 273 = 307 \text{ K}$$

Now we can substitute the conditions into the ideal gas law:

$$(1.21 \text{ atm})\,(V) = (4.22 \text{ mol})\left(0.08205\,\frac{\text{L} \cdot \text{atm}}{\text{mol} \cdot \text{K}}\right)(307 \text{ K})$$

The *atm* unit is in the numerator of both sides, so it cancels. On the right side of the equation, the *mol* and *K* units appear in the numerator and the denominator, so they cancel as well. The only unit remaining is *L*, which is the unit of volume that we are looking for. We isolate the volume variable by dividing both sides of the equation by 1.21:

$$V = \frac{(4.22)(0.08205)(307)}{1.21}\,\text{L}$$

Then solving for volume, we get:

$$V = 87.9 \text{ L}$$

Test Yourself

A 0.0997 mol sample of O_2 has a pressure of 0.692 atm and a temperature of 333 K. What is its volume?

Answer

3.94 L

Example 10

At a given temperature, 0.00332 g of Hg in the gas phase has a pressure of 0.00120 mmHg and a volume of 435 L. What is its temperature?

Solution

We are not given the number of moles of Hg directly, but we are given a mass. We can use the molar mass of Hg to convert to the number of moles.

$$0.00332 \text{ g Hg} \times \frac{1 \text{ mol Hg}}{200.59 \text{ g Hg}} = 0.0000165 \text{ mol} = 1.65 \times 10^{-5} \text{ mol}$$

Pressure is given in units of millimeters of mercury. We can either convert this to atmospheres or use the value of the ideal gas constant that includes the mmHg unit. We will take the second option. Substituting into the ideal gas law,

$$(0.00332 \text{ mmHg})(435 \text{ L}) = (1.65 \times 10^{-5} \text{ mol}) \left(62.36 \frac{\text{L} \cdot \text{mmHg}}{\text{mol} \cdot \text{K}} \right) T$$

The mmHg, L, and mol units cancel, leaving the K unit, the unit of temperature. Isolating T all by itself on one side, we get:

$$T = \frac{(0.00332)(435)}{(1.65 \times 10^{-5})(62.36)} \text{ K}$$

Then solving for K, we get:

$$T = 1,404 \text{ K}$$

Test Yourself

For a 0.00554 mol sample of H_2, $P = 23.44$ torr and $T = 557$ K. What is its volume?

Answer

8.21 L

The ideal gas law can also be used in stoichiometry problems.

Example 11

What volume of H_2 is produced at 299 K and 1.07 atm when 55.8 g of Zn metal react with excess HCl?

$$Zn + 2HCl \rightarrow ZnCl_2 + H_2$$

Solution

Here we have a stoichiometry problem where we need to find the number of moles of H_2 produced. Then we can use the ideal gas law, with the given temperature and pressure, to determine the volume of gas produced. First, the number of moles of H_2 is calculated:

$$55.8 \text{ g Zn} \times \frac{1 \text{ mol Zn}}{65.41 \text{ g Zn}} \times \frac{1 \text{ mol } H_2}{1 \text{ mol Zn}} = 0.853 \text{ mol } H_2$$

Now that we know the number of moles of gas, we can use the ideal gas law to determine the volume, given the other conditions:

$$(1.07 \text{ atm})V = (0.853 \text{ mol}) \left(0.08205 \frac{\text{L} \cdot \text{atm}}{\text{mol} \cdot \text{K}}\right)(299 \text{ K})$$

All the units cancel except for L, for volume, which means

$$V = 19.6 \text{ L}$$

Test Yourself

What pressure of HCl is generated if 3.44 g of Cl_2 are reacted in 4.55 L at 455 K?

$$H_2 + Cl_2 \rightarrow 2HCl$$

Answer

0.796 atm

---

standard temperature and pressure (STP)

A set of benchmark conditions used to compare other properties of gases; about 1 atm for pressure and 273 K for temperature.

molar volume

The volume of exactly 1 mol of a gas; equal to 22.4 L at STP.

FIGURE 11.4
Molar Volume
A mole of gas at STP occupies 22.4 L, the volume of a cube that is 28.2 cm on a side.

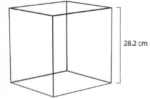

28.2 cm

It should be obvious by now that some physical properties of gases depend strongly on the conditions. What we need is a set of standard conditions so that properties of gases can be properly compared to each other. **Standard temperature and pressure (STP)** is defined as exactly 100 kPa of pressure (0.986 atm) and 273 K (0°C). For simplicity, we will use 1 atm as standard pressure. Defining STP allows us to compare more directly the properties of gases that differ from each other.

One property shared among gases is a molar volume. The **molar volume** is the volume of 1 mol of a gas. At STP, the molar volume of a gas can be determined easily by using the ideal gas law:

$$(1 \text{ atm})V = (1 \text{ mol}) \left(0.08205 \frac{\text{L} \cdot \text{atm}}{\text{mol} \cdot \text{K}}\right)(273 \text{ K})$$

All the units cancel except for L, the unit of volume. So:

$$V = 22.4 \text{ L}$$

Note that we have not specified the identity of the gas; we have specified only that the pressure is 1 atm and the temperature is 273 K. This makes for a very useful approximation: *any gas at STP has a volume of 22.4 L per mole of gas*; that is, the molar volume at STP is 22.4 L/mol (Figure 11.4). This molar volume makes a useful conversion factor in stoichiometry problems if the conditions are at STP. If the conditions are not at STP, a molar volume of 22.4 L/mol is not applicable. However, if the conditions are not at STP, the combined gas law can be used to calculate what the volume of the gas would be if at STP; then the 22.4 L/mol molar volume can be used.

Example 12

How many moles of Ar are present in 38.7 L at STP?

Solution

We can use the molar volume, 22.4 L/mol, as a conversion factor, but we need to reverse the fraction so that the L units cancel and mol units are introduced. It is a one-step conversion:

$$38.7 \text{ \L} \times \frac{1 \text{ mol}}{22.4 \text{ \L}} = 1.73 \text{ mol}$$

Test Yourself

What volume does 4.87 mol of Kr have at STP?

Answer

109 L

Example 13

What volume of H_2 is produced at STP when 55.8 g of Zn metal react with excess HCl?

$$Zn + 2HCl \rightarrow ZnCl_2 + H_2$$

Solution

This is a stoichiometry problem with a twist: we need to use the molar volume of a gas at STP to determine the final answer. The first part of the calculation is the same as in a previous example:

$$55.8 \; \cancel{g \, Zn} \times \frac{1 \; \cancel{mol \, Zn}}{65.41 \; \cancel{g \, Zn}} \times \frac{1 \; mol \; H_2}{1 \; \cancel{mol \, Zn}} = 0.853 \; mol \; H_2$$

Now we can use the molar volume, 22.4 L/mol, because the gas is at STP:

$$0.853 \; \cancel{mol \, H_2} \times \frac{22.4 \; L}{1 \; \cancel{mol \, H_2}} = 19.1 \; L \; H_2$$

Alternatively, we could have applied the molar volume as a third conversion factor in the original stoichiometry calculation.

Test Yourself

What volume of HCl is generated if 3.44 g of Cl_2 are reacted at STP?

$$H_2 + Cl_2 \rightarrow 2HCl$$

Answer

2.17 L

The ideal gas law can also be used to determine the densities of gases. Density, recall, is defined as the mass of a substance divided by its volume:

$$d = \frac{m}{V}$$

Assume that you have exactly 1 mol of a gas. If you know the identity of the gas, you can determine the molar mass of the substance. Using the ideal gas law, you can also determine the volume of that mole of gas, using whatever the temperature and pressure conditions are. Then you can calculate the density of the gas by using

$$density = \frac{molar \; mass}{molar \; volume}$$

Example 14

What is the density of N_2 at 25°C and 0.955 atm?

Solution

First, we must convert the temperature into kelvins:

$$25 + 273 = 298 \; K$$

If we assume exactly 1 mol of N_2, then we know its mass: 28.0 g. Using the ideal gas law, we can calculate the volume:

$$(0.955 \text{ atm})V = (1 \text{ mol}) \left(0.08205 \ \frac{\text{L} \cdot \text{atm}}{\text{mol} \cdot \text{K}}\right)(298 \text{ K})$$

All the units cancel except for L, the unit of volume. So

$$V = 25.6 \text{ L}$$

Knowing the molar mass and the molar volume, we can determine the density of N_2 under these conditions:

$$d = \frac{28.0 \text{ g}}{25.6 \text{ L}} = 1.09 \text{ g/L}$$

Test Yourself

What is the density of CO_2 at a pressure of 0.0079 atm and 227 K? (These are the approximate atmospheric conditions on Mars.)

Answer

0.019 g/L

Chemistry Is Everywhere: Gas Laws and Breathing

Breathing (more properly called *respiration*) is the process by which we draw air into our lungs so that our bodies can take up oxygen from the air. Let us apply the gas laws to breathing.

Start by considering pressure. We draw air into our lungs because the diaphragm, a muscle underneath the lungs, moves down to reduce pressure in the lungs, causing external air to rush in to fill the lower-pressure volume. We expel air by the diaphragm pushing against the lungs, increasing pressure inside the lungs and forcing the high-pressure air out. What are the pressure changes involved? A quarter of an atmosphere? A tenth of an atmosphere? Actually, under normal conditions, it's only 1 or 2 torr of pressure difference that makes us breathe in and out.

FIGURE 11.5 Breathing Mechanics
Breathing involves pressure differences between the inside of the lungs and the air outside. The pressure differences are only a few torr.

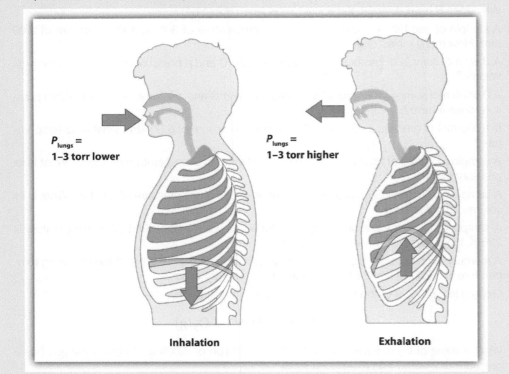

$P_{lungs} =$
1–3 torr lower

$P_{lungs} =$
1–3 torr higher

Inhalation

Exhalation

A normal breath is about 0.50 L. If room temperature is about 22°C, then the air has a temperature of about 295 K. With normal pressure being 1.0 atm, how many moles of air do we take in for every breath? The ideal gas law gives us an answer:

$$(1.0 \text{ atm})(0.50 \text{ L}) = n \left(0.08205 \, \frac{\text{L} \cdot \text{atm}}{\text{mol} \cdot \text{K}} \right) (295 \text{ K})$$

Solving for the number of moles, we get:

$$n = 0.021 \text{ mol air}$$

This ends up being about 0.6 g of air per breath—not much, but enough to keep us alive.

Key Takeaways

- The ideal gas law relates the four independent physical properties of a gas at any time.
- The ideal gas law can be used in stoichiometry problems whose chemical reactions involve gases.
- Standard temperature and pressure (STP) are a useful set of benchmark conditions to compare other properties of gases.
- At STP, gases have a volume of 22.4 L per mole.
- The ideal gas law can be used to determine densities of gases.

Exercises

1. What is the ideal gas law? What is the significance of R?

2. Why does R have different numerical values (see Table 11.1)?

3. A sample of gas has a volume of 3.91 L, a temperature of 305 K, and a pressure of 2.09 atm. How many moles of gas are present?

4. A 3.88 mol sample of gas has a temperature of 28°C and a pressure of 885 torr. What is its volume?

5. A 0.0555 mol sample of Kr has a temperature of 188°C and a volume of 0.577 L. What pressure does it have?

6. If 1.000 mol of gas has a volume of 5.00 L and a pressure of 5.00 atm, what is its temperature?

7. A sample of 7.55 g of He has a volume of 5,520 mL and a temperature of 123°C. What is its pressure in torr?

8. A sample of 87.4 g of Cl_2 has a temperature of –22°C and a pressure of 993 torr. What is its volume in milliliters?

9. A sample of Ne has a pressure of 0.772 atm and a volume of 18.95 L. If its temperature is 295 K, what mass is present in the sample?

10. A mercury lamp contains 0.0055 g of Hg vapor in a volume of 15.0 mL. If the operating temperature is 2,800 K, what is the pressure of the mercury vapor?

11. Oxygen is a product of the decomposition of mercury(II) oxide:

$$2HgO(s) \rightarrow 2Hg(\ell) + O_2(g)$$

What volume of O_2 is formed from the decomposition of 3.009 g of HgO if the gas has a pressure of 744 torr and a temperature of 122°C?

12. Lithium oxide is used to absorb carbon dioxide:

$$Li_2O(s) + CO_2(g) \rightarrow Li_2CO_3(s)$$

What volume of CO_2 can 6.77 g of Li_2O absorb if the CO_2 pressure is 3.5×10^{-4} atm and the temperature is 295 K?

13. What is the volume of 17.88 mol of Ar at STP?

14. How many moles are present in 334 L of H_2 at STP?

15. How many liters, at STP, of CO_2 are produced from 100.0 g of C_8H_{18}, the approximate formula of gasoline?

$$2C_8H_{18}(\ell) + 25O_2(g) \rightarrow 16CO_2(g) + 18H_2O(\ell)$$

16. How many liters, at STP, of O_2 are required to burn 3.77 g of butane from a disposable lighter?

$$2C_4H_{10}(g) + 13O_2(g) \rightarrow 8CO_2(g) + 10H_2O(\ell)$$

17. What is the density of each gas at STP?

   a. He

   b. Ne

   c. Ar

   d. Kr

18. What is the density of each gas at STP?

   a. H_2

   b. O_2

   c. N_2

19. What is the density of SF_6 at 335 K and 788 torr?
20. What is the density of He at –200°C and 33.9 torr?

Answers

1. The ideal gas law is $PV = nRT$. R is the ideal gas law constant, which relates the other four variables.
2. R has different numerical values when its units are different.
3. 0.327 mol
4. 82.3 L
5. 3.64 atm
6. 305 K
7. 8,440 torr
8. 19,400 mL
9. 12.2 g
10. 0.420 atm
11. 0.230 L
12. 15,700 L
13. 401 L
14. 14.9 mol
15. 157 L
16. 9.46 L
17. a. 0.179 g/L
    b. 0.901 g/L
    c. 1.78 g/L
    d. 3.74 g/L
18. a. 0.090 g/L
    b. 1.43 g/L
    c. 1.25 g/L
19. 5.51 g/L
20. 0.0298 g/L

11.6 Gas Mixtures

Learning Objective

1. Learn Dalton's law of partial pressures.

One of the properties of gases is that they mix with each other. When they do so, they become a solution—a homogeneous mixture. Some of the properties of gas mixtures are easy to determine if we know the composition of the gases in the mix.

partial pressure

The pressure that an individual gas in a mixture has.

In gas mixtures, each component in the gas phase can be treated separately. Each component of the mixture shares the same temperature and volume. (Remember that gases expand to fill the volume of their container; gases in a mixture continue to do that as well.) However, each gas has its own pressure. The **partial pressure** of a gas, P_i, is the pressure that an individual gas in a mixture has. Partial pressures are expressed in torr, millimeters of mercury, or atmospheres like any other gas pressure; however, we use the term *pressure* when talking about pure gases and the term *partial pressure* when we are talking about the individual gas components in a mixture.

Dalton's law of partial pressures

The total pressure of a gas mixture, P_{tot}, is equal to the sum of the partial pressures of the components, P_i.

Dalton's law of partial pressures states that the total pressure of a gas mixture, P_{tot}, is equal to the sum of the partial pressures of the components, P_i:

$$P_{tot} = P_1 + P_2 + P_3 + \ldots = \sum_{\# \text{ of gases}} P_i$$

Although this may seem to be a trivial law, it reinforces the idea that gases behave independently of each other.

Example 15

A mixture of H_2 at 2.33 atm and N_2 at 0.77 atm is in a container. What is the total pressure in the container?

Solution

Dalton's law of partial pressures states that the total pressure is equal to the sum of the partial pressures. We simply add the two pressures together:

$$P_{tot} = 2.33 \text{ atm} + 0.77 \text{ atm} = 3.10 \text{ atm}$$

Test Yourself

Air can be thought of as a mixture of N_2 and O_2. In 760 torr of air, the partial pressure of N_2 is 608 torr. What is the partial pressure of O_2?

Answer

152 torr

Example 16

A 2.00 L container with 2.50 atm of H_2 is connected to a 5.00 L container with 1.90 atm of O_2 inside. The containers are opened, and the gases mix. What is the final pressure inside the containers?

Solution

Because gases act independently of each other, we can determine the resulting final pressures using Boyle's law and then add the two resulting pressures together to get the final pressure. The total final volume is 2.00 L + 5.00 L = 7.00 L. First, we use Boyle's law to determine the final pressure of H_2:

$$(2.50 \text{ atm})(2.00 \text{ L}) = P_2(7.00 \text{ L})$$

Solving for P_2, we get:

$$P_2 = 0.714 \text{ atm} = \text{partial pressure of } H_2$$

Now we do that same thing for the O_2:

$$(1.90 \text{ atm})(5.00 \text{ L}) = P_2(7.00 \text{ L})$$

$$P_2 = 1.36 \text{ atm} = \text{partial pressure of } O_2$$

The total pressure is the sum of the two resulting partial pressures:

$$P_{tot} = 0.714 \text{ atm} + 1.36 \text{ atm} = 2.07 \text{ atm}$$

Test Yourself

If 0.75 atm of He in a 2.00 L container is connected to a 3.00 L container with 0.35 atm of Ne and the containers are opened, what is the resulting total pressure?

Answer

0.51 atm

One of the reasons we have to deal with Dalton's law of partial pressures is because gases are frequently collected by bubbling through water. Liquids are constantly evaporating into a vapor until the vapor achieves a partial pressure characteristic of the substance and the temperature. This partial pressure is called a **vapor pressure**. Table 11.2 lists the vapor pressures of H_2O versus temperature. Note that if a substance is normally a gas under a given set of conditions, the term *partial pressure* is used; the term *vapor pressure* is reserved for the partial pressure of a vapor when the liquid is the normal phase under a given set of conditions.

vapor pressure

The partial pressure exerted by evaporation of a liquid.

TABLE 11.2 Vapor Pressure of Water versus Temperature

Temperature (°C)	Vapor Pressure (torr)	Temperature (°C)	Vapor Pressure (torr)
5	6.54	30	31.84
10	9.21	35	42.20
15	12.79	40	55.36
20	17.54	50	92.59
21	18.66	60	149.5
22	19.84	70	233.8
23	21.08	80	355.3
24	22.39	90	525.9
25	23.77	100	760.0

Any time a gas is collected over water, the total pressure is equal to the partial pressure of the gas *plus* the vapor pressure of water. This means that the amount of gas collected will be less than the total pressure suggests.

Example 17

Hydrogen gas is generated by the reaction of nitric acid and elemental iron. The gas is collected in an inverted 2.00 L container immersed in a beaker of water at 22°C. At the end of the collection, the partial pressure inside the container is 733 torr. How many moles of H_2 gas were generated?

Solution

We need to take into account that the total pressure includes the vapor pressure of water. According to Table 11.2, the vapor pressure of water at 22°C is 19.84 torr. According to Dalton's law of partial pressures, the total pressure equals the sum of the pressures of the individual gases, so:

$$733 \text{ torr} = P_{H_2} + P_{H_2O} = P_{H_2} + 19.84 \text{ torr}$$

We solve by subtracting:

$$P_{H_2} = 713 \text{ torr}$$

Now we can use the ideal gas law to determine the number of moles (remembering to convert temperature to kelvins, making it 295 K):

$$(713 \text{ torr})(2.00 \text{ L}) = n\left(62.36 \frac{\text{L} \cdot \text{atm}}{\text{mol} \cdot \text{K}}\right)(295 \text{ K})$$

All the units cancel except for mol, which is what we are looking for. So:

$$n = 0.0775 \text{ mol } H_2 \text{ collected}$$

Test Yourself

CO_2, generated by the decomposition of $CaCO_3$, is collected in a 3.50 L container over water. If the temperature is 50°C and the total pressure inside the container is 833 torr, how many moles of CO_2 were generated?

Answer

0.129 mol

---

mole fraction

The ratio of the number of moles of a component in a mixture divided by the total number of moles in the sample.

Finally, we introduce a new unit that can be useful, especially for gases. The **mole fraction**, χ_i, is the ratio of the number of moles of component i in a mixture divided by the total number of moles in the sample:

$$\chi_i = \frac{\text{moles of component } i}{\text{total number of moles}}$$

(χ is the lowercase Greek letter *chi*.) Note that mole fraction is *not* a percentage; its values range from 0 to 1. For example, consider the combination of 4.00 g of He and 5.0 g of Ne. Converting both to moles, we get:

$$4.00 \text{ g He} \times \frac{1 \text{ mol He}}{4.00 \text{ g He}} = 1.00 \text{ mol He and } 5.0 \text{ g Ne} \times \frac{1 \text{ mol Ne}}{20.0 \text{ g Ne}} = 0.25 \text{ mol Ne}$$

The total number of moles is the sum of the two mole amounts:

$$\text{total moles} = 1.00 \text{ mol} + 0.025 \text{ mol} = 1.25 \text{ mol}$$

The mole fractions are simply the ratio of each mole amount and the total number of moles, 1.25 mol:

$$\chi_{He} = \frac{1.00 \text{ mol}}{1.25 \text{ mol}} = 0.800$$

$$\chi_{Ne} = \frac{0.25 \text{ mol}}{1.25 \text{ mol}} = 0.200$$

The sum of the mole fractions equals exactly 1.

For gases, there is another way to determine the mole fraction. When gases have the same volume and temperature (as they would in a mixture of gases), the number of moles is proportional to partial pressure, so the mole fractions for a gas mixture can be determined by taking the ratio of partial pressure to total pressure:

$$\chi_i = \frac{P_i}{P_{tot}}$$

This expression allows us to determine mole fractions without calculating the moles of each component directly.

Example 18

A container has a mixture of He at 0.80 atm and Ne at 0.60 atm. What are the mole fractions of each component?

Solution

According to Dalton's law, the total pressure is the sum of the partial pressures:

$$P_{tot} = 0.80 \text{ atm} + 0.60 \text{ atm} = 1.40 \text{ atm}$$

The mole fractions are the ratios of the partial pressure of each component and the total pressure:

$$\chi_{He} = \frac{0.80 \text{ atm}}{1.40 \text{ atm}} = 0.57$$
$$\chi_{Ne} = \frac{0.60 \text{ atm}}{1.40 \text{ atm}} = 0.43$$

Again, the sum of the mole fractions is exactly 1.

Test Yourself

What are the mole fractions when 0.65 atm of O_2 and 1.30 atm of N_2 are mixed in a container?

Answer

$$\chi_{O_2} = 0.33; \ \chi_{N_2} = 0.67$$

Food and Drink App: Carbonated Beverages

Carbonated beverages—sodas, beer, sparkling wines—have one thing in common: they have CO_2 gas dissolved in them in such sufficient quantities that it affects the drinking experience. Most people find the drinking experience pleasant—indeed, in the United States alone, over 1.5×10^9 gal of soda are consumed each year, which is almost 50 gal per person! This figure does not include other types of carbonated beverages, so the total consumption is probably significantly higher.

All carbonated beverages are made in one of two ways. First, the flat beverage is subjected to a high pressure of CO_2 gas, which forces the gas into solution. The carbonated beverage is then packaged in a tightly-sealed package (usually a bottle or a can) and sold. When the container is opened, the CO_2 pressure is released, resulting in the well-known *hiss* of an opening container, and CO_2 bubbles come out of solution. This must be done with care: if the CO_2 comes out too violently, a mess can occur!

If you are not careful opening a container of a carbonated beverage, you can make a mess as the CO_2 comes out of solution suddenly.

Source: © Thinkstock

The second way a beverage can become carbonated is by the ingestion of sugar by yeast, which then generates CO_2 as a digestion product. This process is called *fermentation*. The overall reaction is:

$$C_6H_{12}O_6(aq) \rightarrow 2C_2H_5OH(aq) + 2CO_2(aq)$$

When this process occurs in a closed container, the CO_2 produced dissolves in the liquid, only to be released from solution when the container is opened. Most fine sparkling wines and champagnes are turned into carbonated beverages this way. Less-expensive sparkling wines are made like sodas and beer, with exposure to high pressures of CO_2 gas.

Key Takeaways

- The pressure of a gas in a gas mixture is termed the *partial pressure*.
- Dalton's law of partial pressure says that the total pressure in a gas mixture is the sum of the individual partial pressures.
- Collecting gases over water requires that we take the vapor pressure of water into account.
- Mole fraction is another way to express the amounts of components in a mixture.

Exercises

1. What is the total pressure of a gas mixture containing these partial pressures: $P_{N2} = 0.78$ atm, $P_{H2} = 0.33$ atm, and $P_{O2} = 1.59$ atm?

2. What is the total pressure of a gas mixture containing these partial pressures: $P_{Ne} = 312$ torr, $P_{He} = 799$ torr, and $P_{Ar} = 831$ torr?

3. In a gas mixture of He and Ne, the total pressure is 335 torr and the partial pressure of He is 0.228 atm. What is the partial pressure of Ne?

4. In a gas mixture of O_2 and N_2, the total pressure is 2.66 atm and the partial pressure of O_2 is 888 torr. What is the partial pressure of N_2?

5. A 3.55 L container has a mixture of 56.7 g of Ar and 33.9 g of He at 33°C. What are the partial pressures of the gases and the total pressure inside the container?

6. A 772 mL container has a mixture of 2.99 g of H_2 and 44.2 g of Xe at 388 K. What are the partial pressures of the gases and the total pressure inside the container?

7. A sample of O_2 is collected over water in a 5.00 L container at 20°C. If the total pressure is 688 torr, how many moles of O_2 are collected?

8. A sample of H_2 is collected over water in a 3.55 L container at 50°C. If the total pressure is 445 torr, how many moles of H_2 are collected?

9. A sample of CO is collected over water in a 25.00 L container at 5°C. If the total pressure is 0.112 atm, how many moles of CO are collected?

10. A sample of NO_2 is collected over water in a 775 mL container at 25°C. If the total pressure is 0.990 atm, how many moles of NO_2 are collected?

11. A sample of NO is collected over water in a 75.0 mL container at 25°C. If the total pressure is 0.495 atm, how many grams of NO are collected?

12. A sample of ClO_2 is collected over water in a 0.800 L container at 15°C. If the total pressure is 1.002 atm, how many grams of ClO_2 are collected?

13. Determine the mole fractions of each component when 44.5 g of He is mixed with 8.83 g of H_2.

14. Determine the mole fractions of each component when 9.33 g of SO_2 is mixed with 13.29 g of SO_3.

15. In a container, 4.56 atm of F_2 is combined with 2.66 atm of Cl_2. What are the mole fractions of each component?

16. In a container, 77.3 atm of SiF_4 are mixed with 33.9 atm of O_2. What are the mole fractions of each component?

Answers

1. 2.70 atm
2. 1,942 torr
3. 162 torr, or 0.213 atm
4. 1.49 atm
5. $P_{Ar} = 10.0$ atm; $P_{He} = 59.9$ atm; $P_{tot} = 69.9$ atm
6. $P_{H_2} = 61.1$ atm ; $P_{Xe} = 13.9$ atm; $P_{tot} = 75.0$ atm
7. 0.183 mol
8. 0.0621 mol
9. 0.113 mol
10. 0.0304 mol
11. 0.0440 g
12. 2.25 g
13. $\chi_{He} = 0.718$; $\chi_{H_2} = 0.282$
14. $\chi_{SO_2} = 0.467$; $\chi_{SO_3} = 0.533$
15. $\chi_{F_2} = 0.632$; $\chi_{Cl_3} = 0.368$
16. $\chi_{SiF_4} = 0.695$; $\chi_{O_2} = 0.305$

11.7 End-of-Chapter Material

Additional Exercises

1. What is the pressure in pascals if a force of 4.88 kN is pressed against an area of 235 cm^2?

2. What is the pressure in pascals if a force of 3.44×10^4 MN is pressed against an area of 1.09 km^2?

3. What is the final temperature of a gas whose initial conditions are 667 mL, 822 torr, and 67°C and whose final volume and pressure are 1.334 L and 2.98 atm, respectively? Assume the amount remains constant.

4. What is the final pressure of a gas whose initial conditions are 1.407 L, 2.06 atm, and −67°C and whose final volume and temperature are 608 mL and 449 K, respectively? Assume the amount remains constant.

5. Propose a combined gas law that relates volume, pressure, and amount at constant temperature.

6. Propose a combined gas law that relates amount, pressure, and temperature at constant volume.

7. A sample of 6.022×10^{23} particles of gas has a volume of 22.4 L at 0°C and a pressure of 1.000 atm. Although it may seem silly to contemplate, what volume would 1 particle of gas occupy?

8. One mole of liquid N_2 has a volume of 34.65 mL at –196°C. At that temperature, 1 mol of N_2 gas has a volume of 6.318 L if the pressure is 1.000 atm. What pressure is needed to compress the N_2 gas to 34.65 mL?

9. Use two values of R to determine the ratio between an atmosphere and a torr. Does the number make sense?

10. Use two values of R to determine how many joules are in a liter·atmosphere.

11. At an altitude of 40 km above the earth's surface, the atmospheric pressure is 5.00 torr, and the surrounding temperature is –20°C. If a weather balloon is filled with 1.000 mol of He at 760 torr and 22°C, what is its

    a. initial volume before ascent?

    b. final volume when it reaches 40 km in altitude? (Assume the pressure of the gas equals the surrounding pressure.)

12. If a balloon is filled with 1.000 mol of He at 760 torr and 22°C, what is its

    a. initial volume before ascent?

    b. final volume if it descends to the bottom of the Mariana Trench, where the surrounding temperature is 1.4°C and the pressure is 1,060 atm?

13. Air, a mixture of mostly N_2 and O_2, can be approximated as having a molar mass of 28.8 g/mol. What is the density of air at 1.00 atm and 22°C? (This is approximately sea level.)

14. Air, a mixture of mostly N_2 and O_2, can be approximated as having a molar mass of 28.8 g/mol. What is the density of air at 0.26 atm and –26°C? (This is approximately the atmospheric condition at the summit of Mount Everest.)

15. On the surface of Venus, the atmospheric pressure is 91.8 atm, and the temperature is 460°C. What is the density of CO_2 under these conditions? (The Venusian atmosphere is composed largely of CO_2.)

16. On the surface of Mars, the atmospheric pressure is 4.50 torr, and the temperature is –87°C. What is the density of CO_2 under these conditions? (The Martian atmosphere, similar to its Venusian counterpart, is composed largely of CO_2.)

17. HNO_3 reacts with iron metal according to

$$Fe(s) + 2HNO_3(aq) \rightarrow Fe(NO_3)_2(aq) + H_2(g)$$

In a reaction vessel, 23.8 g of Fe are reacted but only 446 mL of H_2 are collected over water at 25°C and a pressure of 733 torr. What is the percent yield of the reaction?

18. $NaHCO_3$ is decomposed by heat according to

$$2NaHCO_3(s) \rightarrow Na_2CO_3(s) + H_2O(\ell) + CO_2(g)$$

If you start with 100.0 g of $NaHCO_3$ and collect 10.06 L of CO_2 over water at 20°C and 0.977 atm, what is the percent yield of the decomposition reaction?

Answers

1. 208,000 Pa

2. 31,600 Pa

3. 1,874 K

4. 10.4 atm

5. $\dfrac{P_1 V_1}{n_1} = \dfrac{P_2 V_2}{n_2}$

6. $\dfrac{P_1}{n_1 T_1} = \dfrac{P_2}{n_2 T_2}$

7. 3.72×10^{-23} L

8. 182 atm

9. 1 atm = 760 torr

10. 101.32 J = 1 L·atm

11. a. 24.2 L

    b. 3155 L

12. a. 24.2 L

    b. 0.0212 L

13. 1.19 g/L

14. 0.369 g/L

15. 67.2 g/L

16. 0.0171 g/L

17. 3.99%

18. 67.1%

CHAPTER 12
Solutions

Opening Essay

More than 70% of the earth's surface is covered by a very important solution—seawater. It is likely that without seawater, no life would exist on earth.

At its simplest, seawater is mostly H_2O. But about 3.5% of seawater is dissolved solids, mostly NaCl but other ions as well. Table 12.1 lists the percentage by mass of the various ions in seawater.

Because it is highly likely that life on earth originated in the oceans, it should not be surprising that many bodily fluids resemble seawater—especially blood. Table 12.1 also lists the percentage by mass of ions in a typical sample of blood.

TABLE 12.1 Percentage by Mass of Ions in Seawater and Blood

Ion	Percentage in Seawater	Percentage in Blood
Na^+	2.36	0.322
Cl^-	1.94	0.366
Mg^{2+}	0.13	0.002
SO_4^{2-}	0.09	—
K^+	0.04	0.016
Ca^{2+}	0.04	0.0096
HCO_3^-	0.002	0.165
HPO_4^{2-}, $H_2PO_4^-$	—	0.01

Most ions are more abundant in seawater than they are in blood, with some notable exceptions. There is far more hydrogen carbonate ion (HCO_3^-) in blood than in seawater; indeed, it is the third most common ion in blood. This difference is significant because the HCO_3^- ion and some related species [CO_3^{2-}, $CO_2(aq)$] have an important role in controlling the acid-base properties of blood. Although there is a negligible amount of the two hydrogen phosphate ions (HPO_4^{2-} and $H_2PO_4^-$) in seawater, there is some in blood, where these ions also impact acid-base properties. Another notable difference is that blood has a negligible amount of the sulfate ion (SO_4^{2-}), but this ion is present in seawater.

Gold is present in seawater—but only a tiny amount. A current estimate of the amount of gold is about 1 part per every 1×10^{13} parts of seawater, which makes the extraction of gold from seawater unfeasible. However, it does mean that there are about 1.4×10^{14} g of gold in the world's oceans!

There are approximately 1.4×10^{14} g of gold in the oceans, but extracting it effectively is beyond current technologies.

Source: © Thinkstock

A solution is a *homogeneous mixture*—a mixture of two or more substances that are so intimately mixed that the mixture behaves in many ways like a single substance. Many chemical reactions occur when the reactants are dissolved in solution. In this chapter, we will introduce concepts that are applicable to solutions and the chemical reactions that occur in them.

12.1 Some Definitions

Learning Objectives

1. Learn some terminology involving solutions.
2. Explain why certain substances dissolve in other substances.

solvent

The major component of a solution.

solute

The minor component of a solution.

The major component of a solution is called the **solvent**. The minor component of a solution is called the **solute**. By major and minor we mean whichever component has the greater presence by mass or by moles. Sometimes this becomes confusing, especially with substances with very different molar masses. However, here we will confine the discussion to solutions for which the major component and the minor component are obvious.

Solutions exist for every possible phase of the solute and the solvent. Salt water, for example, is a solution of solid NaCl in liquid water; soda water is a solution of gaseous CO_2 in liquid water; and air is a solution of a gaseous solute (O_2) in a gaseous solvent (N_2). In all cases, however, the phase of the solution is the same phase as the solvent.

Example 1

A solution is made by dissolving 1.00 g of sucrose ($C_{12}H_{22}O_{11}$) in 100.0 g of liquid water. Identify the solvent and solute in the resulting solution.

Solution

Either by mass or by moles, the obvious minor component is sucrose, so it is the solute. Water—the majority component—is the solvent. The fact that the resulting solution is the same phase as water also indicates that water is the solvent.

Test Yourself

A solution is made by dissolving 3.33 g of HCl(g) in 40.0 g of liquid methyl alcohol (CH_3OH). Identify the solvent and solute in the resulting solution.

Answer

solute: HCl(g); solvent: CH_3OH

One important concept of solutions is in defining how much solute is dissolved in a given amount of solvent. This concept is called **concentration**. Various words are used to describe the relative amounts of solute. **Dilute** describes a solution that has very little solute, while **concentrated** describes a solution that has a lot of solute. One problem is that these terms are qualitative; they describe more or less but not exactly how much.

In most cases, only a certain maximum amount of solute can be dissolved in a given amount of solvent. This maximum amount is called the **solubility** of the solute. It is usually expressed in terms of the amount of solute that can dissolve in 100 g of the solvent at a given temperature. Table 12.2 lists the solubilities of some simple ionic compounds. These solubilities vary widely: NaCl can dissolve up to 36.1 g per 100 g of H_2O, while AgCl can dissolve only 0.00019 g per 100 g of H_2O.

TABLE 12.2 Solubilities of Some Ionic Compounds

Solute	Solubility (g per 100 g of H_2O at 25°C)
AgCl	0.00019
$CaCO_3$	0.0006
KBr	70.7
NaCl	36.1
$NaNO_3$	94.6

When the maximum amount of solute has been dissolved in a given amount of solvent, we say that the solution is **saturated** with solute. When less than the maximum amount of solute is dissolved in a given amount of solute, the solution is **unsaturated**. These terms are also qualitative terms because each solute has its own solubility. A solution of 0.00019 g of AgCl per 100 g of H_2O may be saturated, but with so little solute dissolved, it is also rather dilute. A solution of 36.1 g of NaCl in 100 g of H_2O is also saturated but rather concentrated. Ideally, we need more precise ways of specifying the amount of solute in a solution. We will introduce such ways in Section 2.

In some circumstances, it is possible to dissolve more than the maximum amount of a solute in a solution. Usually, this happens by heating the solvent, dissolving more solute, and letting the solution cool down slowly and carefully. Such solutions are called **supersaturated** solutions and are not stable; given an opportunity (such as dropping a crystal of solute in the solution), the excess solute will precipitate from the solution.

It should be obvious that some solutes dissolve in certain solvents but not others. NaCl, for example, dissolves in water but not in vegetable oil. Beeswax dissolves in liquid hexane but not water. What is it that makes a solute soluble in some solvents but not others?

The answer is intermolecular interactions. The intermolecular interactions include London dispersion forces, dipole-dipole interactions, and hydrogen bonding (as described in Chapter 7). From experimental studies, it has been determined that if molecules of a solute experience the same intermolecular forces that the solvent does, the solute will likely dissolve in that solvent. Therefore, NaCl—a very polar substance because it is composed of ions—dissolves in water, which is very polar, but not in oil, which is generally nonpolar. Nonpolar wax dissolves in nonpolar hexane but not in polar water. This concept leads to the general rule that "like dissolves like" for predicting whether a solute is soluble in a given solvent. However, this is a general rule, not an absolute statement, so it must be applied with care.

concentration

How much solute is dissolved in a given amount of solvent.

dilute

A solution with very little solute.

concentrated

A solution with a lot of solute.

solubility

The maximum amount of a solute that can be dissolved in a given amount of a solvent.

saturated

A solution with the maximum amount of solute dissolved in it.

unsaturated

A solution with less than the maximum amount of solute dissolved in it.

supersaturated

An unstable solution with more than the normal maximum amount of solute in it.

Example 2

Would I_2 be more soluble in CCl_4 or H_2O? Explain your answer.

Solution

I_2 is nonpolar. Of the two solvents, CCl_4 is nonpolar and H_2O is polar, so I_2 would be expected to be more soluble in CCl_4.

Test Yourself

Would C_3H_7OH be more soluble in CCl_4 or H_2O? Explain your answer.

Answer

H_2O because both experience hydrogen bonding

Key Takeaways

- Solutions are composed of a solvent (major component) and a solute (minor component).
- Concentration is the expression of the amount of solute in a given amount of solvent and can be described by several qualitative terms.
- Solubility is a specific amount of solute that can dissolve in a given amount of solvent.
- "Like dissolves like" is a useful rule for deciding if a solute will be soluble in a solvent.

Exercises

1. Define *solute* and *solvent*.
2. Define *saturated*, *unsaturated*, and *supersaturated*.
3. A solution is prepared by combining 2.09 g of CO_2 and 35.5 g of H_2O. Identify the solute and solvent.
4. A solution is prepared by combining 10.3 g of Hg(ℓ) and 45.0 g of Ag(s). Identify the solute and solvent.
5. Use Table 12.2 to decide if a solution containing 45.0 g of NaCl per 100 g of H_2O is unsaturated, saturated, or supersaturated.
6. Use Table 12.2 to decide if a solution containing 0.000092 g of AgCl per 100 g of H_2O is unsaturated, saturated, or supersaturated.
7. Would the solution in Exercise 5 be described as dilute or concentrated? Explain your answer.
8. Would the solution in Exercise 6 be described as dilute or concentrated? Explain your answer.
9. Identify a solute from Table 12.2 whose saturated solution can be described as dilute.
10. Identify a solute from Table 12.2 whose saturated solution can be described as concentrated.
11. Which solvent is Br_2 more likely soluble in—CH_3OH or C_6H_6?
12. Which solvent is NaOH more likely soluble in—CH_3OH or C_6H_6?
13. Compounds with the formula $C_nH_{2n+1}OH$ are soluble in H_2O when n is small but not when n is large. Suggest an explanation for this phenomenon.
14. Glucose has the following structure:

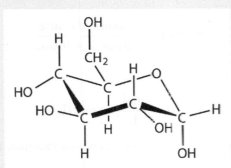

What parts of the molecule indicate that this substance is soluble in water?

Answers

1. The solvent is the majority component of a solution, whereas the solute is the minority component of a solution.

2. An unsaturated solution has less than the maximum amount of solute dissolved, whereas a saturated solution has the maximum amount of solute dissolved. A supersaturated solution has more than the maximum amount of solute dissolved.

3. solute: CO_2; solvent: H_2O

4. solute: Hg; solvent: Ag

5. supersaturated

6. unsaturated

7. concentrated because there is a lot of solute

8. dilute because there is only a tiny amount of solute present

9. AgCl or $CaCO_3$

10. NaCl

11. C_6H_6

12. CH_3OH

13. The nonpolar end dominates intermolecular forces when n is large.

14. the OH groups

12.2 Quantitative Units of Concentration

Learning Objective

1. Learn to determine specific concentrations with several common units.

Rather than qualitative terms (Section 1), we need quantitative ways to express the amount of solute in a solution; that is, we need specific units of concentration. In this section, we will introduce several common and useful units of concentration.

Molarity (M) is defined as the number of moles of solute divided by the number of liters of solution:

$$\text{molarity} = \frac{\text{moles of solute}}{\text{liters of solution}}$$

which can be simplified as

$$M = \frac{\text{mol}}{L}, \text{ or mol/L}$$

As with any mathematical equation, if you know any two quantities, you can calculate the third, unknown, quantity.

For example, suppose you have 0.500 L of solution that has 0.24 mol of NaOH dissolved in it. The concentration of the solution can be calculated as follows:

$$\text{molarity} = \frac{0.24 \text{ mol NaOH}}{0.500 \text{ L}} = 0.48 \text{ M NaOH}$$

The concentration of the solution is 0.48 M, which is spoken as "zero point forty-eight molarity" or "zero point forty-eight molar." If the quantity of the solute is given in mass units, you must convert mass units to mole units before using the definition of molarity to calculate concentration. For example, what is the molar concentration of a solution of 22.4 g of HCl dissolved in 1.56 L? First, convert the mass of solute to moles using the molar mass of HCl (36.5 g/mol):

$$22.4 \text{ g HCl} \times \frac{1 \text{ mol HCl}}{36.5 \text{ g HCl}} = 0.614 \text{ mol HCl}$$

Now we can use the definition of molarity to determine a concentration:

$$M = \frac{0.614 \text{ mol HCl}}{1.56 \text{ L}} = 0.394 \text{ M}$$

Example 3

What is the molarity of a solution made when 32.7 g of NaOH are dissolved to make 445 mL of solution?

Solution

To use the definition of molarity, both quantities must be converted to the proper units. First, convert the volume units from milliliters to liters:

$$445 \text{ mL} \times \frac{1 \text{ L}}{1,000 \text{ mL}} = 0.445 \text{ L}$$

Now we convert the amount of solute to moles, using the molar mass of NaOH, which is 40.0 g/mol:

$$32.7 \text{ g NaOH} \times \frac{1 \text{ mol NaOH}}{40.0 \text{ g NaOH}} = 0.818 \text{ mol NaOH}$$

Now we can use the definition of molarity to determine the molar concentration:

$$M = \frac{0.818 \text{ mol NaOH}}{0.445 \text{ L}} = 1.84 \text{ M NaOH}$$

Test Yourself

What is the molarity of a solution made when 66.2 g of $C_3H_{12}O_6$ are dissolved to make 235 mL of solution?

Answer

1.57 M

   The definition of molarity can be used to determine the amount of solute or the volume of solution, if the other information is given. Example 4 illustrates this situation.

Example 4

How many moles of solute are present in 0.108 L of a 0.887 M NaCl solution?

Solution

We know the volume and the molarity; we can use the definition of molarity to mathematically solve for the amount in moles. Substituting the quantities into the definition of molarity:

$$0.887 \text{ M} = \frac{\text{mol NaCl}}{0.108 \text{ L}}$$

We multiply the 0.108 L over to the other side of the equation and multiply the units together; "molarity × liters" equals moles, according to the definition of molarity. So:

$$\text{mol NaCl} = (0.887 \text{ M})(0.108 \text{ L}) = 0.0958 \text{ mol}$$

Test Yourself

How many moles of solute are present in 225 mL of a 1.44 M $CaCl_2$ solution?

Answer

0.324 mol

   If you need to determine volume, remember the rule that the unknown quantity must be by itself and in the numerator to determine the correct answer. Thus rearrangement of the definition of molarity is required.

Example 5

What volume of a 2.33 M $NaNO_3$ solution is needed to obtain 0.222 mol of solute?

Solution

Using the definition of molarity, we have:

$$2.33 \text{ M} = \frac{0.222 \text{ mol}}{\text{L}}$$

To solve for the number of liters, we bring the 2.33 M over to the right into the denominator, and the number of liters over to the left in the numerator. We now have:

$$\text{L} = \frac{0.222 \text{ mol}}{2.33 \text{ M}}$$

Dividing, the volume is 0.0953 L = 95.3 mL.

Test Yourself

What volume of a 0.570 M K_2SO_4 solution is needed to obtain 0.872 mol of solute?

Answer

1.53 L

A similar unit of concentration is **molality** (m), which is defined as the number of moles of solute per kilogram of solvent, not per liter of solution:

$$\text{molality} = \frac{\text{moles solute}}{\text{kilograms solvent}}$$

molality

The number of moles of solute per kilogram of solvent.

Mathematical manipulation of molality is the same as with molarity.

Another way to specify an amount is **percentage composition by mass** (or *mass percentage*, % m/m). It is defined as follows:

$$\text{\% m/m} = \frac{\text{mass of solute}}{\text{mass of entire sample}} \times 100\%$$

percentage composition by mass

Ratio of mass of solute to the total mass of a sample times 100.

It is not uncommon to see this unit used on commercial products (Figure 12.1).

Example 6

What is the mass percentage of Fe in a piece of metal with 87.9 g of Fe in a 113 g sample?

Solution

Using the definition of mass percentage, we have:

$$\text{\% m/m} = \frac{87.9 \text{ g Fe}}{113 \text{ g sample}} \times 100\% = 77.8\% \text{ Fe}$$

Test Yourself

What is the mass percentage of H_2O_2 in a solution with 1.67 g of H_2O_2 in a 55.5 g sample?

Answer

3.01%

Related concentration units are **parts per thousand (ppth)**, **parts per million (ppm)**, and **parts per billion (ppb)**. Parts per thousand is defined as follows:

$$\text{ppth} = \frac{\text{mass of solute}}{\text{mass of sample}} \times 1{,}000$$

There are similar definitions for parts per million and parts per billion:

$$\text{ppm} = \frac{\text{mass of solute}}{\text{mass of sample}} \times 1{,}000{,}000$$

$$\text{ppb} = \frac{\text{mass of solute}}{\text{mass of sample}} \times 1{,}000{,}000{,}000$$

Each unit is used for progressively lower and lower concentrations. The two masses must be expressed in the same unit of mass, so conversions may be necessary.

Example 7

If there is 0.6 g of Pb present in 277 g of solution, what is the Pb concentration in parts per thousand?

FIGURE 12.1
Concentration in Commercial Applications
The percentage of urea in this package is 5% m/m, meaning that there are 5 g of urea per 100 g of product.

Source: © Thinkstock

parts per thousand (ppth)

Ratio of mass of solute to total mass of sample times 1,000.

parts per million (ppm)

Ratio of mass of solute to total mass of sample times 1,000,000.

parts per billion (ppb)

Ratio of mass of solute to total mass of sample times 1,000,000,000.

Solution

Use the definition of parts per thousand to determine the concentration. Substituting:

$$\frac{0.6 \text{ g Pb}}{277 \text{ g solution}} \times 1,000 = 2.17 \text{ ppth}$$

Test Yourself

If there is 0.551 mg of As in 348 g of solution, what is the As concentration in ppm?

Answer

1.58 ppm

As with molarity and molality, algebraic rearrangements may be necessary to answer certain questions.

Example 8

The concentration of Cl^- ion in a sample of H_2O is 15.0 ppm. What mass of Cl^- ion is present in 240.0 mL of H_2O, which has a density of 1.00 g/mL?

Solution

First, use the density of H_2O to determine the mass of the sample:

$$240.0 \text{ mL} \times \frac{1.00 \text{ g}}{\text{mL}} = 240.0 \text{ g}$$

Now we can use the definition of ppm:

$$15.0 \text{ ppm} = \frac{\text{mass solute}}{240.0 \text{ g solution}} \times 1,000,000$$

Rearranging to solve for the mass of solute,

$$\text{mass solute} = \frac{(15.0 \text{ ppm})(240.0 \text{ g solution})}{1,000,000} = 0.0036 \text{ g} = 3.6 \text{ mg}$$

Test Yourself

The concentration of Fe^{3+} ion in a sample of H_2O is 335.0 ppm. What mass of Fe^{3+} ion is present in 3,450 mL of H_2O, which has a density of 1.00 g/mL?

Answer

1.16 g

For ionic solutions, we need to differentiate between the concentration of the salt versus the concentration of each individual ion. Because the ions in ionic compounds separate from each other when a compound is dissolved in a solution, the resulting concentration of the ion may be different from the concentration of the complete salt. For example, if 1 M NaCl were prepared, the solution could also be described as a solution of 1 M Na^+(aq) and 1 M Cl^-(aq) because there is one Na^+ ion and one Cl^- ion per formula unit of the salt. However, if the solution were 1 M $CaCl_2$, there are two Cl^-(aq) ions for every formula unit dissolved, so the concentration of Cl^-(aq) would be 2 M, not 1 M.

In addition, the total ion concentration is the sum of the individual ion concentrations. Thus, for the 1 M NaCl, the total ion concentration is 2 M; for the 1 M $CaCl_2$, the total ion concentration is 3 M.

Key Takeaway

- Quantitative units of concentration include molarity, molality, mass percentage, parts per thousand, parts per million, and parts per billion.

Exercises

1. Differentiate between molarity and molality.
2. Differentiate between mass percentage and parts per thousand.
3. What is the molarity of a solution made by dissolving 13.4 g of $NaNO_3$ in 345 mL of solution?
4. What is the molarity of a solution made by dissolving 332 g of $C_6H_{12}O_6$ in 4.66 L of solution?
5. How many moles of $MgCl_2$ are present in 0.0331 L of a 2.55 M solution?
6. How many moles of NH_4Br are present in 88.9 mL of a 0.228 M solution?
7. What volume of 0.556 M $NaCl$ is needed to obtain 0.882 mol of $NaCl$?
8. What volume of 3.99 M H_2SO_4 is needed to obtain 4.61 mol of H_2SO_4?
9. What volume of 0.333 M $Al(NO_3)_3$ is needed to obtain 26.7 g of $Al(NO_3)_3$?
10. What volume of 1.772 M $BaCl_2$ is needed to obtain 123 g of $BaCl_2$?
11. What are the individual ion concentrations and the total ion concentration in 0.66 M $Mg(NO_3)_2$?
12. What are the individual ion concentrations and the total ion concentration in 1.04 M $Al_2(SO_4)_3$?
13. If the $C_2H_3O_2^-$ ion concentration in a solution is 0.554 M, what is the concentration of $Ca(C_2H_3O_2)_2$?
14. If the Cl^- ion concentration in a solution is 2.61 M, what is the concentration of $FeCl_3$?

Answers

1. Molarity is moles per liter, whereas molality is moles per kilogram of solvent.
2. Mass percentage is a proportion of the total mass that is the solute, whereas parts per thousand is the number of grams of solute per 1,000 g of solution.
3. 0.457 M
4. 0.396 M
5. 0.0844 mol
6. 0.0203 mol
7. 1.59 L
8. 1.16 L
9. 0.376 L
10. 0.333 L
11. Mg^{2+} = 0.66 M; NO_3^- = 1.32 M; total: 1.98 M
12. Al^{3+} = 2.08 M; SO_4^{2-} = 3.12 M; total: 5.20 M
13. 0.277 M
14. 0.87 M

12.3 Dilutions and Concentrations

Learning Objective

1. Learn how to dilute and concentrate solutions.

Often, a worker will need to change the concentration of a solution by changing the amount of solvent. **Dilution** is the addition of solvent, which decreases the concentration of the solute in the solution. **Concentration** is the removal of solvent, which increases the concentration of the solute in the solution. (Do not confuse the two uses of the word concentration here!)

In both dilution and concentration, the amount of solute stays the same. This gives us a way to calculate what the new solution volume must be for the desired concentration of solute. From the definition of molarity,

$$\text{molarity} = \frac{\text{moles of solute}}{\text{liters of solution}}$$

we can solve for the number of moles of solute:

$$\text{moles of solute} = (\text{molarity})(\text{liters of solution})$$

A simpler way of writing this is to use M to represent molarity and V to represent volume. So the equation becomes:

$$\text{moles of solute} = MV$$

Because this quantity does not change before and after the change in concentration, the product MV must be the same before and after the concentration change. Using numbers to represent the initial and final conditions, we have:

$$M_1 V_1 = M_2 V_2$$

as the **dilution equation**. The volumes must be expressed in the same units. Note that this equation gives only the initial and final conditions, not the amount of the change. The amount of change must be determined by subtraction.

> **dilution**
>
> The addition of solvent, which decreases the concentration of the solute in the solution.

> **concentration**
>
> The removal of solvent, which increases the concentration of the solute in the solution.

> **dilution equation**
>
> The mathematical formula for calculating new concentrations or volumes when a solution is diluted or concentrated.

Example 9

If 25.0 mL of a 2.19 M solution are diluted to 72.8 mL, what is the final concentration?

Solution

It does not matter which set of conditions is labeled 1 or 2, as long as the conditions are paired together properly. Using the dilution equation, we have

$$(2.19 \text{ M})(25.0 \text{ mL}) = M_2(72.8 \text{ mL})$$

Solving for the second concentration (noting that the milliliter units cancel),

$$M_2 = 0.752 \text{ M}$$

The concentration of the solution has decreased. In going from 25.0 mL to 72.8 mL, 72.8 − 25.0 = 47.8 mL of solvent must be added.

Test Yourself

A 0.885 M solution of KBr whose initial volume is 76.5 mL has more water added until its concentration is 0.500 M. What is the new volume of the solution?

Answer

135.4 mL

Concentrating solutions involves removing solvent. Usually this is done by evaporating or boiling, assuming that the heat of boiling does not affect the solute. The dilution equation is used in these circumstances as well.

Chemistry Is Everywhere: Preparing IV Solutions

In a hospital emergency room, a physician orders an intravenous (IV) delivery of 100 mL of 0.5% KCl for a patient suffering from hypokalemia (low potassium levels). Does an aide run to a supply cabinet and take out an IV bag containing this concentration of KCl?

Not likely. It is more probable that the aide must make the proper solution from an IV bag of sterile solution and a more concentrated, sterile solution, called a *stock solution*, of KCl. The aide is expected to use a syringe to draw up some stock solution and inject it into the waiting IV bag and dilute it to the proper concentration. Thus the aide must perform a dilution calculation.

Medical personnel commonly must perform dilutions for IV solutions.

Source: © Thinkstock

If the stock solution is 10.0% KCl and the final volume and concentration need to be 100 mL and 0.50%, respectively, then it is an easy calculation to determine how much stock solution to use:

$$(10\%)V_1 = (0.50\%)(100 \text{ mL})$$

$$V_1 = 5 \text{ mL}$$

Of course, the addition of the stock solution affects the total volume of the diluted solution, but the final concentration is likely close enough even for medical purposes.

Medical and pharmaceutical personnel are constantly dealing with dosages that require concentration measurements and dilutions. It is an important responsibility: calculating the *wrong* dose can be useless, harmful, or even fatal!

Key Takeaway

- Calculate the new concentration or volume for a dilution or concentration of a solution.

Exercises

1. What is the difference between dilution and concentration?

2. What quantity remains constant when you dilute a solution?

3. A 1.88 M solution of NaCl has an initial volume of 34.5 mL. What is the final concentration of the solution if it is diluted to 134 mL?

4. A 0.664 M solution of NaCl has an initial volume of 2.55 L. What is the final concentration of the solution if it is diluted to 3.88 L?

5. If 1.00 mL of a 2.25 M H_2SO_4 solution needs to be diluted to 1.00 M, what will be its final volume?

6. If 12.00 L of a 6.00 M HNO_3 solution needs to be diluted to 0.750 M, what will be its final volume?

7. If 665 mL of a 0.875 M KBr solution are boiled gently to concentrate the solute to 1.45 M, what will be its final volume?

8. If 1.00 L of an LiOH solution is boiled down to 164 mL and its initial concentration is 0.00555 M, what is its final concentration?

9. How much water must be added to 75.0 mL of 0.332 M $FeCl_3(aq)$ to reduce its concentration to 0.250 M?

10. How much water must be added to 1.55 L of 1.65 M $Sc(NO_3)_3(aq)$ to reduce its concentration to 1.00 M?

Answers

1. Dilution is a decrease in a solution's concentration, whereas concentration is an increase in a solution's concentration.

2. moles of solute

3. 0.484 M

4. 0.436 M

5. 2.25 mL

6. 96.0 L

7. 401 mL

8. 0.0338 M

9. 24.6 mL

10. 1.01 L

12.4 Concentrations as Conversion Factors

Learning Objective

1. Apply concentration units as conversion factors.

Concentration can be a conversion factor between the amount of solute and the amount of solution or solvent (depending on the definition of the concentration unit). As such, concentrations can be useful in a variety of stoichiometry problems. In many cases, it is best to use the original definition of the concentration unit; it is that definition that provides the conversion factor.

A simple example of using a concentration unit as a conversion factor is one in which we use the definition of the concentration unit and rearrange; we can do the calculation again as a unit conversion, rather than as a definition. For example, suppose we ask how many moles of solute are present in 0.108 L of a 0.887 M NaCl solution. Because 0.887 M means 0.887 mol/L, we can use this second expression for the concentration as a conversion factor:

$$0.108 \text{ L NaCl} \times \frac{0.887 \text{ mol NaCl}}{\text{L NaCl}} = 0.0958 \text{ mol NaCl}$$

(There is an understood 1 in the denominator of the conversion factor.) If we used the definition approach, we get the same answer, but now we are using conversion factor skills. Like any other conversion factor that relates two different types of units, the reciprocal of the concentration can be also used as a conversion factor.

Example 10

Using concentration as a conversion factor, how many liters of 2.35 M $CuSO_4$ are needed to obtain 4.88 mol of $CuSO_4$?

Solution

This is a one-step conversion, but the concentration must be written as the reciprocal for the units to work out:

$$4.88 \text{ mol CuSO}_4 \times \frac{1 \text{ L}}{2.35 \text{ mol}} = 2.08 \text{ L of solution}$$

Test Yourself

Using concentration as a conversion factor, how many liters of 0.0444 M CH_2O are needed to obtain 0.0773 mol of CH_2O?

Answer

1.74 L

Of course, once quantities in moles are available, another conversion can give the mass of the substance, using molar mass as a conversion factor.

Example 11

What mass of solute is present in 0.765 L of 1.93 M NaOH?

Solution

This is a two-step conversion, first using concentration as a conversion factor to determine the number of moles and then the molar mass of NaOH (40.0 g/mol) to convert to mass:

$$0.765 \text{ L} \times \frac{1.93 \text{ mol NaOH}}{\text{L solution}} \times \frac{40.0 \text{ g NaOH}}{1 \text{ mol NaOH}} = 59.1 \text{ g NaOH}$$

Test Yourself

What mass of solute is present in 1.08 L of 0.0578 M H_2SO_4?

Answer

6.12 g

More complex stoichiometry problems using balanced chemical reactions can also use concentrations as conversion factors. For example, suppose the following equation represents a chemical reaction:

$$2AgNO_3(aq) + CaCl_2(aq) \rightarrow 2AgCl(s) + Ca(NO_3)_2(aq)$$

If we wanted to know what volume of 0.555 M $CaCl_2$ would react with 1.25 mol of $AgNO_3$, we first use the balanced chemical equation to determine the number of moles of $CaCl_2$ that would react and then use concentration to convert to liters of solution:

$$1.25 \text{ mol } AgNO_3 \times \frac{1 \text{ mol } CaCl_2}{2 \text{ mol } AgNO_3} \times \frac{1 \text{ L solution}}{0.555 \text{ mol } CaCl_2} = 1.13 \text{ L } CaCl_2$$

This can be extended by starting with the mass of one reactant, instead of moles of a reactant.

Example 12

What volume of 0.0995 M $Al(NO_3)_3$ will react with 3.66 g of Ag according to the following chemical equation?

$$3Ag + Al(NO_3)_3 \rightarrow 3AgNO_3 + Al$$

Solution

Here, we first must convert the mass of Ag to moles before using the balanced chemical equation and then the definition of molarity as a conversion factor:

$$3.66 \text{ g } Ag \times \frac{1 \text{ mol } Ag}{107.97 \text{ g } Ag} \times \frac{1 \text{ mol } Al(NO_3)_3}{3 \text{ mol } Ag} \times \frac{1 \text{ L solution}}{0.0995 \text{ mol } Al(NO_3)_3} = 0.114 \text{ L}$$

The strikeouts show how the units cancel.

Test Yourself

What volume of 0.512 M NaOH will react with 17.9 g of $H_2C_2O_4(s)$ according to the following chemical equation?

$$H_2C_2O_4 + 2NaOH \rightarrow Na_2C_2O_4 + 2H_2O$$

Answer

0.777 L

We can extend our skills even further by recognizing that we can relate quantities of one solution to quantities of another solution. Knowing the volume and concentration of a solution containing one reactant, we can determine how much of another solution of another reactant will be needed using the balanced chemical equation.

Example 13

A student takes a precisely measured sample, called an *aliquot*, of 10.00 mL of a solution of $FeCl_3$. The student carefully adds 0.1074 M $Na_2C_2O_4$ until all the Fe^{3+}(aq) has precipitated as $Fe_2(C_2O_4)_3$(s). Using a precisely measured tube called a burette, the student finds that 9.04 mL of the $Na_2C_2O_4$ solution was added to precipitate completely the Fe^{3+}(aq). What was the concentration of the $FeCl_3$ in the original solution? (A precisely measured experiment like this, which is meant to determine the amount of a substance in a sample, is called a *titration*.) The balanced chemical equation is as follows:

$$2FeCl_3 + 3Na_2C_2O_4 \rightarrow Fe_2(C_2O_4)_3 + 6NaCl$$

Solution

First we need to determine the number of moles of $Na_2C_2O_4$ that reacted. We will convert the volume to liters and then use the concentration of the solution as a conversion factor:

$$9.04 \; \cancel{mL} \times \frac{1 \; \cancel{L}}{1,000 \; \cancel{mL}} \times \frac{0.1074 \; mol \; Na_2C_2O_4}{\cancel{L}} = 0.000971 \; mol \; Na_2C_2O_4$$

Now we will use the balanced chemical equation to determine the number of moles of Fe^{3+}(aq) that were present in the initial aliquot:

$$0.000971 \; mol \; \cancel{Na_2C_2O_4} \times \frac{2 \; mol \; FeCl_3}{3 \; mol \; \cancel{Na_2C_2O_4}} = 0.000647 \; mol \; FeCl_3$$

Then we determine the concentration of $FeCl_3$ in the original solution. Converting 10.00 mL into liters (0.01000 L), we use the definition of molarity directly:

$$M = \frac{mol}{L} = \frac{0.000647 \; mol \; FeCl_3}{0.01000 \; L} = 0.0647 \; M \; FeCl_3$$

Test Yourself

A student titrates 25.00 mL of H_3PO_4 with 0.0987 M KOH. She uses 54.06 mL to complete the chemical reaction. What is the concentration of H_3PO_4?

$$H_3PO_4 + 3KOH \rightarrow K_3PO_4 + 3H_2O$$

Answer

0.0711 M

When a student performs a titration, a measured amount of one solution is added to another reactant.

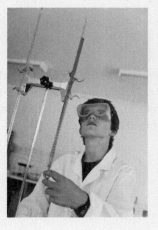

Source: © Thinkstock

We have used molarity exclusively as the concentration of interest, but that will not always be the case. The next example shows a different concentration unit being used.

Example 14

H_2O_2 is used to determine the amount of Mn according to this balanced chemical equation:

$$2MnO_4^- + 5H_2O_2 + 6H^+ \rightarrow 2Mn^{2+} + 5O_2 + 8H_2O$$

What mass of 3.00% m/m H_2O_2 solution is needed to react with 0.355 mol of MnO_4^-(aq)?

Solution

Because we are given an initial amount in moles, all we need to do is use the balanced chemical equation to determine the number of moles of H_2O_2 and then convert to find the mass of H_2O_2. Knowing that the H_2O_2 solution is 3.00% by mass, we can determine the mass of solution needed:

$$0.355 \; \cancel{mol \; MnO_4^-} \times \frac{5 \; \cancel{mol \; H_2O_2}}{2 \; \cancel{mol \; MnO_4^-}} \times \frac{34.02 \; \cancel{g \; H_2O_2}}{\cancel{mol \; H_2O_2}}$$

$$\times \frac{100 \; g \; solution}{3 \; \cancel{g \; H_2O_2}} = 1{,}006 \; g \; solution$$

The first conversion factor comes from the balanced chemical equation, the second conversion factor is the molar mass of H_2O_2, and the third conversion factor comes from the definition of percentage concentration by mass.

Test Yourself

Use the balanced chemical reaction for MnO_4^- and H_2O_2 to determine what mass of O_2 is produced if 258 g of 3.00% m/m H_2O_2 is reacted with MnO_4^-.

Answer

7.28 g

Key Takeaway

- Know how to apply concentration units as conversion factors.

Exercises

1. Using concentration as a conversion factor, how many moles of solute are in 3.44 L of 0.753 M $CaCl_2$?

2. Using concentration as a conversion factor, how many moles of solute are in 844 mL of 2.09 M $MgSO_4$?

3. Using concentration as a conversion factor, how many liters are needed to provide 0.822 mol of NaBr from a 0.665 M solution?

4. Using concentration as a conversion factor, how many liters are needed to provide 2.500 mol of $(NH_2)_2CO$ from a 1.087 M solution?

5. What is the mass of solute in 24.5 mL of 0.755 M $CoCl_2$?

6. What is the mass of solute in 3.81 L of 0.0232 M $Zn(NO_3)_2$?

7. What volume of solution is needed to provide 9.04 g of NiF_2 from a 0.332 M solution?

8. What volume of solution is needed to provide 0.229 g of CH_2O from a 0.00560 M solution?

9. What volume of 3.44 M HCl will react with 5.33 mol of $CaCO_3$?

$$2HCl + CaCO_3 \rightarrow CaCl_2 + H_2O + CO_2$$

10. What volume of 0.779 M NaCl will react with 40.8 mol of $Pb(NO_3)_2$?

$$Pb(NO_3)_2 + 2NaCl \rightarrow PbCl_2 + 2NaNO_3$$

11. What volume of 0.905 M H_2SO_4 will react with 26.7 mL of 0.554 M NaOH?

$$H_2SO_4 + 2NaOH \rightarrow Na_2SO_4 + 2H_2O$$

12. What volume of 1.000 M Na_2CO_3 will react with 342 mL of 0.733 M H_3PO_4?

$$3Na_2CO_3 + 2H_3PO_4 \rightarrow 2Na_3PO_4 + 3H_2O + 3CO_2$$

13. It takes 23.77 mL of 0.1505 M HCl to titrate with 15.00 mL of $Ca(OH)_2$. What is the concentration of $Ca(OH)_2$? You will need to write the balanced chemical equation first.

14. It takes 97.62 mL of 0.0546 M NaOH to titrate a 25.00 mL sample of H_2SO_4. What is the concentration of H_2SO_4? You will need to write the balanced chemical equation first.

15. It takes 4.667 mL of 0.0997 M HNO_3 to dissolve some solid Cu. What mass of Cu can be dissolved?

$$Cu + 4HNO_3(aq) \rightarrow Cu(NO_3)_2(aq) + 2NO_2 + 2H_2O$$

16. It takes 49.08 mL of 0.877 M NH_3 to dissolve some solid AgCl. What mass of AgCl can be dissolved?

$$AgCl(s) + 4NH_3(aq) \rightarrow Ag(NH_3)_4Cl(aq)$$

17. What mass of 3.00% H_2O_2 is needed to produce 66.3 g of $O_2(g)$?

$$2H_2O_2(aq) \rightarrow 2H_2O(\ell) + O_2(g)$$

18. A 0.75% solution of Na_2CO_3 is used to precipitate Ca^{2+} ions from solution. What mass of solution is needed to precipitate 40.7 L of solution with a concentration of 0.0225 M $Ca^{2+}(aq)$?

$$Na_2CO_3(aq) + Ca^{2+}(aq) \rightarrow CaCO_3(s) + 2Na^+(aq)$$

Answers

1. 2.59 mol
2. 1.76 mol
3. 1.24 L
4. 2.300 L
5. 2.40 g
6. 16.7 g
7. 0.282 L
8. 1.36 L
9. 3.10 L
10. 105 L
11. 8.17 mL

12. 0.376 L
13. 0.1192 M
14. 0.107 M
15. 7.39 mg
16. 1.54 g
17. 4.70 kg
18. 12,900 g

12.5 Colligative Properties of Solutions

Learning Objectives

1. Name four colligative properties.
2. Calculate changes in vapor pressure, melting point, and boiling point of solutions.
3. Calculate the osmotic pressure of solutions.

The properties of solutions are very similar to the properties of their respective pure solvents. This makes sense because the majority of the solution *is* the solvent. However, some of the properties of solutions differ from pure solvents in measurable and predictable ways. The differences are proportional to the fraction that the solute particles occupy in the solution. These properties are called **colligative properties**; the word *colligative* comes from the Greek word meaning "related to the number," implying that these properties are related to the number of solute particles, not their identities.

Before we introduce the first colligative property, we need to introduce a new concentration unit. The **mole fraction** of the ith component in a solution, χ_i, is the number of moles of that component divided by the total number of moles in the sample:

$$\chi_i = \frac{\text{moles of } i\text{th component}}{\text{total moles}}$$

(χ is the lowercase Greek letter chi.) The mole fraction is always a number between 0 and 1 (inclusive) and has no units; it is just a number.

colligative property

A property of solutions related to the fraction that the solute particles occupy in the solution, not their identity.

mole fraction

The ratio of the number of moles of a component to the total number of moles in a system.

Example 15

A solution is made by mixing 12.0 g of $C_{10}H_8$ in 45.0 g of C_6H_6. What is the mole fraction of $C_{10}H_8$ in the solution?

Solution

We need to determine the number of moles of each substance, add them together to get the total number of moles, and then divide to determine the mole fraction of $C_{10}H_8$. The number of moles of $C_{10}H_8$ is as follows:

$$12.0 \ \text{g C}_{10}\text{H}_8 \times \frac{1 \ \text{mol C}_{10}\text{H}_8}{128.18 \ \text{g C}_{10}\text{H}_8} = 0.0936 \ \text{mol C}_{10}\text{H}_8$$

The number of moles of C_6H_6 is as follows:

$$45.0 \ \text{g C}_6\text{H}_6 \times \frac{1 \ \text{mol C}_6\text{H}_6}{78.12 \ \text{g C}_6\text{H}_6} = 0.576 \ \text{mol C}_6\text{H}_6$$

The total number of moles is:

$$0.0936 \ \text{mol} + 0.576 \ \text{mol} = 0.670 \ \text{mol}$$

Now we can calculate the mole fraction of $C_{10}H_8$:

$$\chi_{C_{10}H_8} = \frac{0.0936 \ \text{mol}}{0.670 \ \text{mol}} = 0.140$$

The mole fraction is a number between 0 and 1 and is unitless.

Test Yourself

A solution is made by mixing 33.8 g of CH_3OH in 50.0 g of H_2O. What is the mole fraction of CH_3OH in the solution?

Answer

0.275

A useful thing to note is that the sum of the mole fractions of all substances in a mixture equals 1. Thus the mole fraction of C_6H_6 in Example 15 could be calculated by evaluating the definition of mole fraction a second time, or—because there are only two substances in this particular mixture—we can subtract the mole fraction of the $C_{10}H_8$ from 1 to get the mole fraction of C_6H_6.

Now that this new concentration unit has been introduced, the first colligative property can be considered. As was mentioned in Chapter 7, all pure liquids have a characteristic vapor pressure in equilibrium with the liquid phase, the partial pressure of which is dependent on temperature. Solutions, however, have a lower vapor pressure than the pure solvent has, and the amount of lowering is dependent on the fraction of solute particles, as long as the solute itself does not have a significant vapor pressure (the term *nonvolatile* is used to describe such solutes). This colligative property is called **vapor pressure depression** (or *lowering*). The actual vapor pressure of the solution can be calculated as follows:

$$P_{\text{soln}} = \chi_{\text{solv}} \ P^*_{\text{solv}}$$

vapor pressure depression

The decrease of a solution's vapor pressure because of the presence of a solute.

where P_{soln} is the vapor pressure of the solution, χ_{solv} is the mole fraction of the solvent particles, and P^*_{solv} is the vapor pressure of the pure solvent at that temperature (which is data that must be provided). This equation is known as **Raoult's law** (the approximate pronunciation is *rah-OOLT*). Vapor pressure depression is rationalized by presuming that solute particles take positions at the surface in place of solvent particles, so not as many solvent particles can evaporate.

Raoult's law

The mathematical formula for calculating the vapor pressure of a solution.

Example 16

A solution is made by mixing 12.0 g of $C_{10}H_8$ in 45.0 g of C_6H_6. If the vapor pressure of pure C_6H_6 is 95.3 torr, what is the vapor pressure of the solution?

Solution

This is the same solution that was in Example 15, but here we need the mole fraction of C_6H_6. The number of moles of $C_{10}H_8$ is as follows:

$$12.0 \ \cancel{\text{g C}_{10}\text{H}_8} \times \frac{1 \ \text{mol C}_{10}\text{H}_8}{128.18 \ \cancel{\text{g C}_{10}\text{H}_8}} = 0.0936 \ \text{mol C}_{10}\text{H}_8$$

The number of moles of C_6H_6 is as follows:

$$45.0 \ \cancel{\text{g C}_6\text{H}_6} \times \frac{1 \ \text{mol C}_6\text{H}_6}{78.12 \ \cancel{\text{g C}_6\text{H}_6}} = 0.576 \ \text{mol C}_6\text{H}_6$$

So the total number of moles is:

$$0.0936 \ \text{mol} + 0.576 \ \text{mol} = 0.670 \ \text{mol}$$

Now we can calculate the mole fraction of C_6H_6:

$$\chi_{C_6H_6} = \frac{0.576 \ \text{mol}}{0.670 \ \text{mol}} = 0.860$$

(The mole fraction of $C_{10}H_8$ calculated in Example 15 plus the mole fraction of C_6H_6 equals 1, which is mathematically required by the definition of mole fraction.) Now we can use Raoult's law to determine the vapor pressure in equilibrium with the solution:

$$P_2 = (0.860 \ \text{mol})(95.3 \ \text{torr}) = 82.0 \ \text{torr}$$

The solution has a lower vapor pressure than the pure solvent.

Test Yourself

A solution is made by mixing 33.8 g of $C_6H_{12}O_6$ in 50.0 g of H_2O. If the vapor pressure of pure water is 25.7 torr, what is the vapor pressure of the solution?

Answer

24.1 torr

Two colligative properties are related to solution concentration as expressed in molality. Recall the definition of molality:

$$\text{molality} = \frac{\text{moles solute}}{\text{kilograms solvent}}$$

Because the vapor pressure of a solution with a nonvolatile solute is depressed compared to that of the pure solvent, it requires a higher temperature for the solution's vapor pressure to reach 1.00 atm (760 torr). Recall that this is the definition of the normal boiling point: the temperature at which the vapor pressure of the liquid equals 1.00 atm. As such, the normal boiling point of the solution is higher than that of the pure solvent. This property is called **boiling point elevation**.

The change in boiling point (ΔT_b) is easily calculated:

$$\Delta T_b = mK_b$$

where m is the molality of the solution and K_b is called the **boiling point elevation constant**, which is a characteristic of the solvent. Several boiling point elevation constants (as well as boiling point temperatures) are listed in Table 12.3.

boiling point elevation

The increase of a solution's boiling point because of the presence of solute.

boiling point elevation constant

The constant that relates the molality concentration of a solution and its boiling point change.

TABLE 12.3 Boiling Point Data for Various Liquids

Liquid	Boiling Point (°C)	K_b (°C/m)
$HC_2H_3O_2$	117.90	3.07
C_6H_6	80.10	2.53

Liquid	Boiling Point (°C)	K_b (°C/m)
CCl_4	76.8	4.95
H_2O	100.00	0.512

Remember that what is initially calculated is the *change* in boiling point temperature, not the new boiling point temperature. Once the change in boiling point temperature is calculated, it must be added to the boiling point of the pure solvent—because boiling points are always elevated—to get the boiling point of the solution.

Example 17

What is the boiling point of a 2.50 *m* solution of $C_6H_4Cl_2$ in CCl_4? Assume that $C_6H_4Cl_2$ is not volatile.

Solution

Using the equation for the boiling point elevation,

$$\Delta T_b = (2.50\,m)(4.95\,°C/m) = 12.4\,°C$$

Note how the molality units have canceled. However, we are not finished. We have calculated the change in the boiling point temperature, not the final boiling point temperature. If the boiling point goes up by 12.4°C, we need to add this to the normal boiling point of CCl_4 to get the new boiling point of the solution:

$$T_{BP} = 76.8\,°C + 12.4\,°C = 89.2\,°C$$

The boiling point of the solution is predicted to be 89.2°C.

Test Yourself

What is the boiling point of a 6.95 *m* solution of $C_{12}H_{22}O_{11}$ in H_2O?

Answer

103.6°C

freezing point depression

The decrease of a solution's freezing point because of the presence of solute.

The boiling point of a solution is higher than the boiling point of the pure solvent, but the opposite occurs with the freezing point. The freezing point of a solution is lower than the freezing point of the pure solvent. Think of this by assuming that solute particles interfere with solvent particles coming together to make a solid, so it takes a lower temperature to get the solvent particles to solidify. This is called **freezing point depression**.

The equation to calculate the change in the freezing point for a solution is similar to the equation for the boiling point elevation:

$$\Delta T_f = m K_f$$

freezing point depression constant

The constant that relates the molality concentration of a solution and its freezing point change.

where *m* is the molality of the solution and K_f is called the **freezing point depression constant**, which is also a characteristic of the solvent. Several freezing point depression constants (as well as freezing point temperatures) are listed in Table 12.4.

TABLE 12.4 Freezing Point Data for Various Liquids

Liquid	Freezing Point (°C)	K_f (°C/m)
$HC_2H_3O_2$	16.60	3.90
C_6H_6	5.51	4.90
C_6H_{12}	6.4	20.2

Liquid	Freezing Point (°C)	K_f (°C/m)
$C_{10}H_8$	80.2	6.8
H_2O	0.00	1.86

Remember that this equation calculates the change in the freezing point, not the new freezing point. What is calculated needs to be subtracted from the normal freezing point of the solvent because freezing points always go down.

Example 18

What is the freezing point of a 1.77 m solution of CBr_4 in C_6H_6?

Solution

We use the equation to calculate the change in the freezing point and then subtract this number from the normal freezing point of C_6H_6 to get the freezing point of the solution:

$$\Delta T_f = (1.77\,m)(4.90\,°C/m) = 8.67\,°C$$

Now we subtract this number from the normal freezing point of C_6H_6, which is 5.51°C:

$$T_{FP} = 5.51\,°C - 8.67\,°C = -3.16\,°C$$

The freezing point of the solution is –3.16°C.

Test Yourself

What is the freezing point of a 3.05 m solution of CBr_4 in $C_{10}H_8$?

Answer

59.5°C

Freezing point depression is one colligative property we use in everyday life. Many antifreezes used in automobile radiators use solutions that have a lower freezing point than normal so that automobile engines can operate at subfreezing temperatures. We also take advantage of freezing point depression when we sprinkle various compounds on ice to thaw it in the winter for safety (Figure 12.2). The compounds make solutions that have a lower freezing point, so rather than forming slippery ice, any ice is liquefied and runs off, leaving a safer pavement behind.

Before we introduce the final colligative property, we need to present a new concept. A **semipermeable membrane** is a thin membrane that will pass certain small molecules but not others. A thin sheet of cellophane, for example, acts as a semipermeable membrane.

FIGURE 12.2 Salt and Safety
Salt or other compounds take advantage of the freezing point depression to minimize the formation of ice on sidewalks and roads, thus increasing safety.

Source: © Thinkstock

semipermeable membrane

A thin membrane that will pass certain small molecules but not others.

osmosis

The tendency of solvent
molecules to pass through
a semipermeable
membrane due to
concentration differences.

osmotic pressure

The tendency of a solution
to pass solvent through a
semipermeable membrane
due to concentration
differences.

Consider the system in Figure 12.3a. A semipermeable membrane separates two solutions having the different concentrations marked. Curiously, this situation is not stable; there is a tendency for water molecules to move from the dilute side (on the left) to the concentrated side (on the right) until the concentrations are equalized, as in Figure 12.3b. This tendency is called **osmosis**. In osmosis, the solute remains in its original side of the system; only solvent molecules move through the semipermeable membrane. In the end, the two sides of the system will have different volumes. Because a column of liquid exerts a pressure, there is a pressure difference Π on the two sides of the system that is proportional to the height of the taller column. This pressure difference is called the **osmotic pressure**, which is a colligative property.

FIGURE 12.3 Osmosis
(a) Two solutions of differing concentrations are placed on either side of a semipermeable membrane. (b) When osmosis occurs, solvent molecules selectively pass through the membrane from the dilute solution to the concentrated solution, diluting it until the two concentrations are the same. The pressure exerted by the different height of the solution on the right is called the osmotic pressure.

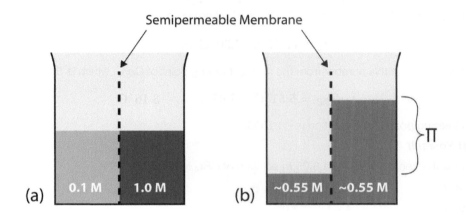

The osmotic pressure of a solution is easy to calculate:

$$\Pi = MRT$$

where Π is the osmotic pressure of a solution, M is the molarity of the solution, R is the ideal gas law constant, and T is the absolute temperature. This equation is reminiscent of the ideal gas law we considered in Chapter 11.

Example 19

What is the osmotic pressure of a 0.333 M solution of $C_6H_{12}O_6$ at 25°C?

Solution

First we need to convert our temperature to kelvins:

$$T = 25 + 273 = 298 \text{ K}$$

Now we can substitute into the equation for osmotic pressure, recalling the value for R:

$$\Pi = (0.333 \text{ M}) \left(0.08205 \frac{\text{L} \cdot \text{atm}}{\text{mol} \cdot \text{K}} \right) (298 \text{ K})$$

The units may not make sense until we realize that molarity is defined as moles per liter:

$$\Pi = \left(0.333\ \frac{mol}{L}\right)\left(0.08205\ \frac{L\cdot atm}{mol\cdot K}\right)(298\ K)$$

Now we see that the moles, liters, and kelvins cancel, leaving atmospheres, which is a unit of pressure. Solving,

$$\Pi = 8.14\ atm$$

This is a substantial pressure! It is the equivalent of a column of water 84 m tall.

Test Yourself

What is the osmotic pressure of a 0.0522 M solution of $C_{12}H_{22}O_{11}$ at 55°C?

Answer

1.40 atm

Osmotic pressure is important in biological systems because cell walls are semipermeable membranes. In particular, when a person is receiving intravenous (IV) fluids, the osmotic pressure of the fluid needs to be approximately the same as blood serum; otherwise bad things can happen. Figure 12.4 shows three red blood cells: Figure 12.4a shows a healthy red blood cell. Figure 12.4b shows a red blood cell that has been exposed to a lower concentration than normal blood serum (a so-called *hypotonic* solution); the cell has plumped up as solvent moves into the cell to dilute the solutes inside. Figure 12.4c shows a red blood cell exposed to a higher concentration than normal blood serum (*hypertonic*); water leaves the red blood cell, so it collapses onto itself. Only when the solutions inside and outside the cell are the same (*isotonic*) will the red blood cell be able to do its job.

FIGURE 12.4 Osmotic Pressure and Red Blood Cells
(a) This is what a normal red blood cell looks like. (b) When a red blood cell is exposed to a hypotonic solution, solvent goes through the cell membrane and dilutes the inside of the cell. (c) When a red blood cell is exposed to a hypertonic solution, solvent goes from the cell to the surrounding solution, diluting the hypertonic solution and collapsing the cell. Neither of these last two cases is desirable, so IV solutions must be isotonic with blood serum so as not to cause deleterious effects.

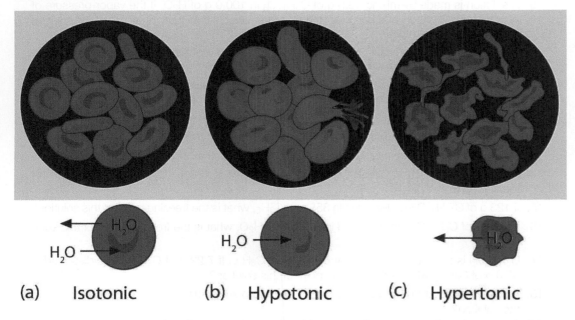

(a)   Isotonic   (b)   Hypotonic   (c)   Hypertonic

Osmotic pressure is also the reason you should not drink seawater if you're stranded in a lifeboat on an ocean; seawater has a higher osmotic pressure than most of the fluids in your body. You *can* drink the water, but ingesting it will pull water out of your cells as osmosis works to dilute the seawater. Ironically, your cells will die of thirst, and you will also die. (It is OK to drink the water if you are stranded on a body of freshwater, at least from an osmotic pressure perspective.) Osmotic pressure is also thought to be important—in addition to capillary action—in getting water to the tops of tall trees.

Key Takeaways

- Colligative properties depend only on the number of dissolved particles (that is, the concentration), not their identity.
- Raoult's law is concerned with the vapor pressure depression of solutions.
- The boiling points of solutions are always higher, and the freezing points of solutions are always lower, than those of the pure solvent.
- Osmotic pressure is caused by concentration differences between solutions separated by a semipermeable membrane and is an important biological issue.

Exercises

1. What are the three colligative properties that involve phase changes?
2. Which colligative property does not involve a phase change? Give an example of its importance.
3. If 45.0 g of C_6H_6 and 60.0 g of $C_6H_5CH_3$ are mixed together, what is the mole fraction of each component?
4. If 125 g of N_2 are mixed with 175 g of O_2, what is the mole fraction of each component?
5. If 36.5 g of NaCl are mixed with 63.5 g of H_2O, what is the mole fraction of each component?
6. An alloy of stainless steel is prepared from 75.4 g of Fe, 12.6 g of Cr, and 10.8 g of C. What is the mole fraction of each component?
7. A solution is made by mixing 12.0 g of $C_{10}H_8$ in 45.0 g of C_6H_6. If the vapor pressure of pure C_6H_6 is 76.5 torr at a particular temperature, what is the vapor pressure of the solution at the same temperature?
8. A solution is made by mixing 43.9 g of $C_6H_{12}C_6$ in 100.0 g of H_2O. If the vapor pressure of pure water is 26.5 torr at a particular temperature, what is the vapor pressure of the solution at the same temperature?
9. At 300°C, the vapor pressure of Hg is 32.97 torr. If 0.775 g of Au were dissolved into 3.77 g of Hg, what would be the vapor pressure of the solution?
10. At 300°C, the vapor pressure of Hg is 32.97 torr. What mass of Au would have to be dissolved in 5.00 g of Hg to lower its vapor pressure to 25.00 torr?
11. If 25.0 g of $C_6H_{12}O_6$ are dissolved in 100.0 g of H_2O, what is the boiling point of this solution?
12. If 123 g of $C_{10}H_{16}O$ are dissolved in 355 g of C_6H_6, what is the boiling point of this solution?
13. If 1 mol of solid CBr_4 is mixed with 2 mol of CCl_4, what is the boiling point of this solution?
14. A solution of $C_2H_2O_4$ in CH_3COOH has a boiling point of 123.40°C. What is the molality of the solution?
15. If 123 g of $C_{10}H_{16}O$ are dissolved in 355 g of C_6H_6, what is the freezing point of this solution?
16. If 25.0 g of $C_6H_{12}O_6$ are dissolved in 100.0 g of H_2O, what is the freezing point of this solution?
17. $C_8H_{17}OH$ is a nonvolatile solid that dissolves in C_6H_{12}. If 7.22 g of $C_8H_{17}OH$ is dissolved in 45.3 g of C_6H_{12}, what is the freezing point of this solution?
18. A solution of $C_2H_2O_4$ in CH_3COOH has a freezing point of 10.00°C. What is the molality of the solution?
19. If 25.0 g of $C_6H_{12}O_6$ are dissolved in H_2O to make 0.100 L of solution, what is the osmotic pressure of this solution at 25°C?
20. If 2.33 g of $C_{27}H_{46}O$ are dissolved in liquid CS_2 to make 50.00 mL of solution, what is the osmotic pressure of this solution at 298 K?

21. At 298 K, what concentration of solution is needed to have an osmotic pressure of 1.00 atm?

22. The osmotic pressure of blood is about 7.65 atm at 37°C. What is the approximate concentration of dissolved solutes in blood? (There are many different solutes in blood, so the answer is indeed an approximation.)

Answers

1. boiling point elevation, freezing point depression, vapor pressure depression
2. osmotic pressure; biological cells (answers will vary)
3. mole fraction C_6H_6: 0.469; mole fraction $C_6H_5CH_3$: 0.531
4. mole fraction N_2: 0.449; mole fraction O_2: 0.551
5. mole fraction NaCl: 0.157; mole fraction H_2O: 0.843
6. mole fraction Fe: 0.542; mole fraction Cr: 0.0971; mole fraction C: 0.361
7. 65.8 torr
8. 25.4 torr
9. 27.26 torr
10. 1.57 g
11. 100.71°C
12. 85.86°C
13. 92.9°C
14. 1.79 m
15. −5.65°C
16. −0.26°C
17. −18.3°C
18. 1.70 m
19. 33.9 atm
20. 2.95 atm
21. 0.0409 M
22. 0.301 M

12.6 Colligative Properties of Ionic Solutes

Learning Objective

1. Determine the colligative properties of solutions of ionic solutes.

In Section 5, we considered the colligative properties of solutions with molecular solutes. What about solutions with ionic solutes? Do they exhibit colligative properties? Yes, they do.

But there is a complicating factor: ionic solutes separate into ions when they dissolve. This increases the total number of particles dissolved in solution and *increases the impact on the resulting colligative property*. Historically, this greater-than-expected impact on colligative properties was one main piece of evidence for ionic compounds separating into ions (increased electrical conductivity was another piece of evidence).

For example, when NaCl dissolves, it separates into two ions:

$$NaCl(s) \rightarrow Na^+(aq) + Cl^-(aq)$$

This means that a 1 M solution of NaCl actually has a net particle concentration of 2 M. The observed colligative property will then be twice as large as expected for a 1 M solution.

It is easy to incorporate this concept into our equations to calculate the respective colligative property. We define the **van't Hoff factor** (i) as the number of particles each solute formula unit breaks apart into when it dissolves. Previously, we have always tacitly assumed that the van't Hoff factor is simply 1. But for some ionic compounds, i is not 1, as shown in Table 12.5.

van't Hoff factor

The number of particles each solute formula unit breaks apart into when it dissolves.

TABLE 12.5 Ideal van't Hoff Factors for Ionic Compounds

Compound	*i*
NaCl	2
KBr	2
LiNO$_3$	2
CaCl$_2$	3
Mg(C$_2$H$_3$O$_2$)$_2$	3
FeCl$_3$	4
Al$_2$(SO$_4$)$_3$	5

The ideal van't Hoff factor is equal to the number of ions that form when an ionic compound dissolves.

Example 20

Predict the van't Hoff factor for Sr(OH)$_2$.

Solution

When Sr(OH)$_2$ dissolves, it separates into one Sr^{2+} ion and two OH$^-$ ions:

$$Sr(OH)_2 \rightarrow Sr^{2+}(aq) + 2OH^-(aq)$$

Because it breaks up into three ions, its van't Hoff factor is 3.

Test Yourself

What is the van't Hoff factor for Fe(NO$_3$)$_3$?

Answer

4

It is the "ideal" van't Hoff factor because this is what we expect from the ionic formula. However, this factor is usually correct only for dilute solutions (solutions less than 0.001 M). At concentrations greater than 0.001 M, there are enough interactions between ions of opposite charge that the net concentration of the ions is less than expected—sometimes significantly. The actual van't Hoff factor is thus less than the ideal one. Here, we will use ideal van't Hoff factors.

Revised equations to calculate the effect of ionization are then easily produced:

$$\Delta T_b = imK_b$$

$$\Delta T_{\mathrm{f}} = imK_{\mathrm{f}}$$

$$\Pi = iMRT$$

where all variables have been previously defined. To calculate vapor pressure depression according to Raoult's law, the mole fraction of solvent particles must be recalculated to take into account the increased number of particles formed on ionization.

Example 21

Determine the freezing point of a 1.77 m solution of NaCl n H_2O. The freezing point constant for H_2O is 1.86°C/m.

Solution

For NaCl, we need to remember to include the van't Hoff factor, which is 2. Otherwise, the calculation of the freezing point is straightforward:

$$imK_{\mathrm{f}} = (2)(1.77\,m)(1.86\,°C/m) = 6.58\,°C$$

This represents the change in the freezing point, which s decreasing. So we have to subtract this change from the normal freezing point of water, 0.00°C

$$0.00 - 6.58 = -6.58\,°C$$

Test Yourself

Determine the boiling point of a 0.887 m solution of $CaCl_2$ in H_2O.

Answer

101.36°C

Food and Drink App: Salting Pasta Cooking Water

When cooking dried pasta, many recipes call for salting the water before cooking the pasta. Some argue—with colligative properties on their side—that adding salt to the water raises the boiling point, thus cooking the pasta faster. Is there any truth to this?

Why do so many recipes call for adding salt to water when boiling pasta? Is it to raise the boiling temperature of the water?

Source: © Thinkstock

To judge the veracity of this claim, we can calculate how much salt should be added to the water to raise the boiling temperature by 1.0°C, with the presumption that dried pasta cooks noticeably faster at 101°C than at 100°C (although a 1° difference may make only a negligible change in cooking times). We can calculate the molality that the water should have:

$$1.0\,°C = m(0.512\,°C/m)$$

$$m = 1.95$$

We have ignored the van't Hoff factor in our estimation because this obviously is not a dilute solution. Let us further assume that we are using 4 L of water (which is very close to 4 qt, which in turn equals 1 gal). Because 4 L of water is about 4 kg (it is actually slightly less at 100°C), we can determine how much salt (NaCl) to add:

$$4 \; \cancel{kg\,H_2O} \times \frac{1.95 \; \cancel{mol\,NaCl}}{\cancel{kg\,H_2O}} \times \frac{58.5 \; g\,NaCl}{1 \; \cancel{mol\,NaCl}} = 456.3 \; g\,NaCl$$

This is just over 1 lb of salt and is equivalent to nearly 1 cup in the kitchen. In your experience, do you add almost a cup of salt to a pot of water to make pasta? Certainly not! A few pinches, perhaps one-fourth of a teaspoon, but not almost a cup! It is obvious that the little amount of salt that most people add to their pasta water is not going to raise the boiling point of the water significantly.

So why do people add some salt to boiling water? There are several possible reasons, the most obvious of which is taste: adding salt adds a little bit of salt flavor to the pasta. It cannot be much because most of the salt remains in the water, not in the cooked pasta. However, it may be enough to detect with our taste buds. The other obvious reason is habit; recipes tell us to add salt, so we do, even if there is little scientific or culinary reason to do so.

Key Takeaways

- For ionic solutes, the calculation of colligative properties must include the fact that the solutes separate into multiple particles when they dissolve.
- The equations for calculating colligative properties of solutions of ionic solvents include the van't Hoff factor, i.

Exercises

1. Explain why we need to consider a van't Hoff factor for ionic solutes but not for molecular solutes.

2. NaCl is often used in winter to melt ice on roads and sidewalks, but calcium chloride ($CaCl_2$) is also used. Which would be better (on a mole-by-mole basis), and why?

3. Calculate the boiling point of an aqueous solution of $NaNO_3$ made by mixing 15.6 g of $NaNO_3$ with 100.0 g of H_2O. Assume an ideal van't Hoff factor.

4. Many labs use a cleaning solution of KOH dissolved in C_2H_5OH. If 34.7 g of KOH were dissolved in 88.0 g of C_2H_5OH, what is the boiling point of this solution? The normal boiling point of C_2H_5OH is 78.4°C and its $K_b = 1.19°C/m$. Assume an ideal van't Hoff factor.

5. What is the freezing point of a solution made by dissolving 345 g of $CaCl_2$ in 1,550 g of H_2O? Assume an ideal van't Hoff factor.

6. A classic homemade ice cream can be made by freezing the ice cream mixture using a solution of 250 g of NaCl dissolved in 1.25 kg of ice water. What is the temperature of this ice water? Assume an ideal van't Hoff factor.

7. Seawater can be approximated as a 3.5% NaCl solution by mass; that is, 3.5 g of NaCl are combined with 96.5 g H_2O. What is the osmotic pressure of seawater? Assume an ideal van't Hoff factor.

8. The osmotic pressure of blood is 7.65 atm at 37°C. If blood were considered a solution of NaCl, what is the molar concentration of NaCl in blood? Assume an ideal van't Hoff factor.

9. What is the vapor pressure of an aqueous solution of 36.4 g of KBr in 199.5 g of H_2O if the vapor pressure of H_2O at the same temperature is 32.55 torr? What other solute(s) would give a solution with the same vapor pressure? Assume an ideal van't Hoff factor.

10. Assuming an ideal van't Hoff factor, what mole fraction is required for a solution of $Mg(NO_3)_2$ to have a vapor pressure of 20.00 torr at 25.0°C? The vapor pressure of the solvent is 23.61 torr at this temperature.

Answers

1. Ionic solutes separate into more than one particle when they dissolve, whereas molecular solutes do not.

2. $CaCl_2$ because it is composed of three ions

3. 101.9°C

4. 95.1°C

5. −7.5°C

6. −12.7°C

7. 30.3 atm

8. 0.150 M

9. 30.86 torr; any two-ion salt should have the same effect.

10. 0.0510

12.7 End-of-Chapter Material

Additional Exercises

1. One brand of ethyl alcohol (Everclear) is 95% ethyl alcohol, with the remaining 5% being water. What is the solvent and what is the solute of this solution?

2. Give an example of each type of solution from your own experience.

    a. A solution composed of a gas solute in a liquid solvent.

    b. A solution composed of a solid solute in a liquid solvent.

    c. A solution composed of a liquid solute in a liquid solvent.

    d. A solution composed of a solid solute in a solid solvent. (Hint: usually such solutions are made as liquids and then solidified.)

3. Differentiate between the terms *saturated* and *concentrated*.

4. Differentiate between the terms *unsaturated* and *dilute*.

5. What mass of $FeCl_2$ is present in 445 mL of 0.0812 M $FeCl_2$ solution?

6. What mass of SO_2 is present in 26.8 L of 1.22 M SO_2 solution?

7. What volume of 0.225 M $Ca(OH)_2$ solution is needed to deliver 100.0 g of $Ca(OH)_2$?

8. What volume of 12.0 M HCl solution is needed to obtain exactly 1.000 kg of HCl?

9. The World Health Organization recommends that the maximum fluoride ion concentration in drinking water be 1.0 ppm. Assuming water has the maximum concentration, if an average person drinks 1,920 mL of water per day, how many milligrams of fluoride ion are being ingested?

10. For sanitary reasons, water in pools should be chlorinated to a maximum level of 3.0 ppm. In a typical 5,000 gal pool that contains 21,200 kg of water, what mass of chlorine must be added to obtain this concentration?

11. Given its notoriety, you might think that uranium is very rare, but it is present at about 2–4 ppm of the earth's crust, which is more abundant than silver or mercury. If the earth's crust is estimated to have a mass of 8.50×10^{20} kg, what range of mass is thought to be uranium in the crust?

12. Chromium is thought to be an ultratrace element, with about 8.9 ng present in a human body. If the average body mass is 75.0 kg, what is the concentration of chromium in the body in pptr?

13. What mass of 3.00% H_2O_2 solution is needed to produce 35.7 g of $O_2(g)$ at 295 K at 1.05 atm pressure?

$$2H_2O_2(aq) \rightarrow 2H_2O(\ell) + O_2(g)$$

14. What volume of pool water is needed to generate 1.000 L of $Cl_2(g)$ at standard temperature and pressure if the pool contains 4.0 ppm HOCl and the water is slightly acidic? The chemical reaction is as follows:

$$HOCl(aq) + HCl(aq) \rightarrow H_2O(\ell) + Cl_2(g)$$

Assume the pool water has a density of 1.00 g/mL.

15. A 0.500 *m* solution of $MgCl_2$ has a freezing point of −2.60°C. What is the true van't Hoff factor of this ionic compound? Why is it less than the ideal value?

16. The osmotic pressure of a 0.050 M LiCl solution at 25.0°C is 2.26 atm. What is the true van't Hoff factor of this ionic compound? Why is it less than the ideal value?

17. Order these solutions in order of increasing boiling point, assuming an ideal van't Hoff factor for each: 0.10 m $C_6H_{12}O_6$, 0.06 m NaCl, 0.4 m Au(NO$_3$)$_3$, and 0.4 m Al$_2$(SO$_4$)$_3$.

18. Order these solutions in order of decreasing osmotic pressure, assuming an ideal van't Hoff factor: 0.1 M HCl, 0.1 M CaCl$_2$, 0.05 M MgBr$_2$, and 0.07 M Ga(C$_2$H$_3$O$_2$)$_3$

Answers

1. solvent: ethyl alcohol; solute: water

3. Saturated means all the possible solute that can dissolve is dissolved, whereas concentrated means that a lot of solute is dissolved.

5. 4.58 g

7. 6.00 L

9. 1.92 mg

11. 1.7×10^{15} to 3.4×10^{15} kg

13. 2,530 g

15. 2.80; it is less than 3 because not all ions behave as independent particles.

17. 0.10 m $C_6H_{12}O_6$ < 0.06 m NaCl < 0.4 m Au(NO$_3$)$_3$ < 0.4 m Al$_2$(SO$_4$)$_3$

CHAPTER 13
Energy and Chemical Reactions

Opening Essay

It takes energy to launch a spaceship into space. If it takes 1 energy unit to warm 0.25 g of water by 1°C, then it takes over 15,100 energy units to put that 0.25 g of water into earth orbit. Some of the most powerful engines designed to lift rockets into space were part of the Saturn V rocket, which was built by the US National Aeronautics and Space Administration (NASA). The rocket had three stages, with the first stage having the capability of launching about 3.5 million kg of mass. About 2.3 million kg was the actual fuel for the first stage; rockets in space have the unpleasant task of having to take their own chemicals with them to provide thrust.

It takes a lot of energy to launch a rocket into space. The Saturn V rocket used five of the most powerful engines ever built to take its initial step into orbit

Source: © Thinkstock

Having to carry its own fuel puts a lot of mass burden on an engine in space. This is why NASA is developing other types of engines to minimize fuel mass. An ion thruster uses xenon atoms that have had at least one electron removed from their atoms. The resulting ions can be accelerated by electric fields, causing a thrust. Because xenon atoms are very large for atoms, the thrusting efficiency is high even though the actual thrust is low. Because of this, ion engines are useful only in space.

Ion drives have low thrust but high efficiency. They have already been used on several space missions, including NASA's *Deep Space 1* spacecraft and Japan's *Hayabusa* asteroid sampling probe.

Source: Photo courtesy of NASA, http://commons.wikimedia.org/wiki/File:Ion_Engine_Test_Firing_-_GPN-2000-000482.jpg.

Energy is a very important quantity in science and the world around us. Although most of our energy ultimately comes from the sun, much of the energy we use on a daily basis is rooted in chemical reactions. The gasoline in your car, the electricity in your house, the food in your diet—all provide substances for chemical reactions to provide energy (gasoline, food) or are produced from chemical reactions (electricity, about 50% of which is generated by burning coal). As such, it is only natural that the study of chemistry involves energy.

13.1 Energy

Learning Objectives

1. Define *energy*.
2. Know the units of energy.
3. Understand the law of conservation of energy.

energy

The ability to do work.

joule

The SI unit of energy.

Energy is the ability to do work. Think about it: when you have a lot of energy, you can do a lot of work; but if you're low on energy, you don't want to do much work. Work (w) itself is defined as a force (F) operating over a distance (Δx):

$$w = F \times \Delta x$$

In SI, force has units of newtons (N), while distance has units of meters. Therefore, work has units of N·m. This compound unit is redefined as a **joule** (J):

$$1 \text{ joule} = 1 \text{ newton} \cdot \text{meter}$$

$$1 \text{ J} = 1 \text{ N} \cdot \text{m}$$

Because energy is the ability to do work, energy is also measured in joules. This is the primary unit of energy we will use here.

How much is 1 J? It is enough to warm up about one-fourth of a gram of water by 1°C. It takes about 12,000 J to warm a cup of coffee from room temperature to 50°C. So a joule is not a lot of energy. It will not be uncommon to measure energies in thousands of joules, so the kilojoule (kJ) is a common unit of energy, with 1 kJ equal to 1,000 J.

An older—but still common—unit of energy is the *calorie*. The calorie (cal) was originally defined in terms of warming up a given quantity of water. The modern definition of calorie equates it to joules:

$$1 \text{ cal} = 4.184 \text{ J}$$

One area where the calorie is used is in nutrition. Energy contents of foods are often expressed in calories. However, the calorie unit used for foods is actually the kilocalorie (kcal). Most foods indicate this by spelling the word with a capital C—Calorie. Figure 13.1 shows one example. So be careful counting calories when you eat!

Example 1

The label in Figure 13.1 states that the serving has 38 Cal. How many joules is this?

Solution

We recognize that with a capital C, the Calories unit is actually kilocalories. To determine the number of joules, we convert first from kilocalories to calories (using the definition of the *kilo*-prefix) and then from calories to joules (using the relationship between calories and joules). So

$$38 \text{ kcal} \times \frac{1{,}000 \text{ cal}}{1 \text{ kcal}} \times \frac{4.184 \text{ J}}{1 \text{ cal}} = 160{,}000 \text{ J}$$

Test Yourself

A serving of breakfast cereal usually has 110 Cal. How many joules of energy is this?

Answer

460,000 J

FIGURE 13.1
Calories on Food Labels
This label expresses the energy content of the food, but in Calories (which are actually kilocalories).

Nutrition Facts		
Serving Size 1/4 Cup (30g)		
Servings Per Container About 38		
Amount Per Serving		
Calories 200	Calories from Fat 150	
		% Daily Value*
Total Fat 17g		26%
Saturated Fat 2.5g		13%
Trans Fat 0g		
Cholesterol 0mg		0%
Sodium 120mg		5%
Total Carbohydrate 7g		2%
Dietary Fiber 2g		8%
Sugars 1g		
Protein 5g		
Vitamin A 0%	•	Vitamin C 0%
Calcium 4%	•	Iron 8%
*Percent Daily Values are based on a 2,000 calorie diet.		

Source: © Thinkstock

In the study of energy, we use the term **system** to describe the part of the universe under study: a beaker, a flask, or a container whose contents are being observed and measured. An **isolated system** is a system that does not allow a transfer of energy or matter into or out of the system. A good approximation of an isolated system is a closed, insulated thermos-type bottle. The fact that the thermos-type bottle is closed keeps matter from moving in or out, and the fact that it is insulated keeps energy from moving in or out.

One of the fundamental ideas about the total energy of an isolated system is that is does not increase or decrease. When this happens to a quantity, we say that the quantity is *conserved*. The statement that the total energy of an isolated system does not change is called the **law of conservation of energy**. As a scientific law, this concept occupies the highest level of understanding we have about the natural universe.

system

The part of the universe under study.

isolated system

A system that does not allow a transfer of energy or matter into or out of the system.

law of conservation of energy

The total energy of an isolated system does not increase or decrease.

Key Takeaways

- Energy is the ability to do work and uses the unit joule.
- The law of conservation of energy states that the total energy of an isolated system does not increase or decrease.

Exercises

1. Define *energy*. How is work related to energy?

2. Give two units of energy and indicate which one is preferred.
3. Express the quantity of 422 J in calories.
4. Express the quantity of 3.225 kJ in calories.
5. Express the quantity 55.69 cal in joules.
6. Express the quantity 965.33 kcal in joules.
7. How does a Calorie differ from a calorie?
8. Express the quantity 965.33 Cal in joules.
9. What is the law of conservation of energy?
10. What does the word *conserved* mean as applied to the law of conservation of energy?

Answers

1. Energy is the ability to do work. Work is a form of energy.
2. Joule and calorie; joule is preferred in science, although calorie (i.e., Calorie) is common when expressing energy content of food.
3. 101 cal
4. 771 cal
5. 233.0 J
6. 4,040,000 J, or 4,040 kJ
7. A Calorie is actually a kilocalorie, or 1,000 calories.
8. 4,040,000 J, or 4,040 kJ
9. The total energy of an isolated system does not increase or decrease.
10. Conserved means that a quantity does not change.

13.2 Work and Heat

Learning Objectives

1. Define a type of work in terms of pressure and volume.
2. Define *heat*.
3. Relate the amount of heat to a temperature change.

We have already defined work as a force acting through a distance. It turns out that there are other equivalent definitions of work that are also important in chemistry.

When a certain volume of a gas expands, it works against an external pressure to expand (Figure 13.2). That is, the gas must perform work. Assuming that the external pressure P_{ext} is constant, the amount of work done by the gas is given by the equation

$$w = -P_{ext} \times \Delta V$$

where ΔV is the change in volume of the gas. This term is always the final volume minus the initial volume,

$$\Delta V = V_{final} - V_{initial}$$

and can be positive or negative, depending on whether V_{final} is larger (is expanding) or smaller (is contracting) than $V_{initial}$. The negative sign in the equation for work is important and implies that as volume expands (ΔV is positive), the gas in the system is *losing* energy as work. On the other hand, if the gas is contracting, ΔV is negative, and the two negative signs make the work positive, so energy is being added to the system.

FIGURE 13.2 Volume versus Pressure
When a gas expands against an external pressure, the gas performs work.

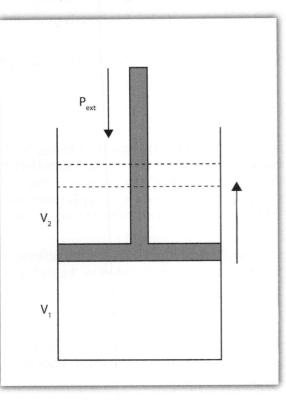

Finally, let us consider units. Volume changes are usually expressed in units like liters, while pressures are usually expressed in atmospheres. When we use the equation to determine work, the unit for work comes out as liter-atmospheres, or L·atm. This is not a very common unit for work. However, there is a conversion factor between L·atm and the common unit of work, joules:

$$1\,\text{L} \cdot \text{atm} = 101.32\,\text{J}$$

Using this conversion factor and the previous equation for work, we can calculate the work performed when a gas expands or contracts.

Example 2

What is the work performed by a gas if it expands from 3.44 L to 6.19 L against a constant external pressure of 1.26 atm? Express the final answer in joules.

Solution

First we need to determine the change in volume, ΔV. A change is always the final value minus the initial value:

$$\Delta V = V_{final} - V_{initial} = 6.19\,\text{L} - 3.44\,\text{L} = 2.75\,\text{L}$$

Now we can use the definition of work to determine the work done:

$$w = -P_{ext} \cdot \Delta V = -(1.26 \text{ atm})(2.75 \text{ L}) = -3.47 \text{ L} \cdot \text{atm}$$

Now we construct a conversion factor from the relationship between liter·atmospheres and joules:

$$-3.47 \text{ L·atm} \times \frac{101.32 \text{ J}}{1 \text{ L·atm}} = -351 \text{ J}$$

We limit the final answer to three significant figures, as appropriate.

Test Yourself

What is the work performed when a gas expands from 0.66 L to 1.33 L against an external pressure of 0.775 atm?

Answer

−53 J

heat

The transfer of energy from one body to another due to a difference in temperature.

Heat is another aspect of energy. **Heat** is the transfer of energy from one body to another due to a difference in temperature. For example, when we touch something with our hands, we interpret that object as either hot or cold depending on how energy is transferred: If energy is transferred into your hands, the object feels hot. If energy is transferred from your hands to the object, your hands feel cold. Because heat is a measure of energy transfer, heat is also measured in joules.

For a given object, the amount of heat (q) involved is proportional to two things: the mass of the object (m) and the temperature change (ΔT) evoked by the energy transfer. We can write this mathematically as

$$q \propto m \times \Delta T$$

specific heat capacity

The proportionality constant between heat, mass, and temperature change; also called specific heat.

where $\propto$ means "is proportional to." To make a proportionality an equality, we include a proportionality constant. In this case, the proportionality constant is labeled c and is called the **specific heat capacity**, or, more succinctly, *specific heat*:

$$q = mc\Delta T$$

where the mass, specific heat, and change in temperature are multiplied together. Specific heat is a measure of how much energy is needed to change the temperature of a substance; the larger the specific heat, the more energy is needed to change the temperature. The units for specific heat are $\frac{J}{g \cdot °C}$ or $\frac{J}{g \cdot K}$, depending on what the unit of ΔT is. You may note a departure from the insistence that temperature be expressed in Kelvin. That is because a *change* in temperature has the same value whether the temperatures are expressed in degrees Celsius or kelvins.

Example 3

Calculate the heat involved when 25.0 g of Fe increase in temperature from 22°C to 76°C. The specific heat of Fe is 0.449 J/g·°C.

Solution

First we need to determine ΔT. A change is always the final value minus the initial value:

$$\Delta T = 76\,°C - 22\,°C = 54\,°C$$

Now we can use the expression for q, substitute for all variables, and solve for heat:

$$q = (25.0 \text{ g}) \left(0.449 \frac{\text{J}}{\text{g} \cdot {}^\circ\text{C}} \right) (54 \, {}^\circ\text{C}) = 610 \text{ J}$$

Note how the g and °C units cancel, leaving J, a unit of heat. Also note that this value of q is inherently positive, meaning that energy is going into the system.

Test Yourself

Calculate the heat involved when 76.5 g of Ag increase in temperature from 17.8°C to 144.5°C. The specific heat of Ag is 0.233 J/g·°C.

Answer

2,260 J

As with any equation, when you know all but one variable in the expression for q, you can determine the remaining variable by using algebra.

Example 4

It takes 5,408 J of heat to raise the temperature of 373 g of Hg by 104°C. What is the specific heat of Hg?

Solution

We can start with the equation for q, but now different values are given, and we need to solve for specific heat. Note that ΔT is given directly as 104°C. Substituting,

$$5{,}408 \text{ J} = (373 \text{ g}) c (104 \, {}^\circ\text{C})$$

We divide both sides of the equation by 373 g and 104°C:

$$c = \frac{5408 \text{ J}}{(373 \text{ g})(104 \, {}^\circ\text{C})}$$

Combining the numbers and bringing together all the units, we get:

$$c = 0.139 \frac{\text{J}}{\text{g} \cdot {}^\circ\text{C}}$$

Test Yourself

Gold has a specific heat of 0.129 J/g·°C. If 1,377 J are needed to increase the temperature of a sample of gold by 99.9°C, what is the mass of the gold?

Answer

107 g

Table 13.1 lists the specific heats of some substances. Specific heat is a physical property of a substance, so it is a characteristic of the substance.

TABLE 13.1 Specific Heats of Various Substances

Substance	Specific Heat (J/g·°C)
water	4.184
iron	0.449
gold	0.129
mercury	0.139
aluminum	0.900

Substance	Specific Heat (J/g·°C)
ethyl alcohol	2.419
magnesium	1.03
helium	5.171
oxygen	0.918

Key Takeaways

- Work can be defined as a gas changing volume against a constant external pressure.
- Heat is the transfer of energy due to temperature differences.
- Heat can be calculated in terms of mass, temperature change, and specific heat.

Exercises

1. Give two definitions of work.

2. What is the sign on work when a sample of gas increases its volume? Explain why work has that sign.

3. What is the work when a gas expands from 3.00 L to 12.60 L against an external pressure of 0.888 atm?

4. What is the work when a gas expands from 0.666 L to 2.334 L against an external pressure of 2.07 atm?

5. What is the work when a gas contracts from 3.45 L to 0.97 L under an external pressure of 0.985 atm?

6. What is the work when a gas contracts from 4.66 L to 1.22 L under an external pressure of 3.97 atm?

7. Like work, the sign on heat can be positive or negative. What is happening to the total energy of a system if heat is positive?

8. Like work, the sign on heat can be positive or negative. What is happening to the total energy of a system if heat is negative?

9. What is the heat when 55.6 g of Fe increase temperature from 25.6°C to 177.9°C? The heat capacity of Fe is in Table 13.1.

10. What is the heat when 0.444 g of Au increases temperature from 17.8°C to 222.5°C? The heat capacity of Au is in Table 13.1.

11. What is the heat when 245 g of H_2O cool from 355 K to 298 K? The heat capacity of H_2O is in Table 13.1.

12. What is the heat when 100.0 g of Mg cool from 725 K to 552 K? The heat capacity of Mg is in Table 13.1.

13. It takes 452 J of heat to raise the temperature of a 36.8 g sample of a metal from 22.9°C to 98.2°C. What is the heat capacity of the metal?

14. It takes 2,267 J of heat to raise the temperature of a 44.5 g sample of a metal from 33.9°C to 288.3°C. What is the heat capacity of the metal?

15. An experimenter adds 336 J of heat to a 56.2 g sample of Hg. What is its change in temperature? The heat capacity of Hg is in Table 13.1.

16. To a 0.444 g sample of H_2O, 23.4 J of heat are added. What is its change in temperature? The heat capacity of H_2O is in Table 13.1.

17. An unknown mass of Al absorbs 187.9 J of heat and increases its temperature from 23.5°C to 35.6°C. What is the mass of the aluminum? How many moles of aluminum is this?

18. A sample of He goes from 19.4°C to 55.9°C when 448 J of energy are added. What is the mass of the helium? How many moles of helium is this?

Answers

1. Work is a force acting through a distance or a volume changing against some pressure.
2. The sign on work is negative because the system expends energy to expand.
3. −864 J
4. −350. J
5. 248 J
6. 1,380 J
7. When heat is positive, the total energy of the system is increasing.
8. When heat is negative, the total energy of the system is decreasing.
9. 3.80×10^3 J
10. 11.7 J
11. −58,400 J
12. −17,800 J
13. 0.163 J/g·°C
14. 0.200 J/g·°C
15. 43.0°C
16. 12.6°C
17. 17.3 g; 0.640 mol
18. 2.37 g; 0.593 mol

13.3 Enthalpy and Chemical Reactions

Learning Objectives

1. Define *enthalpy*.
2. Properly express the enthalpy change of chemical reactions.
3. Explain how enthalpy changes are measured experimentally.

Now that we have shown how energy, work, and heat are related, we are ready to consider energy changes in chemical reactions. A fundamental concept is that *every chemical reaction occurs with a concurrent change in energy*. Now we need to learn how to properly express these energy changes.

Our study of gases in Chapter 11 and our definition of work in Section 2 indicate that conditions like pressure, volume, and temperature affect the energy content of a system. What we need is a definition of energy that holds when some of these conditions are specified (somewhat similar to our definition of standard temperature and pressure in our study of gases). We define the **enthalpy change** (ΔH) as the heat of a process when pressure is held constant:

$$\Delta H \equiv q \quad \text{at constant pressure}$$

The letter H stands for "enthalpy," a kind of energy, while the Δ implies a change in the quantity. We will always be interested in the change in H, rather than the absolute value of H itself.

enthalpy change

The heat of a process at constant pressure; denoted ΔH.

When a chemical reaction occurs, there is a characteristic change in enthalpy. The enthalpy change for a reaction is typically written after a balanced chemical equation and on the same line. For example, when two moles of hydrogen react with one mole of oxygen to make two moles of water, the characteristic enthalpy change is 570 kJ. We write the equation as:

$$2H_2(g) + O_2(g) \rightarrow 2H_2O(\ell) \qquad \Delta H = -570 \text{ kJ}$$

A chemical equation that includes an enthalpy change is called a **thermochemical equation**. A thermochemical equation is assumed to refer to the equation in molar quantities, which means it must be interpreted in terms of moles, not individual molecules.

thermochemical equation

A chemical equation that includes an enthalpy change.

Example 5

Write the thermochemical equation for the reaction of $PCl_3(g)$ with $Cl_2(g)$ to make $PCl_5(g)$, which has an enthalpy change of −88 kJ.

Solution

The thermochemical equation is:

$$PCl_3(g) + Cl_2(g) \rightarrow PCl_5(g) \qquad \Delta H = -88 \text{ kJ}$$

Test Yourself

Write the thermochemical equation for the reaction of $N_2(g)$ with $O_2(g)$ to make $2NO(g)$, which has an enthalpy change of 181 kJ.

Answer

$$N_2(g) + O_2(g) \rightarrow 2NO(g) \qquad \Delta H = 181 \text{ kJ}$$

endothermic

A chemical reaction that has a positive change in enthalpy.

exothermic

A chemical reaction that has a negative change in enthalpy.

You may have noticed that the ΔH for a chemical reaction may be positive or negative. The number is assumed to be positive if it has no sign; a + sign can be added explicitly to avoid confusion. A chemical reaction that has a positive ΔH is said to be **endothermic**, while a chemical reaction that has a negative ΔH is said to be **exothermic**.

What does it mean if the ΔH of a process is positive? It means that the system in which the chemical reaction is occurring is gaining energy. If one considers the energy of a system as being represented as a height on a vertical energy plot, the enthalpy change that accompanies the reaction can be diagrammed as in part (a) in Figure 13.3: the energy of the reactants has some energy, and the system increases its energy as it goes to products. The products are higher on the vertical scale than the reactants. Endothermic, then, implies that the system *gains*, or absorbs, energy. Where does this energy come from? It comes from the surroundings.

An opposite situation exists for an exothermic process, as shown in part (b) in Figure 13.3. If the enthalpy change of a reaction is negative, the system is losing energy, so the products have less energy than the reactants, and the products are lower on the vertical energy scale than the reactants are. Exothermic, then, implies that the system *loses*, or gives off, energy. Where does this energy go? It goes into the surroundings.

FIGURE 13.3 Reaction Energy

(a) In an endothermic reaction, the energy of the system increases (i.e., moves higher on the vertical scale of energy). (b) In an exothermic reaction, the energy of the system decreases (i.e., moves lower on the vertical scale of energy).

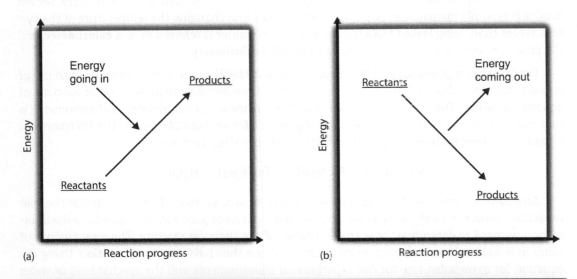

(a)

(b)

Example 6

Consider this thermochemical equation.

$$2CO(g) + O_2(g) \rightarrow 2CO_2(g) \qquad \Delta H = -565 \text{ kJ}$$

Is it exothermic or endothermic? How much energy is given off or absorbed?

Solution

By definition, a chemical reaction that has a negative ΔH is exothermic, meaning that this much energy—in this case, 565 kJ—is given off by the reaction.

Test Yourself

Consider this thermochemical equation.

$$CO_2(g) + H_2(g) \rightarrow CO(g) + H_2O(g) \qquad \Delta H = 42 \text{ kJ}$$

Is it exothermic or endothermic? How much energy is given off or absorbed?

Answer

Endothermic; 42 kJ are absorbed.

How are ΔH values measured experimentally? Actually, ΔH is not measured; q is measured. But the measurements are performed under conditions of constant pressure, so ΔH is equal to the q measured.

Experimentally, q is measured by taking advantage of the equation:

$$q = mc\Delta T$$

calorimeter

A container used to measure the heat of a chemical reaction.

calorimetry

The process of measuring enthalpy changes for chemical reactions.

FIGURE 13.4
Calorimeters
A simple calorimeter can be constructed from some nested foam coffee cups, a cover, a thermometer, and a stirrer.

We pre-measure the mass (m) of the chemicals in a system. Then we let the chemical reaction occur and measure the change in temperature (ΔT) of the system. If we know the specific heat of the materials in the system (typically, we do), we can calculate q. That value of q is numerically equal to the ΔH of the process, which we can scale up to a molar scale. The container in which the system resides is typically insulated, so any energy change goes into changing the temperature of the system, rather than being leaked from the system. The container is referred to as a **calorimeter**, and the process of measuring changes in enthalpy is called **calorimetry**.

For example, suppose 4.0 g of NaOH, or 0.10 mol of NaOH, are dissolved to make 100.0 mL of aqueous solution, while 3.65 g of HCl, or 0.10 mol of HCl, are dissolved to make another 100.0 mL of aqueous solution. The two solutions are mixed in an insulated calorimeter, a thermometer is inserted, and the calorimeter is covered (see Figure 13.4 for an example setup). The thermometer measures the temperature change as the following chemical reaction occurs:

$$\text{NaOH(aq)} + \text{HCl(aq)} \rightarrow \text{NaCl(aq)} + \text{H}_2\text{O}(\ell)$$

An observer notes that the temperature increases from 22.4°C to 29.1°C. Assuming that the heat capacities and densities of the solutions are the same as those of pure water, we now have the information we need to determine the enthalpy change of the chemical reaction. The total amount of solution is 200.0 mL, and with a density of 1.00 g/mL, we thus have 200.0 g of solution. Using the equation for q, we substitute for our experimental measurements and the specific heat of water (Table 13.1):

$$q = (200.0 \ \cancel{g}) \left(4.184 \ \frac{\text{J}}{\cancel{g} \cdot \cancel{°C}} \right) (6.7 \ \cancel{°C})$$

Solving for q, we get:

$$q = 5{,}600 \ \text{J} \equiv \Delta H \ \textbf{for the reaction}$$

The heat q is equal to the ΔH for the reaction because the chemical reaction occurs at constant pressure. However, the reaction is giving off this amount of energy, so the actual sign on ΔH is negative:

$$\Delta H = -5{,}600 \ \text{J} \ \textbf{for the reaction}$$

Thus, we have the following thermochemical equation for the chemical reaction that occurred in the calorimeter:

$$\tfrac{1}{10}\text{NaOH(aq)} + \tfrac{1}{10}\text{HCl(aq)} \rightarrow \tfrac{1}{10}\text{NaCl(aq)} + \tfrac{1}{10}\text{H}_2\text{O}(\ell) \quad \Delta H = -5{,}600 \ \text{J}$$

The 1/10 coefficients are present to remind us that we started with one-tenth of a mole of each reactant, so we make one-tenth of a mole of each product. Typically, however, we report thermochemical equations in terms of moles, not one-tenth of a mole. To scale up to molar quantities, we must multiply the coefficients by 10. However, when we do this, we get 10 times as much energy. Thus, we have:

$$\text{NaOH(aq)} + \text{HCl(aq)} \rightarrow \text{NaCl(aq)} + \text{H}_2\text{O}(\ell) \quad \Delta H = -56{,}000 \ \text{J}$$

The ΔH can be converted into kJ units, so our final thermochemical equation is:

$$\text{NaOH(aq)} + \text{HCl(aq)} \rightarrow \text{NaCl(aq)} + \text{H}_2\text{O}(\ell) \quad \Delta H = -56 \ \text{kJ}$$

We have just taken our experimental data from calorimetry and determined the enthalpy change of a chemical reaction. Similar measurements on other chemical reactions can determine the ΔH values of any chemical reaction you want to study.

Example 7

A 100 mL solution of 0.25 mol of Ca^{2+}(aq) was mixed with 0.50 mol of F^-(aq) ions, and CaF_2 was precipitated:

$$Ca^{2+}(aq) + 2F^-(aq) \rightarrow CaF_2(s)$$

The temperature of the solution increased by 10.5°C. What was the enthalpy change for the chemical reaction? What was the enthalpy change for the production of 1 mol of CaF_2? Assume that the solution has the same density and specific heat as water.

Solution

Because we are given ΔT directly, we can determine the heat of the reaction, which is equal to ΔH:

$$q = (100 \; \cancel{g}) \left(4.184 \; \frac{J}{\cancel{g} \cdot \cancel{°C}}\right) (10.5 \; \cancel{°C})$$

Solving for q, we get:

$$q = 4{,}400 \text{ J}$$

Therefore, $\Delta H = -4{,}400$ J.

According to the stoichiometry of the reaction, exactly 0.25 mol of CaF_2 will form, so this quantity of heat is for 0.25 mol. For 1 mol of CaF_2, we need to scale up the heat by a factor of four:

$$q = 4{,}400 \text{ J} \times 4 = 17{,}600 \text{ J for } 1 \text{ mol } CaF_2$$

On a molar basis, the change in enthalpy is:

$$\Delta H = -17{,}600 \text{ J} = -17.6 \text{ kJ}$$

Test Yourself

In a calorimeter at constant pressure, 0.10 mol of CH_4(g) and 0.20 mol of O_2(g) are reacted.

$$CH_4(g) + 2O_2(g) \rightarrow CO_2(g) + 2H_2O(\ell)$$

The reaction warms 750.0 g of H_2O by 28.4°C. What is ΔH for the reaction on a molar scale (i.e. assuming the coefficients of the chemical reaction represent moles of substance)?

Answer

−891 kJ

Key Takeaways

- Every chemical reaction occurs with a concurrent change in energy.
- The change in enthalpy equals heat at constant pressure.
- Enthalpy changes can be expressed by using thermochemical equations.
- Enthalpy changes are measured by using calorimetry.

Exercises

1. Under what circumstances are q and ΔH the same?

2. Under what circumstances are q and ΔH different?

3. Hydrogen gas and chlorine gas react to make hydrogen chloride gas with an accompanying enthalpy change of −184 kJ. Write a properly balanced thermochemical equation for this process.

4. Propane (C_3H_8) reacts with elemental oxygen gas to produce carbon dioxide and liquid water with an accompanying enthalpy change of −2,220 kJ. Write a properly balanced thermochemical equation for this process.

5. Nitrogen gas reacts with oxygen gas to make NO(g) while absorbing 180 kJ. Write a properly balanced thermochemical equation for this process.

6. Solid sodium reacts with chlorine gas to make solid sodium chloride while giving off 772 kJ. Write a properly balanced thermochemical equation for this process.

7. Hydrogen gas and chlorine gas react to make hydrogen chloride gas with an accompanying enthalpy change of −184 kJ. Is this process endothermic or exothermic?

8. Propane (C_3H_8) reacts with elemental oxygen gas to produce carbon dioxide while giving off 2,220 kJ of energy. Is this process endothermic or exothermic?

9. Nitrogen gas reacts with oxygen gas to make NO(g) while absorbing 180 kJ. Is this process exothermic or endothermic?

10. Sodium metal can react with nitrogen to make sodium azide (NaN_3) with a ΔH of 21.72 kJ. Is this process exothermic or endothermic?

11. Draw an energy level diagram for the chemical reaction in Exercise 8. (See Figure 13.3 for an example.)

12. Draw an energy level diagram for the chemical reaction in Exercise 9. (See Figure 13.3 for an example.)

13. In a 250 mL solution, 0.25 mol of KOH(aq) and 0.25 mol of HNO_3(aq) are combined. The temperature of the solution increases from 22.5°C to 35.9°C. Assume the solution has the same density and heat capacity of water. What is the heat of the reaction, and what is the ΔH of the reaction on a molar basis?

14. In a 600 mL solution, 0.50 mol of $Ca(OH)_2$(aq) and 0.50 mol of H_2SO_4(aq) are combined. The temperature of the solution increases by 22.3°C. What is the heat of the reaction, and what is the ΔH of the reaction on a molar basis? Assume the solution has the same density and heat capacity of water.

15. To warm 400.0 g of H_2O, 0.050 mol of ethanol (C_2H_5OH) is burned. The water warms from 24.6°C to 65.6°C. What is the heat of the reaction, and what is the ΔH of the reaction per mole of ethanol?

16. To warm 100.0 g of H_2O, 0.066 mol beeswax is burned. The water warms from 21.4°C to 25.5°C. What is the heat of the reaction, and what is the ΔH of the reaction on a molar basis?

Answers

1. under conditions of constant pressure

3. $H_2(g) + Cl_2(g) \rightarrow 2HCl(g)$ $\Delta H = -184$ kJ

5. $N_2(g) + O_2(g) \rightarrow 2NO(g)$ $\Delta H = 180$ kJ

7. exothermic

9. endothermic

11.

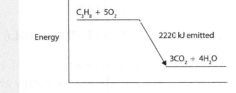

13. heat of reaction = −14.0 kJ; $\Delta H = -56.0$ kJ/mol of reactants

15. heat of reaction = −68.6 kJ; $\Delta H = -1{,}370$ kJ/mol of ethanol

13.4 Stoichiometry Calculations Using Enthalpy

Learning Objective

1. Perform stoichiometry calculations using energy changes from thermochemical equations.

In Chapter 9, we related quantities of one substance to another in a chemical equation by performing calculations that used the balanced chemical equation; the balanced chemical equation provided equivalences that we used to construct conversion factors. For example, in the balanced chemical equation

$$2H_2(g) + O_2(g) \rightarrow 2H_2O(\ell)$$

we recognized the equivalences

$$2 \text{ mol } H_2 \Leftrightarrow 1 \text{ mol } O_2 \Leftrightarrow 2 \text{ mol } H_2O$$

where $\Leftrightarrow$ is the mathematical symbol for "is equivalent to." In our thermochemical equation, however, we have another quantity—energy change:

$$2H_2(g) + O_2(g) \rightarrow 2H_2O(\ell) \qquad \Delta H = -570 \text{ kJ}$$

This new quantity allows us to add another equivalence to our list:

$$2 \text{ mol } H_2 \Leftrightarrow 1 \text{ mol } O_2 \Leftrightarrow 2 \text{ mol } H_2O \Leftrightarrow -570 \text{ kJ}$$

That is, we can now add an energy amount to the equivalences—the enthalpy change of a balanced chemical reaction. This equivalence can also be used to construct conversion factors so that we can relate enthalpy change to amounts of substances reacted or produced.

Note that these equivalences address a concern. When an amount of energy is listed for a balanced chemical reaction, what amount(s) of reactants or products does it refer to? The answer is that it relates to the number of moles of the substance as indicated by its coefficient in the balanced chemical reaction. Thus, 2 mol of H_2 are related to -570 kJ, while 1 mol of O_2 is related to -570 kJ. This is why the unit on the energy change is kJ, not kJ/mol.

For example, consider the thermochemical equation:

$$H_2(g) + Cl_2(g) \rightarrow 2HCl(g) \qquad \Delta H = -184.6 \text{ kJ}$$

The equivalences for this thermochemical equation are:

$$1 \text{ mol } H_2 \Leftrightarrow 1 \text{ mol } Cl_2 \Leftrightarrow 2 \text{ mol } HCl \Leftrightarrow -184.6 \text{ kJ}$$

Suppose we asked how much energy is given off when 8.22 mol of H_2 react. We would construct a conversion factor between the number of moles of H_2 and the energy given off, -184.6 kJ:

$$8.22 \; \cancel{\text{mol } H_2} \times \frac{-184.6 \text{ kJ}}{1 \; \cancel{\text{mol } H_2}} = -1{,}520 \text{ kJ}$$

The negative sign means that this much energy is given off.

Example 8

Given the thermochemical equation

$$N_2(g) + 3H_2(g) \rightarrow 2NH_3(g) \qquad \Delta H = -91.8 \text{ kJ}$$

how much energy is given off when 222.4 g of N_2 reacts?

Solution

The balanced thermochemical equation relates the energy change to moles, not grams, so we first convert the amount of N_2 to moles and then use the thermochemical equation to determine the energy change:

$$222.4 \; \cancel{\text{g } N_2} \times \frac{1 \; \cancel{\text{mol } N_2}}{28.00 \; \cancel{\text{g } N_2}} \times \frac{-91.8 \text{ kJ}}{1 \; \cancel{\text{mol } N_2}} = -729 \text{ kJ}$$

Test Yourself

Given the thermochemical equation

$$N_2(g) + 3H_2(g) \rightarrow 2NH_3(g) \qquad \Delta H = -91.8 \text{ kJ}$$

how much heat is given off when 1.00 g of H_2 reacts?

Answer

-15.1 kJ

Like any stoichiometric quantity, we can start with energy and determine an amount, rather than the other way around.

Chapter 13 Energy and Chemical Reactions 391

Example 9

Given the thermochemical equation

$$N_2(g) + O_2(g) \rightarrow 2NO(g) \qquad \Delta H = 180.6 \text{ kJ}$$

if 558 kJ of energy are supplied, what mass of NO can be made?

Solution

This time, we start with an amount of energy:

$$558 \text{ kJ} \times \frac{2 \text{ mol NO}}{180.6 \text{ kJ}} \times \frac{30.0 \text{ g NO}}{1 \text{ mol NO}} = 185 \text{ g NO}$$

Test Yourself

How many grams of N_2 will react if 100.0 kJ of energy are supplied?

$$N_2(g) + O_2(g) \rightarrow 2NO(g) \qquad \Delta H = 180.6 \text{ kJ}$$

Answer

15.5 g

Chemistry Is Everywhere: Welding with Chemical Reactions

One very energetic reaction is called the *thermite reaction*. Its classic reactants are aluminum metal and iron(III) oxide; the reaction produces iron metal and aluminum oxide:

$$2Al(s) + Fe_2O_3(s) \rightarrow Al_2O_3(s) + 2Fe(s) \qquad \Delta H = -850.2 \text{ kJ}$$

When properly done, the reaction gives off so much energy that the iron product comes off *as a liquid*. (Iron normally melts at 1,536°C.) If carefully directed, the liquid iron can fill spaces between two or more metal parts and weld the metal parts together.

Thermite reactions are used for this purpose even today. For civilian purposes, they are used to reweld broken locomotive axles that cannot be easily removed for repair. They are used to weld railroad tracks together. Thermite reactions can also be used to separate thin pieces of metal if, for whatever reason, a torch doesn't work.

A small clay pot contains a thermite mixture. It is reacting at high temperature in the photo and will eventually produce molten metal to join the railroad tracks below it.

Source: Photo courtesy of Skatebiker, http://commons.wikimedia.org/wiki/File:Velp-thermitewelding-1.jpg.

Thermite reactions are also used for military purposes. Thermite mixtures are frequently used with additional components as incendiary devices—devices that start fires. Thermite reactions are also useful in disabling enemy weapons: a piece of artillery doesn't work so well when it has a hole melted into its barrel because of a thermite reaction!

Key Takeaway

- The energy change of a chemical reaction can be used in stoichiometry calculations.

Exercises

1. Write the equivalences that this balanced thermochemical equation implies.

$$PCl_3(g) + Cl_2(g) \rightarrow PCl_5(g) \qquad \Delta H = -87.9 \text{ kJ}$$

2. Write the equivalences that this balanced thermochemical equation implies.

$$2SO_3(g) \rightarrow 2SO_2(g) + O_2(g) \qquad \Delta H = 197.9 \text{ kJ}$$

3. How many kilojoules are given off when 17.8 mol of $CH_4(g)$ react?

$$CH_4(g) + 2O_2(g) \rightarrow CO_2(g) + 2H_2O(\ell) \qquad \Delta H = -890.1 \text{ kJ}$$

4. How many kilojoules are absorbed when 0.772 mol of $N_2(g)$ reacts?

$$N_2(g) + 2NO(g) \rightarrow 2N_2O(g) \qquad \Delta H = 73.8 \text{ kJ}$$

5. How many kilojoules are absorbed when 23.09 mol of $C_6H_6(\ell)$ are formed?

$$6C(s) + 3H_2(g) \rightarrow C_6H_6(\ell) \qquad \Delta H = 49.0 \text{ kJ}$$

6. How many kilojoules are given off when 8.32 mol of Mg react?

$$2Mg(s) + O_2(g) \rightarrow 2MgO(s) \quad \Delta H = -1{,}213 \text{ kJ}$$

7. Glucose is the main fuel metabolized in animal cells:

$$C_6H_{12}O_6 + 6O_2 \rightarrow 6CO_2 + 6H_2O \qquad \Delta H = -2{,}799 \text{ kJ}$$

   How much energy is given off when 100.0 g of $C_6H_{12}O_6$ react?

8. Given the thermochemical equation

$$2Al(s) + Fe_2O_3(s) \rightarrow Al_2O_3(s) + 2Fe(s) \qquad \Delta H = -850.2 \text{ kJ}$$

   how much energy is given off when 288 g of Fe are produced?

9. Given the thermochemical equation

$$2CO_2(g) \rightarrow 2CO(g) + O_2(g) \qquad \Delta H = 566 \text{ kJ}$$

   how much energy is absorbed when 85.2 g of CO_2 are reacted?

10. Given the thermochemical equation

$$2Na^+(aq) + SO_4^{2-}(aq) \rightarrow Na_2SO_4(s) \qquad \Delta H = 819.8 \text{ kJ}$$

   how much energy is absorbed when 55.9 g of $Na^+(aq)$ are reacted?

11. $NaHCO_3$ decomposes when exposed to heat

$$2NaHCO_3(s) \rightarrow Na_2CO_3(s) + CO_2(g) + H_2O(\ell) \qquad \Delta H = 91.5 \text{ kJ}$$

   What mass of $NaHCO_3$ is decomposed by 256 kJ?

12. HgO decomposes when exposed to heat:

$$2HgO(s) \rightarrow 2Hg(\ell) + O_2(g) \qquad \Delta H = 181.6 \text{ kJ}$$

   What mass of O_2 can be made with 100.0 kJ?

13. For the thermochemical equation

$$Fe_2O_3(s) + 3SO_3(g) \rightarrow Fe_2(SO_4)_3(s) \qquad \Delta H = -570.2 \text{ kJ}$$

   what mass of SO_3 is needed to generate 1,566 kJ?

14. For the thermochemical equation

$$H_2(g) + Br_2(\ell) \rightarrow 2HBr(g) \qquad \Delta H = -72.6 \text{ kJ}$$

   what mass of HBr will be formed when 553 kJ of energy are given off?

Answers

1. 1 mol of PCl_3 ⇔ 1 mol of Cl_2 ⇔ 1 mol of PCl_5 ⇔ −87.9 kJ
2. 2 mol of SO_3 ⇔ 2 mol of SO_2 ⇔ 1 mol of O_2 ⇔ 197.9 kJ

3. 15,800 kJ
4. 57.0 kJ
5. 1,130 kJ
6. 5,050 kJ
7. 1,554 kJ
8. 2,190 kJ
9. 548 kJ
10. 997 kJ
11. 470 g
12. 17.6 g
13. 6.60×10^2 g
14. 1,230 g

13.5 Hess's Law

Learning Objective

1. Learn how to combine chemical equations and their enthalpy changes.

Now that we understand that chemical reactions occur with a simultaneous change in energy, we can apply the concept more broadly. To start, remember that some chemical reactions are rather difficult to perform. For example, consider the combustion of carbon to make carbon monoxide:

$$2C(s) + O_2(g) \rightarrow 2CO(g) \qquad \Delta H = ?$$

In reality, this is extremely difficult to do; given the opportunity, carbon will react to make another compound, carbon dioxide:

$$2C(s) + O_2(g) \rightarrow 2CO_2(g) \qquad \Delta H = -393.5 \text{ kJ}$$

Is there a way around this? Yes. It comes from the understanding that chemical equations can be treated like algebraic equations, with the arrow acting like the equals sign. Like algebraic equations, chemical equations can be combined, and if the same substance appears on both sides of the arrow, it can be canceled out (much like a spectator ion in ionic equations). For example, consider these two reactions:

$$2C(s) + 2O_2(g) \rightarrow 2CO_2(g)$$

$$2CO_2(g) \rightarrow 2CO(g) + O_2(g)$$

If we added these two equations by combining all the reactants together and all the products together, we would get:

$$2C(s) + 2O_2(g) + 2CO_2(g) \rightarrow 2CO_2(g) + 2CO(g) + O_2(g)$$

We note that $2CO_2(g)$ appears on both sides of the arrow, so they cancel:

$$2C(s) + 2O_2(g) + \cancel{2CO_2(g)} \rightarrow \cancel{2CO_2(g)} + 2CO(g) + O_2(g)$$

We also note that there are 2 mol of O_2 on the reactant side, and 1 mol of O_2 on the product side. We can cancel 1 mol of O_2 from both sides:

$$2C(s) + \cancel{2}\,O_2(g) \rightarrow 2CO(g) + \cancel{O_2(g)}$$

What do we have left?

$$2C(s) + O_2(g) \rightarrow 2CO(g)$$

This is the reaction we are looking for! So by algebraically combining chemical equations, we can generate new chemical equations that may not be feasible to perform.

What about the enthalpy changes? **Hess's law** states that when chemical equations are combined algebraically, their enthalpies can be combined in exactly the same way. Two corollaries immediately present themselves:

1. If a chemical reaction is reversed, the sign on ΔH is changed.

2. If a multiple of a chemical reaction is taken, the same multiple of the ΔH is taken as well.

What are the equations being combined? The first chemical equation is the combustion of C, which produces CO_2:

$$2C(s) + 2O_2(g) \rightarrow 2CO_2(g)$$

This reaction is two times the reaction to make CO_2 from C(s) and O_2(g), whose enthalpy change is known:

$$C(s) + O_2(g) \rightarrow CO_2(g) \qquad \Delta H = -393.5 \text{ kJ}$$

According to the first corollary, the first reaction has an energy change of two times –393.5 kJ, or –787.0 kJ:

$$2C(s) + 2O_2(g) \rightarrow 2CO_2(g) \qquad \Delta H = -787.0 \text{ kJ}$$

The second reaction in the combination is related to the combustion of CO(g):

$$2CO(g) + O_2(g) \rightarrow 2CO_2(g) \qquad \Delta H = -566.0 \text{ kJ}$$

The second reaction in our combination is the *reverse* of the combustion of CO. When we reverse the reaction, we change the sign on the ΔH:

$$2CO_2(g) \rightarrow 2CO(g) + O_2(g) \qquad \Delta H = +566.0 \text{ kJ}$$

Now that we have identified the enthalpy changes of the two component chemical equations, we can combine the ΔH values and add them:

$$
\begin{array}{ll}
2C(s) + \cancel{2}O_2(g) \rightarrow \cancel{2CO_2(g)} & \Delta H = -787.0 \text{ kJ} \\
\cancel{2CO_2(g)} \rightarrow 2CO(g) + \cancel{O_2(g)} & \Delta H = +566.0 \text{ kJ} \\
\hline
2C(s) + O_2(g) \rightarrow 2CO(g) & \Delta H = -787.0 + 566.0 \text{ kJ} = -221.0 \text{ kJ}
\end{array}
$$

Hess's law is very powerful. It allows us to combine equations to generate new chemical reactions whose enthalpy changes can be calculated, rather than directly measured.

Example 10

Determine the enthalpy change of

Hess's law

When chemical equations are combined algebraically, their enthalpies can be combined in exactly the same way.

$$C_2H_4 + 3O_2 \rightarrow 2CO_2 + 2H_2O \qquad \Delta H =?$$

from these reactions:

$$C_2H_2 + H_2 \rightarrow C_2H_4 \qquad \Delta H = -174.5 \text{ kJ}$$

$$2C_2H_2 + 5O_2 \rightarrow 4CO_2 + 2H_2O \qquad \Delta H = -1{,}692.2 \text{ kJ}$$

$$2CO_2 + H_2 \rightarrow 2O_2 + C_2H_2 \qquad \Delta H = -167.5 \text{ kJ}$$

Solution

We will start by writing chemical reactions that put the correct number of moles of the correct substance on the proper side. For example, our desired reaction has C_2H_4 as a reactant, and only one reaction from our data has C_2H_4. However, it has C_2H_4 as a product. To make it a reactant, we need to reverse the reaction, changing the sign on the ΔH:

$$C_2H_4 \rightarrow C_2H_2 + H_2 \qquad \Delta H = +174.5 \text{ kJ}$$

We need CO_2 and H_2O as products. The second reaction has them on the proper side, so let us include one of these reactions (with the hope that the coefficients will work out when all our reactions are added):

$$2C_2H_2 + 5O_2 \rightarrow 4CO_2 + 2H_2O \qquad \Delta H = -1{,}692.2 \text{ kJ}$$

We note that we now have 4 mol of CO_2 as products; we need to get rid of 2 mol of CO_2. The last reaction has $2CO_2$ as a reactant. Let us use it as written:

$$2CO_2 + H_2 \rightarrow 2O_2 + C_2H_2 \qquad \Delta H = -167.5 \text{ kJ}$$

We combine these three reactions, modified as stated:

$$C_2H_4 \rightarrow C_2H_2 + H_2 \qquad\qquad \Delta H = +174.5 \text{ kJ}$$
$$2C_2H_2 + 5O_2 \rightarrow 4CO_2 + 2H_2O \qquad\qquad \Delta H = -1{,}692.2 \text{ kJ}$$
$$\underline{2CO_2 + H_2 \rightarrow 2O_2 + C_2H_2 \qquad\qquad \Delta H = -167.5 \text{ kJ}}$$
$$C_2H_4 + 2C_2H_2 + 5O_2 + 2CO_2 + H_2 \rightarrow C_2H_2 + H_2 + 4CO_2 + 2H_2O + 2O_2 + C_2H_2$$

What cancels? $2C_2H_2$, H_2, $2O_2$, and $2CO_2$. What is left is

$$C_2H_4 + 3O_2 \rightarrow 2CO_2 + 2H_2O$$

which is the reaction we are looking for. The ΔH of this reaction is the sum of the three ΔH values:

$$\Delta H = +174.5 - 1{,}692.2 - 167.5 = -1{,}685.2 \text{ kJ}$$

Test Yourself

Given the thermochemical equations

$$Pb + Cl_2 \rightarrow PbCl_2 \qquad \Delta H = -223 \text{ kJ}$$

$$PbCl_2 + Cl_2 \rightarrow PbCl_4 \qquad \Delta H = -87 \text{ kJ}$$

determine ΔH for

$$2PbCl_2 \rightarrow Pb + PbCl_4$$

Answer

+136 kJ

Key Takeaway

- Hess's law allows us to combine reactions algebraically and then combine their enthalpy changes the same way.

Exercises

1. Define *Hess's law*.

2. What does Hess's law require us to do to the ΔH of a thermochemical equation if we reverse the equation?

3. If the ΔH for

$$C_2H_4 + H_2 \rightarrow C_2H_6$$

is −65.6 kJ, what is the ΔH for this reaction?

$$C_2H_6 \rightarrow C_2H_4 + H_2$$

4. If the ΔH for

$$2Na + Cl_2 \rightarrow 2NaCl$$

is −772 kJ, what is the ΔH for this reaction:

$$2NaCl \rightarrow 2Na + Cl_2$$

5. If the ΔH for

$$C_2H_4 + H_2 \rightarrow C_2H_6$$

is −65.6 kJ, what is the ΔH for this reaction?

$$2C_2H_4 + 2H_2 \rightarrow 2C_2H_6$$

6. If the ΔH for

$$2C_2H_6 + 7O_2 \rightarrow 4CO_2 - 6H_2O$$

is −2,650 kJ, what is the ΔH for this reaction?

$$6C_2H_6 + 21O_2 \rightarrow 12CO_2 + 18H_2O$$

7. The ΔH for

$$C_2H_4 + H_2O \rightarrow C_2H_5OH$$

is −44 kJ. What is the ΔH for this reaction?

$$2C_2H_5OH \rightarrow 2C_2H_4 + 2H_2O$$

8. The ΔH for

$$N_2 + O_2 \rightarrow 2NO$$

is 181 kJ. What is the ΔH for this reaction?

$$NO \rightarrow 1/2N_2 + 1/2O_2$$

9. Determine the ΔH for the reaction

$$Cu + Cl_2 \rightarrow CuCl_2$$

given these data:

$$2Cu + Cl_2 \rightarrow 2CuCl \qquad \Delta H = -274 \text{ kJ}$$

$$2CuCl + Cl_2 \rightarrow 2CuCl_2 \qquad \Delta H = -166 \text{ kJ}$$

10. Determine ΔH for the reaction

$$2CH_4 \rightarrow 2H_2 + C_2H_4$$

given these data:

$$CH_4 + 2O_2 \rightarrow CO_2 + 2H_2O \qquad \Delta H = -891 \text{ kJ}$$

$$C_2H_4 + 3O_2 \rightarrow 2CO_2 + 2H_2O \qquad \Delta H = -1{,}411 \text{ kJ}$$

$$2H_2 + O_2 \rightarrow 2H_2O \qquad \Delta H = -571 \text{ kJ}$$

11. Determine ΔH for the reaction

$$Fe_2(SO_4)_3 \rightarrow Fe_2O_3 + 3SO_3$$

given these data:

$$4Fe + 3O_2 \rightarrow 2Fe_2O_3 \qquad \Delta H = -1{,}650 \text{ kJ}$$

$$2S + 3O_2 \rightarrow 2SO_3 \qquad \Delta H = -792 \text{ kJ}$$

$$2Fe + 3S + 6O_2 \rightarrow Fe_2(SO_4)_3 \qquad \Delta H = -2{,}583 \text{ kJ}$$

12. Determine ΔH for the reaction

$$CaCO_3 \rightarrow CaO + CO_2$$

given these data:

$$2Ca + 2C + 3O_2 \rightarrow 2CaCO_3 \qquad \Delta H = -2{,}414 \text{ kJ}$$

$$C + O_2 \rightarrow CO_2 \qquad \Delta H = -393.5 \text{ kJ}$$

$$2Ca + O_2 \rightarrow 2CaO \qquad \Delta H = -1{,}270 \text{ kJ}$$

Answers

1. If chemical equations are combined, their energy changes are also combined.
2. The sign on the ΔH must be changed.
3. $\Delta H = 65.6$ kJ
4. $\Delta H = 772$ kJ
5. $\Delta H = -131.2$ kJ
6. $\Delta H = -7{,}950$ kJ
7. $\Delta H = 88$ kJ
8. $\Delta H = -90.5$ kJ

9. $\Delta H = -220$ kJ

10. $\Delta H = 200$ kJ

11. $\Delta H = 570$ kJ

12. $\Delta H = 178.5$ kJ

13.6 Formation Reactions

Learning Objectives

1. Define a *formation reaction* and be able to recognize one.
2. Use enthalpies of formation to determine the enthalpy of reaction.

Hess's law allows us to construct new chemical reactions and predict what their enthalpies of reaction will be. This is a very useful tool because we no longer have to measure the enthalpy changes of every possible reaction. We only need to measure the enthalpy changes of certain benchmark reactions. We can then use these reactions to algebraically construct any possible reactions, and combine the enthalpies of the benchmark reactions accordingly.

But what are the benchmark reactions? We need to have some agreed-on sets of reactions that provide the central data for any thermochemical equation.

Formation reactions are chemical reactions that form one mole of a substance from its constituent elements in their standard states. By *standard states* we mean as a diatomic molecule if that is how the element exists and the proper phase at normal temperatures (typically room temperature). The product is one mole of substance, which may require that coefficients on the reactant side be fractional (a change from our normal insistence that all coefficients be whole numbers). For example, the formation reaction for methane (CH_4) is:

formation reaction
A chemical reaction that forms one mole of a substance from its constituent elements in their standard states.

$$C(s) + 2H_2(g) \rightarrow CH_4(g)$$

The formation reaction for carbon dioxide (CO_2) is:

$$C(s) + O_2(g) \rightarrow CO_2(g)$$

In both cases, one of the elements is a diatomic molecule because that is the standard state for that particular element. The reaction to form H_2O

$$2H_2(g) + O_2(g) \rightarrow 2H_2O(\ell)$$

is *not* in a standard state because the coefficient on the product is 2; for a proper formation reaction, only one mole of product is formed. Thus, we have to divide all coefficients by 2:

$$H_2(g) + 1/2O_2(g) \rightarrow H_2O(\ell)$$

On a molecular scale, we are using half of an oxygen molecule, which may be problematic to visualize. However, on a molar level, it implies that we are reacting only half of a mole of oxygen molecules, which should be an easy concept to grasp.

Example 11

Which of the following are proper formation reactions?

1. $H_2(g) + Cl_2(g) \rightarrow 2HCl(g)$
2. $Si(s) + 2F_2(g) \rightarrow SiF_4(g)$
3. $CaO(s) + CO_2(g) \rightarrow CaCO_3(s)$

Solution

1. In this reaction, two moles of product are produced, so this is not a proper formation reaction.
2. In this reaction, one mole of a substance is produced from its elements in their standard states, so this is a proper formation reaction.
3. One mole of a substance is produced, but it is produced from two other compounds, not its elements. This is not a proper formation reaction.

Test Yourself

Is this a proper formation reaction? Explain why or why not.

$$2Fe(s) + 3P(s) + 12O(g) \rightarrow Fe_2(PO_4)_3(s)$$

Answer

This is not a proper formation reaction because oxygen is not written as a diatomic molecule.

Given the formula of any substance, you should be able to write the proper formation reaction for that substance.

Example 12

Write formation reactions for each of the following.

1. FeO(s)
2. $C_2H_6(g)$

Solution

In both cases, there is one mole of the substance as product, and the coefficients of the reactants may have to be fractional to balance the reaction.

1. $Fe(s) + 1/2O_2(g) \rightarrow FeO(s)$
2. $2C(s) + 3H_2(g) \rightarrow C_2H_6(g)$

Test Yourself

Write the equation for the formation of $CaCO_3(s)$.

Answer

$$Ca(s) + C(s) + 3/2O_2(g) \rightarrow CaCO_3(s)$$

enthalpy of formation

The enthalpy change for a formation reaction; denoted ΔH_f.

The enthalpy change for a formation reaction is called the **enthalpy of formation** and is given the symbol ΔH_f. The subscript f is the clue that the reaction of interest is a formation reaction. Thus, for the formation of FeO(s),

$$Fe(s) + \frac{1}{2}O_2(g) \rightarrow FeO(s) \qquad \Delta H \equiv \Delta H_f = -272 \text{ kJ/mol}$$

Note that now we are using kJ/mol as the unit because it is understood that the enthalpy change is for one mole of product. Note, too, by definition, that the enthalpy of formation of an element is exactly zero because making an element from an element is no change. For example,

$$H_2(g) \rightarrow H_2(g) \qquad \Delta H_f = 0$$

Formation reactions and their enthalpies are important because *these are the thermochemical data that are tabulated* for any chemical reaction. Table 13.2 lists some enthalpies of formation for a variety of substances; in some cases, note that phases can be important (e.g., for H_2O).

It is easy to show that any general chemical equation can be written in terms of the formation reactions of its reactants and products, some of them reversed (which means the sign must change in accordance with Hess's law). For example, consider

$$2NO_2(g) \rightarrow N_2O_4(g)$$

We can write it in terms of the (reverse) formation reaction of NO_2 and the formation reaction of N_2O_4:

$$2 \times \left[NO_2(g) \rightarrow \frac{1}{2}N_2(g) + O_2(g) \right] \quad \Delta H = -2 \times \Delta H_f \left[NO_2 \right] \quad = -2(33.1 \text{ kJ})$$

$$\underline{N_2(g) + 2O_2(g) \rightarrow N_2O_4(g) \qquad \Delta H = \Delta H_f \left[N_2O_4 \right] \qquad = 9.1 \text{ kJ}}$$

$$2 NO_2(g) \rightarrow N_2O_4 \qquad \Delta H = \qquad\qquad -57.1 \text{ kJ}$$

We must multiply the first reaction by 2 to get the correct overall balanced equation. We are simply using Hess's law in combining the ΔH_f values of the formation reactions.

TABLE 13.2 Enthalpies of Formation for Various Substances

Compound	ΔH_f (kJ/mol)	Compound	ΔH_f (kJ/mol)	Compound	ΔH_f (kJ/mol)	Compound	ΔH_f (kJ/mol)
Ag(s)	0	Ca(s)	0	Hg₂Cl₂(s)	−265.37	NaHCO₃(s)	−950.81
AgBr(s)	−100.37	CaCl₂(s)	−795.80	I₂(s)	0	NaN₃(s)	21.71
AgCl(s)	−127.01	CaCO₃(s, arag)	−1,207.1	K(s)	0	Na₂CO₃(s)	−1,130.77
Al(s)	0	CaCO₃(s, calc)	−1,206.9	KBr(s)	−393.8	Na₂O(s)	−417.98
Al₂O₃(s)	−1,675.7	Cl₂(g)	0	KCl(s)	−436.5	Na₂SO₄(s)	−331.64
Ar(g)	0	Cr(s)	0	KF(s)	−567.3	Ne(g)	0
Au(s)	0	Cr₂O₃(s)	−1,134.70	KI(s)	−327.9	Ni(s)	0
BaSO₄(s)	−1,473.19	Cs(s)	0	Li(s)	0	O₂(g)	0
Br₂(ℓ)	0	Cu(s)	0	LiBr(s)	−351.2	O₃(g)	142.67
C(s, dia)	1.897	F₂(g)	0	LiCl(s)	−408.27	PH₃(g)	22.89
C(s, gra)	0	Fe(s)	0	LiF(s)	−616.0	Pb(s)	0
CCl₄(ℓ)	−128.4	Fe₂(SO₄)₃(s)	−2,583.00	LiI(s)	−270.4	PbCl₂(s)	−359.41
CH₂O(g)	−115.90	Fe₂O₃(s)	−825.5	Mg(s)	0	PbO₂(s)	−274.47
CH₃COOH(ℓ)	−483.52	Ga(s)	0	MgO(s)	−601.60	PbSO₄(s)	−919.97
CH₃OH(ℓ)	−238.4	HBr(g)	−36.29	NH₃(g)	−45.94	Pt(s)	0
CH₄(g)	−74.87	HCl(g)	−92.31	NO(g)	90.29	S(s)	0
CO(g)	−110.5	HF(g)	−273.30	NO₂(g)	33.10	SO₂(g)	−296.81
CO₂(g)	−393.51	HI(g)	26.5	N₂(g)	0	SO₃(g)	−395.77
C₂H₅OH(ℓ)	−277.0	HNO₂(g)	−76.73	N₂O(g)	82.05	SO₃(ℓ)	−438
C₂H₆(g)	−83.8	HNO₃(g)	−134.31	N₂O₄(g)	9.08	Si(s)	0

Compound	ΔH_f (kJ/mol)	Compound	ΔH_f (kJ/mol)	Compound	ΔH_f (kJ/mol)	Compound	ΔH_f (kJ/mol)
$C_6H_{12}(\ell)$	−157.7	$H_2(g)$	0	$N_2O_5(g)$	11.30	U(s)	0
$C_6H_{12}O_6(s)$	−1277	$H_2O(g)$	−241.8	Na(s)	0	$UF_6(s)$	−2,197.0
$C_6H_{14}(\ell)$	−198.7	$H_2O(\ell)$	−285.83	NaBr(s)	−361.1	$UO_2(s)$	−1,085.0
$C_6H_5CH_3(\ell)$	12.0	$H_2O(s)$	−292.72	NaCl(s)	−385.9	Xe(g)	0
$C_6H_6(\ell)$	48.95	He(g)	0	NaF(s)	−576.6	Zn(s)	0
$C_{10}H_8(s)$	77.0	Hg(ℓ)	0	NaI(s)	−287.8	$ZnCl_2(s)$	−415.05
$C_{12}H_{22}O_{11}(s)$	−2,221.2						

Sources: Based on National Institute of Standards and Technology's Chemistry WebBook, http://webbook.nist.gov/chemistry; D. R. Lide, ed., *CRC Handbook of Chemistry and Physics*, 89th ed. (Boca Raton, FL: CRC Press, 2008); J. A. Dean, ed., *Lange's Handbook of Chemistry*, 14th ed. (New York: McGraw-Hill, 1992).

Example 13

Show that the reaction

$$Fe_2O_3(s) + 3SO_3(g) \rightarrow Fe_2(SO_4)_3(s)$$

can be written as a combination of formation reactions.

Solution

There will be three formation reactions. The one for the products will be written as a formation reaction, while the ones for the reactants will be written in reverse. Furthermore, the formation reaction for SO_3 will be multiplied by 3 because there are three moles of SO_3 in the balanced chemical equation. The formation reactions are as follows:

$$Fe_2O_3(s) \rightarrow 2\,Fe(s) + \frac{3}{2}O_2(g)$$

$$3 \times \left[SO_3(g) \rightarrow S(s) + \frac{3}{2}O_2(g) \right]$$

$$2Fe(s) + 3S(s) + 6O_2(g) \rightarrow Fe_2(SO_4)_3(s)$$

When these three equations are combined and simplified, the overall reaction is:

$$Fe_2O_3(s) + 3SO_3(s) \rightarrow Fe_2(SO_4)_3(s)$$

Test Yourself

Write the formation reactions that will yield:

$$2SO_2(g) + O_2(g) \rightarrow 2SO_3(g)$$

Answer

$$2 \times [SO_2(g) \rightarrow S(s) + O_2(g)]$$

$$2 \times \left[S(s) + \frac{3}{2}O_2(g) \rightarrow 2SO_3(g) \right]$$

Now that we have established formation reactions as the major type of thermochemical reaction we will be interested in, do we always need to write all the formation reactions when we want to determine the enthalpy change of any random chemical reaction? No. There is an easier way. You may have noticed in all our examples that we change the signs on all the enthalpies of formation of the reactants, and we don't change the signs on the enthalpies of formation of the products. We also multiply the enthalpies of formation of any substance by its coefficient—technically, even when it is just 1. This allows us to make the following statement: *the enthalpy change of any chemical reaction is equal to the sum of the enthalpies of formation of the products minus the sum of the enthalpies of formation of the reactants.* In mathematical terms,

$$\Delta H_{rxn} = \sum n_p \, \Delta H_{f,p} - \sum n_r \, \Delta H_{f,r}$$

where n_p and n_r are the number of moles of products and reactants, respectively (even if they are just 1 mol), and $\Delta H_{f,p}$ and $\Delta H_{f,r}$ are the enthalpies of formation of the product and reactant species, respectively. This *products-minus-reactants* scheme is very useful in determining the enthalpy change of any chemical reaction, if the enthalpy of formation data are available. Because the mol units cancel when multiplying the amount by the enthalpy of formation, the enthalpy change of the chemical reaction has units of energy (joules or kilojoules) only.

Example 14

Use the products-minus-reactants approach to determine the enthalpy of reaction for:

$$2HBr(g) \ + \ Cl_2(g) \ \rightarrow \ 2HCl(g) \ + \ Br_2(\ell)$$
$$\Delta H_f \quad -36.3 \qquad\quad 0 \qquad\qquad -92.3 \qquad\quad 0 \qquad kJ/mol$$

Solution

The enthalpies of formation are multiplied by the number of moles of each substance in the chemical equation, and the total enthalpy of formation for reactants is subtracted from the total enthalpy of formation of the products:

$$\Delta H_{rxn} = \left[\left(2 \ mol\right)\left(-92.3 \ kJ/mol\right) + \left(1 \ mol\right)\left(0 \ kJ/mol\right) \right]$$
$$- \left[\left(2 \ mol\right)\left(-36.3 \ kJ/mol\right) + \left(1 \ mol\right)\left(0 \ kJ/mol\right) \right]$$

All the mol units cancel. Multiplying and combining all the values, we get:

$$\Delta H_{rxn} = -112.0 \ kJ$$

Test Yourself

What is the enthalpy of reaction for this chemical equation?

$$CO(g) \ + \ H_2O(\ell) \ \rightarrow \ CO_2(g) \ + \ H_2(g)$$
$$\Delta H_f \quad -110.5 \qquad -285.8 \qquad\quad -393.5 \qquad 0 \qquad kJ/mol$$

Answer

+2.8 kJ

Food and Drink App: Calories and Nutrition

Section 1 mentioned the connection between the calorie unit and nutrition: the calorie is the common unit of energy used in nutrition, but we really consider the kilocalorie (spelled Calorie with a capital C). A daily diet of 2,000 Cal is actually 2,000,000 cal, or over 8,000,000 J, of energy.

Nutritionists typically generalize the Calorie content of foods by separating it into the three main food types: proteins, carbohydrates, and fats. The general rule of thumb is as follows:

If the food is	It has this energy content
protein	4 Cal/g
carbohydrate	4 Cal/g
fat	9 Cal/g

This table is very useful. Assuming a 2,000 Cal daily diet, if our diet consists solely of proteins and carbohydrates, we need only about 500 g of food for sustenance—a little more than a pound. If our diet consists solely of fats, we need only about 220 g of food—less than a half pound. Of course, most of us have a mixture of proteins, carbohydrates, and fats in our diets. Water has no caloric value in the diet, so any water in the diet is calorically useless. (However, it is important for hydration; also, many sources of water in our diet are highly flavored and sweetened, which bring other nutritional issues to bear.)

When your body works, it uses calories provided by the diet as its energy source. If we eat more calories than our body uses, we gain weight—about 1 lb of weight for every additional 3,500 Cal we ingest. Similarly, if we want to lose weight, we need to expend an extra 3,500 Cal than we ingest to lose 1 lb of weight. No fancy or fad diets are needed; maintaining an ideal body weight is a straightforward matter of thermochemistry—pure and simple.

Key Takeaways

- A formation reaction is the formation of one mole of a substance from its constituent elements.
- Enthalpies of formation are used to determine the enthalpy change of any given reaction.

Exercises

1. Define *formation reaction* and give an example.
2. Explain the importance of formation reactions in thermochemical equations.
3. Which of the following reactions is a formation reaction? If it is not a formation reaction, explain why.

    a. $H_2(g) + S(s) \rightarrow H_2S(g)$

    b. $2HBr(g) + Cl_2(g) \rightarrow 2HCl(g) + Br_2(\ell)$

4. Which of the following reactions is a formation reaction? If it is not a formation reaction, explain why.

    a. $Fe(g) + 1/2O_2(g) \rightarrow FeO(s)$

    b. $Hg(\ell) + 1/2O_2(g) \rightarrow HgO(s)$

5. Which of the following reactions is a formation reaction? If it is not a formation reaction, explain why.

    a. $H_2(g) + S(s) + 2O_2(g) \rightarrow H_2SO_4(\ell)$

    b. $C_3H_8(g) + 5O_2(g) \rightarrow 3CO_2(g) + 4H_2O(\ell)$

6. Which of the following reactions is a formation reaction? If it is not a formation reaction, explain why.

    a. $Zn(s) + 2HCl(aq) \rightarrow ZnCl_2(aq) + H_2(g)$

    b. $2Na(s) + C(s) + 3/2O_2(g) \rightarrow Na_2CO_3(s)$

7. Write a proper formation reaction for each substance.

   a. $H_3PO_4(s)$
   b. $Na_2O(s)$
   c. $C_3H_7OH(\ell)$

8. Write a proper formation reaction for each substance.
   a. $N_2O_5(g)$
   b. $BaSO_4(s)$
   c. $Fe(OH)_3(s)$

9. Write a proper formation reaction for each substance.
   a. $C_{12}H_{22}O_{11}(s)$
   b. $Zn(NO_3)_2(s)$
   c. $Al(OH)_3(s)$

10. Write a proper formation reaction for each substance.
    a. $O_3(g)$
    b. $Na_2O_2(s)$
    c. $PCl_5(g)$

11. Write this reaction in terms of formation reactions.

$$MgCO_3(s) \rightarrow MgO(s) + CO_2(g)$$

12. Write this reaction in terms of formation reactions.

$$2NO + 4NO_2 \rightarrow 2N_2O_5 + N_2$$

13. Write this reaction in terms of formation reactions.

$$2CuCl(s) \rightarrow Cu(s) + CuCl_2(s)$$

14. Write this reaction in terms of formation reactions.

$$SiH_4 + 4F_2 \rightarrow SiF_4 + 4HF$$

15. Determine the enthalpy change of this reaction. Data can be found in Table 13.2.

$$CH_2O(g) + O_2 \rightarrow CO_2(g) + H_2O(\ell)$$

16. Determine the enthalpy change of this reaction. Data can be found in Table 13.2.

$$2AgBr(s) + Cl_2(g) \rightarrow 2AgCl(s) + Br_2(\ell)$$

17. Determine the enthalpy change of this reaction. Data can be found in Table 13.2.

$$Mg(s) + N_2O_5(g) \rightarrow MgO(s) + 2NO_2(g)$$

18. Determine the enthalpy change of this reaction. Data can be found in Table 13.2.

$$2C_6H_6(\ell) + 15O_2(g) \rightarrow 12CO_2(g) + 6H_2O(\ell)$$

Answers

1. A formation reaction is a reaction that produces one mole of a substance from its elements.
   Example: $C(s) + O_2(g) \rightarrow CO_2(g)$

2. Any chemical reaction can be written as a combination of formation reactions.

3. a. formation reaction

   b. It is not the formation of a single substance, so it is not a formation reaction.

4. a. Iron is normally a solid, not a gas, so it is not a formation reaction.

   b. formation reaction

5. a. formation reaction

   b. It is not the formation of a single substance, so it is not a formation reaction.

6. a. There is not a single substance as a product, so it is not a formation reaction.

   b. formation reaction

7. a. $3/2 H_2(g) + P(s) + 2O_2(g) \rightarrow H_3PO_4(s)$

   b. $2Na(s) + 1/2 O_2(g) \rightarrow Na_2O(s)$

   c. $3C(s) + 1/2 O_2(g) + 4H_2(g) \rightarrow C_3H_7OH(\ell)$

8. a. $N_2(g) + 5/2 O_2(g) \rightarrow N_2O_5(g)$

   b. $Ba(s) + S(s) + 2O_2(g) \rightarrow BaSO_4(s)$

   c. $Fe(s) + 3/2 O_2(g) + 3/2 H_2(g) \rightarrow Fe(OH)_3(s)$

9. a. $12C(s) + 11H_2(g) + 11/2 O_2(g) \rightarrow C_{12}H_{22}O_{11}(s)$

   b. $Zn(s) + N_2(g) + 3O_2(g) \rightarrow Zn(NO_3)_2$

   c. $Al(s) + 3/2 O_2(g) + 3/2 H_2(g) \rightarrow Al(OH)_3(s)$

10. a. $3/2 O_2(g) \rightarrow O_3(g)$

    b. $2Na(s) + O_2(g) \rightarrow Na_2O_2(s)$

    c. $P(s) + 5/2 Cl_2(g) \rightarrow PCl_5(g)$

11. $MgCO_3(s) \rightarrow Mg(s) + C(s) + 3/2 O_2(g)$

    $Mg(s) + 1/2 O_2(g) \rightarrow MgO(s)$

    $C(s) + O_2(g) \rightarrow CO_2(g)$

12. $2 \times [NO \rightarrow 1/2 N_2 + 1/2 O_2]$

    $4 \times [NO_2 \rightarrow 1/2 N_2 + O_2]$

    $2 \times [N_2 + 5/2 O_2 \rightarrow N_2O_5]$

    $N_2 \rightarrow N_2$

13. $2 \times [CuCl(s) \rightarrow Cu(s) + 1/2 Cl_2(g)]$

    $Cu(s) \rightarrow Cu(s)$

    $Cu(s) + Cl_2(g) \rightarrow CuCl_2(s)$

14. $SiH_4 \rightarrow Si + 2H_2$

    $4 \times [F_2 \rightarrow F_2]$

    $Si + 2F_2 \rightarrow SiF_4$

    $4 \times [1/2 H_2 + 1/2 F_2 \rightarrow HF]$

15. $\Delta H = -563.44$ kJ

16. $\Delta H = -53.28$ kJ

17. $\Delta H = -546.7$ kJ

18. $\Delta H = -6{,}534.9$ kJ

13.7 Kinetics: How Reactions Go

Learning Objectives

1. Define *kinetics*.
2. Discuss some of the macroscopic aspects and microscopic aspects of kinetics.
3. Learn how activation energy affects the rates of reactions.

Exactly how do chemical reactions proceed? Consider the following chemical reaction:

$$H_2(g) + F_2(g) \rightarrow 2HF(g)$$

Do the two molecules come together, exchange partners, and make products all at once?

Actually, probably not. Although a chemical equation is written in the macroscopic sense, as reactants rearranging to products, at the *microscopic* level it's usually not this straightforward. The study of exactly how chemical reactions proceed is called **kinetics**. Kinetics has two perspectives, a macroscopic one and a microscopic one.

At the macroscopic level, one concern of kinetics is *how fast* a chemical reaction occurs: Typically, this means how quickly reactants are used up and how quickly products are produced. Because we usually express amounts of chemicals as concentrations, we express the speed of a reaction, or **reaction rate**, in terms of a concentration change per unit time.

Figure 13.5 shows a plot of a concentration of a reactant versus time. The reaction rate, symbolized by R, is the slope of the curve at any given point, and has units of M/s (molarity per second). Because the plot is a curve, the numerical value of R actually changes over the course of the reaction. Initially, a lot of reactant changes to product, so the rate is high. As the reaction proceeds, however, the slope of the curve gets smaller, meaning that the rate is lower and the amount of reactant changing to products is less. Measurements like this are a central part of kinetics.

Rates of reactions can be expressed in terms of any of the reactants or products, with the understanding that reactant concentrations are typically decreasing while product concentrations are typically increasing. However, for any given chemical reaction, the reaction rates are related through the coefficients of the balanced chemical reaction: The rates have the same ratios as the coefficients. For the above reaction between hydrogen and fluorine to make hydrogen fluoride, the coefficients in the balanced chemical reaction are 1 (unwritten), 1 (unwritten), and 2. Therefore, the rates of reaction with respect to hydrogen and fluorine are the same, while the rate with respect to HF is twice that value. If hydrogen is reacting at a rate of 2.0 M/s, the fluorine is reacting at a rate of 2.0 M/s and hydrogen fluoride is being produced at a rate of 4.0 M/s.

kinetics

The study of how chemical reactions actually proceed.

reaction rate

The speed of a reaction, usually expressed in terms of a change in concentration of a reactant or product per unit time.

FIGURE 13.5 Plot of Concentration versus Time
The concentration of a reactant changes over time. Measuring how slow or fast this happens for any reaction is a fundamental part of kinetics.

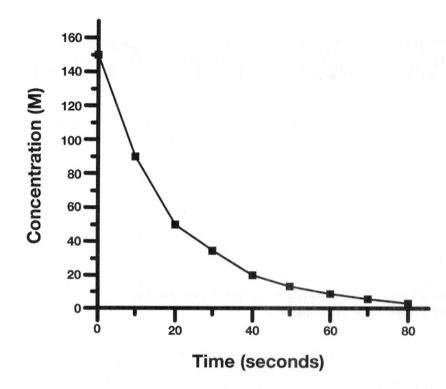

Time (seconds)

Example 15

For the balanced chemical reaction

$$CH_4 + 2O_2 \rightarrow CO_2 + 2H_2O$$

the rate of reaction of CH_4 is 2.6 M/s. What are the rates with respect to the other substances in the reaction?

Solution

The coefficients in the reaction are 1 (unwritten), 2, 1 (unwritten), and 2. Therefore, the rates have to be in this ratio as well. If the rate with respect to CH_4 is 2.6 M/s, then the rate with respect to O_2 is 5.2 M/s (twice the rate with respect to CH_4), the rate with respect to CO_2 is 2.6 M/s, and the rate with respect to H_2O is 5.2 M/s.

Test Yourself

For the reaction

$$2NO + Cl_2 \rightarrow 2NOCl$$

the rate of reaction with respect to NO is 1.8 M/s. What are the rates of reaction with respect to Cl_2 and NOCl?

Answer

0.9 M/s, 1.8 M/s

As you might expect, the rates of chemical reactions are related to how much reactant you start with. Typically, the higher the initial concentration of the reactants, the faster the reaction goes at the start. That is, a rate R is usually proportional to the initial concentrations of reactants, given as [A], [B], and so forth for reactant A, B, etc. Mathematically, we write that as:

$$R \propto [A][B]\ldots$$

What we find experimentally, though, is that the reaction rate is not just proportional to the initial concentration, but the initial concentration raised to some numerical power:

$$R \propto [A]^i[B]^j \ldots$$

where the i and j exponents are usually small whole numbers and are called the **order** with respect to that reactant. In order to make a proportionality an equality, we will include a proportionality constant k to get:

$$R = k[A]^i[B]^j \ldots$$

This final expression is called the **rate law** for the reaction, and the constant k is called the **rate law constant**. Every chemical reaction has its own rate law and rate law constant (which itself varies with temperature). The determination of rate laws is another fundamental aspect of kinetics. One important point is that the orders that appear in the rate law are *not* the same as the coefficients in the balanced chemical reaction. They must be determined experimentally for each chemical reaction.

At the microscopic level, however, the kinetics of a chemical reaction can get more complicated. The **collision theory** of kinetics assumes that reactant molecules much collide with each other in order for the atoms of the reactants to rearrange into products. Reactant molecules, however, are composed of atoms that are connected to chemical bonds. Therefore, collision theory makes two other assumptions about the collisions that cause products to be formed:

- The colliding molecules must have the proper orientation in order to rearrange.
- The colliding molecules must have enough energy to break the old bonds and make new bonds.

The orientation requirement is illustrated in Figure 13.6. In the first reaction between O_3 and NO, the NO molecule is in the proper orientation so that the N atom can accept an O atom from O_3, making the products. In the second reaction, the NO molecule is not in the proper orientation, so a collision between O_3 and NO does not lead to a rearrangement into products.

To understand the energy requirement, it should be understood first that the molecules in a given sample don't all have the same energies, even at a particular temperature. Instead, the molecules have a range of energies, some low and some high. According to collision theory, only those molecules that have a minimum amount of energy will actually react when they collide. This minimum amount of energy is called the **activation energy**, E_A, for the reaction.

This is illustrated in Figure 13.7. The vertical line labeled E_A is the minimum amount of energy the molecules must have in order to rearrange their chemical bonds and react to make products. Because molecules have a range of energies, only so many collisions will have an energy greater than E_A and react to make products.

order

The exponent on the concentration of the reactant in the mathematical expression for the rate.

rate law

A mathematical expression that relates the rate of a chemical reaction to the concentrations of the substances involved.

rate law constant

The proportionality constant k in a rate law.

collision theory

The theory that reactant molecules have to collide in order for atoms to rearrange into products.

FIGURE 13.6 Orientation of Reactants in a Collision
The orientation of reactant molecules affects the chances for reaction. In the first reaction, the orientation allows for a reaction to occur, but in the second reaction it does not.

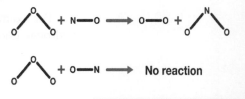

activation energy

The minimum amount of energy needed for colliding reactant molecules to react into products.

FIGURE 13.7 Activation Energy
Only so many collisions will have enough energy to react. The low-temperature line has a small proportion of collisions that result in reactions. At higher temperature, more collisions have an energy higher than the activation energy, and so more collisions result in reactions.

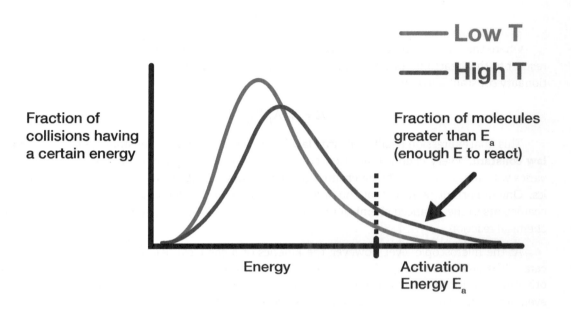

Most chemical reaction speed up when the temperature is increased. Figure 13.7 shows why that happens. At higher temperatures, a larger proportion of the collisions have an energy greater than E_A (because temperature is, after all, an indication of the average energy of the molecules: The higher the temperature, the higher the average energy). Because more of the collisions have enough energy to react, the reaction rate increases.

mechanism

The combination of steps at the atomic and molecular level that yields the overall balanced chemical reaction.

Finally, scientists now understand that most chemical reactions occur in a step-wise fashion that does not necessarily mimic the balanced chemical reaction in every step *but whose combination of steps does agree with the balanced chemical reaction.* This combination of steps at the atomic and molecular level is called the **mechanism** of the chemical reaction. Mechanisms are difficult to prove because we cannot follow individual atoms and molecules when we study chemistry. However, chemists can perform experiments that provide evidence for or against certain proposed mechanisms. The interesting thing about the individual steps is that the species involved do not necessarily have to be the properly-balanced ionic or molecular formulas that we have used in the past.

For example, one proposed mechanism for the reaction of hydrogen and fluorine to make hydrogen fluoride might be:

$$F_2 \rightarrow F \cdot + F \cdot$$

$$F \cdot + H_2 \rightarrow HF + H \cdot$$

$$H \cdot + F \cdot \rightarrow HF$$

The dots next to the atomic symbol imply that a bond is broken and the atom has an unpaired electron on it. If you combine all three of the steps in this mechanism, you get the overall balanced chemical reaction:

$$H_2 + F_2 \rightarrow 2HF$$

However, the three individual steps of the mechanism propose exactly how, at the atomic level, the two reactant molecules interact to make the product molecules. Is this mechanism correct? We don't know because we can't follow individual hydrogen and fluorine molecules during the course of the reaction. The best we can do is perform experiments that provide evidence for or against this particular proposed mechanism.

Key Takeaways

- Kinetics is the study of how chemical reactions actually occur.
- Reaction rates are an important part of kinetics and are expressed in a rate law.
- Collision theory suggests that colliding molecules have to have proper orientation and enough energy to react.
- A mechanism is a list of the individual steps reactants undergo to make products.

Exercises

1. Define *kinetics*.

2. In what units are rates of reactions expressed?

3. For the reaction

$$N_2 + 3H_2 \rightarrow 2NH_3$$

the rate of reaction with respect to N_2 is 0.66 M/s. What are the rates with respect to H_2 and NH_3?

4. For the reaction

$$P_4 + 6Cl_2 \rightarrow 4PCl_3$$

the rate of reaction with respect to PCl_3 is 1.28 M/s. What are the rates with respect to P_4 and Cl_2?

5. Under what circumstances, if any, will all rates of a reaction be numerically equal?

6. If the rate of a reaction with respect to H_2 is 0.75 mol/s, what is the rate in g/hr?

7. What are the three assumptions of collision theory?

8. Explain why most rates of reaction increase when the temperature is increased.

9. Propose a mechanism for the reaction between H_2 and Cl_2. (Hint: Write the balanced chemical reaction first.)

10. Propose a mechanism for the reaction between H_2 and C_2. (Hint: Write the balanced chemical reaction first.)

Answers

1. Kinetics is the study how how chemical reactions proceed at both the macroscopic and microscopic levels.

3. 1.98 M/s, 1.32 M/s

5. Only if all of the coefficients in the chemical reaction are 1.

7. 1. Reactant molecules collide in order to react. 2. Collisions must have the proper orientation in order to react. 3. Collisions must have some minimum energy in order to react.

9. Proposed mechanism:

$$Cl_2 \rightarrow Cl \cdot + Cl \cdot$$

$$Cl\cdot\ + H_2 \rightarrow HCl + H\cdot$$

$$H\cdot\ + Cl\cdot \rightarrow HCl$$

13.8 End-of-Chapter Material

Additional Exercises

1. What is the work when 124 mL of gas contract to 72.0 mL under an external pressure of 822 torr?

2. What is the work when 2,345 mL of gas contract to 887 mL under an external pressure of 348 torr?

3. A 3.77 L volume of gas is exposed to an external pressure of 1.67 atm. As the gas contracts, 156 J of work are added to the gas. What is the final volume of the gas?

4. A 457 mL volume of gas contracts when 773 torr of external pressure act on it. If 27.4 J of work are added to the gas, what is its final volume?

5. What is the heat when 1,744 g of Hg increase in temperature by 334°C? Express your final answer in kJ.

6. What is the heat when 13.66 kg of Fe cool by 622°C? Express your final answer in kJ.

7. What is final temperature when a 45.6 g sample of Al at 87.3°C gains 188 J of heat?

8. What is final temperature when 967 g of Au at 557°C lose 559 J of heat?

9. Plants take CO_2 and H_2O and make glucose ($C_6H_{12}O_6$) and O_2. Write a balanced thermochemical equation for this process. Use data in Table 13.2.

10. Exercise 9 described the formation of glucose in plants, which take in CO_2 and H_2O and give off O_2. Is this process exothermic or endothermic? If exothermic, where does the energy go? If endothermic, where does the energy come from?

11. The basic reaction in the refining of aluminum is to take Al_2O_3(s) and turn it into Al(s) and O_2(g). Write the balanced thermochemical equation for this process. Use data in Table 13.2.

12. Is the enthalpy change of the reaction

$$H_2O(\ell) \rightarrow H_2O(g)$$

zero or nonzero? Use data in Table 13.2 to determine the answer.

13. What mass of H_2O can be heated from 22°C to 80°C in the combustion of 1 mol of CH_4? You will need the balanced thermochemical equation for the combustion of CH_4. Use data in Table 13.2.

14. What mass of H_2O can be heated from 22°C to 80°C in the combustion of 1 mol of C_2H_6? You will need the balanced thermochemical equation for the combustion of C_2H_6. Use data in Table 13.2. Compare your answer to Exercise 13.

15. What is the enthalpy change for the unknown reaction?

$$Pb(s) + Cl_2(g) \rightarrow PbCl_2(s) \qquad \Delta H = -359\ kJ$$

$$PbCl_2(s) + Cl_2(g) \rightarrow PbCl_4(\ell) \qquad \Delta H = ?$$

$$Pb(s) + 2Cl_2(g) \rightarrow PbCl_4(\ell) \qquad \Delta H = -329\ kJ$$

16. What is the enthalpy change for the unknown reaction?

$$P(s) + 3/2Br_2(\ell) \rightarrow PBr_3(\ell) \qquad \Delta H = -185\ kJ$$

$$PI_3(s) \rightarrow P(s) + 3/2I_2(s) \qquad \Delta H = ?$$

$$PI_3(s) + 3/2Br_2(\ell) \rightarrow PBr_3(\ell) + 3/2I_2(s) \qquad \Delta H = -139 \text{ kJ}$$

17. What is the ΔH for this reaction? The label *gra* means graphite, and the label *dia* means diamond. What does your answer mean? Use data in Table 13.2

$$C(s, gra) \rightarrow C(s, dia)$$

18. Without consulting any tables, determine the ΔH for this reaction. Explain your answer.

$$H_2O(\ell, 25\,^\circ C) \rightarrow H_2O(\ell, 25\,^\circ C)$$

19. Which reaction is likely to go faster at a given temperature, a reaction with a high activation energy or a reaction with a low activation energy? Explain your answer.

Answers

1. 5.70 J

3. 4.69 L

5. 80.97 kJ

7. 91.9°C

9. $6CO_2(g) + 6H_2O(\ell) \rightarrow C_6H_{12}O_6(s) + 6O_2(g) \qquad \Delta H = 2,799$ kJ

11. $2Al_2O_3(s) \rightarrow 4Al(s) + 3O_2(g) \qquad \Delta H = 3351.4$ kJ

13. 3,668 g

15. $\Delta H = 30$ kJ

17. $\Delta H = 1.897$ kJ; the reaction is endothermic.

19. A reaction with a low activation energy will likely go faster because more of its reactant molecules have an energy higher than E_A and will react.

CHAPTER 14
Chemical Equilibrium

Opening Essay

Imagine you are stranded in a rowboat in the middle of the ocean. Suddenly, your boat springs a small leak, and you need to bail out water. You grab a bucket and begin to bail. After a few minutes, your efforts against the leak keep the water to about half an inch, but any further bailing doesn't change the water level; the leak brings in as much water as you bail out.

You are at *equilibrium*. Two opposing processes have reached the same speed, and there is no more overall change in the process.

Chemical reactions are like that as well. Most of them come to an equilibrium. The actual position of the equilibrium—whether it favors the reactants or the products—is characteristic of a chemical reaction; it is difficult to see just by looking at the balanced chemical equation. But chemistry has tools to help you understand the equilibrium of chemical reactions—the focus of our study in this chapter.

So far in this text, when we present a chemical reaction, we have usually assumed that the reaction goes to completion. Indeed, our stoichiometric calculations were based on this; when we asked how much of a product is produced when so much of a reactant reacts, we are assuming that *all* of a reactant reacts. However, this is usually not the case many reactions do not go to completion, and many chemists have to deal with that. In this chapter, we will study this phenomenon and see ways in which we can affect the extent of chemical reactions.

14.1 Chemical Equilibrium

Learning Objectives

1. Define *chemical equilibrium*.
2. Recognize chemical equilibrium as a dynamic process.

Consider the following reaction occurring in a closed container (so that no material can go in or out):

$$H_2 + I_2 \rightarrow 2HI$$

This is simply the reaction between elemental hydrogen and elemental iodine to make hydrogen iodide. The way the equation is written, we are led to believe that the reaction goes to completion, that all the H_2 and the I_2 react to make HI.

However, this is not the case. The reverse chemical reaction starts taking place:

$$2HI \rightarrow H_2 + I_2$$

It acts to undo what the first reaction does. Eventually, the reverse reaction proceeds so quickly that it matches the speed of the forward reaction. When that happens, any continued overall reaction stops: the reaction has reached **chemical equilibrium** (sometimes just spoken as *equilibrium*; plural *equilibria*), the point at which the forward and reverse processes balance each other's progress.

Because two opposing processes are occurring at once, it is conventional to represent an equilibrium using a double arrow, like this:

$$H_2 + I_2 \rightleftarrows 2HI$$

The double arrow implies that the reaction is going in both directions. Note that the reaction must still be balanced.

Example 1

Write the equilibrium equation that exists between calcium carbonate as a reactant and calcium oxide and carbon dioxide as products.

Solution

As this is an equilibrium situation, a double arrow is used. The equilibrium equation is written as follows:

$$CaCO_3 \rightleftarrows CaO + CO_2$$

Test Yourself

Write the equilibrium equation between elemental hydrogen and elemental oxygen as reactants and water as the product.

Answer

$$2H_2 + O_2 \rightleftarrows 2H_2O$$

One thing to note about equilibrium is that the reactions do not stop; both the forward reaction and the reverse reaction continue to occur. They both occur at the same rate, so any overall change by one reaction is cancelled by the reverse reaction. We say that chemical equilibrium is *dynamic*, rather than static. Also, because both reactions are occurring simultaneously, the equilibrium can be written backward. For example, representing an equilibrium as

$$H_2 + I_2 \rightleftarrows 2HI$$

is the same thing as representing the same equilibrium as

$$2HI \rightleftarrows H_2 + I_2$$

The reaction must be at equilibrium for this to be the case, however.

Key Takeaways

- Chemical reactions eventually reach equilibrium, a point at which forward and reverse reactions balance each other's progress.
- Chemical equilibria are dynamic: the chemical reactions are always occurring; they just cancel each other's progress.

Exercises

1. Define *chemical equilibrium*. Give an example.
2. Explain what is meant when it is said that chemical equilibrium is dynamic.
3. Write the equilibrium equation between elemental hydrogen and elemental chlorine as reactants and hydrochloric acid as the product.
4. Write the equilibrium equation between iron(III) sulfate as the reactant and iron(III) oxide and sulfur trioxide as the products.
5. Graphite and diamond are two forms of elemental carbon. Write the equilibrium equation between these two forms in two different ways.
6. At 1,500 K, iodine molecules break apart into iodine atoms. Write the equilibrium equation between these two species in two different ways.

Answers

1. the situation when the forward and reverse chemical reactions occur, leading to no additional net change in the reaction position; $H_2 + I_2 \rightleftarrows 2HI$ (answers will vary)
2. The term *dynamic* means that the forward and reverse chemical reactions still occur; there is just no net change in the position of the reaction.
3. $H_2 + Cl_2 \rightleftarrows 2HCl$
4. $Fe_2(SO_4)_3 \rightleftarrows Fe_2O_3 + 3SO_3$
5. $C\,(gra) \rightleftarrows C\,(dia);\ C\,(dia) \rightleftarrows C\,(gra)$
6. $I_2 \rightleftarrows 2I;\ 2I \rightleftarrows I_2$

14.2 The Equilibrium Constant

Learning Objectives

1. Explain the importance of the equilibrium constant.
2. Construct an equilibrium constant expression for a chemical reaction.

In the mid 1860s, Norwegian scientists C. M. Guldberg and P. Waage noted a peculiar relationship between the amounts of reactants and products in an equilibrium. No matter how many reactants they started with, a certain ratio of reactants and products was achieved at equilibrium. Today, we call this observation the **law of mass action**. It relates the amounts of reactants and products at equilibrium for a chemical reaction. For a general chemical reaction occurring in solution,

$$aA + bB \rightleftarrows cC + dD$$

the **equilibrium constant**, also known as K_{eq}, is defined by the following expression:

$$K_{eq} = \frac{[C]^c[D]^d}{[A]^a[B]^b}$$

law of mass action

The relationship of the amounts of reactants and products at equilibrium.

equilibrium constant

A numerical value that relates to the ratio of products and reactants at equilibrium.

where [A] is the molar concentration of species A at equilibrium, and so forth. The coefficients *a*, *b*, *c*, and *d* in the chemical equation become exponents in the expression for K_{eq}. The K_{eq} is a characteristic numerical value for a given reaction at a given temperature; that is, each chemical reaction has its own characteristic K_{eq}. The concentration of each reactant and product in a chemical reaction at equilibrium is *related*; the concentrations cannot be random values, but they depend on each other. The numerator of the expression for K_{eq} has the concentrations of every product (however many products there are), while the denominator of the expression for K_{eq} has the concentrations of every reactant, leading to the common *products over reactants* definition for the K_{eq}.

Let us consider a simple example. Suppose we have this equilibrium:

$$A \rightleftarrows B$$

There is one reactant, one product, and the coefficients on each are just 1 (as usual, not written). The K_{eq} expression for this equilibrium is:

$$K_{eq} = \frac{[B]}{[A]}$$

(Exponents of 1 on each concentration are understood.) Suppose the numerical value of K_{eq} for this chemical reaction is 2.0. If [B] = 4.0 M, then [A] must equal 2.0 M so that the value of the fraction equals 2.0:

$$K_{eq} = \frac{[B]}{[A]} = \frac{4.0}{2.0} = 2.0$$

By convention, the units are understood to be M and are omitted from the K_{eq} expression. Suppose [B] were 6.0 M. For the K_{eq} value to remain constant (it is, after all, called the equilibrium *constant*), then [A] would have to be 3.0 M at equilibrium:

$$K_{eq} = \frac{[B]}{[A]} = \frac{6.0}{3.0} = 2.0$$

If [A] were *not* equal to 3.0 M, the reaction would not be at equilibrium, and a net reaction would occur until that ratio was indeed 2.0. At that point, the reaction is at equilibrium, and any net change would cease. (Recall, however, that the forward and reverse reactions do not stop because chemical equilibrium is dynamic.)

The issue is the same with more complex expressions for the K_{eq}; only the mathematics becomes more complex. Generally speaking, given a value for the K_{eq} and all but one concentration at equilibrium, the missing concentration can be calculated.

Example 2

Given the following reaction:

$$H_2 + I_2 \rightleftarrows 2HI$$

If the equilibrium [HI] is 0.75 M and the equilibrium [H$_2$] is 0.20 M, what is the equilibrium [I$_2$] if the K_{eq} is 0.40?

Solution

We start by writing the K_{eq} expression. Using the *products over reactants* approach, the K_{eq} expression is as follows:

$$K_{eq} = \frac{[HI]^2}{[H_2][I_2]}$$

Note that [HI] is squared because of the coefficient 2 in the balanced chemical equation. Substituting for the equilibrium [H_2] and [HI] and for the given value of K_{eq}:

$$0.40 = \frac{(0.75)^2}{(0.20)[I_2]}$$

To solve for [I_2], we have to do some algebraic rearrangement: divide the 0.40 into both sides of the equation and multiply both sides of the equation by [I_2]. This brings [I_2] into the numerator of the left side and the 0.40 into the denominator of the right side:

$$[I_2] = \frac{(0.75)^2}{(0.20)(0.40)}$$

Solving,

$$[I_2] = 7.0 \text{ M}$$

The concentration unit is assumed to be molarity. This value for [I_2] can be easily verified by substituting 0.75, 0.20, and 7.0 into the expression for K_{eq} and evaluating: you should get 0.40, the numerical value of K_{eq} (and you do).

Test Yourself

Given the following reaction:

$$H_2 + I_2 \rightleftarrows 2HI$$

If the equilibrium [HI] is 0.060 M and the equilibrium [I_2] is 0.90 M, what is the equilibrium [H_2] if the K_{eq} is 0.40?

Answer

0.010 M

In some types of equilibrium problems, square roots, cube roots, or even higher roots need to be analyzed to determine a final answer. Make sure you know how to perform such operations on your calculator; if you do not know, ask your instructor for assistance.

Example 3

The following reaction is at equilibrium:

$$N_2 + 3H_2 \rightleftarrows 2NH_3$$

The K_{eq} at a particular temperature is 13.7. If the equilibrium [N_2] is 1.88 M and the equilibrium [NH_3] is 6.62 M, what is the equilibrium [H_2]?

Solution

We start by writing the K_{eq} expression from the balanced chemical equation:

$$K_{eq} = \frac{[NH_3]^2}{[N_2][H_2]^3}$$

Substituting for the known equilibrium concentrations and the K_{eq}, this becomes:

$$13.7 = \frac{(6.62)^2}{(1.88)[H_2]^3}$$

Rearranging algebraically and then evaluating the numerical expression, we get:

$$[H_2]^3 = \frac{(6.22)^2}{(1.88)(13.7)} = 1.502112129$$

To solve for [H₂], we need to take the cube root of the equation. Performing this operation, we get:

$$[H_2] = 1.15 \text{ M}$$

You should verify that this is correct using your own calculator to confirm that you know how to do a cube root correctly.

Test Yourself

The following reaction is at equilibrium:

$$N_2 + 3H_2 \rightleftarrows 2NH_3$$

The K_{eq} at a particular temperature is 13.7. If the equilibrium [N₂] is 0.055 M and the equilibrium [H₂] is 1.62 M, what is the equilibrium [NH₃]?

Answer

1.79 M

The K_{eq} was defined earlier in terms of concentrations. For gas-phase reactions, the K_{eq} can also be defined in terms of the partial pressures of the reactants and products, P_i. For the gas-phase reaction

$$aA(g) + bB(g) \rightleftarrows cC(g) + dD(g)$$

the pressure-based equilibrium constant, K_P, is defined as follows:

$$K_P = \frac{P_C^c P_D^d}{P_A^a P_B^b}$$

where P_A is the partial pressure of substance A at equilibrium in atmospheres, and so forth. As with the concentration-based equilibrium constant, the units are omitted when substituting into the expression for K_P.

Example 4

What is the K_P for this reaction, given the equilibrium partial pressures of 0.664 atm for NO₂ and 1.09 atm for N₂O₄?

$$2NO_2(g) \rightleftarrows N_2O_4(g)$$

Solution

Write the K_P expression for this reaction:

$$K_P = \frac{P_{N_2O_4}}{P_{NO_2}^2}$$

Then substitute the equilibrium partial pressures into the expression and evaluate:

$$K_P = \frac{(1.09)}{(0.664)^2} = 2.47$$

Test Yourself

What is the K_P for this reaction, given the equilibrium partial pressures of 0.44 atm for H_2, 0.22 atm for Cl_2, and 2.98 atm for HCl?

$$H_2 + Cl_2 \rightleftarrows 2HCl$$

Answer

91.7

There is a simple relationship between K_{eq} (based on concentration units) and K_P (based on pressure units):

$$K_P = K_{eq} \cdot (RT)^{\Delta n}$$

where R is the ideal gas law constant (in units of L·atm/mol·K), T is the absolute temperature, and Δn is the change in the number of moles of gas in the balanced chemical equation, defined as $n_{gas,prods} - n_{gas,rcts}$. Note that this equation implies that if the number of moles of gas are the same in reactants and products, $K_{eq} = K_P$.

Example 5

What is the K_P at 25°C for this reaction if the K_{eq} is 4.2×10^{-2}?

$$N_2(g) + 3H_2(g) \rightleftarrows 2NH_3(g)$$

Solution

Before we use the relevant equation, we need to do two things: convert the temperature to kelvins and determine Δn. Converting the temperature is easy:

$$T = 25 + 273 = 298 \text{ K}$$

To determine the change in the number of moles of gas, take the number of moles of gaseous products and subtract the number of moles of gaseous reactants. There are 2 mol of gas as product and 4 mol of gas of reactant:

$$\Delta n = 2 - 4 = -2 \text{ mol}$$

Note that Δn is negative. Now we can substitute into our equation, using $R = 0.08205$ L·atm/mol·K. The units are omitted for clarity:

$$K_P = (4.2 \times 10^{-2})(0.08205)(298)^{-2}$$

Solving,

$$K_P = 7.0 \times 10^{-5}$$

Test Yourself

What is the K_P at 25°C for this reaction if the K_{eq} is 98.3?

$$I_2(g) \rightleftarrows 2I(g)$$

Answer

2.40×10^3

Finally, we recognize that many chemical reactions involve substances in the solid or liquid phases. For example, a particular chemical reaction is represented as follows:

$$2NaHCO_3(s) \rightleftharpoons Na_2CO_3(s) + CO_2(g) + H_2O(\ell)$$

heterogeneous equilibrium

An equilibrium in which more than one phase of reactants or products is present.

This chemical equation includes all three phases of matter. This kind of equilibrium is called a **heterogeneous equilibrium** because there is more than one phase present.

The rule for heterogeneous equilibria is as follows: *Do not include the concentrations of pure solids and pure liquids in K_{eq} expressions.* Only partial pressures for gas-phase substances or concentrations in solutions are included in the expressions of equilibrium constants. As such, the equilibrium constant expression for this reaction would simply be

$$K_P = P_{CO_2}$$

because the two solids and one liquid would not appear in the expression.

Key Takeaways

- Every chemical equilibrium can be characterized by an equilibrium constant, known as K_{eq}.
- The K_{eq} and K_P expressions are formulated as amounts of products divided by amounts of reactants; each amount (either a concentration or a pressure) is raised to the power of its coefficient in the balanced chemical equation.
- Solids and liquids do not appear in the expression for the equilibrium constant.

Exercises

1. Define the *law of mass action*.
2. What is an equilibrium constant for a chemical reaction? How is it constructed?
3. Write the K_{eq} expression for each reaction.
   a. $H_2 + Cl_2 \rightleftharpoons 2HCl$
   b. $NO + NO_2 \rightleftharpoons N_2O_3$
4. Write the K_{eq} expression for each reaction.
   a. $C_2H_5OH + NaI \rightleftharpoons C_2H_5I + NaOH$
   b. $PCl_3 + Cl_2 \rightleftharpoons PCl_5$
5. Write the K_P expression for each reaction.
   a. $2H_2(g) + O_2(g) \rightleftharpoons 2H_2O(g)$
   b. $2H_2O_2(g) \rightleftharpoons 2H_2O(g) + O_2(g)$
6. Write the K_P expression for each reaction.
   a. $CH_4(g) + 2O_2(g) \rightleftharpoons CO_2(g) + 2H_2O(g)$
   b. $CH_4(g) + 4Cl_2(g) \rightleftharpoons CCl_4(g) + 4HCl(g)$
7. The following reaction is at equilibrium:

$$PBr_3 + Br_2 \rightleftharpoons PBr_5$$

   The equilibrium [Br$_2$] and [PBr$_5$] are 2.05 M and 0.55 M, respectively. If the K_{eq} is 1.65, what is the equilibrium [PBr$_3$]?
8. The following reaction is at equilibrium:

$$CO + Cl_2 \rightleftharpoons COCl_2$$

   The equilibrium [CO] and [Cl$_2$] are 0.088 M and 0.103 M, respectively. If the K_{eq} is 0.225, what is the equilibrium [COCl$_2$]?

9. The following reaction is at equilibrium:

$$CH_4 + 2Cl_2 \rightleftarrows CH_2Cl_2 + 2HCl$$

If $[CH_4]$ is 0.250 M, $[Cl_2]$ is 0.150 M, and $[CH_2Cl_2]$ is 0.175 M at equilibrium, what is $[HCl]$ at equilibrium if the K_{eq} is 2.30?

10. The following reaction is at equilibrium:

$$4HBr + O_2 \rightleftarrows 2H_2O + 2Br_2$$

If $[HBr]$ is 0.100 M, $[O_2]$ is 0.250 M, and $[H_2O]$ is 0.0500 M at equilibrium, what is $[Br_2]$ at equilibrium if the K_{eq} is 0.770?

11. Write the K_P expression for the following gas-phase reaction:

$$4NO_2(g) + O_2(g) \rightleftarrows 2N_2O_5(g)$$

12. Write the K_P expression for the following gas-phase reaction:

$$ClO(g) + O_3(g) \rightleftarrows ClO_2(g) + O_2(g)$$

13. What is the equilibrium partial pressure of $COBr_2$ if the equilibrium partial pressures of CO and Br_2 are 0.666 atm and 0.235 atm and the K_P for this equilibrium is 4.08?

$$CO(g) + Br_2(g) \rightleftarrows COBr_2(g)$$

14. What is the equilibrium partial pressure of O_3 if the equilibrium partial pressure of O_2 is 0.0044 atm and K_P for this equilibrium is 0.00755?

$$3O_2(g) \rightleftarrows 2O_3(g)$$

15. Calculate the K_P for this reaction at 298 K if the $K_{eq} = 1.76 \times 10^{-3}$.

$$3O_2(g) \rightleftarrows 2O_3(g)$$

16. Calculate the K_P for this reaction at 310 K if the $K_{eq} = 6.22 \times 10^3$.

$$4NO_2(g) + O_2(g) \rightleftarrows 2N_2O_5(g)$$

17. Calculate the K_{eq} for this reaction if the $K_P = 5.205 \times 10^{-3}$ at 660°C.

$$CO(g) + F_2(g) \rightleftarrows COF_2(g)$$

18. Calculate the K_{eq} for this reaction if the $K_P = 78.3$ at 100°C.

$$4HCl(g) + O_2(g) \rightleftarrows 2H_2O(g) + 2Cl_2(g)$$

19. Write the correct K_{eq} expression for this reaction.

$$NaOH(aq) + HCl(aq) \rightleftarrows NaCl(aq) + H_2O(\ell)$$

20. Write the correct K_{eq} expression for this reaction.

$$AgNO_3(aq) + NaCl(aq) \rightleftarrows AgCl(s) + NaNO_3(aq)$$

21. Write the correct K_P expression for this reaction.

$$CaCO_3(s) \rightleftarrows CaO(s) + CO_2(g)$$

22. Write the correct K_P expression for this reaction.

$$C_2H_2(g) + 2I_2(s) \rightleftarrows C_2H_2I_4(g)$$

Answers

1. the relationship between the concentrations of reactants and products of a chemical reaction at equilibrium

2. An equilibrium constant is a characteristic ratio of products to reactants for an equilibrium. It is constructed as the concentrations of the products divided by the concentrations of the reactants.

3. a. $K_{eq} = \dfrac{[HCl]^2}{[H_2][Cl_2]}$

   b. $K_{eq} = \dfrac{[N_2O_3]}{[NO][NO_2]}$

4. a. $K_{eq} = \dfrac{[C_2H_5I][NaOH]}{[C_2H_5OH][NaI]}$

   b. $K_{eq} = \dfrac{[PCl_5]}{[PCl_3][Cl_2]}$

5. a. $K_P = \dfrac{P_{H_2O}^2}{P_{H_2}^2 P_{O_2}}$

   b. $K_P = \dfrac{P_{H_2O}^2 P_{O_2}}{P_{H_2O_2}^2}$

6. a. $K_P = \dfrac{P_{CO_2} P_{H_2O}^2}{P_{CH_4} P_{O_2}^2}$

   b. $K_P = \dfrac{P_{CCl_4} P_{HCl}^4}{P_{CH_4} P_{Cl_2}^4}$

7. 0.163 M

8. 0.00204 M

9. 0.272 M

10. 0.0877 M

11. $K_P = \dfrac{P_{N_2O_5}^2}{P_{NO_2}^4 P_{O_2}}$

12. $K = \dfrac{P_{ClO_2} P_{O_2}}{P_{ClO} P_{O_3}}$

13. 0.639 atm

14. 2.54×10^{-5} atm

15. 7.20×10^{-5}

16. $K_p = 0.378$

17. $K_{eq} = 3.98 \times 10^{-1}$

18. $K_{eq} = 2.40 \times 10^3$

19. $K_{eq} = \dfrac{[NaCl]}{[NaOH][HCl]}$

20. $K_{eq} = \dfrac{[NaNO_3]}{[AgNO_3][NaCl]}$

21. $K_P = P_{CO_2}$

22. $K_P = \dfrac{P_{C_2H_2I_4}}{P_{C_2H_2}}$

14.3 Shifting Equilibria: Le Chatelier's Principle

Learning Objectives

1. Define *Le Chatelier's principle*.
2. Predict the direction of shift for an equilibrium under stress.

Once equilibrium is established, the reaction is over, right? Not exactly. An experimenter has some ability to affect the equilibrium.

Chemical equilibria can be shifted by changing the conditions that the system experiences. We say that we "stress" the equilibrium. When we stress the equilibrium, the chemical reaction is no longer at equilibrium, and the reaction starts to move back toward equilibrium in such a way as to decrease the stress. The formal statement is called **Le Chatelier's principle**: If an equilibrium is stressed, then the reaction shifts to reduce the stress.

There are several ways to stress an equilibrium. One way is to add or remove a product or a reactant in a chemical reaction at equilibrium. When additional reactant is added, the equilibrium shifts to reduce this stress: it makes more product. When additional product is added, the equilibrium shifts to reactants to reduce the stress. If reactant or product is removed, the equilibrium shifts to make more reactant or product, respectively, to make up for the loss.

Le Chatelier's principle

If an equilibrium is stressed, then the reaction shifts to reduce the stress.

Example 6

Given this reaction at equilibrium:

$$N_2 + 3H_2 \rightleftarrows 2NH_3$$

In which direction—toward reactants or toward products—does the reaction shift if the equilibrium is stressed by each change?

1. H_2 is added.
2. NH_3 is added.
3. NH_3 is removed.

Solution

1. If H_2 is added, there is now more reactant, so the reaction will shift toward products to reduce the added H_2.
2. If NH_3 is added, there is now more product, so the reaction will shift toward reactants to reduce the added NH_3.
3. If NH_3 is removed, there is now less product, so the reaction will shift toward products to replace the product removed.

Test Yourself

Given this reaction at equilibrium:

$$CO(g) + Br_2(g) \rightleftarrows COBr_2(g)$$

In which direction—toward reactants or toward products—does the reaction shift if the equilibrium is stressed by each change?

1. Br_2 is removed.
2. $COBr_2$ is added.

Answers

1. toward reactants
2. toward reactants

It is worth noting that when reactants or products are added or removed, *the value of the K_{eq} does not change*. The chemical reaction simply shifts, in a predictable fashion, to reestablish concentrations so that the K_{eq} expression reverts to the correct value.

How does an equilibrium react to a change in pressure? Pressure changes do not markedly affect the solid or liquid phases. However, pressure strongly impacts the gas phase. Le Chatelier's principle implies that a pressure increase shifts an equilibrium to the side of the reaction with the fewer number of moles of gas, while a pressure decrease shifts an equilibrium to the side of the reaction with the greater number of moles of gas. If the number of moles of gas is the same on both sides of the reaction, pressure has no effect.

Example 7

What is the effect on this equilibrium if pressure is increased?

$$N_2(g) + 3H_2(g) \rightleftarrows 2NH_3(g)$$

Solution

According to Le Chatelier's principle, if pressure is increased, then the equilibrium shifts to the side with the fewer number of moles of gas. This particular reaction shows a total of 4 mol of gas as reactants and 2 mol of gas as products, so the reaction shifts toward the products side.

Test Yourself

What is the effect on this equilibrium if pressure is decreased?

$$3O_2(g) \rightleftarrows 2O_3(g)$$

Answer

Reaction shifts toward reactants.

What is the effect of temperature changes on an equilibrium? It depends on whether the reaction is endothermic or exothermic. Recall that *endothermic* means that energy is absorbed by a chemical reaction, while *exothermic* means that energy is given off by the reaction. As such, energy can be thought of as a reactant or a product, respectively, of a reaction:

$$\text{endothermic : energy + reactants} \rightarrow \text{products}$$

$$\text{exothermic : reactants} \rightarrow \text{products + energy}$$

Because temperature is a measure of the energy of the system, increasing temperature can be thought of as adding energy. The reaction will react as if a reactant or a product is being added and will act accordingly by shifting to the other side. For example, if the temperature is increased for an endothermic reaction, essentially a reactant is being added, so the equilibrium shifts toward products. Decreasing the temperature is equivalent to decreasing a reactant (for endothermic reactions) or a product (for exothermic reactions), and the equilibrium shifts accordingly.

Example 8

Predict the effect of increasing the temperature on this equilibrium.

$$PCl_3 + Cl_2 \rightleftarrows PCl_5 + 60 \text{ kJ}$$

Solution

Because energy is listed as a product, it is being produced, so the reaction is exothermic. If the temperature is increasing, a product is being added to the equilibrium, so the equilibrium shifts to minimize the addition of extra product: it shifts back toward reactants.

Test Yourself

Predict the effect of decreasing the temperature on this equilibrium.

$$N_2O_4 + 57 \text{ kJ} \rightleftarrows 2NO_2$$

Answer

Equilibrium shifts toward reactants.

In the case of temperature, the value of the equilibrium has changed because the K_{eq} is dependent on temperature. That is why equilibria shift with changes in temperature.

A **catalyst** is a substance that increases the speed of a reaction. Overall, a catalyst is not a reactant and is not used up, but it still affects how fast a reaction proceeds. However, a catalyst does not affect the extent or position of a reaction at equilibrium. It helps a reaction achieve equilibrium faster.

catalyst

A substance that increases the speed of a reaction.

Chemistry Is Everywhere: Equilibria in the Garden

Hydrangeas are common flowering plants around the world. Although many hydrangeas are white, there is one common species (*Hydrangea macrophylla*) whose flowers can be either red or blue, as shown in the accompanying figure. How is it that a plant can have different colored flowers like this?

FIGURE 14.1 Garden Equilibria
This species of hydrangea has flowers that can be either red or blue. Why the color difference?

Source: © Thinkstock

Interestingly, the color of the flowers is due to the acidity of the soil that the hydrangea is planted in. An astute gardener can adjust the pH of the soil and actually change the color of the flowers. However, it is not the H^+ or OH^- ions that affect the color of the flowers. Rather, it is the presence of aluminum that causes the color change.

The solubility of aluminum in soil—and thus the ability of plants to absorb it—is dependent on the acidity of the soil. If the soil is relatively acidic, the aluminum is more soluble, and plants can absorb it more easily. Under these conditions, hydrangea flowers are blue as Al ions interact with anthocyanin pigments in the plant. In more basic soils, aluminum is less soluble, and under these conditions the hydrangea flowers are red. Gardeners who change the pH of their soils to change the color of their hydrangea flowers are therefore employing Le Chatelier's principle: the amount of acid in the soil changes the equilibrium of aluminum solubility, which in turn affects the color of the flowers.

Key Takeaways

- Le Chatelier's principle addresses how an equilibrium shifts when the conditions of an equilibrium are changed.
- The direction of shift can be predicted for changes in concentrations, temperature, or pressure.
- Catalysts do not affect the position of an equilibrium; they help reactions achieve equilibrium faster.

Exercises

1. Define *Le Chatelier's principle*.
2. What is meant by a stress? What are some of the ways an equilibrium can be stressed?
3. Given this equilibrium, predict the direction of shift for each stress.

$$H_2(g) + I_2(s) + 53 \text{ kJ} \rightleftarrows 2HI(g)$$

   a. decreased temperature
   b. increased pressure
   c. removal of HI

4. Given this equilibrium, predict the direction of shift for each stress.

$$H_2(g) + F_2(g) \rightleftarrows 2HF(g) + 546 \text{ kJ}$$

   a. increased temperature
   b. addition of H_2
   c. decreased pressure

5. Given this equilibrium, predict the direction of shift for each stress.

$$2SO_2(g) + O_2(g) \rightleftarrows 2SO_3(g) + 196 \text{ kJ}$$

   a. removal of SO_3
   b. addition of O_2
   c. decreased temperature

6. Given this equilibrium, predict the direction of shift for each stress.

$$CO_2(g) + C(s) + 171 \text{ kJ} \rightleftarrows 2CO(g)$$

   a. addition of CO
   b. increased pressure
   c. addition of a catalyst

7. The synthesis of NH_3 uses this chemical reaction.

$$N_2(g) + 3H_2(g) \rightleftharpoons 2NH_3(g) + 92 \text{ kJ}$$

Identify three stresses that can be imposed on the equilibrium to maximize the amount of NH_3.

8. The synthesis of $CaCO_3$ uses this chemical reaction.

$$CaO(s) + CO_2(g) \rightleftharpoons CaCO_3(s) - 180 \text{ kJ}$$

Identify three stresses that can be imposed on the equilibrium to maximize the amount of $CaCO_3$.

Answers

1. When an equilibrium is stressed, the equilibrium shifts to minimize that stress.
2. A stress is a change in a condition of the equilibrium. Equilibria can be stressed by changing temperature, pressure, or the amounts of reactants or products.
3. a. toward reactants
   b. toward reactants
   c. toward products
4. a. toward reactants
   b. toward products
   c. no effect
5. a. toward products
   b. toward products
   c. toward products
6. a. toward reactants
   b. toward reactants
   c. no effect
7. increased pressure, decreased temperature, removal of NH_3
8. increased pressure, decreased temperature, increasing CO_2 amount

14.4 Calculating Equilibrium Constant Values

Learning Objective

1. Calculate equilibrium concentrations from the values of the initial amounts and the K_{eq}.

There are some circumstances in which, given some initial amounts and the K_{eq}, you will have to determine the concentrations of all species when equilibrium is achieved. Such calculations are not difficult to do, especially if a consistent approach is applied. We will consider such an approach here.

Suppose we have this simple equilibrium. Its associated K_{eq} is 4.0, and the initial concentration of each reactant is 1.0 M:

$$H_2(g) \quad + \quad Cl_2(g) \quad \rightleftarrows \quad 2HCl(g) \qquad\qquad K_{eq} = 4.0$$
$$1.0 \text{ M} \qquad\qquad 1.0 \text{ M}$$

Because we have concentrations for the reactants but not the products, we presume that the reaction will proceed in the forward direction to make products. But by how much will it proceed? We don't know, so let us assign it a variable. Let us assume that x M H_2 reacts as the reaction goes to equilibrium. This means that at equilibrium, we have (1.0 - x) M H_2 left over.

According to the balanced chemical equation, H_2 and Cl_2 react in a 1:1 ratio. How do we know that? The coefficients of these two species in the balanced chemical equation are 1 (unwritten, of course). This means that if x M H_2 reacts, x M Cl_2 reacts as well. If we start with 1.0 M Cl_2 at the beginning and we react x M, we have (1.0 - x) M Cl_2 left at equilibrium.

How much HCl is made? We start with zero, but we also see that 2 mol of HCl are made for every mole of H_2 (or Cl_2) that reacts (from the coefficients in the balanced chemical equation), so if we lose x M H_2, we gain $2x$ M HCl. So now we know the equilibrium concentrations of our species:

$$H_2(g) \qquad + \qquad Cl_2(g) \quad \rightleftarrows \quad 2HCl(g) \qquad\qquad K_{eq} = 4.0$$
$$(1.0 - x) \text{ M} \qquad (1.0 - x) \text{ M} \qquad 2x \text{ M}$$

We can substitute these concentrations into the K_{eq} expression for this reaction and combine it with the known value of K_{eq}:

$$K_{eq} = \frac{[HCl]^2}{[H_2][Cl_2]} = \frac{(2x)^2}{(1-x)(1-x)} = 4.0$$

This is an equation with only one variable, so we should be able to solve for the unknown value. This expression may look formidable, but first we can simplify the denominator and write it as a perfect square as well:

$$\frac{(2x)^2}{(1-x)^2} = 4.0$$

The fraction is a perfect square, as is the 4.0 on the right. So we can take the square root of both sides:

$$\frac{2x}{1-x} = 2.0$$

Now we rearrange and solve (be sure you can follow each step):

$$2x = 2.0 - 2.0x$$
$$4x = 2.0$$
$$x = 0.50$$

Now we have to remind ourselves what x is—the amount of H_2 and Cl_2 that reacted—and $2x$ is the equilibrium [HCl]. To determine the equilibrium concentrations, we need to go back and evaluate the expressions 1 - x and $2x$ to get the equilibrium concentrations of our species:

$$1.0 - x = 1.0 - 0.50 = 0.50 \text{ M} = [H_2] = [Cl_2]$$

$$2x = 2(0.50) = 1.0 \text{ M} = [HCl]$$

The units are assumed to be molarity. To check, we simply substitute these concentrations and verify that we get the numerical value of the K_{eq}, in this case 4.0:

$$\frac{(1.0)^2}{(0.50)(0.50)} = 4.0$$

We formalize this process by introducing the ICE chart, where ICE stands for initial, change, and equilibrium. The initial values go in the first row of the chart. The change values, usually algebraic expressions because we do not yet know their exact numerical values, go in the next row. However, the change values *must* be in the proper stoichiometric ratio as indicated by the balanced chemical equation. Finally, the equilibrium expressions in the last row are a combination of the initial value and the change value for each species. The expressions in the equilibrium row are substituted into the K_{eq} expression, which yields an algebraic equation that we try to solve.

The ICE chart for the above example would look like this:

	H₂(g)	+	Cl₂(g)	⇌	2HCl(g)	K_{eq} = 4.0
I	1.0		1.0		0	
C	−x		−x		+2x	
E	1.0 − x		1.0 − x		+2x	

Substituting the last row into the expression for the K_{eq} yields

$$K_{eq} = \frac{[HCl]^2}{[H_2][Cl_2]} = \frac{(2x)^2}{(1-x)(1-x)} = 4.0$$

which, of course, is the same expression we have already solved and yields the same answers for the equilibrium concentrations. The ICE chart is a more formalized way to do these types of problems. The + sign is included explicitly in the change row of the ICE chart to avoid any confusion.

Sometimes when an ICE chart is set up and the K_{eq} expression is constructed, a more complex algebraic equation will result. One of the more common equations has an x^2 term in it and is called a *quadratic equation*. There will be two values possible for the unknown x, and for a quadratic equation with the general formula $ax^2 + bx + c = 0$ (where a, b, and c are the *coefficients* of the quadratic equation), the two possible values are as follows:

$$x = \frac{-b \pm \sqrt{b^2 - 4ac}}{2a}$$

One value of x is the + sign used in the numerator, and the other value of x is the − sign used in the numerator. In this case, one value of x typically makes no sense as an answer and can be discarded as physically impossible, leaving only one possible value and the resulting set of concentrations. Example 9 illustrates this.

Example 9

Set up an ICE chart and solve for the equilibrium concentrations in this chemical reaction.

$$COI_2(g) \rightleftharpoons CO(g) + I_2(g) \qquad K_{eq} = 0.00088$$
$$0.55\,M \qquad\quad 0 \qquad 0$$

Solution

The ICE chart is set up like this. First, the initial values:

	$COI_2(g)$	$\rightleftharpoons$	$CO(g)$	+	$I_2(g)$
I	0.55		0		0
C					
E					

Some of the COI_2 will be lost, but how much? We don't know, so we represent it by the variable x. So x M COI_2 will be lost, and for each COI_2 that is lost, x M CO and x M I_2 will be produced. These expressions go into the change row:

	$COI_2(g)$	$\rightleftharpoons$	$CO(g)$	+	$I_2(g)$
I	0.55		0		0
C	$-x$		$+x$		$+x$
E					

At equilibrium, the resulting concentrations will be a combination of the initial amount and the changes:

	$COI_2(g)$	$\rightleftharpoons$	$CO(g)$	+	$I_2(g)$
I	0.55		0		0
C	$-x$		$+x$		$+x$
E	$0.55 - x$		$+x$		$+x$

The expressions in the equilibrium row go into the K_{eq} expression:

$$K_{eq} = \frac{[CO][I_2]}{[COI_2]} = 0.00088 = \frac{(x)(x)}{(0.55 - x)}$$

We rearrange this into a quadratic equation that equals 0:

$$0.000484 - 0.00088x = x^2$$

$$x^2 + 0.00088x - 0.000484 = 0$$

Now we use the quadratic equation to solve for the two possible values of x:

$$x = \frac{-0.00088 \pm \sqrt{(0.00088)^2 - 4(1)(-0.000484)}}{2(1)}$$

Evaluate for both signs in the numerator—first the + sign and then the − sign:

$$x = 0.0216 \text{ or } x = -0.0224$$

Because x is the final concentration of both CO and I_2, it cannot be negative, so we discount the second numerical answer as impossible. Thus $x = 0.0216$.

Going back to determine the final concentrations using the expressions in the E row of our ICE chart, we have:

$$[COI_2] = 0.55 - x = 0.55 - 0.0216 = 0.53 \text{ M}$$

$$[CO] = x = 0.0216 \text{ M}$$

$$[I_2] = x = 0.0216 \text{ M}$$

You can verify that these numbers are correct by substituting them into the K_{eq} expression and evaluating and comparing to the known K_{eq} value.

Set up an ICE chart and solve for the equilibrium concentrations in this chemical reaction.

$$N_2H_2(g) \ \rightleftarrows \ N_2(g) + H_2(g) \qquad K_{eq} = 0.052$$
$$0.075 \, M \qquad\quad 0 \qquad\quad 0$$

Answer

The completed ICE chart is as follows:

	N$_2$H$_2$(g)	$\rightleftarrows$ N$_2$(g)	+ H$_2$(g)
I	0.075	0	0
C	$-x$	$+x$	$+x$
E	$0.075 - x$	$+x$	$+x$

Solving for x gives the equilibrium concentrations as [N$_2$H$_2$] = 0.033 M; [N$_2$] = 0.042 M; and [H$_2$] = 0.042 M

Key Takeaway

- An ICE chart is a convenient way to determine equilibrium concentrations from starting amounts.

Exercises

1. Describe the three parts of an ICE chart.
2. What is the relationship between the equilibrium row in an ICE chart and the other two rows?
3. Set up (but do not solve) an ICE chart for this reaction, given the initial conditions.

$$3O_2(g) \ \rightleftarrows \ 2O_3(g)$$
$$0.075 \, M$$

4. Set up (but do not solve) an ICE chart for this reaction, given the initial conditions.

$$CH_4(g) + 2O_2(g) \rightleftarrows CO_2(g) + 2H_2O(g)$$
$$0.750 \, M \qquad 0.450 \, M$$

5. Given that pure solids and liquids do not appear in K_{eq} expressions, set up the ICE chart for this reaction, given the initial conditions.

$$CH_4(g) + 2O_2(g) \rightleftarrows CO_2(g) + 2H_2O(\ell)$$
$$0.0060 \, M \qquad 0.055 \, M$$

6. Given that pure solids and liquids do not appear in K_{eq} expressions, set up the ICE chart for this reaction, given the initial conditions.

$$N_2H_4(\ell) + O_2(g) \rightleftarrows N_2(g) + 2H_2O(\ell)$$
$$2.33 \, M \qquad 1.09 \, M$$

7. Determine the equilibrium concentrations for this chemical reaction with the given K_{eq}.

$$HCN(g) \rightleftarrows HNC(g) \qquad K_{eq} = 4.50$$
$$2.00\,M$$

8. Determine the equilibrium concentrations for this chemical reaction with the given K_{eq}.

$$IF_3(g) + F_2(g) \rightleftarrows IF_5(g) \qquad K_{eq} = 7.59$$
$$1.0\,M \qquad 0.50\,M$$

9. Determine the equilibrium concentrations for this chemical reaction with the given K_{eq}.

$$N_2O_3(g) \rightleftarrows NO(g) + NO_2(g) \qquad K_{eq} = 2.50$$
$$0.0663\,M$$

10. Determine the equilibrium concentrations for this chemical reaction with the given K_{eq}.

$$CO(g) + H_2O(g) \rightleftarrows CO_2(g) + H_2(g) \qquad K_{eq} = 16.0$$
$$0.750\,M \qquad 0.750\,M$$

11. Determine the equilibrium concentrations for this chemical reaction with the given K_{eq}.

$$H_2S(g) \rightleftarrows H_2(g) + S(s) \qquad K_{eq} = 0.055$$
$$0.882\,M$$

12. Determine the equilibrium concentrations for this chemical reaction with the given K_{eq}.

$$2AgCl(s) + F_2(g) \rightleftarrows 2AgF(s) + Cl_2(g) \qquad K_{eq} = 1.2 \times 10^2$$
$$1.99M$$

Answers

1. I = initial concentrations; C = change in concentrations; E = equilibrium concentrations
2. The equilibrium row is the sum of the initial and change rows in an ICE chart.

3.

	$3O_2$	$\rightleftarrows$	$2O_3$
I	0.075		0
C	$-3x$		$+2x$
E	$0.075 - 3x$		$+2x$

4.

	CH_4	+	$2O_2$	$\rightleftarrows$	CO_2	+	$2H_2O$
I	0.750		0.450		0		0
C	$-x$		$-2x$		$+x$		$+2x$
E	$0.750 - x$		$0.450 - 2x$		$+x$		$+2x$

5.

	CH_4	+	$2O_2$	$\rightleftarrows$	CO_2	+	$2H_2O$
I	0.0060		0.055		0		0
C	$-x$		$-2x$		$+x$		—
E	$0.0060 - x$		$0.055 - 2x$		$+x$		—

6.

	N₂H₄	+	O₂	⇌	N₂	+	2H₂O
I	2.33		1.09		0		0
C	—		−x		+x		—
E	—		1.09 −x		+x		—

7. [HCN] = 0.364 M; [HNC] = 1.64 M
8. [IF₃] = 0.591 M; [F₂] = 0.091 M; [IF₅] = 0.409 M
9. [N₂O₃] = 0.0017 M; [NO] = [NO₂] = 0.0646 M
10. [CO] = [H₂O] = 0.150 M; [CO₂] = [H₂] = 0.600 M
11. [H₂S] = 0.836 M; [H₂] = 0.046 M
12. [F₂] = 0.016 M; [Cl₂] = 1.974 M

14.5 Solubility Product Equilibria

Learning Objective

1. Identify equilibrium constant expressions for slightly-soluble salts.

In one sense, all chemical equilibria are treated the same. However, there are several classes of reactions that are noteworthy because of either the identities of the reactants and products or the form of the K_{eq} expression. Here we will consider one class of equilibrium. In Chapter 15, we will introduce some other types. The idea to keep in mind, however, is that all of these are still simply equilibrium constants—just for certain types of chemical reactions.

Insoluble Compounds

In Chapter 8 Section 2, on chemical reactions, the concept of soluble and insoluble compounds was introduced. Solubility rules were presented that allow a person to predict whether certain simple ionic compounds will or will not dissolve.

Describing a substance as soluble or insoluble is a bit misleading because virtually all substances are soluble; they are just soluble to different extents. In particular for ionic compounds, what we typically describe as an *insoluble* compound can actually be ever so slightly soluble; an equilibrium is quickly established between the solid compound and the ions that do form in solution. Thus the hypothetical compound MX does in fact dissolve but only very slightly. That means we can write an equilibrium for it:

$$MX(s) \rightleftharpoons M^+(aq) + X^-(aq)$$

The equilibrium constant for a compound normally considered insoluble is called a **solubility product constant** and is labeled K_{sp} (with the subscript sp, meaning "solubility product"). Because the reactant is a solid, its concentration does not appear in the K_{sp} expression, so expressions for K_{sp} do not have denominators. For example, the chemical equation and the expression for the K_{sp} for AgCl, normally considered insoluble, are as follows:

$$AgCl(s) \rightleftarrows Ag^+(aq) + Cl^-(aq) \qquad K_{sp} = [Ag^+][Cl^-]$$

Table 14.1 lists some values of the K_{sp} for slightly soluble ionic compounds.

TABLE 14.1 Solubility Product Constants for Slightly Soluble Ionic Compounds

Compound	K_{sp}
$BaSO_4$	1.1×10^{-10}
$Ca(OH)_2$	5.0×10^{-6}
$Ca_3(PO_4)_2$	2.1×10^{-33}
$Mg(OH)_2$	5.6×10^{-12}
HgI_2	2.9×10^{-29}
$AgCl$	1.8×10^{-10}
AgI	8.5×10^{-17}
Ag_2SO_4	1.5×10^{-5}

Example 10

Write the K_{sp} expression for $Ca_3(PO_4)_2$.

Solution

Recall that when an ionic compound dissolves, it separates into its individual ions. For $Ca_3(PO_4)_2$, the ionization reaction is as follows:

$$Ca_3(PO_4)_2(s) \rightleftarrows 3Ca^{2+}(aq) + 2PO_4^{3-}(aq)$$

Hence the K_{sp} expression is:

$$K_{sp} = [Ca^{2+}]^3[PO_4^{3-}]^2$$

Test Yourself

Write the K_{sp} expression Ag_2SO_4.

Answer

$K_{sp} = [Ag^+]^2[SO_4^{2-}]$

Equilibrium problems involving the K_{sp} can also be done, and they are usually more straightforward than other equilibrium problems because there is no denominator in the K_{sp} expression. Care must be taken, however, in completing the ICE chart and evaluating exponential expressions.

Example 11

What are $[Ag^+]$ and $[Cl^-]$ in a saturated solution of AgCl? The K_{sp} of AgCl is 1.8×10^{-10}.

Solution

The chemical equation for the dissolving of AgCl is:

$$AgCl(s) \rightleftharpoons Ag^+(aq) + Cl^-(aq)$$

The K_{sp} expression is as follows:

$$K_{sp} = [Ag^+][Cl^-]$$

The ICE chart for the equilibrium is as follows:

	AgCl(s)	$\rightleftharpoons$	Ag$^+$(aq)	+	Cl$^-$(aq)
I			0		0
C	$-x$		$+x$		$+x$
E			$+x$		$+x$

Notice that we have little in the column under AgCl except the stoichiometry of the change; we do not need to know its initial or equilibrium concentrations because its concentration does not appear in the K_{sp} expression. Substituting the equilibrium values into the expression:

$$(x)(x) = 1.8 \times 10^{-10}$$

Solving,

$$x^2 = 1.8 \times 10^{-10}$$

$$x = 1.3 \times 10^{-5}$$

Thus [Ag$^+$] and [Cl$^-$] are both 1.3×10^{-5} M.

Test Yourself

What are [Ba^{2+}] and [SO$_4^{2-}$] in a saturated solution of BaSO$_4$? The K_{sp} of BaSO$_4$ is 1.1×10^{-10}.

Answer

1.0×10^{-5} M

Example 12

What are [Ca^{2+}] and [PO$_4^{3-}$] in a saturated solution of Ca$_3$(PO$_4$)$_2$? The K_{sp} of Ca$_3$(PO$_4$)$_2$ is 2.1×10^{-33}.

Solution

This is similar to Example 11, but the ICE chart is much different because of the number of ions formed.

	Ca$_3$(PO$_4$)$_2$(s)	$\rightleftharpoons$	3Ca^{2+}(aq)	+	2PO$_4^{3-}$(aq)
I			0		0
C	$-x$		$+3x$		$+2x$
E			$+3x$		$+2x$

For every unit of Ca$_3$(PO$_4$)$_2$ that dissolves, three Ca^{2+} ions and two PO$_4^{3-}$ ions are formed. The expression for the K_{sp} is also different:

$$K_{sp} = [Ca^{2+}]^3[PO_4^{3-}]^2 = 2.1 \times 10^{-33}$$

Now when we substitute the unknown concentrations into the expression, we get:

$$(3x)^3(2x)^2 = 2.1 \times 10^{-33}$$

When we raise each expression inside parentheses to the proper power, remember that the power affects everything inside the parentheses, including the number. So:

$$(27x^3)(4x^2) = 2.1 \times 10^{-33}$$

Simplifying,

$$108x^5 = 2.1 \times 10^{-33}$$

Dividing both sides of the equation by 108, we get:

$$x^5 = 1.9 \times 10^{-35}$$

Now we take the fifth root of both sides of the equation (be sure you know how to do this on your calculator):

$$x = 1.1 \times 10^{-7}$$

We are not done yet. We still need to determine the concentrations of the ions. According to the ICE chart, $[Ca^{2+}]$ is 3x, not x. So:

$$[Ca^{2+}] = 3x = 3 \times 1.1 \times 10^{-7} = 3.3 \times 10^{-7} \text{ M}$$

$[PO_4{}^{3-}]$ is 2x, so:

$$[PO_4^{3-}] = 2x = 2 \times 1.1 \times 10^{-7} = 2.2 \times 10^{-7} \text{ M}$$

Test Yourself

What are $[Mg^{2+}]$ and $[OH^-]$ in a saturated solution of $Mg(OH)_2$? The K_{sp} of $Mg(OH)_2$ is 5.6 × 10^{-12}.

Answer

$[Mg^{2+}] = 1.1 \times 10^{-4}$ M; $[OH^-] = 2.2 \times 10^{-4}$ M

Food and Drink App: Solids in Your Wine Bottle

People who drink wine from bottles (as opposed to boxes) will occasionally notice some insoluble materials in the wine, either encrusting the bottle, stuck to the cork, or suspended in the liquid wine itself. The accompanying figure shows a cork encrusted with colored crystals. What are these crystals?

The red crystals on the top of the wine cork are from insoluble compounds that are not soluble in the wine.

Source: Photo courtesy of Paul A. Hernandez, http://www.flickr.com/photos/paul_a_hernandez/2940862302/.

One of the acids in wine is tartaric acid ($H_2C_4H_4O_6$). Like the other acids in wine (citric and malic acids, among others), tartaric acid imparts a slight tartness to the wine. Tartaric acid is rather soluble in H_2O, dissolving over 130 g of the acid in only 100 g of H_2O. However, the potassium salt of singly ionized tartaric acid, potassium hydrogen tartrate ($KHC_4H_4O_6$; also known as potassium bitartrate and better known in the kitchen as cream of tartar), has a solubility of only 6 g per 100 g of H_2O. Thus, over time, wine stored at cool temperatures will slowly precipitate potassium hydrogen tartrate. The crystals precipitate in the wine or grow on the insides of the wine bottle and, if the bottle is stored on its side, on the bottom of the cork. The color of the crystals comes from pigments in the wine; pure potassium hydrogen tartrate is clear in its crystalline form, but in powder form it is white.

The crystals are harmless to ingest; indeed, cream of tartar is used as an ingredient in cooking. However, most wine drinkers don't like to chew their wine, so if tartrate crystals are present in a wine, the wine is usually filtered or decanted to remove the crystals. Tartrate crystals are almost exclusively in red wines; white and rose wines do not have as much tartaric acid in them.

Key Takeaway

- Equilibrium constants exist for certain groups of equilibria, such as weak acids, weak bases, the autoionization of water, and slightly soluble salts.

Exercises

1. Explain the difference between the K_{eq} and the K_{sp}.

2. Write the balanced chemical equation that represents the equilibrium between CaF_2(s) as reactants and Ca^{2+}(aq) and F^-(aq) as products.

3. Noting the phase labels, write the K_{sp} expression for the chemical equation in Exercise 2.

4. Write the balanced chemical equation and the K_{sp} expression for the slight solubility of $Mg(OH)_2$(s).

5. Write the balanced chemical equation and the K_{sp} expression for the slight solubility of $Fe_2(SO_4)_3$(s).

6. What are $[Sr^{2+}]$ and $[SO_4^{2-}]$ in a saturated solution of $SrSO_4$(s)? The K_{sp} of $SrSO_4$(s) is 3.8×10^{-4}.

7. What are $[Ba^{2+}]$ and $[F^-]$ in a saturated solution of BaF_2(s)? The K_{sp} of BaF_2(s) is 1.8×10^{-7}.

8. What are $[Ca^{2+}]$ and $[OH^-]$ in a saturated solution of $Ca(OH)_2$(s)? The K_{sp} of $Ca(OH)_2$(s) is 5.0×10^{-6}.

9. What are $[Pb^{2+}]$ and $[I^-]$ in a saturated solution of PbI_2? The K_{sp} for PbI_2 is 9.8×10^{-9}.

Answers

1. The K_{sp} is a special type of the K_{eq} and applies to compounds that are only slightly soluble.

2. $CaF_2(s) \rightleftarrows Ca^{2+}(aq) + 2F^-(aq)$

3. $K_{sp} = [Ca^{2+}][F^-]^2$

4. $MgOH_2(s) \rightleftarrows Mg^{2+}(aq) + 2OH^-(aq); \quad K_{sp} = [Mg^{2+}][OH^-]^2$

5. $Fe_2(SO_4)_3(s) \rightleftarrows 2Fe^{3+}(aq) + 3SO_4^{2-}(aq); \quad K_{sp} = [Fe^{3+}]^2[SO_4^{2-}]^3$

6. $[Sr^{2+}] = [SO_4^{2-}] = 1.9 \times 10^{-2}$ M

7. $[Ba^{2+}] = 3.6 \times 10^{-3}$ M; $[F^-] = 7.1 \times 10^{-3}$ M

8. $[Ca^{2+}] = 0.011$ M; $[OH^-] = 0.022$ M

9. $[Pb^{2+}] = 1.3 \times 10^{-3}$ M; $[I^-] = 2.7 \times 10^{-3}$ M

14.6 End-of-Chapter Material

Additional Exercises

1. What is the relationship between the K_{sp} expressions for a chemical reaction and its reverse chemical reaction?
2. For the equilibrium

$$PCl_3(g) + Cl_2(g) \rightleftharpoons PCl_5(g) + 60 \text{ kJ}$$

   list four stresses that serve to increase the amount of PCl_5.
3. For the equilibrium

$$N_2O_4 + 57 \text{ kJ} \rightleftharpoons 2NO_2$$

   list four stresses that serve to increase the amount of NO_2.
4. Does a very large K_{eq} favor the reactants or the products? Explain your answer.
5. Is the K_{eq} for reactions that favor reactants large or small? Explain your answer.
6. What is the solubility in moles per liter of AgCl? Use data from Table 14.1.
7. What is the solubility in moles per liter of $Ca(OH)_2$? Use data from Table 14.1.
8. Under what conditions is $K_{eq} = K_P$?
9. Under what conditions is $K_{eq} > K_P$ when the temperature is 298 K?
10. For a salt that has the general formula MX, an ICE chart shows that the K_{sp} is equal to x^2, where x is the concentration of the cation. What is the appropriate formula for the K_{sp} of a salt that has a general formula of MX_2?
11. Referring to Exercise 10, what is the appropriate formula for the K_{sp} of a salt that has a general formula of M_2X_3 if the concentration of the cation is defined as $2x$, rather than x?
12. Consider a saturated solution of $PbBr_2(s)$. If $[Pb^{2+}]$ is 1.33×10^{-5} M, find each of the following.

    a. $[Br^-]$

    b. the K_{sp} of $PbBr_2(s)$

13. Consider a saturated solution of $Pb_3(PO_4)_2(s)$. If $[Pb^{2+}]$ is 7.34×10^{-14} M, find each of the following.

    a. $[PO_4^{3-}]$

    b. the K_{sp} of $Pb_3(PO_4)_2(s)$

Answers

1. They are reciprocals of each other.
2. increase the pressure; decrease the temperature; add PCl_3; add Cl_2; remove PCl_5
3. decrease the pressure; increase the temperature; add N_2O_4; remove NO_2
4. favor products because the numerator of the ratio for the K_{eq} is larger than the denominator
5. small because the denominator of the ratio is larger than the numerator
6. 1.3×10^{-5} mol/L
7. 0.0108 mol/L
8. $K_{eq} = K_P$ when the number of moles of gas on both sides of the reaction is the same.

9. when the number of moles of gas of products is less than the number of moles of gas of reactants

10. $4x^3$

11. If [M] is defined as x, the formula is $\frac{27}{8}x^5$. If [M] is defined as $2x$, the formula is $108x^5$.

12. a. 2.66×10^{-5} M

    b. 9.41×10^{-15}

13. a. $[PO_4^{3-}] = 4.89 \times 10^{-14}$ M

    b. $K_{sp} = 9.46 \times 10^{-67}$

CHAPTER 15
Acids and Bases

Opening Essay

Formerly there were rather campy science-fiction television shows in which the hero was always being threatened with death by being plunged into a vat of boiling acid: "Mwa ha ha, Buck Rogers [or whatever the hero's name was], prepare to meet your doom by being dropped into a vat of boiling acid!" (The hero always escapes, of course.) This may have been interesting drama, but it was not very good chemistry. If the villain knew his/her/its science, the hero would have been dropped into a vat of boiling base.

The active component of a classic acid is the H^+ ion, while the active part of a classic base is the OH^- ion. Both ions are related to water in that all H^+ ion needs to become a water molecule is an OH^- ion, while all an OH^- ion needs to become water is an H^- ion. Consider the relative masses involved: an ion of mass 1 needs an ion of mass 17 to make water, while an ion of mass 17 needs an ion of mass 1 to make water. Which process do you think will be easier?

In fact, bases are more potentially dangerous than acids because it is much easier for an OH^- ion to rip off an H^+ ion from surrounding matter than it is for an H^+ ion to rip off an OH^- ion. Certain household chemicals, such as some brands of cleanser, can be very concentrated bases, which makes them among the most potentially hazardous substances found around the home; if spilled on the skin, the strong caustic compound can immediately remove H^+ ions from the flesh, resulting in chemical burns. Compare that to the fact that we occasionally purposefully ingest substances such as citrus fruits, vinegar, and wine—all of which contain acids. (Of course, some parts of the body, such as the eyes, are extremely sensitive to acids as well as bases.) It seems that our bodies are more capable of dealing with acids than with bases.

On the left is a common acid, and on the right is a common base. Which one is more potentially hazardous?

Source: © Thinkstock

So a note to all the villains out there: get your chemistry right if you want to be successful!

Acids and bases are important classes of chemical compounds. They are part of the foods and beverages we ingest, they are present in medicines and other consumer products, and they are prevalent in the world around us. In this chapter, we will focus on acids and bases and their chemistry.

15.1 Acids and Their Nomenclature

Learning Objectives

1. Define *acid*.
2. Name a simple acid.

acid

An ionic compound of the H^+ cation dissolved in water.

There is one other group of compounds that is important to us—acids—and these compounds have interesting chemical properties. Initially, we will define an **acid** as an ionic compound of the H^+ cation dissolved in water. To indicate that something is dissolved in water, we will use the phase label (aq) next to a chemical formula (where aq stands for "aqueous," a word that describes something dissolved in water). If the formula does not have this label, then the compound is treated as a molecular compound rather than an acid.

binary acids

Acids with hydrogen and one additional element as the anion.

Acids have their own nomenclature, or system of naming. **Binary acids** are acids with hydrogen and one other element as the anion. The name of a binary acid is constructed from three parts: the prefix *hydro-* + the *stem* of the anion name + the suffix *-ic acid*. For example, HCl(aq) is "hydro-" + "-chlor-" + "-ic acid" or hydrochloric acid. Other binary acids are named similarly.

If a compound is composed of hydrogen ions and a polyatomic anion, then the name of the acid is derived from the stem of the polyatomic ion's name. Typically, if the anion name ends in -ate, the name of the acid is the stem of the anion name plus *-ic acid*; if the related anion's name ends in -ite, the name of the corresponding acid is the stem of the anion name plus *-ous acid*. Table 15.1 lists the formulas and names of a variety of acids that you should be familiar with. You should recognize most of the anions in the formulas of the acids.

TABLE 15.1 Names and Formulas of Acids

Formula	Name
$HC_2H_3O_2$	acetic acid
$HClO_3$	chloric acid
HCl	hydrochloric acid
HBr	hydrobromic acid
HI	hydriodic acid
HF	hydrofluoric acid
HNO_3	nitric acid
$H_2C_2O_4$	oxalic acid
Note: The "aq" label is omitted for clarity.	

Formula	Name
$HClO_4$	perchloric acid
H_3PO_4	phosphoric acid
H_2SO_4	sulfuric acid
H_2SO_3	sulfurous acid
Note: The "aq" label is omitted for clarity.	

Example 1

Name each acid without consulting Table 15.1.

1. HBr
2. H_2SO_4

Solution

1. As a binary acid, the acid's name is *hydro-* + stem name + *-ic acid*. Because this acid contains a bromine atom, the name is hydrobromic acid.
2. Because this acid is derived from the sulfate ion, the name of the acid is the stem of the anion name + *-ic acid*. The name of this acid is sulfuric acid.

Test Yourself

Name each acid.

1. HF
2. HNO_2

Answers

1. hydrofluoric acid
2. nitrous acid

All acids have some similar properties. For example, acids have a sour taste; in fact, the sour taste of some of our foods, such as citrus fruits and vinegar, is caused by the presence of acids in food. Many acids react with some metallic elements to form metal ions and elemental hydrogen. Acids make certain plant pigments change colors; indeed, the ripening of some fruits and vegetables is caused by the formation or destruction of excess acid in the plant.

Acids are very prevalent in the world around us. We have already mentioned that citrus fruits contain acid; among other compounds, they contain citric acid, $H_3C_6H_5O_7(aq)$. Oxalic acid, $H_2C_2O_4(aq)$, is found in spinach and other green leafy vegetables. Hydrochloric acid not only is found in the stomach (stomach acid) but also can be bought in hardware stores as a cleaner for concrete and masonry. Phosphoric acid is an ingredient in some soft drinks.

Key Takeaways

- An acid is a compound of the H^+ ion dissolved in water.
- Acids have their own naming system.
- Acids have certain chemical properties that distinguish them from other compounds.

Exercises

1. Give the formula for each acid.

   a. perchloric acid
   b. hydriodic acid

2. Give the formula for each acid.

   a. hydrosulfuric acid
   b. phosphorous acid

3. Name each acid.

   a. $HF(aq)$
   b. $HNO_3(aq)$
   c. $H_2C_2O_4(aq)$

4. Name each acid.

   a. $H_2SO_4(aq)$
   b. $H_3PO_4(aq)$
   c. $HCl(aq)$

5. Name an acid found in food.
6. Name some properties that acids have in common.

Answers

1. a. $HClO_4(aq)$
   b. $HI(aq)$

2. a. $H_2S(aq)$
   b. $H_3PO_4(aq)$

3. a. hydrofluoric acid
   b. nitric acid
   c. oxalic acid

4. a. sulfuric acid
   b. phosphoric acid
   c. hydrochloric acid

5. oxalic acid (answers will vary)
6. They have a sour taste, feel rough on the skin, and react with bases.

15.2 Arrhenius Acids and Bases

Learning Objectives

1. Identify an Arrhenius acid and an Arrhenius base.
2. Write the chemical reaction between an Arrhenius acid and an Arrhenius base.

Historically, the first chemical definition of an acid and a base was put forward by Svante Arrhenius, a Swedish chemist, in 1884. An **Arrhenius acid** is a compound that increases the H^+ ion concentration in aqueous solution. Although it is usual, it is not necessary that the compound be an ionic compound of the H^+ ion. Classic acids, like the ones discussed in the last section, are also Arrhenius acids.

The H^+ ion is just a bare proton, and it is rather clear that bare protons are not floating around in an aqueous solution. Instead, chemistry has defined the **hydronium ion** (H_3O^+) as the actual chemical species that represents an H^+ ion. H^- ions and H_3O^+ ions are often considered interchangeable when writing chemical equations (although a properly balanced chemical equation should also include the additional H_2O).

An **Arrhenius base** is a compound that increases the OH^- ion concentration in aqueous solution. Ionic compounds of the OH^- ion are classic Arrhenius bases. Again, however, it is not necessary that an Arrhenius acid be an ionic compound that contains the OH^- ion.

Arrhenius acid

A compound that increases the hydrogen ion concentration in aqueous solution.

hydronium ion

The actual chemical species that represents a hydrogen ion.

Arrhenius base

A compound that increases the hydroxide ion concentration in aqueous solution.

Example 2

Identify each compound as an Arrhenius acid, an Arrhenius base, or neither.

1. HNO_3
2. CH_3OH
3. $Mg(OH)_2$

Solution

1. This compound is an ionic compound between H^+ ions and NO_3^- ions, so it is an Arrhenius acid.
2. Although this formula has an OH in it, we do not recognize the remaining part of the molecule as a cation. It is neither an acid nor a base. (In fact, it is the formula for methanol, an organic compound.)
3. This formula also has an OH in it, but this time we recognize that the magnesium is present as Mg^{2+} cations. As such, this is an ionic compound of the OH^- ion and is an Arrhenius base.

Test Yourself

Identify each compound as an Arrhenius acid, an Arrhenius base, or neither.

1. KOH
2. H_2SO_4
3. C_2H_6

Answer

1. Arrhenius base
2. Arrhenius acid
3. neither

As introduced in the previous section, Arrhenius acids have some properties in common. They turn litmus, a plant extract, red. They react with some metals to give off H_2 gas. They react with carbonate and hydrogen carbonate salts to give off CO_2 gas, a chemical property sometimes utilized in the kitchen. Acids that are ingested typically have a sour, sharp taste. (The name *acid* comes from the Latin word *acidus*, meaning "sour.") Bases also have some properties in common. They are slippery to the touch, turn litmus blue, and have a bitter flavor if ingested.

salt

Any ionic compound that is formed from a reaction between an acid and a base.

neutralization reaction

The reaction of an acid and a base to produce water and a salt.

Acids and bases have another property: they react with each other to make water and an ionic compound called a salt. A **salt**, in chemistry, is any ionic compound made by combining an acid with a base. A reaction between an acid and a base is called a **neutralization reaction** and can be represented as follows:

$$\text{acid} + \text{base} \rightarrow H_2O + \text{salt}$$

The stoichiometry of the balanced chemical equation depends on the number of H^+ ions in the acid and the number of OH^- ions in the base.

Example 3

Write the balanced chemical equation for the neutralization reaction between H_2SO_4 and KOH. What is the name of the salt that is formed?

Solution

The general reaction is as follows:

$$H_2SO_4 + KOH \rightarrow H_2O + \text{salt}$$

Because the acid has two H^+ ions in its formula, we need two OH^- ions to react with it, making two H_2O molecules as product. The remaining ions, K^+ and SO_4^{2-}, make the salt potassium sulfate (K_2SO_4). The balanced chemical reaction is as follows:

$$H_2SO_4 + 2KOH \rightarrow 2H_2O + K_2SO_4$$

Test Yourself

Write the balanced chemical equation for the neutralization reaction between HCl and $Mg(OH)_2$. What is the name of the salt that is formed?

Answer

$2HCl + Mg(OH)_2 \rightarrow 2H_2O + MgCl_2$; magnesium chloride

Key Takeaways

- An Arrhenius acid is a compound that increases the H^+ ion concentration in aqueous solution.
- An Arrhenius base is a compound that increases the OH^- ion concentration in aqueous solution.
- The reaction between an Arrhenius acid and an Arrhenius base is called neutralization and results in the formation of water and a salt.

Exercises

1. Define *Arrhenius acid*.
2. Define *Arrhenius base*.
3. What are some general properties of Arrhenius acids?
4. What are some general properties of Arrhenius bases?
5. Identify each substance as an Arrhenius acid, an Arrhenius base, or neither.
   a. NaOH
   b. C_2H_5OH
   c. H_3PO_4

6. Identify each substance as an Arrhenius acid, an Arrhenius base, or neither.

   a. $C_6H_{12}O_6$

   b. HNO_2

   c. $Ba(OH)_2$

7. Write the balanced chemical equation for the neutralization reaction between KOH and $H_2C_2O_4$. What is the salt?

8. Write the balanced chemical equation for the neutralization reaction between $Sr(OH)_2$ and H_3PO_4. What is the salt?

9. Write the balanced chemical equation for the neutralization reaction between HCl and $Fe(OH)_3$. What is the salt?

10. Write the balanced chemical equation for the neutralization reaction between H_2SO_4 and $Cr(OH)_3$. What is the salt?

11. $CaCl_2$ would be the product of the reaction of what acid and what base?

12. $Zn(NO_3)_2$ would be product of the reaction of what acid and what base?

13. $BaSO_4$ would be product of the reaction of what acid and what base?

14. Na_3PO_4 would be product of the reaction of what acid and what base?

Answers

1. a compound that increases the H^+ concentration in water

2. a compound that increases the OH^- concentration in water

3. sour taste, react with metals, and turn litmus red

4. rough feel, react with acids to neutralize them, taste bitter, and turn litmus blue

5. a. Arrhenius base

   b. neither

   c. Arrhenius acid

6. a. neither

   b. Arrhenius acid

   c. Arrhenius base

7. $2KOH + H_2C_2O_4 \rightarrow 2H_2O + K_2C_2O_4$; $K_2C_2O_4$

8. $3Sr(OH)_2 + 2H_3PO_4 \rightarrow 6H_2O + Sr_3(PO_4)_2$; $Sr_3(PO_4)_2$

9. $3HCl + Fe(OH)_3 \rightarrow 3H_2O + FeCl_3$; $FeCl_3$

10. $3H_2SO_4 + 2Cr(OH)_3 \rightarrow 6H_2O + Cr_2(SO_4)_3$; $Cr_2(SO_4)_3$

11. HCl and $Ca(OH)_2$

12. HNO_3 and $Zn(OH)_2$

13. H_2SO_4 and $Ba(OH)_2$

14. H_3PO_4 and NaOH

15.3 Brønsted-Lowry Acids and Bases

Learning Objectives

1. Identify a Brønsted-Lowry acid and a Brønsted-Lowry base.
2. Identify conjugate acid-base pairs in an acid-base reaction.

Brønsted-Lowry acid

Any species that can donate a proton to another molecule.

Brønsted-Lowry base

Any species that can accept a proton from another molecule.

The Arrhenius definition of acid and base is limited to aqueous (that is, water) solutions. Although this is useful because water is a common solvent, it is limited to the relationship between the H^+ ion and the OH^- ion. What would be useful is a more general definition that would be more applicable to other chemical reactions and, importantly, independent of H_2O.

In 1923, Danish chemist Johannes Brønsted and English chemist Thomas Lowry independently proposed new definitions for acids and bases, ones that focus on proton transfer. A **Brønsted-Lowry acid** is any species that can donate a proton (H^+) to another molecule. A **Brønsted-Lowry base** is any species that can accept a proton from another molecule. In short, a Brønsted-Lowry acid is a proton donor (PD), while a Brønsted-Lowry base is a proton acceptor (PA).

It is easy to see that the Brønsted-Lowry definition covers the Arrhenius definition of acids and bases. Consider the prototypical Arrhenius acid-base reaction:

$$\underset{\text{acid}}{H^+(aq)} + \underset{\text{base}}{OH^-(aq)} \rightarrow H_2O(\ell)$$

The acid species and base species are marked. The proton, however, is (by definition) a proton donor (labeled PD), while the OH^- ion is acting as the proton acceptor (labeled PA):

$$\underset{\text{PD}}{H^+(aq)} + \underset{\text{PA}}{OH^-(aq)} \rightarrow H_2O(\ell)$$

The proton donor is a Brønsted-Lowry acid, and the proton acceptor is the Brønsted-Lowry base:

$$\underset{\text{BL acid}}{H^+(aq)} + \underset{\text{BL base}}{OH^-(aq)} \rightarrow H_2O(\ell)$$

Thus H^+ is an acid by both definitions, and OH^- is a base by both definitions.

Ammonia (NH_3) is a base even though it does not contain OH^- ions in its formula. Instead, it generates OH^- ions as the product of a proton-transfer reaction with H_2O molecules; NH_3 acts like a Brønsted-Lowry base, and H_2O acts like a Brønsted-Lowry acid:

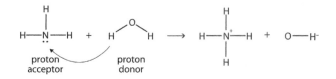

hydrolysis

A reaction with water.

A reaction with water is called **hydrolysis**; we say that NH_3 hydrolyzes to make NH_4^+ ions and OH^- ions.

Even the dissolving of an Arrhenius acid in water can be considered a Brønsted-Lowry acid-base reaction. Consider the process of dissolving $HCl(g)$ in water to make an aqueous solution of hydrochloric acid. The process can be written as follows:

$$HCl(g) + H_2O(\ell) \rightarrow H_3O^+(aq) + Cl^-(aq)$$

HCl(g) is the proton donor and therefore a Brønsted-Lowry acid, while H_2O is the proton acceptor and a Brønsted-Lowry base. These two previous examples show that H_2O can act as both a proton donor and a proton acceptor, depending on what other substance is in the chemical reaction. A substance that can act as a proton donor or a proton acceptor is called **amphiprotic**. Water is probably the most common amphiprotic substance we will encounter, but other substances are also amphiprotic.

Example 4

Identify the Brønsted-Lowry acid and the Brønsted-Lowry base in this chemical equation.

$$C_6H_5OH + NH_2^- \rightarrow C_6H_5O^- + NH_3$$

Solution

The C_6H_5OH molecule is losing an H^+; it is the proton donor and the Brønsted-Lowry acid. The NH_2^- ion (called the amide ion) is accepting the H^+ ion to become NH_3, so it is the Brønsted-Lowry base.

Test Yourself

Identify the Brønsted-Lowry acid and the Brønsted-Lowry base in this chemical equation.

$$Al(H_2O)_6^{3+} + H_2O \rightarrow Al(H_2O)_5(OH)^{2+} + H_3O^+$$

Answer

Brønsted-Lowry acid: $Al(H_2O)_6^{3+}$; Brønsted-Lowry base: H_2O

In the reaction between NH_3 and H_2O,

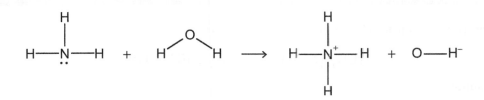

the chemical reaction does not go to completion; rather, the reverse process occurs as well, and eventually the two processes cancel out any additional change. At this point, we say the chemical reaction is at *equilibrium*. Both processes still occur, but any net change by one process is countered by the same net change by the other process; it is a *dynamic*, rather than a *static*, equilibrium. Because both reactions are occurring, it makes sense to use a double arrow instead of a single arrow:

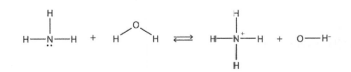

What do you notice about the reverse reaction? The NH_4^- ion is donating a proton to the OH^- ion, which is accepting it. This means that the NH_4^+ ion is acting as the proton donor, or Brønsted-Lowry acid, while OH^- ion, the proton acceptor, is acting as a Brønsted-Lowry base. The reverse reaction is also a Brønsted-Lowry acid base reaction:

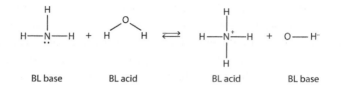

BL base   BL acid   BL acid   BL base

This means that both reactions are acid-base reactions by the Brønsted-Lowry definition. If you consider the species in this chemical reaction, two sets of similar species exist on both sides. Within each set, the two species differ by a proton in their formulas, and one member of the set is a Brønsted-Lowry acid, while the other member is a Brønsted-Lowry base. These sets are marked here:

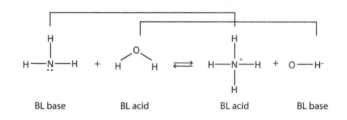

BL base   BL acid   BL acid   BL base

The two sets—NH_3/NH_4^+ and H_2O/OH^-—are called **conjugate acid-base pairs**. We say that NH_4^+ is the conjugate acid of NH_3, OH^- is the conjugate base of H_2O, and so forth. Every Brønsted-Lowry acid-base reaction can be labeled with two conjugate acid-base pairs.

conjugate acid-base pair

Two species whose formulas differ by only a hydrogen ion.

Example 5

Identify the conjugate acid-base pairs in this equilibrium.

$$(CH_3)_3N + H_2O \rightleftarrows (CH_3)_3NH^+ + OH^-$$

Solution

One pair is H_2O and OH^-, where H_2O has one more H^+ and is the conjugate acid, while OH^- has one less H^+ and is the conjugate base. The other pair consists of $(CH_3)_3N$ and $(CH_3)_3NH^+$, where $(CH_3)_3NH^+$ is the conjugate acid (it has an additional proton) and $(CH_3)_3N$ is the conjugate base.

Test Yourself

Identify the conjugate acid-base pairs in this equilibrium.

$$NH_2^- + H_2O \rightleftarrows NH_3 + OH^-$$

Answer

H_2O (acid) and OH^- (base); NH_2^- (base) and NH_3 (acid)

Chemistry Is Everywhere: Household Acids and Bases

Many household products are acids or bases. For example, the owner of a swimming pool may use muriatic acid to clean the pool. Muriatic acid is another name for HCl(aq). Vinegar is a dilute solution of acetic acid [$HC_2H_3O_2$(aq)] in water. In a medicine chest, one may find a bottle of vitamin C tablets; the chemical name of vitamin C is ascorbic acid ($HC_6H_7O_6$).

One of the more familiar household bases is NH_3, which is found in numerous cleaning products. NH_3 is a base because it increases the OH^- ion concentration by reacting with H_2O:

$$NH_3(aq) + H_2O(\ell) \rightarrow NH_4^+(aq) + OH^-(aq)$$

Many soaps are also slightly basic because they contain compounds that act as Brønsted-Lowry bases, accepting protons from H_2O and forming excess OH^- ions. This is one explanation for why soap solutions are slippery.

Perhaps the most dangerous household chemical is the lye-based drain cleaner. Lye is a common name for NaOH, although it is also used as a synonym for KOH. Lye is an extremely caustic chemical that can react with grease, hair, food particles, and other substances that may build up and clog a water pipe. Unfortunately, lye can also attack body tissues and other substances in our bodies. Thus when we use lye-based drain cleaners, we must be very careful not to touch any of the solid drain cleaner or spill the water it was poured into. Safer, nonlye drain cleaners (like the one in the accompanying figure) use peroxide compounds to react on the materials in the clog and clear the drain.

Drain cleaners can be made from a reactive material that is less caustic than a base.

Source: © Shutterstock

Key Takeaways

- A Brønsted-Lowry acid is a proton donor; a Brønsted-Lowry base is a proton acceptor.
- Acid-base reactions include two sets of conjugate acid-base pairs.

Exercises

1. Define *Brønsted-Lowry acid*. How does it differ from an Arrhenius acid?
2. Define *Brønsted-Lowry base*. How does it differ from an Arrhenius base?
3. Write the dissociation of hydrogen bromide in water as a Brønsted-Lowry acid-base reaction and identify the proton donor and proton acceptor.
4. Write the dissociation of nitric acid in water as a Brønsted-Lowry acid-base reaction and identify the proton donor and proton acceptor.

5. Pyridine (C_5H_5N) acts as a Brønsted-Lowry base in water. Write the hydrolysis reaction for pyridine and identify the Brønsted-Lowry acid and Brønsted-Lowry base.

6. The methoxide ion (CH_3O^-) acts as a Brønsted-Lowry base in water. Write the hydrolysis reaction for the methoxide ion and identify the Brønsted-Lowry acid and Brønsted-Lowry base.

7. Identify the Brønsted-Lowry acid and Brønsted-Lowry base in this chemical equation.

$$H_3PO_4 + OH^- \rightarrow H_2PO_4^- + H_2O$$

8. Identify the Brønsted-Lowry acid and Brønsted-Lowry base in this chemical equation.

$$H_2C_2O_4 + 2F^- \rightarrow 2HF + C_2O_4^{2-}$$

9. Predict the products of this reaction, assuming it undergoes a Brønsted-Lowry acid-base reaction.

$$HC_2H_3O_2 + C_5H_5N \rightarrow ?$$

10. Predict the products of this reaction, assuming it undergoes a Brønsted-Lowry acid-base reaction.

$$(C_2H_5)_3N + H_2O \rightarrow ?$$

11. What is the conjugate acid of H_2O? of NH_3?

12. What is the conjugate acid of $H_2PO_4^-$? of NO_3^-?

13. What is the conjugate base of HSO_4^-? of H_2O?

14. What is the conjugate base of H_3O^+? of H_2SO_4?

15. Identify the conjugate acid-base pairs in this reaction.

$$HSO_4^- + PO_4^{3-} \rightarrow SO_4^{2-} + HPO_4^{2-}$$

16. Identify the conjugate acid-base pairs in this reaction.

$$HClO_3 + (C_2H_5)_3N \rightarrow ClO_3^- + (C_2H_5)_3NH^+$$

17. Identify the conjugate acid-base pairs in this reaction.

$$NH_3 + C_6H_5O^- \rightarrow C_6H_5OH + NH_2^-$$

18. Identify the conjugate acid-base pairs in this reaction.

$$C_5H_5NH^+ + C_2O_4^{2-} \rightarrow C_5H_5N + HC_2O_4^-$$

Answers

1. A Brønsted-Lowry acid is a proton donor. It does not necessarily increase the H^+ concentration in water.

2. A Brønsted-Lowry base is a proton acceptor, rather than producing OH^- ions in solution.

3. $HBr + H_2O \rightarrow H_3O^+ + Br^-$; PD: HBr; PA: H_2O

4. $HNO_3 + H_2O \rightarrow H_3O^+ + NO_3^-$; PD: HNO_3; PA: H_2O

5. $C_5H_5N + H_2O \rightarrow C_5H_5NH^+ + OH^-$; PD: H_2O; PA: C_5H_5N

6. $CH_3O^- + H_2O \rightarrow CH_3OH + OH^-$; PD: H_2O; PA: CH_3O^-

7. BL acid: H_3PO_4; BL base: OH^-

8. BL acid: $H_2C_2O_4$; BL base: F^-
9. $C_2H_3O_2^-$ and $C_5H_5NH^+$
10. $(C_2H_5)_3NH^+ + OH^-$
11. H_3O^+; NH_4^+
12. H_3PO_4; HNO_3
13. SO_4^{2-}; OH^-
14. H_2O; HSO_4^-
15. HSO_4^- and SO_4^{2-}; PO_4^{3-} and HPO_4^{2-}
16. $HClO_3$ and ClO_3^-; $(C_2H_5)_3N$ and $(C_2H_5)_3NH^+$
17. NH_3 and NH_2^-; $C_6H_5O^-$ and C_6H_5OH
18. $C_5H_5NH^+$ and C_5H_5N; $C_2O_4^{2-}$ and $HC_2O_4^-$

15.4 Acid-Base Titrations

Learning Objectives

1. Describe a titration experiment.
2. Explain what an indicator does.
3. Perform a titration calculation correctly.

The reaction of an acid with a base to make a salt and water is a common reaction in the laboratory, partly because so many compounds can act as acids or bases. Another reason that acid-base reactions are so prevalent is because they are often used to determine quantitative amounts of one or the other. Performing chemical reactions quantitatively to determine the exact amount of a reagent is called a **titration**. A titration can be performed with almost any chemical reaction for which the balanced chemical equation is known. Here, we will consider titrations that involve acid-base reactions.

In a titration, one reagent has a known concentration or amount, while the other reagent has an unknown concentration or amount. Typically, the known reagent (the **titrant**) is added to the unknown quantity and is dissolved in solution. The unknown amount of substance (the **analyte**) may or may not be dissolved in solution (but usually is). The titrant is added to the analyte using a precisely calibrated volumetric delivery tube called a burette (also spelled buret; see Figure 15.1). The burette has markings to determine how much volume of solution has been added to the analyte. When the reaction is complete, it is said to be at the **equivalence point**; the number of moles of titrant can be calculated from the concentration and the volume, and the balanced chemical equation can be used to determine the number of moles (and then concentration or mass) of the unknown reactant.

titration

A chemical reaction performed quantitatively to determine the exact amount of a reagent.

titrant

The reagent of known concentration.

analyte

The reagent of unknown concentration.

equivalence point

The point of the reaction when all the analyte has been reacted with the titrant.

FIGURE 15.1
Equipment for Titrations
A burette is a type of liquid dispensing system that can accurately indicate the volume of liquid dispensed.

For example, suppose 25.66 mL (or 0.02566 L) of 0.1078 M HCl was used to titrate an unknown sample of NaOH. What mass of NaOH was in the sample? We can calculate the number of moles of HCl reacted:

$$\text{\# mol HCl} = (0.02566 \text{ L})(0.1078 \text{ M}) = 0.002766 \text{ mol HCl}$$

We also have the balanced chemical reaction between HCl and NaOH:

$$\text{HCl} + \text{NaOH} \rightarrow \text{NaCl} + \text{H}_2\text{O}$$

So we can construct a conversion factor to convert to number of moles of NaOH reacted:

$$0.002766 \text{ mol HCl} \times \frac{1 \text{ mol NaOH}}{1 \text{ mol HCl}} = 0.002766 \text{ mol NaOH}$$

Then we convert this amount to mass, using the molar mass of NaOH (40.00 g/mol):

$$0.002766 \text{ mol NaOH} \times \frac{40.00 \text{ g NaOH}}{1 \text{ mol NaOH}} = 0.1106 \text{ g NaOH}$$

This is type of calculation is performed as part of a titration.

Example 6

What mass of $Ca(OH)_2$ is present in a sample if it is titrated to its equivalence point with 44.02 mL of 0.0885 M HNO_3? The balanced chemical equation is as follows:

$$2\text{HNO}_3 + \text{Ca(OH)}_2 \rightarrow \text{Ca(NO}_3)_2 + 2\text{H}_2\text{O}$$

Solution

In liters, the volume is 0.04402 L. We calculate the number of moles of titrant:

$$\text{\# moles HNO}_3 = (0.04402 \text{ L})(0.0885 \text{ M}) = 0.00390 \text{ mol HNO}_3$$

Using the balanced chemical equation, we can determine the number of moles of $Ca(OH)_2$ present in the analyte:

$$0.00390 \text{ mol HNO}_3 \times \frac{1 \text{ mol Ca(OH)}_2}{2 \text{ mol HNO}_3} = 0.00195 \text{ mol Ca(OH)}_2$$

Then we convert this to a mass using the molar mass of $Ca(OH)_2$:

$$0.00195 \text{ mol Ca(OH)}_2 \times \frac{74.1 \text{ g Ca(OH)}_2}{1 \text{ mol Ca(OH)}_2} = 0.144 \text{ g Ca(OH)}_2$$

Test Yourself

What mass of $H_2C_2O_4$ is present in a sample if it is titrated to its equivalence point with 18.09 mL of 0.2235 M NaOH? The balanced chemical reaction is as follows:

$$\text{H}_2\text{C}_2\text{O}_4 + 2\text{NaOH} \rightarrow \text{Na}_2\text{C}_2\text{O}_4 + 2\text{H}_2\text{O}$$

Answer

0.182 g

How does one know if a reaction is at its equivalence point? Usually, the person performing the titration adds a small amount of an **indicator**, a substance that changes color depending on the acidity or basicity of the solution. Because different indicators change colors at different levels of acidity, choosing the correct one is important in performing an accurate titration.

indicator

A substance whose color change indicates the equivalence point of a titration.

Key Takeaways

- A titration is the quantitative reaction of an acid and a base.
- Indicators are used to show that all the analyte has reacted with the titrant.

Exercises

1. Define *titration*.
2. What is the difference between the titrant and the analyte?
3. True or false: An acid is always the titrant. Explain your answer.
4. True or false: An analyte is always dissolved before reaction. Explain your answer.
5. If 55.60 mL of 0.2221 M HCl was needed to titrate a sample of NaOH to its equivalence point, what mass of NaOH was present?
6. If 16.33 mL of 0.6664 M KOH was needed to titrate a sample of $HC_2H_3O_2$ to its equivalence point, what mass of $HC_2H_3O_2$ was present?
7. It takes 45.66 mL of 0.1126 M HBr to titrate 25.00 mL of $Ca(OH)_2$ to its equivalence point. What is the original concentration of the $Ca(OH)_2$ solution?
8. It takes 9.77 mL of 0.883 M H_2SO_4 to titrate 15.00 mL of KOH to its equivalence point. What is the original concentration of the KOH solution?

Answers

1. a chemical reaction performed in a quantitative fashion
2. The analyte is the initial substance, whereas the titrant is the substance that is added to the analyte.
3. False; a base can be a titrant, or the reaction being performed may not even be an acid-base reaction.
4. False; a solid analyte can also be used.
5. 0.494 g
6. 0.654 g
7. 0.1028 M
8. 1.15 M

15.5 Strong vs. Weak Acids and Bases and Their Salts

Learning Objectives

1. Define a strong and a weak acid and base.
2. Recognize an acid or a base as strong or weak.
3. Determine if a salt produces an acidic or a basic solution.

Except for their names and formulas, so far we have treated all acids as equals, especially in a chemical reaction. However, acids can be very different in a very important way. Consider HCl(aq). When HCl is dissolved in H_2O, it completely dissociates into $H^+(aq)$ and $Cl^-(aq)$ ions; all the HCl molecules become ions:

$$HCl \xrightarrow{100\%} H^+(aq) + Cl^-(aq)$$

strong acid

Any acid that is 100% dissociated into ions in aqueous solution.

Any acid that dissociates 100% into ions is called a **strong acid**. If it does not dissociate 100%, it is a **weak acid**. $HC_2H_3O_2$ is an example of a weak acid:

$$HC_2H_3O_2 \xrightarrow{\sim 5\%} H^+(aq) + C_2H_3O_2^-(aq)$$

weak acid

Any acid that is less than 100% dissociated into ions in aqueous solution.

Because this reaction does not go 100% to completion, it is more appropriate to write it as an equilibrium:

$$HC_2H_3O_2 \rightleftarrows H^+(aq) + C_2H_3O_2^-(aq)$$

As it turns out, there are very few strong acids, which are given in Table 15.2. If an acid is not listed here, it is a weak acid. It may be 1% ionized or 99% ionized, but it is still classified as a weak acid.

strong base

Any base that is 100% dissociated into ions in aqueous solution.

The issue is similar with bases: a **strong base** is a base that is 100% ionized in solution. If it is less than 100% ionized in solution, it is a **weak base**. There are very few strong bases (see Table 15.2); any base not listed is a weak base. Note that all strong bases are ionic OH^- compounds. So a base based on some other mechanism, such as NH_3 (which does not contain OH^- ions as part of its formula), will be a weak base.

weak base

Any base that is less than 100% dissociated into ions in aqueous solution.

TABLE 15.2 Strong Acids and Bases

Acids	Bases
HCl	LiOH
HBr	NaOH
HI	KOH
HNO_3	RbOH
H_2SO_4	CsOH
$HClO_3$	$Mg(OH)_2$
$HClO_4$	$Ca(OH)_2$

Acids	Bases
	$Sr(OH)_2$
	$Ba(OH)_2$

Example 7

Identify each acid or base as strong or weak.

1. HCl
2. $Mg(OH)_2$
3. C_5H_5N

Solution

1. Because HCl is listed in Table 15.2, it is a strong acid.
2. Because $Mg(OH)_2$ is listed in Table 15.2, it is a strong base.
3. The nitrogen in C_5H_5N would act as a proton acceptor and therefore can be considered a base, but because it does not contain a OH^- ion, it cannot be considered a strong base; it is a weak base.

Test Yourself

Identify each acid or base as strong or weak.

1. RbOH
2. HNO_2

Answers

1. strong base
2. weak acid

Example 8

Write the balanced chemical equation for the dissociation of $Ca(OH)_2$ and indicate whether it proceeds 100% to products or not.

Solution

This is an ionic compound of Ca^{2+} ions and OH^- ions. When an ionic compound dissolves, it separates into its constituent ions:

$$Ca(OH)_2 \rightarrow Ca^{2+}(aq) + 2OH^-(aq)$$

Because $Ca(OH)_2$ is listed in Table 15.2, this reaction proceeds 100% to products.

Test Yourself

Write the balanced chemical equation for the dissociation of hydrazoic acid (HN_3) and indicate whether it proceeds 100% to products or not.

Answer

The reaction is as follows:

$$HN_3 \rightarrow H^+(aq) + N_3^-(aq)$$

It does not proceed 100% to products because hydrazoic acid is not a strong acid.

Certain salts will also affect the acidity or basicity of aqueous solutions because some of the ions will undergo hydrolysis, just like NH_3 does to make a basic solution. The general rule is that salts with ions that are part of strong acids or bases will not hydrolyze, while salts with ions that are part of weak acids or bases will hydrolyze.

Consider NaCl. When it dissolves in an aqueous solution, it separates into Na^+ ions and Cl^- ions:

$$NaCl \rightarrow Na^+\,(aq) + Cl^-\,(aq)$$

Will the $Na^+(aq)$ ion hydrolyze? If it does, it will interact with the OH^- ion to make NaOH:

$$Na^+\,(aq) + H_2O \rightarrow NaOH + H^+\,(aq)$$

However, NaOH is a strong base, which means that it is 100% ionized in solution:

$$NaOH \rightarrow Na^+\,(aq) + OH^-\,(aq)$$

The free $OH^-(aq)$ ion reacts with the $H^+(aq)$ ion to remake a water molecule:

$$H^+\,(aq) + OH^-\,(aq) \rightarrow H_2O$$

The net result? There is no change, so there is no effect on the acidity or basicity of the solution from the $Na^+(aq)$ ion. What about the Cl^- ion? Will it hydrolyze? If it does, it will take an H^+ ion from a water molecule:

$$Cl^-\,(aq) + H_2O \rightarrow HCl + OH^-$$

However, HCl is a strong acid, which means that it is 100% ionized in solution:

$$HCl \rightarrow H^+\,(aq) + Cl^-\,(aq)$$

The free $H^+(aq)$ ion reacts with the $OH^-(aq)$ ion to remake a water molecule:

$$H^+\,(aq) + OH^-\,(aq) \rightarrow H_2O$$

neutral salt

An ionic compound that does not affect the acidity of its aqueous solution.

The net result? Again there is no change, so there is no effect on the acidity or basicity of the solution from the $Cl^-(aq)$ ion. Because neither ion in NaCl affects the acidity or basicity of the solution, NaCl is an example of a **neutral salt**.

Things change, however, when we consider a salt like $NaC_2H_3O_2$. We already know that the Na^+ ion won't affect the acidity of the solution. What about the acetate ion? If it hydrolyzes, it will take an H^+ from a water molecule:

$$C_2H_3O_2^-\,(aq) + H_2O \rightarrow HC_2H_3O_2 + OH^-\,(aq)$$

basic salt

An ionic compound whose aqueous solution is slightly basic.

Does this happen? Yes, it does. Why? *Because $HC_2H_3O_2$ is a weak acid.* Any chance a weak acid has to form, it will (the same with a weak base). As some $C_2H_3O_2^-$ ions hydrolyze with H_2O to make the molecular weak acid, OH^- ions are produced. OH^- ions make solutions basic. Thus $NaC_2H_3O_2$ solutions are slightly basic, so such a salt is called a **basic salt**.

There are also salts whose aqueous solutions are slightly acidic. NH_4Cl is an example. When NH_4Cl is dissolved in H_2O, it separates into NH_4^+ ions and Cl^- ions. We have already seen that the Cl^- ion does not hydrolyze. However, the NH_4^+ ion will:

$$NH_4^+\,(aq) + H_2O \rightarrow NH_3\,(aq) + H_3O^+\,(aq)$$

acidic salt

An ionic compound whose aqueous solution is slightly acidic.

Recall from Section 2 that H_3O^+ ion is the hydronium ion, the more chemically proper way to represent the H^+ ion. This is the classic acid species in solution, so a solution of $NH_4^+(aq)$ ions is slightly acidic. NH_4Cl is an example of an **acidic salt**. The molecule NH_3 is a weak base, and it will form when it can, just like a weak acid will form when it can.

So there are two general rules: (1) If an ion derives from a strong acid or base, it will not affect the acidity of the solution. (2) If an ion derives from a weak acid, it will make the solution basic; if an ion derives from a weak base, it will make the solution acidic.

Example 9

Identify each salt as acidic, basic, or neutral.

1. KCl
2. KNO$_2$
3. NH$_4$Br

Solution

1. The ions from KCl derive from a strong acid (HCl) and a strong base (KOH). Therefore, neither ion will affect the acidity of the solution, so KCl is a neutral salt.

2. Although the K$^+$ ion derives from a strong base (KOH), the NO$_2^-$ ion derives from a weak acid (HNO$_2$). Therefore the solution will be basic, and KNO$_2$ is a basic salt.

3. Although the Br$^-$ ions derive from a strong acid (HBr), the NH$_4^+$ ion derives from a weak base (NH$_3$), so the solution will be acidic, and NH$_4$Br is an acidic salt.

Test Yourself

Identify each salt as acidic, basic, or neutral.

1. (C$_5$H$_5$NH)Cl
2. Na$_2$SO$_3$

Answers

1. acidic
2. basic

Some salts are composed of ions that come from both weak acids and weak bases. The overall effect on an aqueous solution depends on which ion exerts more influence on the overall acidity. We will not consider such salts here.

Key Takeaways

- Strong acids and bases are 100% ionized in aqueous solution
- Weak acids and bases are less than 100% ionized in aqueous solution.
- Salts of weak acids or bases can affect the acidity or basicity of their aqueous solutions.

Exercises

1. Differentiate between a strong acid and a weak acid.
2. Differentiate between a strong base and a weak base.
3. Identify each as a strong acid or a weak acid. Assume aqueous solutions.
   a. HF
   b. HCl
   c. HC$_2$O$_4$
4. Identify each as a strong base or a weak base. Assume aqueous solutions.
   a. NaOH
   b. Al(OH)$_3$
   c. C$_4$H$_9$NH$_2$

5. Write a chemical equation for the ionization of each acid and indicate whether it proceeds 100% to products or not.

   a. HNO_3

   b. HNO_2

   c. HI_3

6. Write a chemical equation for the ionization of each base and indicate whether it proceeds 100% to products or not.

   a. NH_3

   b. $(CH_3)_3N$

   c. $Mg(OH)_2$

7. Write the balanced chemical equation for the reaction of each acid and base pair.

   a. $HCl + C_5H_5N$

   b. $H_2C_2O_4 + NH_3$

   c. $HNO_2 + C_7H_9N$

8. Write the balanced chemical equation for the reaction of each acid and base pair.

   a. $H_3C_5H_5O_7 + Mg(OH)_2$

   b. $HC_3H_3O_3 + (CH_3)_3N$

   c. $HBr + Fe(OH)_3$

9. Identify each salt as neutral, acidic, or basic.

   a. $NaBr$

   b. $Fe(NO_3)_2$

   c. $Fe(NO_3)_3$

10. Identify each salt as neutral, acidic, or basic.

    a. NH_4I

    b. $C_2H_5NH_3Cl$

    c. KI

11. Identify each salt as neutral, acidic, or basic.

    a. $NaNO_2$

    b. $NaNO_3$

    c. NH_4NO_3

12. Identify each salt as neutral, acidic, or basic.

    a. $KC_2H_3O_2$

    b. $KHSO_4$

    c. $KClO_3$

13. Write the hydrolysis reaction that occurs, if any, when each salt dissolves in water.

    a. K_2SO_3

    b. KI

    c. NH_4ClO_3

14. Write the hydrolysis reaction that occurs, if any, when each salt dissolves in water.

    a. $NaNO_3$

    b. CaC_2O_4

    c. C_5H_5NHCl

15. When NH_4NO_2 dissolves in H_2O, both ions hydrolyze. Write chemical equations for both reactions. Can you tell if the solution will be acidic or basic overall?

16. When pyridinium acetate ($C_5H_5NHC_2H_3O_2$) dissolves in H_2O, both ions hydrolyze. Write chemical equations for both reactions. Can you tell if the solution will be acidic or basic overall?

17. A lab technician mixes a solution of 0.015 M $Mg(OH)_2$. Is the resulting OH^- concentration greater than, equal to, or less than 0.015 M? Explain your answer.

18. A lab technician mixes a solution of 0.55 M HNO_3. Is the resulting H^+ concentration greater than, equal to, or less than 0.55 M? Explain your answer.

Answers

1. A strong acid is 100% ionized in aqueous solution, whereas a weak acid is not 100% ionized.

2. A strong base is 100% ionized in aqueous solution, whereas a weak base is not 100% ionized.

3. a. weak acid
    b. strong acid
    c. weak acid

4. a. strong base
    b. weak base
    c. weak base

5. a. $HNO_3(aq) \rightarrow H^+(aq) + NO_3^-(aq)$; proceeds 100%
    b. $HNO_2(aq) \rightarrow H^+(aq) + NO_2^-(aq)$; does not proceed 100%
    c. $HI_3(aq) \rightarrow H^+(aq) + I_3^-(aq)$; does not proceed 100%

6. a. $NH_3 + H_2O \rightarrow NH_4^+ + OH^-$; does not proceed 100%
    b. $(CH_3)_3N + H_2O \rightarrow (CH_3)_3NH^+ + OH^-$; does not proceed 100%
    c. $Mg(OH)_2 \rightarrow Mg^{2+} + 2OH^-$; proceeds 100%

7. a. $HCl + C_5H_5N \rightarrow Cl^- + C_5H_5NH^+$
    b. $H_2C_2O_4 + 2NH_3 \rightarrow C_2O_4^{2-} + 2NH_4^+$
    c. $HNO_2 + C_7H_9N \rightarrow NO_2^- + C_7H_9NH^+$

8. a. $2H_3C_5H_5O_7 + 3Mg(OH)_2 \rightarrow Mg_3(C_5H_5O_7)_2 + 6H_2O$
    b. $HC_3H_3O_3 + (CH_3)_3N \rightarrow C_3H_3O_3^- + (CH_3)_3NH^+$
    c. $3HBr + Fe(OH)_3 \rightarrow FeBr_3 + 3H_2O$

9. a. neutral
    b. acidic
    c. acidic

10. a. acidic
    b. acidic
    c. neutral

11. a. basic
    b. neutral
    c. acidic

12. a. basic
    b. acidic
    c. neutral

13. a. $SO_3^{2-} + H_2O \rightarrow HSO_3^- + OH^-$

    b. no reaction

    c. $NH_4^+ + H_2O \rightarrow NH_3 + H_3O^+$

14. a. no reaction

    b. $C_2O_4^{2-} + H_2O \rightarrow HC_2O_4^- + OH^-$

    c. $C_5H_5NH^+ + H_2O \rightarrow C_5H_5N + H_3O^+$

15. $NH_4^+ + H_2O \rightarrow NH_3 + H_3O^+$; $NO_2^- + H_2O \rightarrow HNO_2 + OH^-$; it is not possible to determine whether the solution will be acidic or basic.

16. $C_5H_5NH^+ + H_2O \rightarrow C_5H_5N + H_3O^+$; $C_2H_3O_2^- + H_2O \rightarrow HC_2H_3O_2 + OH^-$; it is not possible to determine whether the solution will be acidic or basic.

17. greater than 0.015 M because there are two OH^- ions per formula unit of $Mg(OH)_2$

18. equal to 0.55 M because HNO_3 is a strong acid

15.6 Autoionization of Water

Learning Objectives

1. Describe the autoionization of water.
2. Calculate the concentrations of H^+ and OH^- in solutions, knowing the other concentration.

We have already seen that H_2O can act as an acid or a base:

$$NH_3 + H_2O \rightarrow NH_4^+ + OH^- \text{ (}H_2O \text{ acts as an acid)}$$

$$HCl + H_2O \rightarrow H_3O^+ + Cl^- \text{ (}H_2O \text{ acts as a base)}$$

It may not surprise you to learn, then, that within any given sample of (even pure) water, some H_2O molecules are acting as acids, and other H_2O molecules are acting as bases. The chemical equation is as follows:

$$H_2O + H_2O \rightarrow H_3O^+ + OH^-$$

autoionization of water

Water molecules act as acids (proton donors) and bases (proton acceptors) with each other to a tiny extent in all aqueous solutions.

This occurs only to a very small degree: only about 6 in 10^8 H_2O molecules are participating in this process, which is called the **autoionization of water**. The concentration of both $H^+(aq)$ and $OH^-(aq)$ in a sample of pure H_2O is about 1.0×10^{-7} M. If we use square brackets—[ ]—around a dissolved species to imply the molar concentration of that species, we have

$$[H^+] = [OH^-] = 1.0 \times 10^{-7} \text{ M}$$

for *any* sample of pure water because H_2O can act as both an acid and a base. The product of these two concentrations is 1.0×10^{-14}:

$$[H^+] \times [OH^-] = (1.0 \times 10^{-7})(1.0 \times 10^{-7}) = 1.0 \times 10^{-14}$$

In acids, the concentration of $H^+(aq)$—$[H^+]$—is greater than 1.0×10^{-7} M, while for bases the concentration of $OH^-(aq)$—$[OH^-]$—is greater than 1.0×10^{-7} M. However, the *product* of the two concentrations—$[H^+][OH^-]$—is *always* equal to 1.0×10^{-14}, no matter whether the aqueous solution is an acid, a base, or neutral:

$$[H^+][OH^-] = 1.0 \times 10^{-14}$$

This value of the product of concentrations is so important for aqueous solutions that it is called the **autoionization constant of water** and is denoted K_w:

$$K_w = [H^+][OH^-] = 1.0 \times 10^{-14}$$

The autoionization of water is simply a special type of equilibrium constant, which means that all of the implications of equilibrium constants apply. Thus, if you know $[H^+]$ for a solution, you can calculate what $[OH^-]$ has to be for the product to equal 1.0×10^{-14}, or if you know $[OH^-]$, you can calculate $[H^+]$. As one concentration goes up, the other must go down to compensate so that their product always equals the value of K_w—again, behaving like any other equilibrium constant.

> **autoionization constant of water**
>
> The product of the hydrogen ion and hydroxide ion concentrations.

Example 10

What is $[OH^-]$ of an aqueous solution if $[H^+]$ is 1.0×10^{-4} M?

Solution

Using the expression and known value for K_w,

$$K_w = [H^+][OH^-] = 1.0 \times 10^{-14} = (1.0 \times 10^{-4})[OH^-]$$

We solve by dividing both sides of the equation by 1.0×10^{-4}:

$$[OH^-] = \frac{1.0 \times 10^{-14}}{1.0 \times 10^{-4}} = 1.0 \times 10^{-10} \text{ M}$$

It is assumed that the concentration unit is molarity, so $[OH^-]$ is 1.0×10^{-10} M.

Test Yourself

What is $[H^+]$ of an aqueous solution if $[OH^-]$ is 1.0×10^{-9} M?

Answer

1.0×10^{-5} M

When you have a solution of a particular acid or base, you need to look at the formula of the acid or base to determine the number of H^+ or OH^- ions in the formula unit because $[H^+]$ or $[OH^-]$ may not be the same as the concentration of the acid or base itself.

Example 11

What is $[H^+]$ in a 0.0044 M solution of $Ca(OH)_2$?

Solution

We begin by determining $[OH^-]$. The concentration of the solute is 0.0044 M, but because $Ca(OH)_2$ is a strong base, there are two OH^- ions in solution for every formula unit dissolved, so the actual $[OH^-]$ is two times this, or 2×0.0044 M = 0.0088 M. Now we can use the K_w expression:

$$[H^+][OH^-] = 1.0 \times 10^{-14} = [H^+](0.0088 \text{ M})$$

Dividing both sides by 0.0088:

$$[H^+] = \frac{1.0 \times 10^{-14}}{(0.0088)} = 1.1 \times 10^{-12} \text{ M}$$

$[H^+]$ has decreased significantly in this basic solution.

Test Yourself

What is [OH⁻] in a 0.00032 M solution of H_2SO_4? (Hint: assume both H⁺ ions ionize.)

Answer

1.6×10^{-11} M

For strong acids and bases, [H⁺] and [OH⁻] can be determined directly from the concentration of the acid or base itself because these ions are 100% ionized by definition. However, for weak acids and bases, this is not so. The degree, or percentage, of ionization would need to be known before we can determine [H⁺] and [OH⁻].

Example 12

A 0.0788 M solution of $HC_2H_3O_2$ is 3.0% ionized into H⁺ ions and $C_2H_3O_2^-$ ions. What are [H⁺] and [OH⁻] for this solution?

Solution

Because the acid is only 3.0% ionized, we can determine [H⁺] from the concentration of the acid. Recall that 3.0% is 0.030 in decimal form:

$$[H^+] = 0.030 \times 0.0788 = 0.00236 \text{ M}$$

With this [H⁺], then [OH⁻] can be calculated as follows:

$$[OH^-] = \frac{1.0 \times 10^{-14}}{0.00236} = 4.2 \times 10^{-12} \text{ M}$$

This is much different than would be expected in a strong acid of the same concentration.

Test Yourself

A 0.0222 M solution of pyridine (C_5H_5N) is 0.44% ionized into pyridinium ions ($C_5H_5NH^+$) and OH⁻ ions. What are [OH⁻] and [H⁺] for this solution?

Answer

[OH⁻] = 9.77×10^{-5} M; [H⁺] = 1.02×10^{-10} M

Key Takeaway

- In any aqueous solution, the product of [H⁺] and [OH⁻] equals 1.0×10^{-14}.

Exercises

1. Does [H⁺] remain constant in all aqueous solutions? Why or why not?

2. Does [OH⁻] remain constant in all aqueous solutions? Why or why not?

3. What is the relationship between [H⁺] and K_w? Write a mathematical expression that relates them.

4. What is the relationship between [OH⁻] and K_w? Write a mathematical expression that relates them.

5. Write the chemical equation for the autoionization of water and label the conjugate acid-base pairs.

6. Write the reverse of the reaction for the autoionization of water. It is still an acid-base reaction? If so, label the acid and base.

7. For a given aqueous solution, if $[H^+] = 1.0 \times 10^{-3}$ M, what is $[OH^-]$?

8. For a given aqueous solution, if $[H^+] = 1.0 \times 10^{-9}$ M, what is $[OH^-]$?

9. For a given aqueous solution, if $[H^+] = 7.92 \times 10^{-5}$ M, what is $[OH^-]$?

10. For a given aqueous solution, if $[H^+] = 2.07 \times 10^{-1}$ M, what is $[H^-]$?

11. For a given aqueous solution, if $[OH^-] = 1.0 \times 10^{-5}$ M, what is $[H^+]$?

12. For a given aqueous solution, if $[OH^-] = 1.0 \times 10^{-12}$ M, what is $[H^+]$?

13. For a given aqueous solution, if $[OH^-] = 3.77 \times 10^{-4}$ M, what is $[H^+]$?

14. For a given aqueous solution, if $[OH^-] = 7.11 \times 10^{-10}$ M, what is $[H^+]$?

15. What are $[H^+]$ and $[OH^-]$ in a 0.344 M solution of HNO_3?

16. What are $[H^+]$ and $[OH^-]$ in a 2.86 M solution of HBr?

17. What are $[H^+]$ and $[OH^-]$ in a 0.00338 M solution of KOH?

18. What are $[H^+]$ and $[OH^-]$ in a 6.02×10^{-4} M solution of $Ca(OH)_2$?

19. If HNO_2 is dissociated only to an extent of 0.445%, what are $[H^+]$ and $[OH^-]$ in a 0.307 M solution of HNO_2?

20. If $(C_2H_5)_2NH$ is dissociated only to an extent of 0.077%, what are $[H^+]$ and $[OH^-]$ in a 0.0955 M solution of $(C_2H_5)_2NH$?

Answers

1. $[H^+]$ varies with the amount of acid or base in a solution.

2. $[OH^-]$ varies if there is an acid or base in the solution.

3. $[H^+] = \dfrac{K_w}{[OH^-]}$

4. $[OH^-] = \dfrac{K_w}{[H^+]}$

5. $H_2O + H_2O \rightarrow H_3O^+ + OH^-$; H_2O/H_3O^+ and H_2O/OH^-

6. $H_3O^+ + OH^- \rightarrow H_2O + H_2O$; acid: H_3O^+; base: OH^-

7. 1.0×10^{-11} M

8. 1.0×10^{-5} M

9. 1.26×10^{-10} M

10. 4.83×10^{-4} M

11. 1.0×10^{-9} M

12. 1.0×10^{-2} M

13. 2.65×10^{-11} M

14. 1.41×10^{-5} M

15. $[H^+] = 0.344$ M; $[OH^-] = 2.91 \times 10^{-14}$ M

16. $[H^+] = 2.86$ M; $[OH^-] = 3.50 \times 10^{-15}$ M

17. $[OH^-] = 0.00338$ M; $[H^+] = 2.96 \times 10^{-12}$ M

18. $[OH^-] = 1.20 \times 10^{-3}$ M; $[H^+] = 8.31 \times 10^{-12}$ M

19. $[H^+] = 0.00137$ M; $[OH^-] = 7.32 \times 10^{-12}$ M

20. $[OH^-] = 7.35 \times 10^{-5}$ M; $[H^+] = 1.36 \times 10^{-10}$ M

15.7 The pH Scale

Learning Objectives

1. Define *pH*.
2. Determine the pH of acidic and basic solutions.

As we have seen, [H⁺] and [OH⁻] values can be markedly different from one aqueous solution to another. So chemists defined a new scale that succinctly indicates the concentrations of either of these two ions.

pH is a logarithmic function of [H⁺]:

$$pH = -\log[H^+]$$

pH is usually (but not always) between 0 and 14. Knowing the dependence of pH on [H⁺], we can summarize as follows:

- If pH < 7, then the solution is acidic.
- If pH = 7, then the solution is neutral.
- If pH > 7, then the solution is basic.

This is known as the **pH scale**. You can use pH to make a quick determination whether a given aqueous solution is acidic, basic, or neutral.

pH

The negative logarithm of the hydrogen ion concentration.

pH scale

The range of values from 0 to 14 that describes the acidity or basicity of a solution.

Example 13

Label each solution as acidic, basic, or neutral based only on the stated pH.

1. milk of magnesia, pH = 10.5
2. pure water, pH = 7
3. wine, pH = 3.0

Solution

1. With a pH greater than 7, milk of magnesia is basic. (Milk of magnesia is largely $Mg(OH)_2$.)
2. Pure water, with a pH of 7, is neutral.
3. With a pH of less than 7, wine is acidic.

Test Yourself

Identify each substance as acidic, basic, or neutral based only on the stated pH.

1. human blood, pH = 7.4
2. household ammonia, pH = 11.0
3. cherries, pH = 3.6

Answers

1. basic
2. basic
3. acidic

Table 15.3 gives the typical pH values of some common substances. Note that several food items are on the list, and most of them are acidic.

TABLE 15.3 Typical pH Values of Various Substances*

Substance	pH
stomach acid	1.7
lemon juice	2.2
vinegar	2.9
soda	3.0
wine	3.5
coffee, black	5.0
milk	6.9
pure water	7.0
blood	7.4
seawater	8.5
milk of magnesia	10.5
ammonia solution	12.5
1.0 M NaOH	14.0
*Actual values may vary depending on conditions.	

pH is a *logarithmic* scale. A solution that has a pH of 1.0 has 10 times the $[H^+]$ as a solution with a pH of 2.0, which in turn has 10 times the $[H^+]$ as a solution with a pH of 3.0, and so forth.

Using the definition of pH, it is also possible to calculate $[H^+]$ (and $[OH^-]$) from pH and vice versa. The general formula for determining $[H^+]$ from pH is as follows:

$$[H^+] = 10^{-pH}$$

You need to determine how to evaluate the above expression on your calculator. Ask your instructor if you have any questions. The other issue that concerns us here is significant figures. Because the number(s) before the decimal point in a logarithm relate to the power on 10, the number of digits *after* the decimal point is what determines the number of significant figures in the final answer:

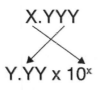

X.YYY

Y.YY x 10ˣ

Example 14

What are $[H^+]$ and $[OH^-]$ for an aqueous solution whose pH is 4.88?

Solution

We need to evaluate the expression:

$$[H^+] = 10^{-4.88}$$

Depending on the calculator you use, the method for solving this problem will vary. In some cases, the "−4.88" is entered and a "10ˣ" key is pressed; for other calculators, the sequence of keystrokes is reversed. In any case, the correct numerical answer is as follows:

$$[H^+] = 1.3 \times 10^{-5} \text{ M}$$

Because 4.88 has two digits after the decimal point, $[H^+]$ is limited to two significant figures. From this, $[OH^-]$ can be determined:

$$[OH^-] = \frac{1 \times 10^{-14}}{1.3 \times 10^{-5}} = 7.7 \times 10^{-10} \text{ M}$$

Test Yourself

What are $[H^+]$ and $[OH^-]$ for an aqueous solution whose pH is 10.36?

Answer

$[H^+] = 4.4 \times 10^{-11}$ M; $[OH^-] = 2.3 \times 10^{-4}$ M

---

pOH

The negative logarithm of the hydroxide ion concentration.

There is an easier way to relate $[H^+]$ and $[OH^-]$. We can also define **pOH** similar to pH:

$$\text{pOH} = -\log[OH^-]$$

(In fact, p"anything" is defined as the negative logarithm of that anything.) This also implies that:

$$[OH^-] = 10^{-\text{pOH}}$$

A simple and useful relationship is that for any aqueous solution,

$$\text{pH} + \text{pOH} = 14$$

This relationship makes it simple to determine pH from pOH or pOH from pH and then calculate the resulting ion concentration.

Example 15

The pH of a solution is 8.22. What are pOH, $[H^+]$, and $[OH^-]$?

Solution

Because the sum of pH and pOH equals 14, we have

$$8.22 + \text{pOH} = 14$$

Subtracting 8.22 from 14, we get:

$$\text{pOH} = 5.78$$

Now we evaluate the following two expressions:

$$[H^+] = 10^{-8.22}$$

$$[OH^-] = 10^{-5.78}$$

So:

$$[H^+] = 6.0 \times 10^{-9} \text{ M}$$

$$[OH^-] = 1.7 \times 10^{-6} \text{ M}$$

Test Yourself

The pOH of a solution is 12.04. What are pH, $[H^+]$, and $[OH^-]$?

Answer

pH = 1.96; $[H^+] = 1.1 \times 10^{-2}$ M; $[OH^-] = 9.1 \times 10^{-13}$ M

In Section 5, we noted how some acids and bases are strong and some are weak. If an acid or base is weak, then they are not ionized 100% and the compounds exist in an equilibrium with their ionic parts. If they are in equilibrium, then they must have equilibrium constants associated with them.

An **acid dissociation constant**, K_a, is the equilibrium constant for the dissociation of a weak acid into ions. For example, acetic acid is a weak acid, and its equilibrium is:

$$HC_2H_3O_2(aq) \rightleftharpoons H^-(aq) + C_2H_3O_2^-(aq)$$

acid dissociation constant

The equilibrium constant for the dissociation of a weak acid into ions.

The expression for K_a is, just like any other equilibrium constant expression, the concentrations of products over reactants:

$$K_a = \frac{[H^+][C_2H_3O_2^-]}{[HC_2H_3O_2]}$$

In the case of acetic acid, the value of K_a is 1.8×10^{-5}. Table 15.4 lists values of several acid dissociation constants. Keep in mind that they are just equilibrium constants, despite the introduction of a new name.

TABLE 15.4 Acid Dissociation Constants for Some Weak Acids

Acid	K_a
$HC_2H_3O_2$	1.8×10^{-5}
$HClO_2$	1.1×10^{-2}
$H_2PO_4^-$	6.2×10^{-8}
HCN	6.2×10^{-10}
HF	6.3×10^{-4}
HNO_2	5.6×10^{-4}
H_3PO_4	7.5×10^{-3}

Note also that the acid dissociation constant refers to *one* H^+ ion coming off the initial reactant. Thus the acid dissociation constant for H_3PO_4 refers to this equilibrium:

$$H_3PO_4(aq) \rightleftharpoons H^+(aq) + H_2PO_4^-(aq) \qquad K_a = 7.5 \times 10^{-3}$$

The $H_2PO_4^-$ ion, called the hydrogen phosphate ion, is also a weak acid with its own acid dissociation constant:

$$H_2PO_4^-(aq) \rightleftharpoons H^+(aq) + HPO_4^{2-}(aq) \qquad K_a = 6.2 \times 10^{-8}$$

Thus for so-called *polyprotic acids*, each H^+ ion comes off in sequence, and each H^+ ion that ionizes does so with its own characteristic K_a.

Example 16

Write the equilibrium equation and the K_a expression for HSO_4^- acting as a weak acid.

Solution

HSO_4^- acts as a weak acid by separating into an H^+ ion and an SO_4^{2-} ion:

$$HSO_4^-(aq) \rightleftharpoons H^+(aq) + SO_4^{2-}(aq)$$

The K_a is written just like any other equilibrium constant expression, in terms of the concentrations of products divided by concentrations of reactants:

$$K_a = \frac{[\text{H}^+][\text{SO}_4{}^{2-}]}{[\text{HSO}_4{}^-]}$$

Test Yourself

Write the equilibrium equation and the K_a expression for $\text{HPO}_4{}^{2-}$ acting as a weak acid.

Answer

$$\text{HPO}_4{}^{2-}(\text{aq}) \rightleftarrows \text{H}^+(\text{aq}) + \text{PO}_4{}^{3-}(\text{aq}) \qquad K_a = \frac{[\text{H}^+][\text{PO}_4{}^{3-}]}{[\text{HSO}_4{}^{2-}]}$$

The K_a is used in equilibrium constant problems just like other equilibrium constants are. However, in some cases, we can simplify the mathematics if the numerical value of K_a is small, much smaller than the concentration of the acid itself. Example 17 illustrates this.

Example 17

What is the pH of a 1.00 M solution of $\text{HC}_2\text{H}_3\text{O}_2$? The K_a of $\text{HC}_2\text{H}_3\text{O}_2$ is 1.8×10^{-5}.

Solution

This is a two-part problem. We need to determine $[\text{H}^+]$ and then use the definition of pH to determine the pH of the solution. For the first part, we can use an ICE chart:

	$\text{HC}_2\text{H}_3\text{O}_2(\text{aq})$	$\rightleftarrows$	$\text{H}^+(\text{aq})$	+	$\text{C}_2\text{H}_3\text{O}_2{}^-(\text{aq})$
I	1.00		0		0
C	-x		+x		+x
E	1.00 - x		+x		+x

$$K_a = \frac{[\text{H}^+][\text{C}_2\text{H}_3\text{O}_2{}^-]}{[\text{HC}_2\text{H}_3\text{O}_2]} = \frac{(x)(x)}{1.00 - x} = 1.8 \times 10^{-5}$$

Here is where a useful approximation comes in: at 1.8×10^{-5}, $\text{HC}_2\text{H}_3\text{O}_2$ will not ionize very much, so we expect that the value of x will be small. It should be so small that in the denominator of the fraction, the term (1.00 - x) will likely be very close to 1.00. As such, we would introduce very little error if we simply neglect the x in that term, making it equal to 1.00:

$$(1.00 - x) \approx 1.00 \text{ for small values of } x$$

This simplifies the mathematical expression we need to solve:

$$\frac{(x)(x)}{1.00} = 1.8 \times 10^{-5}$$

This is much easier to solve than a more complicated quadratic equation. The new expression becomes:

$$x^2 = 1.8 \times 10^{-5}$$

Because x is the equilibrium concentration of H^+ and $\text{C}_2\text{H}_3\text{O}_2{}^-$, we thus have:

$$[\text{H}^+] = 4.2 \times 10^{-3} \text{ M}$$

Notice that we are justified in neglecting the x in the denominator; it truly is small compared to 1.00. Now we can determine the pH of the solution:

$$pH = -\log[H^+] = -\log(4.2 \times 10^{-3}) = 2.38$$

Test Yourself

What is the pH of a 0.500 M solution of HCN? The K_a for HCN is 6.2×10^{-10}.

Answer

4.75

Weak bases also have dissociation constants, labeled K_b (the b subscript stands for base). However, values of K_b are rarely tabulated because there is a simple relationship between the K_b of a base and the K_a of its conjugate acid:

$$K_a \times K_b = 1.0 \times 10^{-14}$$

Thus it is simple to calculate the K_b of a base from the K_a of its conjugate acid.

Example 18

What is the value of K_b for $C_2H_3O_2^-$, which can accept a proton and therefore act as a base?

Solution

To determine the K_b for $C_2H_3O_2^-$, we need to know the K_a of its conjugate acid. The conjugate acid of $C_2H_3O_2^-$ is $HC_2H_3O_2$. The K_a for $HC_2H_3O_2$ is in Table 15.4 and is 1.8×10^{-5}. Using the mathematical relationship between K_a and K_b:

$$(1.85 \times 10^{-5}) \times K_b = 1.0 \times 10^{-14}$$

Solving:

$$K_b = \frac{1.0 \times 10^{-14}}{1.8 \times 10^{-5}} = 5.6 \times 10^{-10}$$

Test Yourself

What is the value of K_b for PO_4^{3-}, which can accept a proton and act as a base? The K_a for HPO_4^{2-} is 2.2×10^{-13}.

Answer

4.5×10^{-2}

Key Takeaways

- pH is a logarithmic function of [H+].
- [H+] can be calculated directly from pH.
- pOH is related to pH and can be easily calculated from pH.

Exercises

1. Define *pH*. How is it related to pOH?

2. Define *pOH*. How is it related to pH?

3. What is the pH range for an acidic solution?

4. What is the pH range for a basic solution?

5. What is $[H^+]$ for a neutral solution?

6. What is $[OH^-]$ for a neutral solution? Compare your answer to Exercise 6. Does this make sense?

7. Which substances in Table 15.3 are acidic?

8. Which substances in Table 15.3 are basic?

9. What is the pH of a solution when $[H^+]$ is 3.44×10^{-4} M?

10. What is the pH of a solution when $[H^+]$ is 9.04×10^{-13} M?

11. What is the pH of a solution when $[OH^-]$ is 6.22×10^{-7} M?

12. What is the pH of a solution when $[OH^-]$ is 0.0222 M?

13. What is the pOH of a solution when $[H^+]$ is 3.44×10^{-4} M?

14. What is the pOH of a solution when $[H^+]$ is 9.04×10^{-13} M?

15. What is the pOH of a solution when $[OH^-]$ is 6.22×10^{-7} M?

16. What is the pOH of a solution when $[OH^-]$ is 0.0222 M?

17. If a solution has a pH of 0.77, what is its pOH, $[H^+]$, and $[OH^-]$?

18. If a solution has a pOH of 13.09, what is its pH, $[H^+]$, and $[OH^-]$?

19. Explain the difference between K_a and K_b.

20. If the K_a for HNO_2 is 5.6×10^{-4}, what is K_b for $NO_2^-(aq)$?

21. If the K_a for HCN is 6.2×10^{-10}, what is the K_b for $CN^-(aq)$?

Answers

1. pH is the negative logarithm of $[H^+]$ and is equal to 14 – pOH.

2. pOH is the negative logarithm of $[OH^-]$ and is equal to 14 – pH.

3. pH < 7

4. pH > 7

5. 1.0×10^{-7} M

6. 1.0×10^{-7} M. It is the same as $[H^+]$. The answer makes sense because for a neutral solution, $[H^+] = [OH^-]$.

7. Every entry above pure water is acidic.

8. Every entry below pure water is basic.

9. 3.46

10. 12.04

11. 7.79

12. 12.35

13. 10.54

14. 1.96

15. 6.21

16. 1.65

17. pOH = 13.23; $[H^+] = 1.70 \times 10^{-1}$ M; $[OH^-] = 5.89 \times 10^{-14}$ M

18. pH = 0.91; $[H^+] = 1.23 \times 10^{-1}$ M; $[OH^-] = 8.13 \times 10^{-14}$ M

19. K_a is for the dissociation of a compound acting as an acid, while K_b is for the dissociation of a compound acting as a base.

20. 1.8×10^{-10}
21. 1.6×10^{-5}

15.8 Buffers

Learning Objectives

1. Define *buffer*.
2. Correctly identify the two components of a buffer.

As indicated in Section 5, weak acids are relatively common, even in the foods we eat. But we occasionally encounter a strong acid or base, such as stomach acid, which has a strongly acidic pH of 1.7. By definition, strong acids and bases can produce a relatively large amount of H^+ or OH^- ions and consequently have marked chemical activities. In addition, very small amounts of strong acids and bases can change the pH of a solution very quickly. If 1 mL of stomach acid [approximated as 0.1 M HCl(aq)] were added to the bloodstream and no correcting mechanism were present, the pH of the blood would decrease from about 7.4 to about 4.7—a pH that is not conducive to continued living. Fortunately, the body has a mechanism for minimizing such dramatic pH changes.

The mechanism involves a **buffer**, a solution that resists dramatic changes in pH. Buffers do so by being composed of certain pairs of solutes: either a weak acid plus a salt derived from that weak acid or a weak base plus a salt of that weak base. For example, a buffer can be composed of dissolved $HC_2H_3O_2$ (a weak acid) and $NaC_2H_3O_2$ (the salt derived from that weak acid). Another example of a buffer is a solution containing NH_3 (a weak base) and NH_4Cl (a salt derived from that weak base).

> **buffer**
>
> A solution that resists dramatic changes in pH.

Let us use an $HC_2H_3O_2/NaC_2H_3O_2$ buffer to demonstrate how buffers work. If a strong base—a source of $OH^-(aq)$ ions—is added to the buffer solution, those OH^- ions will react with the $HC_2H_3O_2$ in an acid-base reaction:

$$HC_2H_3O_2(aq) + OH^-(aq) \rightarrow H_2O(\ell) + C_2H_3O_2^-(aq)$$

Rather than changing the pH dramatically by making the solution basic, the added OH^- ions react to make H_2O, so the pH does not change much.

If a strong acid—a source of H^+ ions—is added to the buffer solution, the H^+ ions will react with the anion from the salt. Because $HC_2H_3O_2$ is a weak acid, it is not ionized much. This means that if lots of H^+ ions and $C_2H_3O_2^-$ ions are present in the same solution, they will come together to make $HC_2H_3O_2$:

$$H^+(aq) + C_2H_3O_2^-(aq) \rightarrow HC_2H_3O_2(aq)$$

Rather than changing the pH dramatically and making the solution acidic, the added H^+ ions react to make molecules of a weak acid. Figure 15.2 illustrates both actions of a buffer.

FIGURE 15.2 The Actions of Buffers
Buffers can react with both strong acids (top) and strong bases (side) to minimize large changes in pH.

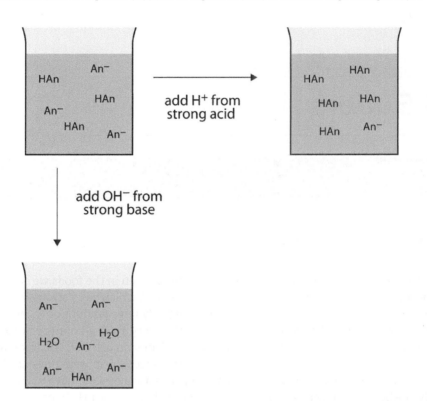

Buffers made from weak bases and salts of weak bases act similarly. For example, in a buffer containing NH_3 and NH_4Cl, NH_3 molecules can react with any excess H^+ ions introduced by strong acids:

$$NH_3(aq) + H^+(aq) \rightarrow NH_4^+(aq)$$

while the $NH_4^+(aq)$ ion can react with any OH^- ions introduced by strong bases:

$$NH_4^+(aq) + OH^-(aq) \rightarrow NH_3(aq) + H_2O(\ell)$$

Example 19

Which combinations of compounds can make a buffer solution?

1. $HCHO_2$ and $NaCHO_2$
2. HCl and $NaCl$
3. CH_3NH_2 and CH_3NH_3Cl
4. NH_3 and $NaOH$

Solution

1. $HCHO_2$ is formic acid, a weak acid, while $NaCHO_2$ is the salt made from the anion of the weak acid (the formate ion [CHO_2^-]). The combination of these two solutes would make a buffer solution.
2. HCl is a strong acid, not a weak acid, so the combination of these two solutes would not make a buffer solution.

3. CH_3NH_2 is methylamine, which is like NH_3 with one of its H atoms substituted with a CH_3 group. Because it is not listed in Table 15.2, we can assume that it is a weak base. The compound CH_3NH_3Cl is a salt made from that weak base, so the combination of these two solutes would make a buffer solution.

4. NH_3 is a weak base, but NaOH is a strong base. The combination of these two solutes would not make a buffer solution.

Test Yourself

Which combinations of compounds can make a buffer solution?

1. $NaHCO_3$ and NaCl
2. H_3PO_4 and NaH_2PO_4
3. NH_3 and $(NH_4)_3PO_4$
4. NaOH and NaCl

Answers

1. no
2. yes
3. yes
4. no

Buffers work well only for limited amounts of added strong acid or base. Once either solute is completely reacted, the solution is no longer a buffer, and rapid changes in pH may occur. We say that a buffer has a certain **capacity**. Buffers that have more solute dissolved in them to start with have larger capacities, as might be expected.

Human blood has a buffering system to minimize extreme changes in pH. One buffer in blood is based on the presence of HCO_3^- and H_2CO_3 [the second compound is another way to write $CO_2(aq)$]. With this buffer present, even if some stomach acid were to find its way directly into the bloodstream, the change in the pH of blood would be minimal. Inside many of the body's cells, there is a buffering system based on phosphate ions.

> **capacity**
>
> The amount of strong acid or base a buffer can counteract.

Food and Drink App: The Acid That Eases Pain

Although medicines are not exactly "food and drink," we do ingest them, so let's take a look at an acid that is probably the most common medicine: acetylsalicylic acid, also known as aspirin. Aspirin is well known as a pain reliever and antipyretic (fever reducer).

The structure of aspirin is shown in the accompanying figure. The acid part is circled; it is the H atom in that part that can be donated as aspirin acts as a Brønsted-Lowry acid. Because it is not listed in Table 15.2, acetylsalicylic acid is a weak acid. However, it is still an acid, and given that some people consume relatively large amounts of aspirin daily, its acidic nature can cause problems in the stomach lining, despite the stomach's defenses against its own stomach acid.

FIGURE 15.3 The Molecular Structure of Aspirin
The circled atoms are the acid part of the molecule.

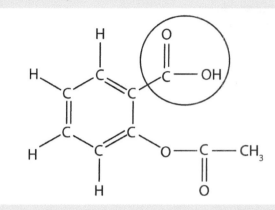

Because the acid properties of aspirin may be problematic, many aspirin brands offer a "buffered aspirin" form of the medicine. In these cases, the aspirin also contains a buffering agent—usually MgO—that regulates the acidity of the aspirin to minimize its acidic side effects.

Aspirin was formally marketed as a drug starting in 1899. The US Food and Drug Administration (FDA), the governmental agency charged with overseeing and approving drugs in the United States, wasn't formed until 1906. Some have argued that if the FDA had been formed before aspirin was introduced, aspirin may never have gotten approval due to its potential for side effects—gastrointestinal bleeding, ringing in the ears, Reye's syndrome (a liver problem), and some allergic reactions. However, recently aspirin has been touted for its effects in lessening heart attacks and strokes, so it is likely that aspirin is here to stay.

Key Takeaway

- A buffer is a solution that resists sudden changes in pH.

Exercises

1. Define *buffer*. What two related chemical components are required to make a buffer?
2. Can a buffer be made by combining a strong acid with a strong base? Why or why not?
3. Which combinations of compounds can make a buffer? Assume aqueous solutions.
   a. HCl and NaCl
   b. HNO_2 and $NaNO_2$
   c. NH_4NO_3 and HNO_3
   d. NH_4NO_3 and NH_3
4. Which combinations of compounds can make a buffer? Assume aqueous solutions.
   a. H_3PO_4 and Na_3PO_4
   b. $NaHCO_3$ and Na_2CO_3
   c. $NaNO_3$ and $Ca(NO_3)_2$
   d. HN_3 and NH_3
5. For each combination in Exercise 3 that is a buffer, write the chemical equations for the reactions of the buffer components when a strong acid and a strong base is added.
6. For each combination in Exercise 4 that is a buffer, write the chemical equations for the reactions of the buffer components when a strong acid and a strong base is added.

7. The complete phosphate buffer system is based on four substances: H_3PO_4, $H_2PO_4^-$, HPO_4^{2-}, and PO_4^{3-}. What different buffer solutions can be made from these substances?

8. Explain why NaBr cannot be a component in either an acidic or a basic buffer.

9. Two solutions are made containing the same concentrations of solutes. One solution is composed of H_3PO_4 and Na_3PO_4, while the other is composed of HCN and NaCN. Which solution should have the larger capacity as a buffer?

10. Two solutions are made containing the same concentrations of solutes. One solution is composed of NH_3 and NH_4NO_3, while the other is composed of H_2SO_4 and Na_2SO_4. Which solution should have the larger capacity as a buffer?

Answers

1. A buffer is the combination of a weak acid or base and a salt of that weak acid or base.

2. Because a weak acid or base and its salt are necessary, a buffer cannot be composed of a strong acid and a strong base. They would just react with each other in a neutralization reaction.

3. a. no
   b. yes
   c. no
   d. yes

4. a. yes
   b. yes
   c. no
   d. no

5. 3b: strong acid: $NO_2^- + H^+ \rightarrow HNO_2$; strong base: $HNO_2 + OH^- \rightarrow NO_2^- + H_2O$; 3d: strong base: $NH_4^+ + OH^- \rightarrow NH_3 + H_2O$; strong acid: $NH_3 + H^+ \rightarrow NH_4^+$

6. a: strong base: $H_3PO_4 + OH^- \rightarrow H_2PO_4^- + H_2O$; strong acid: $PO_4^{3-} + H^+ \rightarrow HPO_4^{2-}$; 4b: strong base: $HCO_3^- + OH^- \rightarrow H_2O + CO_3^{2-}$; strong acid: $CO_3^{2-} + H^+ \rightarrow HCO_3^-$

7. Buffers can be made from three combinations: (1) H_3PO_4 and $H_2PO_4^-$, (2) $H_2PO_4^-$ and HPO_4^{2-}, and (3) HPO_4^{2-} and PO_4^{3-}. (Technically, a buffer can be made from any two components.)

8. NaBr is a salt that derives from a strong acid and a strong base, so it is not a salt of either a weak acid or weak base and cannot be a component of a buffer.

9. The phosphate buffer should have the larger capacity.

10. Neither has the larger capacity. They can accept or donate only a single H^+ or OH^-.

15.9 End-of-Chapter Material

Additional Exercises

1. Write the balanced chemical equation between Zn metal and HCl(aq). The other product is $ZnCl_2$.

2. Write the neutralization reaction in which $ZnCl_2$, also found in Exercise 1, is the salt product.

3. Why isn't an oxide compound like CaO considered a salt? (Hint: what acid-base combination would be needed to make it if it were a salt?)

4. Metal oxides are considered basic because they react with H_2O to form OH compounds. Write the chemical equation for a reaction that forms a base when CaO is combined with H_2O.

5. Write the balanced chemical equation between aluminum hydroxide and sulfuric acid.

6. Write the balanced chemical equation between phosphoric acid and barium hydroxide.

7. Write the equation for the chemical reaction that occurs when caffeine ($C_8H_{10}N_4O_2$) acts as a Brønsted-Lowry base.

8. Citric acid ($C_6H_8O_7$) is the acid found in citrus fruits. It can lose a maximum of three H^+ ions in the presence of a base. Write the chemical equations for citric acid acting stepwise as a Brønsted-Lowry acid.

9. Can an amphiprotic substance be a strong acid and a strong base at the same time? Explain your answer.

10. Can an amphiprotic substance be a weak acid and a weak base at the same time? If so, explain why and give an example.

11. Under what conditions will the equivalence point of a titration be slightly acidic?

12. Under what conditions will the equivalence point of a titration be slightly basic?

13. Write the chemical equation for the autoionization of NH_3.

14. Write the chemical equation for the autoionization of HF.

15. What is the pOH range for an acidic solution?

16. What is the pOH range for a basic solution?

17. The concentration of commercial HCl is about 12 M. What is its pH and pOH?

18. The concentration of concentrated H_2SO_4 is about 18 M. Assuming only one H^+ comes off the H_2SO_4 molecule, what is its pH and pOH? What would the pH and pOH be if the second H^+ were also ionized?

19. What is the relationship between the K_w value for H_2O and its reverse chemical reaction?

20. Is the conjugate base of a strong acid weak or strong? Explain your answer.

21. What is the pH of a saturated solution of $Mg(OH)_2$? Use the data from Table 14.1.

22. What are the pH and the pOH of a saturated solution of $Fe(OH)_3$? The K_{sp} of $Fe(OH)_3$ is 2.8×10^{-39}.

Answers

1. $Zn + 2HCl \rightarrow ZnCl_2 + H_2$

2. $Zn(OH)_2 + 2HCl \rightarrow 2H_2O + ZnCl_2$

3. The O^{2-} ion would come from H_2O, which is not considered a classic acid in the Arrhenius sense.

4. $CaO + H_2O \rightarrow Ca(OH)_2$

5. $2Al(OH)_3 + 3H_2SO_4 \rightarrow Al_2(SO_4)_3 + 6H_2O$

6. $2H_3PO_4 + 3Ba(OH)_2 \rightarrow Ba_3(PO_4)_2 + 6H_2O$

7. $C_8H_{10}N_4O_2 + H_2O \rightarrow C_8H_{10}N_4O_2H^+ + OH^-$; the H^+ ion attaches to one of the N atoms in the caffeine molecule.

8. $C_6H_8O_7 + OH^- \rightarrow C_6H_7O_7^- + H_2O$; $C_6H_7O_7^- + OH^- \rightarrow C_6H_6O_7^{2-} + H_2O$; $C_6H_6O_7^{2-} + OH^- \rightarrow C_6H_5O_7^{3-} + H_2O$

9. As a strong acid or base, an amphiprotic substance reacts 100% as an acid or a base, so it cannot be a base or an acid at the same time.

10. Because a weak acid or base does not react 100% in either direction, an amphiprotic substance can be a weak acid or a weak base at the same time. HCO_3^- is one example.

11. if the salt produced is an acidic salt

12. if the salt produced is a basic salt

13. $NH_3 + NH_3 \rightarrow NH_4^+ + NH_2^-$

14. $HF + HF \rightarrow H_2F^+ + F^-$

15. $pOH > 7$

16. $pOH < 7$

17. $pH = -1.08$; $pOH = 15.08$

18. 1 H^+ ionized: $pH = -1.26$; $pOH = 15.26$; 2 H^+ ionized: $pH = -1.56$, $pOH = 15.56$

19. It would be $1/K_w$, or 1.0×10^{14}.

20. Weak, because the acid prefers to be ionized.

21. 10.35

22. 10.00

CHAPTER 16
Nuclear Chemistry

Opening Essay

Most of us have at least one device in our homes that guards our safety and, at the same time, depends on radioactivity to operate properly. This device is a smoke detector.

A typical smoke detector contains an electric circuit that includes two metal plates about 1 cm apart. A battery in the circuit creates a voltage between the plates. Next to the plates is a small disk containing a tiny amount (~0.0002 g) of the radioactive element americium. The radioactivity of americium ionizes the air between the plates, causing a tiny current to flow constantly between them. (This constant drain on the battery explains why the batteries in smoke detectors should be replaced regularly, whether the alarm has been triggered or not.)

When particles of smoke from a fire enter the smoke detector, they interfere with the ions between the metal plates, interrupting the flow of current. When the current drops beneath a set value, another circuit triggers a loud alarm, warning of the possible presence of fire.

Although radioactive, the americium in a smoke detector is embedded in plastic and is not harmful unless the plastic package is taken apart, which is unlikely. Although many people have an unfounded fear of radioactivity, smoke detectors save thousands of lives every year.

Many people think of nuclear chemistry in connection with the nuclear power industry and atomic bombs but do not realize that most smoke detectors rely on nuclear chemistry and save countless lives every year. The applications of nuclear chemistry may be more widespread than you think.

Source: © Thinkstock

Most chemists pay little attention to the nucleus of an atom except to consider the number of protons it contains, because that determines an element's identity. However, in nuclear chemistry, the composition of the nucleus and the changes that occur there are very important.

Applications of nuclear chemistry may be more widespread than you realize. Many people are aware of nuclear power plants and nuclear bombs, but nuclear chemistry also has applications ranging from smoke detectors to medicine, from the sterilization of food to the analysis of ancient artifacts. In this chapter, we will examine some of the basic concepts of nuclear chemistry and some of the nuclear reactions that are important in our everyday lives.

16.1 Radioactivity

1. Define and give examples of the major types of radioactivity.

We saw in Chapter 3 that atoms are composed of subatomic particles—protons, neutrons, and electrons. Protons and neutrons are located in the nucleus and provide most of the mass of an atom, while electrons circle the nucleus in shells and subshells and account for an atom's size.

We also introduced in Chapter 3 the notation for succinctly representing an isotope of a particular atom:

$$^{12}_{6}\text{C}$$

The element in this example, represented by the symbol C, is carbon. Its atomic number, 6, is the subscript next to the symbol and is the number of protons in the atom. The mass number, the superscript next to the symbol, is the sum of the number of protons and neutrons in the nucleus of this particular isotope. In this case, the mass number is 12, which means that the number of neutrons in the atom is 12 − 6 = 6 (that is, the mass number of the atom minus the number of protons in the nucleus equals the number of neutrons). Occasionally, the atomic number is omitted in this notation because the symbol of the element itself conveys its characteristic atomic number. Because they are relatively common, the two isotopes of hydrogen—^{2}H and ^{3}H—are given their own names and symbols: deuterium (D) and tritium (T), respectively.

radioactivity

Emanations of particles and radiation from atomic nuclei.

Atomic theory in the nineteenth century presumed that nuclei had fixed compositions. But in 1896, the French scientist Henri Becquerel found that a uranium compound placed near a photographic plate made an image on the plate, even if the compound was wrapped in black cloth. He reasoned that the uranium compound was emitting some kind of radiation that passed through the cloth to expose the photographic plate. Further investigations showed that the radiation was a combination of particles and electromagnetic rays, with its ultimate source being the atomic nucleus. These emanations were ultimately called, collectively, **radioactivity**.

alpha particle

A type of radioactive emission equivalent to a helium nucleus.

There are three main forms of radioactive emissions. The first is called an **alpha particle**, which is symbolized by the Greek letter α. An alpha particle is composed of two protons and two neutrons and is the same as a helium nucleus. (We often use $^{4}_{2}\text{He}$ to represent an alpha particle.) It has a 2+ charge. When a radioactive atom emits an alpha particle, the original atom's atomic number decreases by two (because of the loss of two protons), and its mass number decreases by four (because of the loss of four nuclear particles). We can represent the emission of an alpha particle with a chemical equation—for example, the alpha-particle emission of uranium-235 is as follows:

$$^{235}_{92}\text{U} \rightarrow {}^{4}_{2}\text{He} + {}^{231}_{90}\text{Th}$$

nuclear equation

A chemical equation that emphasizes changes in atomic nuclei.

Rather than calling this equation a chemical equation, we call it a **nuclear equation** to emphasize that the change occurs in an atomic nucleus. How do we know that a product of this reaction is $^{231}_{90}\text{Th}$? We use the law of conservation of matter, which says that matter cannot be created or destroyed. This means we must have the same number of protons and neutrons on both sides of the nuclear equation. If our uranium nucleus loses two protons, there are 90 protons remaining, identifying the element as thorium. Moreover, if we lose four nuclear particles of the original 235, there are 231 remaining. Thus, we use subtraction to identify the isotope of the Th atom—in this case, $^{231}_{90}\text{Th}$.

Chemists often use the names **parent isotope** and **daughter isotope** to represent the original atom and the product other than the alpha particle. In the previous example, $^{235}_{92}U$ is the parent isotope, and $^{231}_{90}Th$ is the daughter isotope. When one element changes into another in this manner, it undergoes **radioactive decay**.

parent isotope

The reactant in a nuclear equation.

daughter isotope

The product left over from the parent isotope in a nuclear equation.

radioactive decay

The spontaneous change of a nucleus from one element to another.

Example 1

Write the nuclear equation that represents the radioactive decay of radon-222 by alpha particle emission and identify the daughter isotope.

Solution

Radon has an atomic number of 86, so the parent isotope is represented as $^{222}_{86}Rn$. We represent the alpha particle as $^{4}_{2}He$ and use subtraction (222 – 4 = 218 and 86 – 2 = 84) to identify the daughter isotope as polonium:

$$^{222}_{86}Rn \rightarrow ^{4}_{2}He + ^{218}_{84}Po$$

Test Yourself

Write the nuclear equation that represents radioactive decay of polonium-208 by alpha particle emission and identify the daughter isotope.

Answer

$^{208}_{84}Po \rightarrow ^{4}_{2}He + ^{204}_{82}Pb$; daughter isotope: $^{204}_{82}Pb$

The second major type of radioactive emission is called a **beta particle**, symbolized by the Greek letter β. A beta particle is an electron ejected from the nucleus (not from the shells of electrons about the nucleus) and has a –1 charge. We can also represent a beta particle as $^{0}_{-1}e$. The net effect of beta particle emission on a nucleus is that a neutron is converted to a proton. The mass number stays the same, but because the number of protons increases by one, the atomic number goes up by one. Carbon-14 decays by emitting a beta particle:

$$^{14}_{6}C \rightarrow ^{14}_{7}N + ^{0}_{-1}e$$

beta particle

A type of radioactive emission equivalent to an electron.

Again, the sum of the atomic numbers is the same on both sides of the equation, as is the sum of the mass numbers. (Note that the electron is assigned an "atomic number" of –1, equal to its charge.)

The third major type of radioactive emission is not a particle but rather a very energetic form of electromagnetic radiation called **gamma rays**, symbolized by the Greek letter γ. Gamma rays themselves do not carry an electrical charge, but they may knock electrons out of atoms in a sample of matter and make it electrically charged (for which gamma rays are termed *ionizing radiation*). For example, in the radioactive decay of radon-222, both alpha and gamma radiation are emitted, with the latter having an energy of 8.2 × 10^{-14} J per nucleus decayed:

gamma rays

A type of radioactive emission that is a very energetic form of electromagnetic radiation.

$$^{222}_{86}Rn \rightarrow ^{218}_{84}Po + ^{4}_{2}He + \gamma$$

This may not seem like much energy, but if 1 mol of Rn atoms were to decay, the gamma ray energy would be 4.9 × 10^{7} kJ!

Example 2

Write the nuclear equation that represents the radioactive decay of boron-12 by beta particle emission and identify the daughter isotope. A gamma ray is emitted simultaneously with the beta particle.

Solution

The parent isotope is $^{12}_{5}\text{B}$, while one of the products is $^{0}_{-1}\text{e}$. So that the mass and atomic numbers have the same value on both sides, the mass number of the daughter isotope must be 12, and its atomic number must be 6. The element having an atomic number of 6 is carbon. Thus the complete nuclear equation is as follows:

$$^{12}_{5}\text{B} \rightarrow {}^{12}_{6}\text{C} + {}^{0}_{-1}\text{e} + \gamma$$

The daughter isotope is carbon-12.

Test Yourself

Write the nuclear equation that represents the radioactive decay of technetium-133 by beta particle emission and identify the daughter isotope. A gamma ray is emitted simultaneously with the beta particle.

Answer

$^{133}_{43}\text{Tc} \rightarrow {}^{133}_{44}\text{Ru} + {}^{0}_{-1}\text{e} + \gamma$; daughter isotope: ruthenium-133

Alpha, beta, and gamma emissions have different abilities to penetrate matter. The relatively large alpha particle is easily stopped by matter (although it may impart a significant amount of energy to the matter it contacts). Beta particles penetrate slightly into matter, perhaps a few centimeters at most. Gamma rays can penetrate deeply into matter and can impart a large amount of energy into the surrounding matter. Table 16.1 summarizes the properties of the three main types of radioactive emissions.

TABLE 16.1 The Three Main Forms of Radioactive Emissions

Characteristic	Alpha Particles	Beta Particles	Gamma Rays
symbols	α, $^{4}_{2}\text{He}$	β, $^{0}_{-1}\text{e}$	γ
identity	helium nucleus	electron	electromagnetic radiation
charge	2+	1−	none
mass number	4	0	0
penetrating power	minimal (will not penetrate skin)	short (will penetrate skin and some tissues slightly)	deep (will penetrate tissues deeply)

spontaneous fission (or fission)

The breaking apart of an atomic nucleus into smaller nuclei.

Occasionally, an atomic nucleus breaks apart into smaller pieces in a radioactive process called **spontaneous fission (or fission)**. Typically, the daughter isotopes produced by fission are a varied mix of products, rather than a specific isotope as with alpha and beta particle emission. Often, fission produces excess neutrons that will sometimes be captured by other nuclei, possibly inducing additional radioactive events. Uranium-235 undergoes spontaneous fission to a small extent. One typical reaction is

$$^{235}_{92}\text{U} \rightarrow {}^{139}_{56}\text{Ba} + {}^{94}_{36}\text{Kr} + 2^{1}_{0}\text{n}$$

where $^{1}_{0}\text{n}$ is the symbol for a neutron. As with any nuclear process, the sums of the atomic numbers and mass numbers must be the same on both sides of the equation. Spontaneous fission is found only in large nuclei. The smallest nucleus that exhibits spontaneous fission is lead-208. (Fission is the radioactive process used in nuclear power plants and one type of nuclear bomb.)

Key Takeaways

- The major types of radioactivity include alpha particles, beta particles, and gamma rays.
- Fission is a type of radioactivity in which large nuclei spontaneously break apart into smaller nuclei.

Exercises

1. Define *radioactivity*.

2. Give an example of a radioactive element. How do you know if it is radioactive?

3. How many protons and neutrons are in each isotope?

   a. $^{11}_{5}B$

   b. $^{27}_{13}Al$

   c. ^{56}Fe

   d. ^{224}Rn

4. How many protons and neutrons are in each isotope?

   a. $^{2}_{1}H$

   b. $^{112}_{48}Cd$

   c. ^{252}Es

   d. ^{40}K

5. Describe an alpha particle. What nucleus is it equivalent to?

6. Describe a beta particle. What subatomic particle is it equivalent to?

7. What are gamma rays?

8. Why is it inappropriate to refer to gamma rays as "gamma particles"?

9. Plutonium has an atomic number of 94. Write the nuclear equation for the alpha particle emission of plutonium-244. What is the daughter isotope?

10. Francium has an atomic number of 87. Write the nuclear equation for the alpha particle emission of francium-212. What is the daughter isotope?

11. Tin has an atomic number of 50. Write the nuclear equation for the beta particle emission of tin-121. What is the daughter isotope?

12. Technetium has an atomic number of 43. Write the nuclear equation for the beta particle emission of technetium-99. What is the daughter isotope?

13. Energies of gamma rays are typically expressed in units of megaelectron volts (MeV), where 1 MeV = 1.602×10^{-13} J. Using the data provided in the text, calculate the energy in megaelectron volts of the gamma ray emitted when radon-222 decays.

14. The gamma ray emitted when oxygen-19 gives off a beta particle is 0.197 MeV. What is its energy in joules? (See Exercise 13 for the definition of a megaelectron volt.)

15. Which penetrates matter more deeply—alpha particles or beta particles? Suggest ways to protect yourself against both particles.

16. Which penetrates matter more deeply—alpha particles or gamma rays? Suggest ways to protect yourself against both emissions.

17. Define *nuclear fission*.

18. What general characteristic is typically necessary for a nucleus to undergo spontaneous fission?

Answers

1. Radioactivity is the spontaneous emission of particles and electromagnetic radiation from nuclei of unstable atoms.

2. Uranium (answers will vary); it is difficult to know in advance if any given isotope is radioactive, but all elements with an atomic number greater than that of bismuth are radioactive

3. a. 5 protons; 6 neutrons
    b. 13 protons; 14 neutrons
    c. 26 protons; 30 neutrons
    d. 86 protons; 138 neutrons

4. a. 1 proton; 1 neutron
    b. 48 protons; 64 neutrons
    c. 99 protons; 153 neutrons
    d. 19 protons; 21 neutrons

5. An alpha particle is a collection of two protons and two neutrons and is equivalent to a helium nucleus.

6. A beta particle is an electron emitted from the nucleus.

7. Gamma rays are high-energy electromagnetic radiation given off in radioactive decay.

8. Gamma rays are actually electromagnetic radiation, not particles.

9. $^{244}_{94}\text{Pu} \rightarrow \,^{240}_{92}\text{U} + \,^{4}_{2}\text{He}$; daughter isotope: ^{240}U

10. $^{212}_{87}\text{Fr} \rightarrow \,^{208}_{85}\text{At} + \,^{4}_{2}\text{He}$; daughter isotope: ^{208}At

11. $^{121}_{50}\text{Sn} \rightarrow \,^{121}_{51}\text{Sb} + \,^{0}_{-1}\text{e}$; daughter isotope: ^{121}Sb

12. $^{99}_{43}\text{Tc} \rightarrow \,^{99}_{44}\text{Ru} + \,^{0}_{-1}\text{e}$; daughter isotope: ^{99}Ru

13. 0.51 MeV

14. 3.16×10^{-14} J

15. Beta particles penetrate more. A thick wall of inert matter is sufficient to block both particles.

16. Gamma rays penetrate more. A thick slab of some dense material is necessary for complete protection.

17. Nuclear fission is the breaking down of large nuclei into smaller nuclei, usually with the release of excess neutrons.

18. Generally, very large nuclei undergo spontaneous fission.

16.2 Half-Life

Learning Objectives

1. Define *half-life*.
2. Determine the amount of radioactive substance remaining after a given number of half-lives.

Whether or not a given isotope is radioactive is a characteristic of that particular isotope. Some isotopes are stable indefinitely, while others are radioactive and decay through a characteristic form of emission. As time passes, less and less of the radioactive isotope will be present, and the level of radioactivity decreases. An interesting and useful aspect of radioactive decay is **half-life**, which is the amount of time it takes for one-half of a radioactive isotope to decay. The half-life of a specific radioactive isotope is constant; it is unaffected by conditions and is independent of the initial amount of that isotope.

Consider the following example. Suppose we have 100.0 g of tritium (a radioactive isotope of hydrogen). It has a half-life of 12.3 y. After 12.3 y, half of the sample will have decayed from hydrogen-3 to helium-3 by emitting a beta particle, so that only 50.0 g of the original tritium remains. After another 12.3 y—making a total of 24.6 y—another half of the remaining tritium will have decayed, leaving 25.0 g of tritium. After another 12.3 y—now a total of 36.9 y—another half of the remaining tritium will have decayed, leaving 12.5 g. This sequence of events is illustrated in Figure 16.1.

FIGURE 16.1 Radioactive Decay
During each successive half-life, half of the initial amount will radioactivey decay.

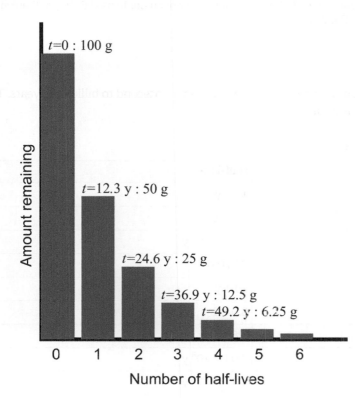

We can determine the amount of a radioactive isotope remaining after a given number half-lives by using the following expression:

$$\text{amount remaining} = \text{initial amount} \times \left(\frac{1}{2}\right)^{n}$$

where n is the number of half-lives. This expression works even if the number of half-lives is not a whole number.

half-life

The amount of time it takes for one-half of a radioactive isotope to decay.

Example 3

The half-life of fluorine-20 is 11.0 s. If a sample initially contains 5.00 g of fluorine-20, how much remains after 44.0 s?

Solution

If we compare the time that has passed to the isotope's half-life, we note that 44.0 s is exactly 4 half-lives, so using the previous expression, $n = 4$. Substituting and solving results in the following:

$$\text{amount remaining} = 5.00\,\text{g} \times \left(\tfrac{1}{2}\right)^4$$

$$\text{amount remaining} = 5.00\,\text{g} \times \tfrac{1}{16}$$

$$\text{amount remaining} = 0.313\,\text{g}$$

Less than one-third of a gram of fluorine-20 remains.

Test Yourself

The half-life of titanium-44 is 60.0 y. A sample of titanium contains 0.600 g of titanium-44. How much remains after 240.0 y?

Answer

0.0375 g

Half-lives of isotopes range from fractions of a microsecond to billions of years. Table 16.2 lists the half-lives of some isotopes.

TABLE 16.2 Half-Lives of Various Isotopes

Isotope	Half-Life
^{3}H	12.3 y
^{14}C	5730 y
^{40}K	1.26×10^9 y
^{51}Cr	27.70 d
^{90}Sr	29.1 y
^{131}I	8.04 d
^{222}Rn	3.823 d
^{235}U	7.04×10^8 y
^{238}U	4.47×10^9 y
^{241}Am	432.7 y
^{248}Bk	23.7 h
^{260}Sg	4 ms

Chemistry Is Everywhere: Radioactive Elements in the Body

You may not think of yourself as radioactive, but you are. A small portion of certain elements in the human body are radioactive and constantly undergo decay. The following table summarizes radioactivity in the normal human body.

Radioactive Iso-tope	Half-Life (y)	Isotope Mass in the Body (g)	Activity in the Body (decays/s)
^{40}K	1.26×10^9	0.0164	4,340
^{14}C	5,730	1.6×10^{-8}	3,080
^{87}Rb	4.9×10^{10}	0.12	600
^{210}Pb	22.3	5.4×10^{-10}	15
^{3}H	12.3	2×10^{-14}	7
^{238}U	4.47×10^9	1×10^{-4}	5
^{228}Ra	5.76	4.6×10^{-14}	5
^{226}Ra	1,620	3.6×10^{-11}	3

The average human body experiences about 9,000 radioactive decays per second.

Most of the radioactivity in the human body comes from potassium-40 and carbon-14. Potassium and carbon are two elements that we absolutely cannot live without, so unless we can remove all the radioactive isotopes of these elements from our bodies, there is no way to escape at least some radioactivity. There is debate about which radioactive element is more problematic. There is more potassium-40 in the body than carbon-14, and it has a much longer half-life. Potassium-40 also decays with about 10 times more energy than carbon-14, making each decay potentially more problematic. However, carbon is the element that makes up the backbone of most living molecules, making carbon-14 more likely to be present around important molecules, such as proteins and DNA molecules. Most experts agree that while it is foo hardy to expect absolutely no exposure to radioactivity, we can and should minimize exposure to excess radioactivity.

What if the elapsed time is not an exact number of half-lives? We can still calculate the amount of material we have left, but the equation is more complicated. The equation is

$$\textbf{amount remaining} = (\textbf{amount initially}) \times e^{-0.693t/t_{1/2}}$$

where e is the base of natural logarithms (2.71828182...), t is the elapsed time, and $t_{1/2}$ is the half-life of the radioactive isotope. The variables t and $t_{1/2}$ should have the same units of time, and you may need to make sure you know how to evaluate natural-logarithm powers on your calculator (for many calculators, there is an "inverse logarithm" function that you can use; consult your instructor if you are not sure how to use your calculator). Although this is a more complicated formula, the length of time t need not be an exact multiple of half-lives.

Example 4

The half-life of fluorine-20 is 11.0 s. If a sample initially contains 5.00 g of fluorine-20, how much remains after 60.0 s?

Solution

Although similar to Example 3, the amount of time is not an exact multiple of a half-life. Here we identify the initial amount as 5.00 g, $t = 60.0$ s, and $t_{1/2} = 11.0$ s. Substituting into the equation:

$$\textbf{amount remaining} = (5.00\ \textbf{g}) \times e^{-(0.693)(60.0\ \text{s})/11.0\ \text{s}}$$

Evaluating the exponent (and noting that the s units cancel), we get

$$\textbf{amount remaining} = (5.00\ \textbf{g}) \times e^{-3.78}$$

Solving, the amount remaining is 0.114 g. (You may want to verify this answer to confirm that you are using your calculator properly.)

Test Yourself

The half-life of titanium-44 is 60.0 y. A sample of titanium contains 0.600 g of titanium-44. How much remains after 100.0 y?

Answer

0.189 g

Key Takeaways

- Natural radioactive processes are characterized by a half-life, the time it takes for half of the material to decay radioactively.
- The amount of material left over after a certain number of half-lives can be easily calculated.

Exercises

1. Do all isotopes have a half-life? Explain your answer.

2. Which is more radioactive—an isotope with a long half-life or an isotope with a short half-life?

3. How long does it take for 1.00 g of palladium-103 to decay to 0.125 g if its half-life is 17.0 d?

4. How long does it take for 2.00 g of niobium-94 to decay to 0.0625 g if its half-life is 20,000 y?

5. It took 75 y for 10.0 g of a radioactive isotope to decay to 1.25 g. What is the half-life of this isotope?

6. It took 49.2 s for 3.000 g of a radioactive isotope to decay to 0.1875 g. What is the half-life of this isotope?

7. The half-live of americium-241 is 432 y. If 0.0002 g of americium-241 is present in a smoke detector at the date of manufacture, what mass of americium-241 is present after 100.0 y? After 1,000.0 y?

8. If the half-life of tritium (hydrogen-3) is 12.3 y, how much of a 0.00444 g sample of tritium is present after 5.0 y? After 250.0 y?

9. Explain why the amount left after 1,000.0 y in Exercise 7 is not one-tenth of the amount present after 100.0 y, despite the fact that the amount of time elapsed is 10 times as long.

10. Explain why the amount left after 250.0 y in Exercise 8 is not one-fiftieth of the amount present after 5.0 y, despite the fact that the amount of time elapsed is 50 times as long.

11. An artifact containing carbon-14 contains 8.4×10^{-9} g of carbon-14 in it. If the age of the artifact is 10,670 y, how much carbon-14 did it have originally? The half-life of carbon-14 is 5,730 y.

12. Carbon-11 is a radioactive isotope used in positron emission tomography (PET) scans for medical diagnosis. Positron emission is another, though rare, type of radioactivity. The half-life of carbon-11 is 20.3 min. If 4.23×10^{-6} g of carbon-11 is left in the body after 4.00 h, what mass of carbon-11 was present initially?

Answers

1. Only radioactive isotopes have a half-life.

2. An isotope with a shorter half-life is generally considered more radioactive (although it also depends on the energy emitted).

3. 51.0 d

4. 1.0×10^5 y

5. 25 y

6. 12.3 s

7. 0.000170 g; 0.0000402 g

8. 0.00335 g; 3.39×10^{-9} g

9. Radioactive decay is an exponential process, not a linear process.

10. Radioactive decay is an exponential process, not a linear process.

11. 3.1×10^{-8} g

12. 0.0153 g

16.3 Units of Radioactivity

Learning Objective

1. Express amounts of radioactivity in a variety of units.

In Section 2, we used mass to indicate the amount of radioactive substance present. This is only one of several units used to express amounts of radiation. Some units describe the number of radioactive events occurring per unit time, while others express the amount of a person's exposure to radiation.

Perhaps the direct way of reporting radioactivity is the number of radioactive decays per second. One decay per second is called one **becquerel (Bq)**. Even in a small mass of radioactive material, however, there are thousands upon thousands of decays or disintegrations per second. The unit **curie (Ci)**, now defined as 3.7×10^{10} decays/s, was originally defined as the number of decays per second in 1 g of radium. Many radioactive samples have activities that are on the order of microcuries (μCi) or more. Both the becquerel and the curie can be used in place of grams to describe quantities of radioactive material. As an example, the amount of americium in an average smoke detector has an activity of 0.9 μCi. (The curie is named after Polish scientist Marie Curie, who performed some of the initial investigations into radioactive phenomena in the early 1900s; the becquerel is named after Henri Becquerel, who discovered radioactivity in 1896.)

becquerel (Bq)

A unit of radioactivity equal to 1 decay per second.

curie (Ci)

A unit of radioactivity equal to 3.7×10^{10} decays/s.

Example 5

A sample of radium has an activity of 16.0 mCi (millicuries). If the half-life of radium is 1,600 y, how long before the sample's activity is 1.0 mCi?

Solution

The following table shows the activity of the radium sample over multiple half-lives:

Time in Years	Activity
0	16.0 mCi
1,600	8.0 mCi
3,200	4.0 mCi
4,800	2.0 mCi
6,400	1.0 mCi

Over a period of four half-lives, the activity of the radium will be halved four times, at which point its activity will be 1.0 mCi. Thus it takes four half-lives, or 4 × 1,600 y = 6,400 y, for the activity to decrease to 1.0 mCi.

Test Yourself

A sample of radon has an activity of 60,000 Bq. If the half-life of radon is 15 h, how long before the sample's activity is 3,750 Bq?

Answer

60 h

Example 6

A sample of radium has an activity of 16.0 mCi. If the half-life of radium is 1,600 y, how long before the sample's activity is 5.6 mCi?

Solution

In this case we do not have an exact number of half-lives, so we need to use the more complicated equation (in Section 2) and solve for time. If the initial amount is represented by 16.0 mCi and the final amount is 5.6 mCi, we have:

$$5.6 \text{ mCi} = (16.0 \text{ mCi})e^{-0.693t/(1,600 \text{ y})}$$

To solve, we divide both sides of the equation by 16.0 mCi to cancel the millicurie units:

$$\frac{5.6}{16.0} = e^{-0.693t/(1,600 \text{ y})}$$

By taking the natural logarithm of both sides; the natural logarithm cancels the exponential function. The natural logarithm of 5.6/16.0 is –1.050. So:

$$-1.050 = -0.693t/(1,600 \text{ y})$$

The negative sign cancels, and we solve for t. Thus:

$$t = 2,420 \text{ y}$$

It makes sense that the time is greater than one half-life (1,600 y) because we have less than one-half of the original activity left.

Test Yourself

A sample of radon has an activity of 60,000 Bq. If the half-life of radon is 15 h, how long before the sample's activity is 10,000 Bq?

Answer

38.8 h

Other measures of radioactivity are based on the effects it has on living tissue. Radioactivity can transfer energy to tissues in two ways: through the kinetic energy of the particles hitting the tissue and through the electromagnetic energy of the gamma rays being absorbed by the tissue. Either way, the transferred energy—like the thermal energy from boiling water—can damage the tissue.

The **rad** (an acronym for "radiation absorbed dose") is a unit equivalent to 1 g of tissue absorbing 0.01 J:

$$1 \text{ rad} = 0.01 \text{ J/g}$$

Another unit of radiation absorption is the gray (Gy):

$$1 \text{ Gy} = 100 \text{ rad}$$

The rad is more common. To get an idea of the amount of energy this represents, consider that the absorption of 1 rad by 70,000 g of water (approximately the same mass as a 150 lb person) would increase the temperature of the water by only 0.002°C. This may not seem like a lot, but it is enough energy to break about 1×10^{21} molecular C–C bonds in a person's body. That amount of damage would not be desirable.

Predicting the effects of radiation is complicated by the fact that different types of emissions affect various tissues differently. To quantify these effects, the unit **rem** (an acronym for röntgen equivalent man) is defined as

$$\text{rem} = \text{rad} \times \text{factor}$$

where "factor" is a number greater than or equal to 1 that takes into account the type of radioactive emission and sometimes the type of tissue being exposed. For beta particles, the factor equals 1. For alpha particles striking most tissues, the factor is 10, but for eye tissue the factor is 30. Most radioactive emissions that people are exposed to are on the order of a few dozen millirems (mrem) or less; a medical X-ray is about 20 mrem. A sievert (Sv) is a related unit and is defined as 100 rem.

What is a person's annual exposure to radioactivity and radiation? Table 16.3 lists the sources and annual amounts of radiation exposure. It may surprise you to learn that fully 82% of the radioactivity and radiation exposure we receive is from natural sources—sources we cannot avoid. Fully 10% of the exposure comes from our own bodies—largely from carbon-14 and potassium-40.

rad
A unit of radioactive exposure equal to 0.01 J/g of tissue.

rem
A unit of radioactive exposure that includes a factor to account for the type of radioactivity.

TABLE 16.3 Average Annual Radiation Exposure (Approximate)

Source	Amount (mrem)
radon gas	200
medical sources	53
radioactive atoms in the body naturally	39
terrestrial sources	28
cosmic sources	28*
consumer products	10
nuclear energy	0.05
Total	**358**

*Flying from New York City to San Francisco adds 5 mrem to your overall radiation exposure because the plane flies above much of the atmosphere, which protects us from cosmic radiation.

The actual effects of radioactivity and radiation exposure on a person's health depend on the type of radioactivity, the length of exposure, and the tissues exposed. Table 16.4 lists the potential threats to health at various amounts of exposure over short periods of time (hours or days).

TABLE 16.4 Effects of Short-Term Exposure to Radioactivity and Radiation

Exposure (rem)	Effect
1 (over a full year)	no detectable effect
~20	increased risk of some cancers
~100	damage to bone marrow and other tissues; possible internal bleeding; decrease in white blood cell count
200–300	visible "burns" in skin, nausea, vomiting, fatigue
>300	loss of white blood cells; hair loss
~600	death

One of the simplest ways of detecting radioactivity is by using a piece of photographic film embedded in a badge or a pen. On a regular basis, the film is developed and checked for exposure. Comparing the exposure level of the film with a set of standard exposures indicates the amount of radiation a person was exposed to.

Geiger counter

An electrical device that detects radioactivity.

Another means of detecting radioactivity is an electrical device called a **Geiger counter** (Figure 16.2). It contains a gas-filled chamber with a thin membrane on one end that allows radiation emitted from radioactive nuclei to enter the chamber and knock electrons off atoms of gas (usually argon). The presence of electrons and positively charged ions causes a small current, which is detected by the Geiger counter and converted to a signal on a meter or, commonly, an audio circuit to produce an audible "click."

FIGURE 16.2 Detecting Radioactivity
A Geiger counter is a common instrument used to detect radioactivity.

Source: © Thinkstock

Key Takeaway

- Radioactivity can be expressed in a variety of units, including rems, rads, and curies.

Exercises

1. Define *rad*.
2. Define *rem*.
3. How does a becquerel differ from a curie?
4. Define *curie*.
5. A sample of radon gas has an activity of 140.0 mCi. If the half-life of radon is 1,500 y, how long before the activity of the sample is 8.75 mCi?
6. A sample of curium has an activity of 1,600 Bq. If the half-life of curium is 24.0 s, how long before its activity is 25.0 Bq?
7. If a radioactive sample has an activity of 65 μCi, how many disintegrations per second are occurring?
8. If a radioactive sample has an activity of 7.55×10^5 Bq, how many disintegrations per second are occurring?
9. A sample of fluorine-20 has an activity of 2.44 mCi. If its half-life is 11.0 s, what is its activity after 50.0 s?
10. Strontium-90 has a half-life of 28.1 y. If 66.7 Bq of pure strontium-90 were allowed to decay for 15.0 y, what would the activity of the remaining strontium-90 be?
11. How long does it take 100.0 mCi of fluorine-20 to decay to 10.0 mCi if its half-life is 11.0 s?
12. Technetium-99 is used in medicine as a source of radiation. A typical dose is 25 mCi. How long does it take for the activity to reduce to 0.100 mCi? The half-life of ^{99}Tc is 210,000 y.
13. Describe how a radiation exposure in rems is determined
14. Which contributes more to the rems of exposure—alpha or beta particles? Why?
15. Use Table 16.4 to determine which sources of radiation exposure are inescapable and which can be avoided. What percentage of radiation is unavoidable?
16. Name two isotopes that contribute to the radioactivity in our bodies.
17. Explain how a film badge works to detect radiation.
18. Explain how a Geiger counter works to detect radiation.

Answers

1. a unit of radioactive exposure equal to 0.01 J of energy per gram of tissue
2. the rad amount of exposure times a quality factor that depends on the type of radioactivity and the tissue exposed to the radiation
3. A becquerel is 1 decay/s, whereas a curie is 3.7×10^{10} decays/s.
4. 3.7×10^{10} decays/s
5. 6.0×10^3 y
6. 144 s
7. 2.41×10^6 disintegrations per second
8. 7.55×10^5 disintegrations per second
9. 0.104 mCi
10. 46.1 Bq
11. 36.5 s
12. 1.68×10^6 y
13. by using a film badge, which is exposed by the radiation, or a Geiger counter
14. alpha particles because they are more massive

15. Radioactive atoms in the body, most terrestrial sources, cosmic sources, and nuclear energy sources are likely unavoidable, which is about 27% of the total exposure. If exposure to radon gas is added, the total unavoidable exposure increases to 82%.

16. carbon-14 and potassium-40 (answers may vary)

17. Film is exposed by the radiation. The more radiation film is subjected to, the more exposed it becomes.

18. A Geiger counter has a tube with a thin window that allows radioactive emissions through. These radioactive emissions ionize the gas inside the tube, which allows for a current to flow and a "click" to be heard over an audio circuit.

16.4 Uses of Radioactive Isotopes

Learning Objective

1. Learn some applications of radioactivity.

Radioactive isotopes have a variety of applications. Generally, however, they are useful because either we can detect their radioactivity or we can use the energy they release.

Radioactive isotopes are effective tracers because their radioactivity is easy to detect. A **tracer** is a substance that can be used to follow the pathway of that substance through some structure. For instance, leaks in underground water pipes can be discovered by running some tritium-containing water through the pipes and then using a Geiger counter to locate any radioactive tritium subsequently present in the ground around the pipes. (Recall that tritium is a radioactive isotope of hydrogen.)

Tracers can also be used to follow the steps of a complex chemical reaction. After incorporating radioactive atoms into reactant molecules, scientists can track where the atoms go by following their radioactivity. One excellent example of this is the use of carbon-14 to determine the steps involved in photosynthesis in plants. We know these steps because researchers followed the progress of carbon-14 throughout the process.

tracer

A substance that can be used to follow the pathway of that substance through a structure.

Radioactive Dating

Radioactive isotopes are useful for establishing the ages of various objects. The half-life of radioactive isotopes is unaffected by any environmental factors, so the isotope acts like an internal clock. For example, if a rock is analyzed and is found to contain a certain amount of uranium-235 and a certain amount of its daughter isotope, we can conclude that a certain fraction of the original uranium-235 has radioactively decayed. If half of the uranium has decayed, then the rock has an age of one half-life of uranium-235, or about 4.5×10^9 y. Many analyses like this, using a wide variety of isotopes, have indicated that age of the earth itself is over 4×10^9 y. In another interesting example of radioactive dating, hydrogen-3 dating has been used to verify the stated vintages of some old fine wines.

One isotope, carbon-14, is particularly useful in determining the age of once-living artifacts. A tiny amount of carbon-14 is produced naturally in the upper reaches of the atmosphere, and living things incorporate some of it into their tissues, building up to a constant, albeit very low, level.

Once a living thing dies, it no longer acquires carbon-14; as time passes the carbon-14 that was in the tissues decays. (The half-life of carbon-14 is 5,370 y.) If a once-living artifact is discovered and analyzed many years after its death and the remaining carbon-14 is compared to the known constant level, an approximate age of the artifact can be determined. Using such methods, scientists determined that the age of the Shroud of Turin (Figure 16.3; purported by some to be the burial cloth of Jesus Christ and composed of flax fibers, a type of plant) is about 600–700 y, not 2,000 y as claimed by some. Scientists were also able to use radiocarbon dating to show that the age of a mummified body found in the ice of the Alps was 5,300 y.

FIGURE 16.3 Shroud of Turin
In 1989, several groups of scientists used carbon-14 dating to demonstrate that the Shroud of Turin was only 600–700 y. Many people still cling to a different notion, despite the scientific evidence.

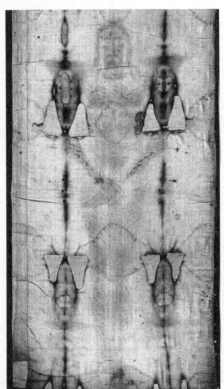

Source: https://commons.wikimedia.org/wiki/File:Shroudofturin1.jpg.

Irradiation of Food

The radiation emitted by some radioactive substances can be used to kill microorganisms on a variety of foodstuffs, extending the shelf life of these products. Produce such as tomatoes, mushrooms, sprouts, and berries are irradiated with the emissions from cobalt-60 or cesium-137. This exposure kills a lot of the bacteria that cause spoilage, so the produce stays fresh longer. Eggs and some meat, such as beef, pork, and poultry, can also be irradiated. Contrary to the belief of some people, irradiation of food *does not* make the food itself radioactive.

Medical Applications

Radioactive isotopes have numerous medical applications—diagnosing and treating illness and diseases. One example of a diagnostic application is using radioactive iodine-131 to test for thyroid activity (Figure 16.4). The thyroid gland in the neck is one of the few places in the body with a significant concentration of iodine. To evaluate thyroid activity, a measured dose of ^{131}I is administered to a patient, and the next day a scanner is used to measure the amount of radioactivity in the thyroid gland. The amount of radioactive iodine that collects there is directly related to the activity of the thyroid, allowing trained physicians to diagnose both hyperthyroidism and hypothyroidism. Iodine-131 has a half-life of only 8 d, so the potential for damage due to exposure is minimal. Technetium-99 can also be used to test thyroid function. Bones, the heart, the brain, the liver, the lungs, and many other organs can be imaged in similar ways by using the appropriate radioactive isotope.

FIGURE 16.4 Medical Diagnostics
Radioactive iodine can be used to image the thyroid gland for diagnostic purposes.

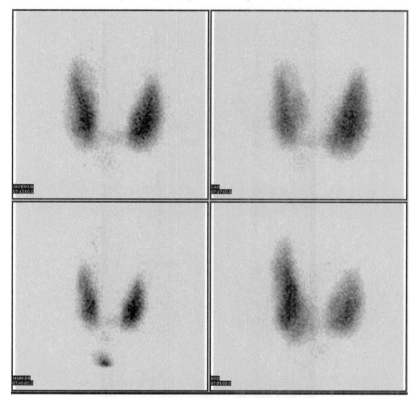

Source: Scan courtesy of Myo Han, http://en.wikipedia.org/wiki/File:Thyroid_scan.jpg.

Very little radioactive material is needed in these diagnostic techniques because the radiation emitted is so easy to detect. However, therapeutic applications usually require much larger doses because their purpose is to preferentially kill diseased tissues. For example, if a thyroid tumor were detected, a much larger infusion (thousands of rem, as opposed to a diagnostic dose of less than 40 rem) of iodine-131 could help destroy the tumor cells. Similarly, radioactive strontium is used to not only detect but also ease the pain of bone cancers. Table 16.5 lists several radioactive isotopes and their medical uses.

TABLE 16.5 Some Radioactive Isotopes with Medical Applications

Isotope	Use
^{32}P	cancer detection and treatment, especially in eyes and skin
^{59}Fe	anemia diagnosis
^{60}Co	gamma ray irradiation of tumors
^{99m}Tc*	brain, thyroid, liver, bone marrow, lung, heart, and intestinal scanning; blood volume determination
^{131}I	diagnosis and treatment of thyroid function

Isotope	Use
^{133}Xe	lung imaging
^{198}Au	liver disease diagnosis

*The "m" means that it is a metastable form of this isotope of technetium.

In addition to the direct application of radioactive isotopes to diseased tissue, the gamma ray emissions of some isotopes can be directed toward the tissue to be destroyed. Cobalt-60 is a useful isotope for this kind of procedure.

Food and Drink App: Radioactivity in Wines

Wine lovers put some stock in *vintages*, or the years in which the wine grapes were grown before they were turned into wine. Wine can differ in quality depending on the vintage. Some wine lovers willingly pay much more for a bottle of wine with a certain vintage. But how does one verify that a bottle of wine was in fact part of a certain vintage? Is the label a fake? Is that stash of wine found in the basement of a French chateau really from the 1940s, or was it made in 2009?

This wine label from a bottle of wine claims a vintage of 1991. Is the wine really from this vintage, or is it a fake? Radioactivity can help determine the answer.

Source: Used by permission of Ralph E. Wermuth.

Cesium-137 is a radioactive isotope that has a half-life of 30.1 y. It was introduced into the atmosphere in the 1940s and 1950s by the atmospheric testing of nuclear weapons by several countries after World War II. A significant amount of cesium-137 was released during the Chernobyl nuclear disaster in 1986. As a result of this atmospheric contamination, scientists have precise measurements of the amount of cesium-137 available in the environment since 1950. Some of the isotope of cesium is taken up by living plants, including grape vines. Using known vintages, oenologists (wine scientists) can construct a detailed analysis of the cesium-137 of various wines through the years.

The verification of a wine's vintage requires the measurement of the activity of cesium-137 in the wine. By measuring the current activity of cesium-137 in a sample of wine (the gamma rays from the radioactive decay pass through glass wine bottles easily, so there's no need to open the bottle), comparing it to the known amount of cesium-137 from the vintage, and taking into account the passage of time, researchers can collect evidence for or against a claimed wine vintage.

Before about 1950, the amount of cesium-137 in the environment was negligible, so if a wine dated before 1950 shows any measurable cesium-137 activity, it is almost surely a fake, so don't shell out lots of money for it! It may be a good wine, but it is almost definitely not over 60 years old.

Key Takeaway

- Radioactivity has several practical applications, including tracers, medical applications, dating once-living objects, and preservation of food.

Exercises

1. Define *tracer* and give an example of how tracers work.
2. Name two isotopes that have been used as tracers.
3. Explain how radioactive dating works.
4. Name two isotopes that have been used in radioactive dating.
5. The current disintegration rate for carbon-14 is 14.0 Bq. A sample of burnt wood discovered in an archeological excavation is found to have a carbon-14 disintegration rate of 3.5 Bq. If the half-life of carbon-14 is 5,730 y, approximately how old is the wood sample?
6. A small asteroid crashes to Earth. After chemical analysis, it is found to contain 1 g of technetium-99 to every 3 g of ruthenium-99, its daughter isotope. If the half-life of technetium-99 is 210,000 y, approximately how old is the asteroid?
7. What is a positive aspect of the irradiation of food?
8. What is a negative aspect of the irradiation of food?
9. Describe how iodine-131 is used to both diagnose and treat thyroid problems.
10. List at least five organs that can be imaged using radioactive isotopes.
11. Which radioactive emissions can be used therapeutically?
12. Which isotope is used in therapeutics primarily for its gamma ray emissions?

Answers

1. A tracer is a radioactive isotope that can be detected far from its original source to trace the path of certain chemicals. Hydrogen-3 can be used to trace the path of water underground.
2. hydrogen-3 and carbon-14 (answers will vary)
3. If the initial amount of a radioactive isotope is known, then by measuring the amount of the isotope remaining, a person can calculate how old that object is since it took up the isotope.
4. carbon-14 and uranium-235 (answers will vary)
5. 11,500 y
6. 420,000 y
7. increased shelf life (answers will vary)
8. Public acceptance is low because of a misunderstanding of the process.
9. The thyroid gland absorbs most of the iodine, allowing it to be imaged for diagnostic purposes or preferentially irradiated for treatment purposes.
10. Eyes, skin, blood, brain, thyroid, liver, bone marrow, lungs, heart, and intestines are among the organs that can be targeted.
11. gamma rays
12. cobalt-60

16.5 Nuclear Energy

Learning Objectives

1. Explain where nuclear energy comes from.
2. Describe the difference between fission and fusion.

Nuclear changes occur with a simultaneous release of energy. Where does this energy come from? If we could precisely measure the masses of the reactants and products of a nuclear reaction, we would notice that the amount of mass drops slightly in the conversion from reactants to products. Consider the following nuclear equation, in which the molar mass of each species is indicated to four decimal places:

$$\underset{235.0439}{^{235}\text{U}} \rightarrow \underset{138.9088}{^{139}\text{Ba}} - \underset{93.9343}{^{94}\text{Kr}} + \underset{2 \times 1.0087}{2^1\text{n}}$$

If we compare the mass of the reactant (235.0439) to the masses of the products (sum = 234.8605), we notice a mass difference of −0.1834 g, or −0.0001834 kg. Where did this mass go?

According to Albert Einstein's theory of relativity, energy (E) and mass (m) are related by the following equation:

$$E = mc^2$$

where c is the speed of light, or 3.00×10^8 m/s. In the course of the chemical reaction for uranium, the mass difference is converted to energy, which is given off by the reaction:

$$E = (-0.0001834 \text{ kg})(3.00 \times 10^8 \text{ m/s})^2 = -1.65 \times 10^{13} \text{ J} = -1.65 \times 10^{10} \text{ kJ}$$

(For the units to work out, mass must be expressed in units of kilograms.) That is, 16.5 billion kJ of energy is given off every time 1 mol of uranium-235 undergoes this nuclear reaction. This is an extraordinary amount of energy. Compare it to combustion reactions of hydrocarbons, which give off about 650 kJ/mol of energy for every CH_2 unit in the hydrocarbon—on the order of *hundreds* of kilojoules per mole. Nuclear reactions give off *billions* of kilojoules per mole.

If this energy could be properly harvested, it would be a significant source of energy for our society. **Nuclear energy** involves the controlled harvesting of energy from fission reactions. The reaction can be controlled because the fission of uranium-235 (and a few other isotopes, such as plutonium-239) can be artificially initiated by injecting a neutron into a uranium nucleus. The overall nuclear equation, with energy included as a product, is as follows:

$$^{235}\text{U} + {}^1\text{n} \rightarrow {}^{139}\text{Ba} + {}^{94}\text{Kr} + 3^1\text{n} + \textbf{energy}$$

Thus by the careful addition of extra neutrons into a sample of uranium, we can control the fission process and obtain energy that can be used for other purposes. (Artificial or induced radioactivity, in which neutrons are injected into a sample of matter that subsequently cause fission, was first demonstrated in 1934 by Irène Joliot-Curie and Frédéric Joliot, the daughter and son-in-law of Marie Curie.)

nuclear energy

The controlled harvesting of energy from fission reactions.

Example 7

Plutonium-239 can absorb a neutron and undergo a fission reaction to make an atom of gold-204 and an atom of phosphorus-31. Write the balanced nuclear equation for the process and determine the number of neutrons given off as part of the reaction.

Solution

Using the information given, we can write the following initial equation:

$$\text{}_0^1\text{n} + \text{}_{94}^{239}\text{Pu} \rightarrow \text{}_{79}^{204}\text{Au} + \text{}_{15}^{31}\text{P} + ?\text{}_0^1\text{n}$$

In balanced nuclear equations, the sums of the subscripts on each side of the equation are the same, as are the sums of the superscripts. The subscripts are already balanced: $0 + 94 = 94$ and $79 + 15 = 94$. The superscripts on the left equal 240 ($1 + 239$) but equal 235 ($204 + 31$) on the right. We need five more mass number units on the right. Five neutrons should be products of the process for the mass numbers to balance. (Because the atomic number of a neutron is zero, including five neutrons on the right does not change the overall sum of the subscripts.) Thus the balanced nuclear equation is as follows:

$$\text{}_0^1\text{n} + \text{}_{94}^{239}\text{Pu} \rightarrow \text{}_{79}^{204}\text{Au} + \text{}_{15}^{31}\text{P} + 5\text{}_0^1\text{n}$$

We predict that the overall process will give off five neutrons.

Test Yourself

Uranium-238 can absorb a neutron and undergo a fission reaction to produce an atom of cesium-135 and an atom of rubidium-96. Write the balanced nuclear equation for the process and determine the number of neutrons given off as part of the reaction.

Answer

$\text{}_0^1\text{n} + \text{}_{92}^{238}\text{U} \rightarrow \text{}_{37}^{96}\text{Rb} + \text{}_{55}^{135}\text{Cs} + 8\text{}_0^1\text{n}$; eight neutrons

Example 8

One balanced nuclear reaction for the fission of plutonium-239 is as follows:

$$\underset{1.0087}{\text{}_0^1\text{n}} + \underset{239.0522}{\text{}_{94}^{239}\text{Pu}} \rightarrow \underset{203.9777}{\text{}_{79}^{204}\text{Au}} + \underset{30.9738}{\text{}_{15}^{31}\text{P}} + \underset{5 \times 1.0087}{5\text{}_0^1\text{n}}$$

The molar mass in grams of each species is given for each particle. What is the energy change of this fission reaction?

Solution

We start by adding the masses of all species on each side of the nuclear equation. Then we determine the difference in mass as the reaction proceeds and convert this to an equivalent amount of energy. The total mass of the reactants is:

$1.0087 + 239.0522 = 240.0609$ g

The total mass of the products is:

$203.9777 + 30.9738 + (5 \times 1.0087) = 239.9950$ g

The change is mass is determined by subtracting the mass of the reactants from the mass of the products:

change in mass $= 239.9950 - 240.0609 = -0.0659$ g

This mass change must be converted into kilogram units:

$$-0.0659 \text{ g} \times \frac{1 \text{ kg}}{1,000 \text{ g}} = -0.0000659 \text{ kg}$$

Now we can use Einstein's equation to determine the energy change of the nuclear reaction:

$$E = (-0.0000659 \text{ kg})(3.00 \times 10^8 \text{ m/s})^2 = -5.93 \times 10^{12} \text{ J}$$

This is almost 6 *trillion* joules given off.

Test Yourself

The nuclear equation for the fission of uranium-238 is as follows:

$$\underset{1.0087}{_0^1\text{n}} + \underset{238.0508}{_{92}^{238}\text{U}} \rightarrow \underset{95.9342}{_{37}^{96}\text{Rb}} + \underset{134.9060}{_{55}^{135}\text{Cs}} + \underset{8 \times 1.0087}{8_0^1\text{n}}$$

The molar mass in grams of each species is given for each particle. What is the energy change of this fission reaction?

Answer

-1.35×10^{13} J

A **nuclear reactor** is an apparatus designed to carefully control the progress of a nuclear reaction and extract the resulting energy for useful purposes. Figure 16.5 shows a simplified diagram of a nuclear reactor. The energy from the controlled nuclear reaction converts water into high-pressure steam, which is used to run turbines that generate electricity.

nuclear reactor

An apparatus designed to carefully control the progress of a nuclear reaction and extract the resulting energy for useful purposes.

FIGURE 16.5 A Diagram of a Nuclear Power Plant for Generating Electricity
The two main components of the power plant are the nuclear reactor itself and the steam-driven turbine and electricity generator.

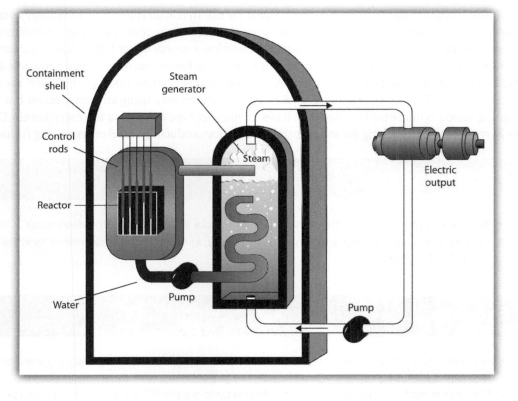

Although the fission of large nuclei can produce different products, on average the fission of uranium produces two more free neutrons than were present to begin with. These neutrons can themselves stimulate other uranium nuclei to undergo fission, releasing yet more energy and even more neutrons, which can in turn induce even more uranium fission. A single neutron can thus begin a process that grows exponentially in a phenomenon called a **chain reaction**:

chain reaction

An exponential growth in a phenomenon.

$$1 \rightarrow 2 \rightarrow 4 \rightarrow 8 \rightarrow 16 \rightarrow 32 \rightarrow 64 \rightarrow 128 \rightarrow 256 \rightarrow 512$$
$$\rightarrow 1,024 \rightarrow 2,048 \rightarrow 4,096 \rightarrow 8,192 \rightarrow 16,384 \rightarrow \dots$$

atomic bomb

A weapon that depends on a nuclear chain reaction to generate immense forces.

Because energy is produced with each fission event, energy is also produced exponentially and in an uncontrolled fashion. The quick production of energy creates an explosion. This is the mechanism behind the **atomic bomb**. (The first controlled chain reaction was achieved on December 2, 1942, in an experiment supervised by Enrico Fermi in a laboratory underneath the football stadium at the University of Chicago.)

Although fairly simple in theory, an atomic bomb is difficult to produce, in part because uranium-235, the isotope that undergoes fission, makes up only 0.7% of natural uranium; the rest is mostly uranium-238, which does not undergo fission. (Remember that the radioactive process that a nucleus undergoes is characteristic of the isotope.) To make uranium useful for nuclear reactors, the uranium in uranium-235 must be *enriched* to about 3%. The enrichment of uranium is a laborious and costly series of physical and chemical separations. To be useful in an atomic bomb, uranium must be enriched to 70% or more. At lesser concentrations, the chain reaction cannot sustain itself, so no explosion is produced.

fusion

A nuclear process in which small nuclei are combined into larger nuclei, releasing energy.

Fusion is another nuclear process that can be used to produce energy. In this process, smaller nuclei are combined to make larger nuclei, with an accompanying release of energy. One example is hydrogen fusion, which makes helium:

$$4\,^1\text{H} \rightarrow {}^4\text{He} + 2.58 \times 10^{12}\ \text{J}$$

Notice that the amount of energy given off per mole of reactant is only one-tenth of the amount given off by the fission of 1 mol of uranium-235. On a mass (per gram) basis, however, hydrogen fusion gives off 10 times more energy than fission does. In addition, the product of fission is helium gas, not a wide range of isotopes (some of which are also radioactive) produced by fission.

Fusion occurs in nature: The sun and other stars use fusion as their ultimate energy source. Fusion is also the basis of very destructive weapons that have been developed by several countries around the world. However, one current goal is to develop a source of *controlled* fusion for use as an energy source. The practical problem is that to perform fusion, extremely high pressures and temperatures are necessary. Currently, the only known stable systems undergoing fusion are the interiors of stars. The conditions necessary for fusion can be created using an atomic bomb, but the resulting fusion is uncontrollable (and the basis for another type of bomb, a hydrogen bomb). Currently, researchers are looking for safe, controlled ways for producing useful energy using fusion.

Key Takeaways

- Nuclear energy comes from tiny mass changes in nuclei as radioactive processes occur.
- In fission, large nuclei break apart and release energy; in fusion, small nuclei merge together and release energy.

Exercises

1. According to Einstein's equation, the conversion of 1.00 g of matter into energy generates how much energy?

2. How much matter needs to be converted to energy to supply 400 kJ of energy, the approximate energy of 1 mol of C–H bonds? What conclusion does this suggest about energy changes of chemical reactions?

3. In the spontaneous fission of lead-208, the following reaction occurs:

$$^{208}\text{Pb} \rightarrow {}^{129}\text{I} + {}^{76}\text{Cu} + 3\,^1\text{n}$$

For every mole of lead-208 that decays, 0.1002 g of mass is lost. How much energy is given off per mole of lead-208 reacted?

4. In the spontaneous fission of radium-226, the following reaction occurs:

$$^{226}\text{Ra} \rightarrow {}^{156}\text{Pm} + {}^{68}\text{Co} + 2\,{}^{1}\text{n}$$

For every mole of radium-226 that decays, 0.1330 g of mass is lost. How much energy is given off per mole of radium-226 reacted?

5. Recalculate the amount of energy from Exercise 3 in terms of the number of grams of lead-208 reacted.

6. Recalculate the amount of energy from Exercise 4 in terms of the number of grams of radium-226 reacted.

7. What is the energy change of this fission reaction? Masses in grams are provided.

$$\underset{241.0569}{^{241}\text{Pu}} \rightarrow \underset{139.9106}{^{140}\text{Ba}} + \underset{89.9077}{^{90}\text{Sr}} - \underset{11 \times 1.0087}{11\,{}^{1}\text{n}}$$

8. What is the energy change of this fission reaction? Masses in grams are provided.

$$\underset{247.0704}{^{247}\text{Cm}} \rightarrow \underset{106.9099}{^{107}\text{Ru}} + \underset{130.9085}{^{131}\text{Te}} + \underset{9 \times 1.0087}{9\,{}^{1}\text{n}}$$

9. The two rarer isotopes of hydrogen—deuterium and tritium—can also be fused to make helium by the following reaction:

$$^{2}\text{H} + {}^{3}\text{H} \rightarrow {}^{4}\text{He} + {}^{1}\text{n}$$

In the course of this reaction, 0.01888 g of mass is lost. How much energy is given off in the reaction of 1 mol of deuterium and tritium?

10. A process called *helium burning* is thought to occur inside older stars, forming carbon:

$$3\,{}^{4}\text{He} \rightarrow {}^{12}\text{C}$$

If the reaction proceeds with 0.00781 g of mass lost on a molar basis, how much energy is given off?

11. Briefly describe how a nuclear reactor generates electricity.

12. Briefly describe the difference between how a nuclear reactor works and how a nuclear bomb works.

13. What is a chain reaction?

14. Why must uranium be enriched to supply nuclear energy?

Answers

1. 9.00×10^{13} J

2. Mass changes in normal chemical reactions are negligible because 4×10^{-12} g of matter must be converted.

3. 9.02×10^{12} J

4. 1.20×10^{13} J

5. 4.34×10^{10} J/g

6. 5.30×10^{10} J/g

7. -1.28×10^{13} J

8. -1.56×10^{13} J

9. 1.70×10^{12} J

10. 7.03×10^{11} J

11. A nuclear reactor controls a nuclear reaction to produce energy in usable amounts. The energy produced generates steam, which is used to turn a turbine that generates electricity for general use.

12. A nuclear reactor controls a nuclear reaction to produce energy in usable amounts, whereas a nuclear bomb produces an uncontrolled nuclear reaction to release a large amount of energy suddenly and destructively.

13. a process that generates more reaction pathways for each previous reaction

14. Naturally occurring uranium does not have enough uranium-235 to produce useful amounts of energy. The amount of uranium-235 must be increased, which is a very intensive and costly procedure.

16.6 End-of-Chapter Material

Additional Exercises

1. Given that many elements are metals, suggest why it would be unsafe to have radioactive materials in contact with acids.

2. Many alpha-emitting radioactive substances are relatively safe to handle, but inhaling radioactive dust can be very dangerous. Why?

3. Uranium can be separated from its daughter isotope thorium by dissolving a sample in acid and adding sodium iodide, which precipitates thorium(III) iodide:

$$Th^{3+}(aq) + 3I^-(aq) \rightarrow ThI_3(s)$$

If 0.567 g of Th^{3+} were dissolved in solution, how many milliliters of 0.500 M NaI(aq) would have to be added to precipitate all the thorium?

4. Thorium oxide can be dissolved in acidic solution:

$$ThO_2(s) + 4H^+ \rightarrow Th^{4+}(aq) + 2H_2O(\ell)$$

How many milliliters of 1.55 M HCl(aq) are needed to dissolve 10.65 g of ThO_2?

5. Radioactive strontium is dangerous because it can chemically replace calcium in the human body. The bones are particularly susceptible to radiation damage. Write the nuclear equation for the beta emission of strontium-90.

6. Write the nuclear equation for the beta emission of iodine-131, the isotope used to diagnose and treat thyroid problems.

7. A common uranium compound is uranyl nitrate hexahydrate [$UO_2(NO_3)_2 \cdot 6H_2O$]. What is the formula mass of this compound?

8. Plutonium forms three oxides: PuO, PuO_2, and Pu_2O_3. What are the formula masses of these three compounds?

9. A banana contains 600 mg of potassium, 0.0117% of which is radioactive potassium-40. If 1 g of potassium-40 has an activity of 2.626×10^5 Bq, what is the activity of a banana?

10. Smoke detectors typically contain about 0.25 mg of americium-241 as part of the smoke detection mechanism. If the activity of 1 g of americium-241 is 1.26×10^{11} Bq, what is the activity of americium-241 in the smoke detector?

11. Uranium hexafluoride (UF_6) reacts with water to make uranyl fluoride (UO_2F_2) and HF. Balance the following reaction:

$$UF_6 + H_2O \rightarrow UO_2F_2 + HF$$

12. The cyclopentadienyl anion ($C_5H_5^-$) is an organic ion that can make ionic compounds with positive ions of radioactive elements, such as Np^{3+}. Balance the following reaction:

$$NpCl_3 + Be(C_5H_5)_2 \rightarrow Np(C_5H_5)_3 + BeCl_2$$

13. If the half-life of hydrogen-3 is 12.3 y, how much time does it take for 99.0% of a sample of hydrogen-3 to decay?

14. If the half-life of carbon-14 is 5,730 y, how long does it take for 10.0% of a sample of carbon-14 to decay?

15. Although bismuth is generally considered stable, its only natural isotope, bismuth-209, is estimated to have a half-life of 1.9×10^{19} y. If the universe is estimated to have a lifetime of 1.38×10^{10} y, what percentage of bismuth-209 has decayed over the lifetime of the universe? (Hint: Be prepared to use a lot of decimal places.)

16. The most common isotope of uranium (uranium-238) has a half-life of 4.5×10^9 y. If the universe is estimated to have a lifetime of 1.38×10^{10} y, what percentage of uranium-238 has decayed over the lifetime of the universe?

17. Refer to Table 16.3 and separate the sources of radioactive exposure into voluntary and involuntary sources. What percentage of radioactive exposure is involuntary?

18. With reference to Table 16.3 and Exercise 17, suggest ways that a practical person can minimize exposure to radioactivity.

Answers

1. Acids can dissolve many metals; a spilled acid can lead to contamination.

2. Alpha particles exposed to the lungs can be dangerous.

3. 14.7 mL

4. 104 mL

5. $^{90}_{38}Sr \rightarrow {}^{90}_{39}Y + {}^{0}_{-1}e$

6. $^{131}_{53}I \rightarrow {}^{131}_{54}Xe + {}^{0}_{-1}e$

7. 502.15 g/mol

8. about 260, 276, and 536 g/mol, respectively

9. about 18 Bq

10. 3.15×10^7 Bq

11. $UF_6 + 2H_2O \rightarrow UO_2F_2 + 4HF$

12. $2NpCl_3 + 3Be(C_5H_5)_2 \rightarrow 2Np(C_5H_5)_3 + 3BeCl_2$

13. 81.7 y

14. 871 y

15. about 0.000000005%

16. 88.1%

17. Radioactive atoms in the body, terrestrial sources, and cosmic sources are truly involuntary, which is about 27% of the total. Radon exposure, medical sources, consumer products, and even nuclear energy sources can be avoided.

18. Removing exposure to radon (venting basements) and minimizing unnecessary (but not necessary) medical procedures that use radioactivity are the best ways to minimize radioactivity exposure.

CHAPTER 17
Organic Chemistry

Opening Essay

All life on Earth is ultimately based on photosynthesis—the process by which plants absorb CO_2 and H_2O from their environment and, in the presence of sunlight, convert those substances into a simple sugar (glucose) and ultimately starches and other building blocks of life. The net photosynthesis chemical reaction is as follows:

$$6CO_2 + 6H_2O \xrightarrow{\text{light}} C_6H_{12}O_6 + 6O_2$$

Oxygen is also a product of photosynthesis. Most forms of animal life (including people) depend on oxygen to breathe, which makes plants indispensible. Virtually all food sources come from plants, eaten either directly (as fruits, vegetables, or grains) or indirectly (as feedstock for meat animals such as cattle, poultry, pigs, sheep, goats, and the like). Plants are absolutely necessary for life to exist.

The net reaction for photosynthesis is misleadingly simple. A series of reactions, called light-dependent reactions, start by the absorption of light by pigments (not just chlorophyll, as is commonly misunderstood) in plant cells. This is followed by a series of light-independent reactions, so named not because they happen in the dark but because they do not directly involve light; however, they involve the products of reactions stimulated by light, so they ultimately depend on light. The whole series of reactions involves many chemicals, enzymes, breaking and making chemical bonds, the transfer of electrons and H^+ ions, and other chemical processes. The elucidation of the actual steps of photosynthesis—a process still unduplicated artificially—is a major achievement of modern chemistry.

In the presence of the sun, plants perform photosynthesis, the chemical reactions that convert CO_2 and H_2O to glucose. The reaction also produces O_2, which is necessary for animal life. Virtually all life on Earth depends on photosynthesis.

Source: © Thinkstock

Organic chemistry is the study of the chemistry of carbon compounds. Why focus on carbon? Carbon has properties that give its chemistry unparalleled complexity. It forms four covalent bonds, which give it great flexibility in bonding. It makes fairly strong bonds with itself (a characteristic called *catenation*), allowing for the formation of large molecules; it also forms fairly strong bonds with other elements, allowing for the possibility of a wide variety of substances. No other element demonstrates the versatility of carbon when it comes to making compounds. Because of this, an entire field of chemistry is devoted to the study of the compounds and reactivity of one element.

Because of the potential for complexity, chemists have defined a rather rigorous system to describe the chemistry of carbon. We will introduce some of that system in this chapter. Should you continue your study of chemistry beyond this text, you will find a much larger world of organic chemistry than we can cover in a single chapter.

17.1 Hydrocarbons

Learning Objectives

1. Identify alkanes, alkenes, alkynes, and aromatic compounds.
2. List some properties of hydrocarbons.

hydrocarbon

An organic compound composed of carbon and hydrogen.

aliphatic hydrocarbon

A hydrocarbon based on chains of C atoms.

alkane

An aliphatic hydrocarbon with only single covalent bonds.

alkene

An aliphatic hydrocarbon that contains a C–C double bond.

alkyne

An aliphatic hydrocarbon that contains a C–C triple bond.

aromatic hydrocarbon

A hydrocarbon that contains a benzene ring.

The simplest organic compounds are those composed of only two elements: carbon and hydrogen. These compounds are called **hydrocarbons**. Hydrocarbons themselves are separated into two types: aliphatic hydrocarbons and aromatic hydrocarbons. **Aliphatic hydrocarbons** are hydrocarbons based on chains of C atoms. There are three types of aliphatic hydrocarbons. **Alkanes** are aliphatic hydrocarbons with only single covalent bonds. **Alkenes** are hydrocarbons that contain at least one C–C double bond, and **alkynes** are hydrocarbons that contain a C–C triple bond. Occasionally, we find an aliphatic hydrocarbon with a ring of C atoms; these hydrocarbons are called *cycloalkanes* (or *cycloalkenes* or *cycloalkynes*).

Aromatic hydrocarbons have a special six-carbon ring called a *benzene* ring. Electrons in the benzene ring have special energetic properties that give benzene physical and chemical properties that are markedly different from alkanes. Originally, the term *aromatic* was used to describe this class of compounds because they were particularly fragrant. However, in modern chemistry the term *aromatic* denotes the presence of a six-membered ring that imparts different and unique properties to a molecule.

The simplest alkanes have their C atoms bonded in a straight chain; these are called *normal* alkanes. They are named according to the number of C atoms in the chain. The smallest alkane is methane:

To make four covalent bonds, the C atom bonds to four H atoms, making the molecular formula for methane CH_4. The diagram for methane is misleading, however; the four covalent bonds that the C atom makes are oriented three dimensionally toward the corners of a tetrahedron. A better representation of the methane molecule is shown in Figure 17.1.

The next-largest alkane has two C atoms that are covalently bonded to each other. For each C atom to make four covalent bonds, each C atom must be bonded to three H atoms. The resulting molecule, whose formula is C_2H_6, is ethane:

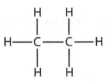

Propane has a backbone of three C atoms surrounded by H atoms. You should be able to verify that the molecular formula for propane is C_3H_8:

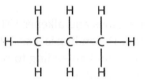

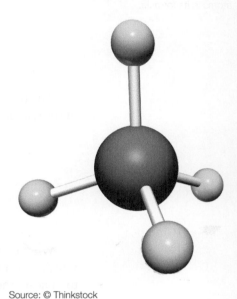

FIGURE 17.1 Three-Dimensional Representation of Methane
The methane molecule is three dimensional, with the H atoms in the positions of the four corners of a tetrahedron.

Source: © Thinkstock

The diagrams representing alkanes are called **structural formulas** because they show the structure of the molecule. As molecules get larger, structural formulas become more and more complex. One way around this is to use a **condensed structural formula**, which lists the formula of each C atom in the backbone of the molecule. For example, the condensed structural formula for ethane is CH_3CH_3, while for propane it is $CH_3CH_2CH_3$. Table 17.1 gives the molecular formulas, the condensed structural formulas, and the names of the first 10 alkanes.

structural formula

A diagram that represents how the atoms in a molecule are bonded.

condensed structural formula

A listing of the atoms bonded to each C atom in a chain.

TABLE 17.1 The First 10 Alkanes

Molecular Formula	Condensed Structural Formula	Name
CH_4	CH_4	methane
C_2H_6	CH_3CH_3	ethane
C_3H_8	$CH_3CH_2CH_3$	propane
C_4H_{10}	$CH_3CH_2CH_2CH_3$	butane
C_5H_{12}	$CH_3CH_2CH_2CH_2CH_3$	pentane
C_6H_{14}	$CH_3(CH_2)_4CH_3$	hexane
C_7H_{16}	$CH_3(CH_2)_5CH_3$	heptane
C_8H_{18}	$CH_3(CH_2)_6CH_3$	octane
C_9H_{20}	$CH_3(CH_2)_7CH_3$	nonane
$C_{10}H_{22}$	$CH_3(CH_2)_8CH_3$	decane

Because alkanes have the maximum number of H atoms possible according to the rules of covalent bonds, alkanes are also referred to as **saturated hydrocarbons**.

saturated hydrocarbon

A carbon compound with the maximum possible number of H atoms in its formula.

unsaturated hydrocarbon

A carbon compound with less than the maximum possible number of H atoms in its formula.

Alkenes have a C–C double bond. Because they have less than the maximum number of H atoms possible, they are called **unsaturated hydrocarbons**. The smallest alkene—ethene—has two C atoms and is also known by its common name ethylene:

The next largest alkene—propene—has three C atoms with a C–C double bond between two of the C atoms. It is also known as propylene:

What do you notice about the names of alkanes and alkenes? The names of alkenes are the same as their corresponding alkanes except that the ending is -*ene*, rather than -*ane*. Using a stem to indicate the number of C atoms in a molecule and an ending to represent the type of organic compound is common in organic chemistry, as we shall see.

With the introduction of the next alkene, butene, we begin to see a major issue with organic molecules: options. With four C atoms, the C–C double bond can go between the first and second C atoms or between the second and third C atoms:

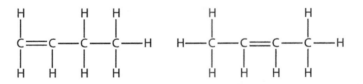

(A double bond between the third and fourth C atoms is the same as having it between the first and second C atoms, only flipped over.) The rules of naming in organic chemistry require that these two substances have different names. The first molecule is named *1-butene*, while the second molecule is named *2-butene*. The number at the beginning of the name indicates where the double bond originates. The lowest possible number is used to number a feature in a molecule; hence, calling the second molecule 3-butene would be incorrect. Numbers are common parts of organic chemical names because they indicate which C atom in a chain contains a distinguishing feature.

isomer

A molecule with the same molecular formula as another molecule but a different structure.

The compounds 1-butene and 2-butene have different physical and chemical properties, even though they have the same molecular formula—C_4H_8. Different molecules with the same molecular formula are called **isomers**. Isomers are common in organic chemistry and contribute to its complexity.

Example 1

Based on the names for the butene molecules, propose a name for this molecule.

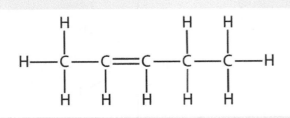

Solution

With five C atoms, we will use the *pent-* stem, and with a C–C double bond, this is an alkene, so this molecule is a pentene. In numbering the C atoms, we use the number 2 because it is the lower possible label. So this molecule is named 2-pentene.

Test Yourself

Based on the names for the butene molecules, propose a name for this molecule.

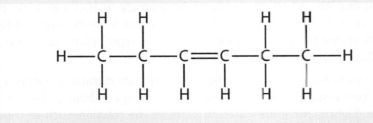

Answer

3-hexene

Alkynes, with a C–C triple bond, are named similarly to alkenes except their names end in *-yne*. The smallest alkyne is ethyne, which is also known as acetylene:

$$H—C≡C—H$$

Propyne has the structure

$$H—C≡C—\overset{\displaystyle H}{\underset{\displaystyle H}{C}}—H$$

With butyne, we need to start numbering the position of the triple bond, just as we did with alkenes:

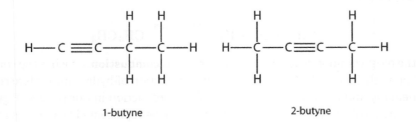

| 1-butyne | 2-butyne |

Aromatic compounds contain the benzene unit. Benzene itself is composed of six C atoms in a ring, with alternating single and double C–C bonds:

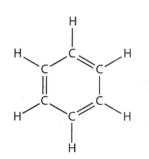

The alternating single and double C–C bonds give the benzene ring a special stability, and it does not react like an alkene as might be suspected. Benzene has the molecular formula C_6H_6; in larger aromatic compounds, a different atom replaces one or more of the H atoms.

As fundamental as hydrocarbons are to organic chemistry, their properties and chemical reactions are rather mundane. Most hydrocarbons are nonpolar because of the close electronegativities of the C and H atoms. As such, they dissolve only sparingly in H_2O and other polar solvents. Small hydrocarbons, such as methane and ethane, are gases at room temperature, while larger hydrocarbons, such as hexane and octane, are liquids. Even larger hydrocarbons are solids at room temperature and have a soft, waxy consistency.

Hydrocarbons are rather unreactive, but they do participate in some classic chemical reactions. One common reaction is substitution with a halogen atom by combining a hydrocarbon with an elemental halogen. Light is sometimes used to promote the reaction, such as this one between methane and chlorine:

$$CH_4 + Cl_2 \xrightarrow{\text{light}} CH_3Cl + HCl$$

addition reaction

The reaction of a halogen molecule across a C–C double or triple bond.

Halogens can also react with alkenes and alkynes, but the reaction is different. In these cases, the halogen reacts with the C–C double or triple bond and inserts itself onto each C atom involved in the multiple bonds. This reaction is called an **addition reaction**. One example is:

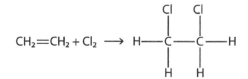

The reaction conditions are usually mild; in many cases, the halogen reacts spontaneously with an alkene or an alkyne.

hydrogenation reaction

The reaction of hydrogen across a C–C double or triple bond, usually in the presence of a catalyst.

Hydrogen can also be added across a multiple bond; this reaction is called a **hydrogenation reaction**. In this case, however, the reaction conditions may not be mild; high pressures of H_2 gas may be necessary. A platinum or palladium catalyst is usually employed to get the reaction to proceed at a reasonable pace:

$$CH_2{=}CH_2 + H_2 \xrightarrow{\text{metal catalyst}} CH_3CH_3$$

combustion

The combination of a hydrocarbon with O_2 to make CO_2 and H_2O.

By far the most common reaction of hydrocarbons is **combustion**, which is the combination of a hydrocarbon with O_2 to make CO_2 and H_2O. The combustion of hydrocarbons is accompanied by a release of energy and is a primary source of energy production in our society (Figure 17.2). The combustion reaction for gasoline, for example, which can be represented by C_8H_{18}, is as follows:

$$2C_8H_{18} + 25O_2 \rightarrow 16CO_2 + 18H_2O + 5060 \text{ kJ}$$

FIGURE 17.2 Combustion
The combustion of hydrocarbons is a primary source of energy in our society.

Source: © Thinkstock

Key Takeaways

- The simplest organic compounds are hydrocarbons and are composed of carbon and hydrogen.
- Hydrocarbons can be aliphatic or aromatic; aliphatic hydrocarbons are divided into alkanes, alkenes, and alkynes.
- The combustion of hydrocarbons is a primary source of energy for our society.

Exercises

1. Define *hydrocarbon*. What are the two general types of hydrocarbons?

2. What are the three different types of aliphatic hydrocarbons? How are they defined?

3. Indicate whether each molecule is an aliphatic or an aromatic hydrocarbon; if aliphatic, identify the molecule as an alkane, an alkene, or an alkyne.

    a.

    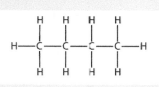

    b.

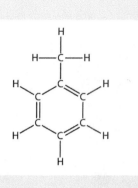

c.

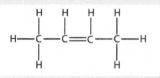

4. Indicate whether each molecule is an aliphatic or an aromatic hydrocarbon; if aliphatic, identify the molecule as an alkane, an alkene, or an alkyne.

a.

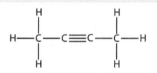

b.

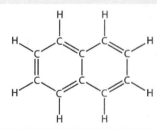

c.

5. Indicate whether each molecule is an aliphatic or an aromatic hydrocarbon; if aliphatic, identify the molecule as an alkane, an alkene, or an alkyne.

a.

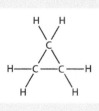

b.

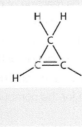

c.

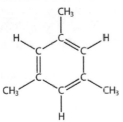

6. Indicate whether each molecule is an aliphatic or an aromatic hydrocarbon; if aliphatic, identify the molecule as an alkane, an alkene, or an alkyne.

a.

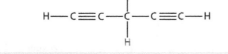

b.

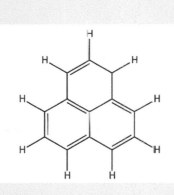

c.

7. Name and draw the structural formulas for the four smallest alkanes.
8. Name and draw the structural formulas for the four smallest alkenes.
9. What does the term *aromatic* imply about an organic molecule?
10. What does the term *normal* imply when used for alkanes?
11. Explain why the name *1-propene* is incorrect. What is the proper name for this molecule?
12. Explain why the name *3-butene* is incorrect. What is the proper name for this molecule?
13. Name and draw the structural formula of each isomer of pentene.
14. Name and draw the structural formula of each isomer of hexyne.
15. Write a chemical equation for the reaction between methane and bromine.
16. Write a chemical equation for the reaction between ethane and chlorine.

17. Draw the structure of the product of the reaction of bromine with propene.
18. Draw the structure of the product of the reaction of chlorine with 2-butene.
19. Draw the structure of the product of the reaction of hydrogen with 1-butene.
20. Draw the structure of the product of the reaction of hydrogen with 2-pentene.
21. Write the balanced chemical equation for the combustion of heptane.
22. Write the balanced chemical equation for the combustion of nonane.

Answers

1. an organic compound composed of only carbon and hydrogen; aliphatic hydrocarbons and aromatic hydrocarbons
2. Alkanes have all single bonds, alkenes have a C–C double bond, and alkynes have a C–C triple bond.
3. a. aliphatic; alkane
   b. aromatic
   c. aliphatic; alkene
4. a. aliphatic; alkyne
   b. aromatic
   c. aliphatic; alkene
5. a. aliphatic; alkane
   b. aliphatic; alkene
   c. aromatic
6. a. aliphatic; alkene
   b. aromatic
   c. aliphatic; alkyne

7.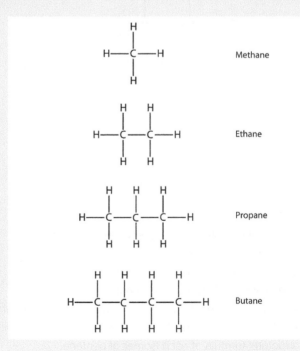

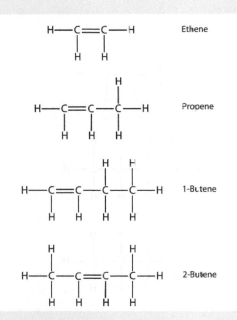

8.

9. Aromatic means that the molecule has a benzene ring.

10. All the C atoms are in a single row.

11. The 1 is not necessary. The name of the compound is simply *propene*.

12. The lowest possible number should be used. The correct name is *2-butene*.

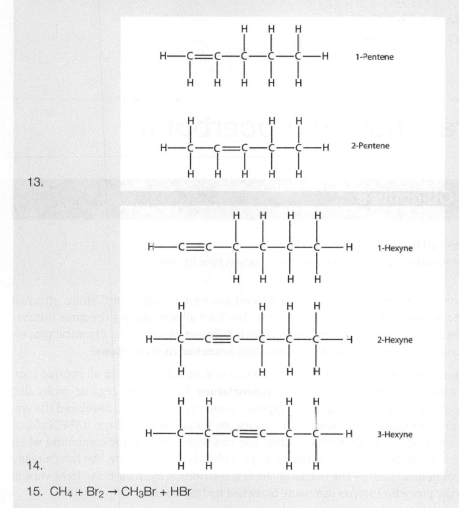

13.

14.

15. $CH_4 + Br_2 \rightarrow CH_3Br + HBr$

16. $C_2H_6 + Cl_2 \rightarrow C_2H_5Cl + HCl$

17.

18.

19.

20.

21. $C_7H_{16} + 11O_2 \rightarrow 7CO_2 + 8H_2O$

22. $C_9H_{20} + 14O_2 \rightarrow 9CO_2 + 10H_2O$

17.2 Branched Hydrocarbons

Learning Objectives

1. Name a branched hydrocarbon from its structure.
2. Draw the structural formula of a branched hydrocarbon from its name.

branched hydrocarbon

A carbon compound that is not a straight chain but has branches attached to the longest chain.

nomenclature

The rules of naming in organic chemistry.

Not all hydrocarbons are straight chains. Many hydrocarbons have branches of C atoms attached to a chain. These branched alkanes are isomers of straight-chain alkanes having the same number of C atoms. However, they are different compounds with different physical and chemical properties. As such, they need different names. How do we name **branched hydrocarbons**?

There are a series of rules for naming branched alkanes (and, ultimately, for all organic compounds). These rules make up the system of **nomenclature** for naming organic molecules. Worldwide, the International Union of Pure and Applied Chemistry (IUPAC) has developed the system of nomenclature for organic compounds. These rules are sometimes called the *IUPAC rules of nomenclature*. By learning and applying these rules, you can name any organic compound when given its structure or determine the unique structure of a molecule from its name. You have already learned the basics of nomenclature—the names of the first ten normal hydrocarbons. Here, we will add some steps to the procedure so you can name branched hydrocarbons.

First, given the structure of an alkane, identify the longest continuous chain of C atoms. Note that the longest chain may not be drawn in a straight line. The longest chain determines the parent name of the hydrocarbon. For example, in the molecule

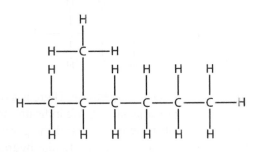

the longest chain of carbons has six C atoms. Therefore, it will be named as a hexane. However, in the molecule

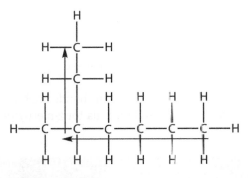

the longest chain of C atoms is not six, but seven, as shown. Therefore, this molecule will be named as a heptane.

The next step is to identify the branches, or **substituents**, on the main chain. The names of the substituents, or *alkyl groups*, are derived from the names of the parent hydrocarbons; however, rather than having the ending *-ane*, the substituent name has the ending *-yl*. Table 17.2 lists the substituent names for the five smallest substituents.

TABLE 17.2 Substituent Names

Substituent Formula	Number of C Atoms	Name of Substituent
CH$_3$	1	*methyl-*
CH$_3$CH$_2$	2	*ethyl-*
CH$_3$CH$_2$CH$_2$	3	*propyl-*
CH$_3$CH$_2$CH$_2$CH$_2$	4	*butyl-*
CH$_3$CH$_2$CH$_2$CH$_2$CH$_2$	5	*pentyl-*
and so forth	and so forth	and so forth

In naming the branched hydrocarbon, the name of the substituent is combined with the parent name of the hydrocarbon without spaces. However, there is likely one more step. The longest chain of the hydrocarbon must be numbered, and the numerical position of the substituent must be included to account for possible isomers. As with double and triple bonds, the main chain is numbered to give the substituent the lowest possible number. For example, in this alkane

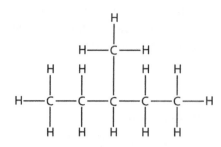

the longest chain is five C atoms long, so it is a pentane. There is a one-carbon substituent on the third C atom, so there is a methyl group at position 3. We indicate the position using the number, which is followed by a hyphen, the substituent name, and the parent hydrocarbon name—in this case, 3-methylpentane. That name is specific to that particular hydrocarbon and no other molecule. Organic chemistry nomenclature is very specific!

It is common to write the structural formula of a hydrocarbon without the H atoms, for clarity. We can also represent 3-methylpentane as

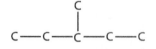

where it is understood that any unwritten covalent bonds are bonds with H atoms. With this understanding, we recognize that the structural formula for 3-methylpentane refers to a molecule with the formula of C_6H_{14}.

Example 2

Name this molecule.

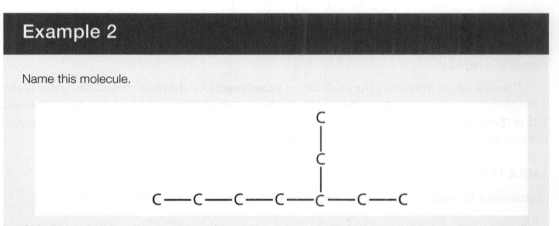

Solution

The longest continuous carbon chain has seven C atoms, so this molecule will be named as a heptane. There is a two-carbon substituent on the main chain, which is an ethyl group. To give the substituent the lowest numbering, we number the chain from the *right* side and see that the substituent is on the third C atom. This hydrocarbon is 3-ethylheptane.

Test Yourself

Name this molecule.

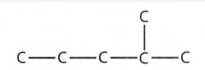

Answer

2-methylpentane

Branched hydrocarbons may have more than one substituent. If the substituents are different, then give each substituent a number (using the smallest possible numbers) and list the substituents in alphabetical order, with the numbers separated by hyphens and with no spaces in the name. Using these rules, the molecule

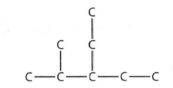

is 3-ethyl-2-methylpentane.

If the substituents are the same, then use the name of the substituent only once, but use more than one number, separated by a comma. Also, put a numerical prefix before the substituent name that indicates the number of substituents of that type. The numerical prefixes are listed in Table 17.3. The number of the position values must agree with the numerical prefix before the substituent.

TABLE 17.3 Numerical Prefixes to Use for Multiple Substituents

Number of Same Substituent	Numerical Prefix
2	di-
3	tri-
4	tetra-
5	penta-
and so forth	and so forth

Consider this molecule:

The longest chain has four C atoms, so it is a butane. There are two substituents, each of which consists of a single C atom; they are methyl groups. The methyl groups are on the second and third C atoms in the chain (no matter which end the numbering starts from), so we would name this molecule 2,3-dimethylbutane. Note the comma between the numbers, the hyphen between the numbers and the substituent name, and the presence of the prefix di- before the *methyl*. Other molecules—even with larger numbers of substituents—can be named similarly.

Example 3

Name this molecule.

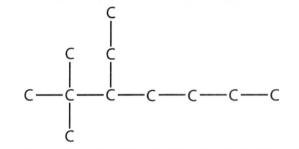

Solution

The longest chain has seven C atoms, so we name this molecule as a heptane. We find two one-carbon substituents on the second C atom and a two-carbon substituent on the third C atom. Therefore, this molecule is named 3-ethyl-2,2-dimethylheptane.

Test Yourself

Name this molecule.

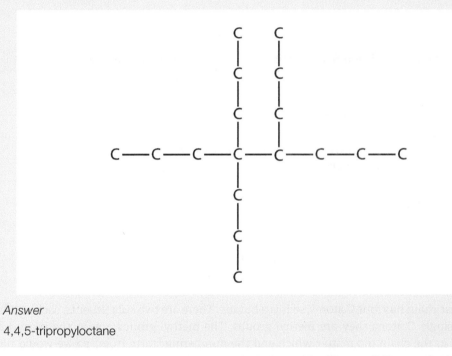

Answer

4,4,5-tripropyloctane

Alkenes and alkynes are named in a similar fashion. The biggest difference is that when identifying the longest carbon chain, it *must* contain the C–C double or triple bond. Furthermore, when numbering the main chain, the double or triple bond gets the lowest possible number. This means that there may be longer or higher-numbered substituents than may be allowed if the molecule were an alkane. For example, this molecule

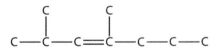

is 2,4-dimethyl-3-heptene (note the number and the hyphens that indicate the position of the double bond).

Example 4

Name this molecule.

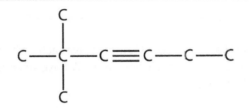

Solution

The longest chain that contains the C–C triple bond has six C atoms, so this is a hexyne molecule. The triple bond starts at the third C atom, so this is a 3-hexyne. Finally, there are two methyl groups on the chain; to give them the lowest possible number, we number the chain from the left side, giving the methyl groups the second position. The name of this molecule is 2,2-dimethyl-3-hexyne.

Test Yourself

Name this molecule.

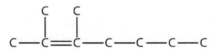

Answer

2,3,4-trimethyl-2-pentene

Once you master naming hydrocarbons from their given structures, it is rather easy to draw a structure from a given name. Just draw the parent chain with the correct number of C atoms (putting the double or triple bond in the right position, as necessary) and add the substituents in the proper positions. If you start by drawing the C atom backbone, you can go back and complete the structure by adding H atoms to give each C atom four covalent bonds. From the name 2,3-dimethyl-4-propyl-2-heptene, we start by drawing the seven-carbon parent chain with a double bond starting at the second carbon:

$$C-C=C-C-C-C-C$$

We add to this structure two one-carbon substituents on the second and third C atoms:

$$
\begin{array}{ccc}
& C & C \\
& | & | \\
C-C&=&C-C-C-C-C
\end{array}
$$

We finish the carbon backbone by adding a three-carbon propyl group to the fourth C atom in the parent chain:

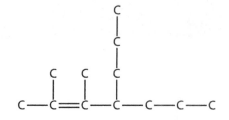

If we choose, we can add H atoms to each C atom to give each carbon four covalent bonds, being careful to note that the C atoms in the double bond already have an additional covalent bond. (How many H atoms do you think are required?[1])

Example 5

Draw the carbon backbone for 2,3,4-trimethylpentane.

Solution

First, we draw the five-carbon backbone that represents the pentane chain:

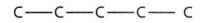

According to the name, there are three one-carbon methyl groups attached to the second, the third, and the fourth C atoms in the chain. We finish the carbon backbone by putting the three methyl groups on the pentane main chain:

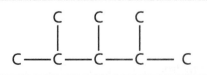

Test Yourself

Draw the carbon backbone for 3-ethyl-6,7-dimethyl-2-octene.

Answer

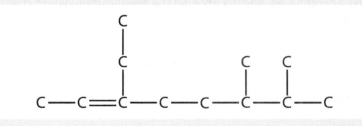

Naming substituted benzene molecules is straightforward. If there is only one substituent, the substituent is named as a side chain on a benzene molecule, like this:

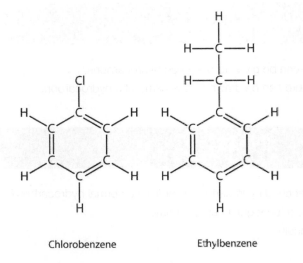

Chlorobenzene   Ethylbenzene

If there are two or more substituents on a benzene molecule, the relative positions must be numbered, just as an aliphatic chain of C atoms is numbered. The substituent that is first alphabetically is assigned position 1, and the ring is numbered in a circle to give the other substituents the lowest possible number(s).

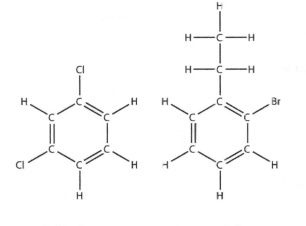

1,3-Dichlorobenzene   1-Bromo-2-ethylbenzene

If a benzene ring is treated as a substituent, it is given the name *phenyl-*. The following molecule is 3-phenylpentane:

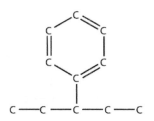

where the H atoms have been omitted for clarity.

Key Takeaways

- A unique name can be given to branched hydrocarbons.
- A unique structure can be drawn for the name of a hydrocarbon.

Exercises

1. How does a branched hydrocarbon differ from a normal hydrocarbon?
2. How does a substituent get its unique name?
3. Name this molecule.

4. Name this molecule.

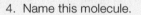

5. Name this molecule.

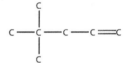

6. Name this molecule.

7. Name this molecule.

8. Name this molecule.

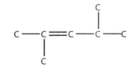

9. Name this molecule.

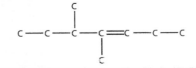

10. Name this molecule.

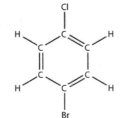

11. Name this molecule.

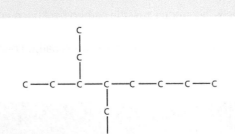

12. Name this molecule.

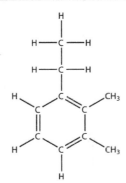

13. Draw the carbon backbone for each molecule.

   a. 3,4-diethyloctane

   b. 2,2-dimethyl-4-propylnonane

14. Draw the carbon backbone for each molecule.

   a. 3-ethyl-4-methyl-3-heptene

   b. 3,3-diethyl-1-pentyne

15. Draw the carbon backbone for each molecule.

   a. 4-ethyl-4-propyl-2-octyne

   b. 5-butyl-2,2-dimethyldecane

16. Draw the carbon backbone for each molecule.

   a. 3,4-diethyl-1-hexyne

   b. 4-propyl-3-ethyl-2-methyloctane

17. The name 2-ethylhexane is incorrect. Draw the carbon backbone and write the correct name for this molecule.

18. The name 3-butyl-7-methyloctane is incorrect. Draw the carbon backbone and write the correct name for this molecule.

Answers

1. A branched hydrocarbon does not have all of its C atoms in a single row.

3. 3-methyl-2-hexene

5. 4,4-dimethyl-1-pentene

7. 2,4-dimethyl-2-pentene

9. 3,4-diethyloctane

11. 1-bromo-4-chlorobenzene

13. a.

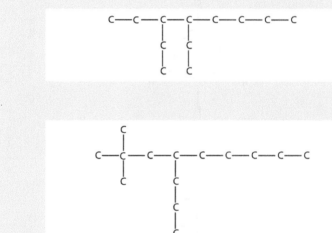

   b.

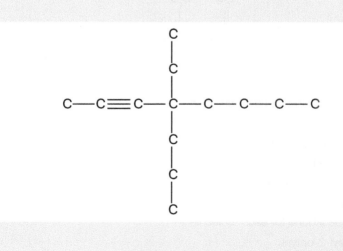

15. a.

   b.

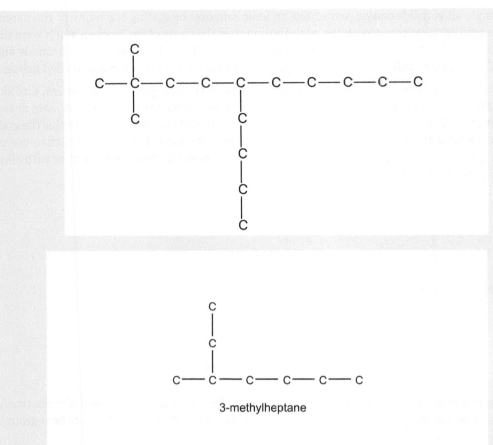

3-methylheptane

17.

17.3 Alkyl Halides and Alcohols

Learning Objectives

1. Define *functional group*.
2. Identify and name a simple alkyl halide.
3. Identify and name a simple alcohol.
4. Predict the product(s) of an elimination reaction of an alkyl halide or an alcohol.

A **functional group** is any collection of atoms and/or bonds with certain characteristic chemical reactions. We have already seen two functional groups: the C–C double bond and the C–C triple bond. They undergo certain characteristic chemical reactions—for example, the addition of a halogen across the multiple bond.

The presence of a halogen atom (F, Cl, Br, or I; also, X is used to represent any halogen atom) is one of the simplest functional groups. Organic compounds that contain a halogen atom are called **alkyl halides**. We have already seen some examples of alkyl halides when the addition of halogens across double and triple bonds was introduced in Section 2; the products of these reactions were alkyl halides.

functional group

A collection of atoms or bonds with certain characteristic reactions.

alkyl halide

An organic compound that contains a halogen atom.

A simple alkyl halide can be named like an ionic salt, first by stating the name of the parent alkane as a substituent group (with the *-yl* suffix) and then the name of the halogen as if it were the anion. So CH_3Cl has the common name of methyl chloride, while CH_3CH_2Br is ethyl bromide and $CH_3CH_2CH_2I$ is propyl iodide. However, this system is not ideal for more complicated alkyl halides.

The systematic way of naming alkyl halides is to name the halogen as a substituent, just like an alkyl group, and use numbers to indicate the position of the halogen atom on the main chain. The name of the halogen as a substituent comes from the stem of the element's name plus the ending *-o*, so the substituent names are *fluoro-*, *chloro-*, *bromo-* and *iodo-*. If there is more than one of a certain halogen, we use numerical prefixes to indicate the number of each kind, just as with alkyl groups. For example, this molecule

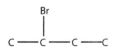

is 2-bromobutane, while this molecule

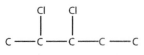

is 2,3-dichloropentane. If alkyl groups are present, the substituents are listed alphabetically. Numerical prefixes are ignored when determining the alphabetical ordering of substituent groups.

Example 6

Name this molecule.

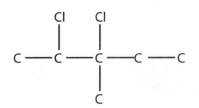

Solution

The longest carbon chain has five C atoms, so the molecule is a pentane. There are two chlorine substituents located on the second and third C atoms, with a one-carbon methyl group on the third C atom as well. The correct name for this molecule is 2,3-dichloro-3-methylpentane.

Test Yourself

Name this molecule.

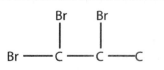

Answer

1,1,2-tribromopropane

Another simple functional group is the covalently bonded OH group. This is the **alcohol** functional group. It is not the hydroxide ion; rather than being present as a negatively charged species, in organic chemistry it is a covalently bonded functional group.

Like alkyl halides, alcohols have a common naming system and a more formal system. The common system is similar to that of alkyl halides: name the alkyl group attached to the OH group, ending with the suffix -yl, and add the word *alcohol* as a second word. So CH_3OH is methyl alcohol; CH_3CH_2OH is ethyl alcohol, and $CH_3CH_2CH_2OH$ is propyl alcohol.

As with alkyl halides, though, this system is limited (although for smaller alcohols, it is very common in everyday usage). The formal system of naming uses the name of the hydrocarbon containing the OH group and having the correct number of C atoms, dropping the final -e of the name and appending the suffix -ol. Thus CH_3OH is methanol and CH_3CH_2OH is ethanol. For larger alcohol molecules, we use a number to indicate the position of the OH group on the longest carbon chain, similar to the number needed for alkenes and alkynes. Again, the carbon chain is numbered to give the OH group the lowest number, no matter how large the other numbers are. So $CH_3CH_2CH_2OH$ is 1-propanol, while $CH_3CHOHCH_3$ is 2-propanol. (A common component in many medicine cabinets, 2-propanol is also known as isopropanol or isopropyl alcohol [Figure 17.3]).

Another acceptable way of naming an alcohol—especially a more complicated molecule—is to name the OH group as the hydroxy substituent and give it a numerical position like an alkyl group or a halogen atom. Thus 2-propanol would be called 2-hydroxypropane by this convention.

alcohol
An organic compound that contains an OH functional group.

FIGURE 17.3
Isopropyl Alcohol
What you find labeled *isopropyl alcohol* in a medicine cabinet is more formally called 2-propanol.

Source: Photo courtesy of Craig Spurrier, http://en.wikipedia.org/wiki/File:Rubbing_alcohol.JPG.

Example 7

Name this molecule as an alcohol and as a substituted alkane.

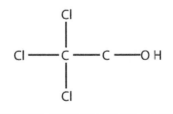

Solution

The longest carbon chain containing the OH group has four C atoms, so the parent hydrocarbon is butane. Because the OH group is on the first C atom, it is 1-butanol. There is a methyl group on the second C atom, as well as a Cl atom, so the formal name for this alcohol is 2-chloro-2-methyl-1-butanol. If naming the alcohol group as a substituent, it would be 2-chloro-1-hydroxy-2-methylbutane.

Test Yourself

Name this molecule as an alcohol and as a substituted alkane.

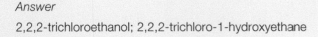

Answer

2,2,2-trichloroethanol; 2,2,2-trichloro-1-hydroxyethane

Most alkyl halides are insoluble in H_2O. Smaller alcohols, however, are very soluble in H_2O because these molecules can engage in hydrogen bonding with H_2O molecules. For larger molecules, however, the polar OH group is overwhelmed by the nonpolar alkyl part of the molecule. While methanol is soluble in H_2O in all proportions, only about 2.6 g of pentanol will dissolve in 100 g of H_2O. Larger alcohols have an even lower solubility in H_2O.

elimination

The removal of an HZ (Z = halogen, OH) from an alkyl halide or an alcohol.

One reaction common to alcohols and alkyl halides is **elimination**, the removal of the functional group (either X or OH) and an H atom from an adjacent carbon. The general reaction can be written as follows:

where Z represents either the X or the OH group. The biggest difference between elimination in alkyl halides and elimination in alcohols is the identity of the catalyst: for alkyl halides, the catalyst is a strong base; for alcohols, the catalyst is a strong acid. For compounds in which there are H atoms on more than one adjacent carbon, a mixture of products results.

Example 8

Predict the organic product(s) of this reaction.

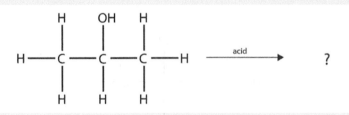

Solution

Under these conditions, an HOH (otherwise known as H_2O) molecule will be eliminated, and an alkene will be formed. It does not matter which adjacent carbon loses the H atom; in either case the product will be

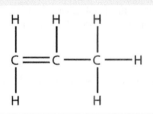

which is propene.

Test Yourself

Predict the organic product(s) of this reaction.

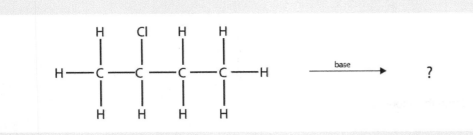

Answer

1-butene and 2-butene

Key Takeaways

- Alkyl halides have a halogen atom as a functional group.
- Alcohols have an OH group as a functional group.
- Nomenclature rules allow us to name alkyl halides and alcohols.
- In an elimination reaction, a double bond is formed as an HX or an HOH molecule is removed.

Exercises

1. Define *functional group* and give two examples.
2. What is elimination? How does it differ for alkyl halides and alcohols?
3. Name this molecule.

4. Name this molecule.

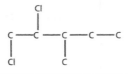

5. Name this molecule.

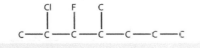

6. Name this molecule.

7. Name this molecule.

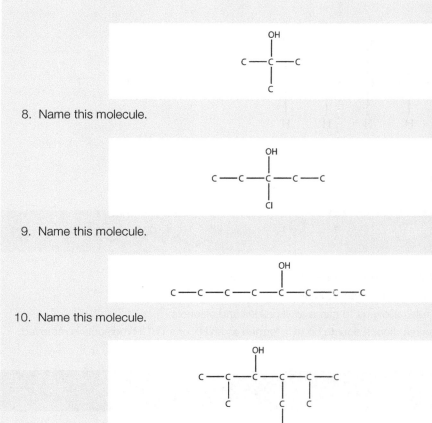

8. Name this molecule.

9. Name this molecule.

10. Name this molecule.

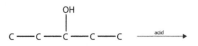

11. Predict the product(s) of this elimination reaction.

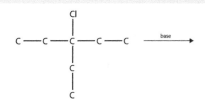

12. Predict the product(s) of this elimination reaction.

13. Predict the product(s) of this elimination reaction.

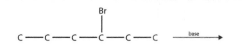

14. Predict the product(s) of this elimination reaction.

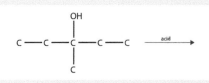

Answers

1. A group of atoms with a certain reactivity; halogen atoms and alcohol groups (answers will vary).
2. Elimination is the removal of two substituents from two adjacent C atoms in an alkyl halide or an alcohol. An alkyl halide uses a base as a catalyst, while an alcohol uses an acid as a catalyst.
3. 2-bromobutane
4. 1,2-dichloro-3-methylpentane
5. 2-chloro-3-fluoro-4-methylheptane
6. dibromo-diiodomethane
7. 2-methyl-2-propanol
8. 3-chloro-3-pentanol
9. 4-octanol
10. 2,5-dimethyl-4-ethyl-3-hexanol
11. 2-pentene
12. 3-ethyl-2-pentene
13. 2-hexene and 3-hexene
14. 3-methyl-2-pentene and 2-ethyl-1-butene

17.4 Other Oxygen-Containing Functional Groups

Learning Objective

1. Identify the aldehyde, ketone, acid, ester, and ether functional groups.

There are other functional groups that contain O atoms. Before we introduce them, we define the **carbonyl group**, which is formed when an O atom and a C atom are joined by a double bond:

$$\overset{\text{O}}{\underset{\quad}{\overset{\|}{-\text{C}-}}}$$

The other two bonds on the C atom are attached to other atoms. It is the identities of these other atoms that define what specific type of compound an organic molecule is.

If one bond of the carbonyl group is made to an H atom, then the molecule is classified as an **aldehyde**. (If there are two H atoms, there is only 1 C atom.) When naming aldehydes, the main chain of C atoms must include the carbon in the carbonyl group, which is numbered as position 1 in the carbon chain. The parent name of the hydrocarbon is used, but the suffix *-al* is appended. (Do not confuse *-al* with *-ol*, which is the suffix used for alcohols.) So we have:

carbonyl group

A functional group formed when an O atom and a C atom are joined with a double bond.

aldehyde

A compound that has a carbonyl functional group at the end of a chain of C atoms.

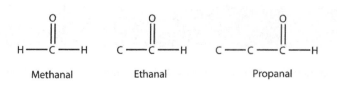

Methanal   Ethanal   Propanal

Methanal has a common name with which you may be familiar: formaldehyde. The main thing to note about aldehydes is that the carbonyl group is at the *end* of a carbon chain.

A carbonyl group in the middle of a carbon chain implies that both remaining bonds of the carbonyl group are made to C atoms. This type of molecule is called a **ketone**. Despite the fact that aldehydes and ketones have the same carbonyl group, they have different chemical and physical properties and are properly grouped as two different types of compounds. The smallest ketone has three C atoms in it. When naming a ketone, we take the name of the parent hydrocarbon and change the suffix to *-one*:

ketone

A compound that has a carbonyl group in the middle of a carbon chain.

Propanone

The common name for propanone is acetone. With larger ketones, we must use a number to indicate the position of the carbonyl group, much like a number is used with alkenes and alkynes:

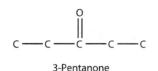

3-Pentanone

There is another way to name ketones: name the alkyl groups that are attached to the carbonyl group and add the word *ketone* to the name. So propanone can also be called dimethyl ketone, while 2-butanone is called methyl ethyl ketone.

Example 9

Draw the structure of 2-pentanone.

Solution

This molecule has five C atoms in a chain, with the carbonyl group on the second C atom. Its structure is as follows:

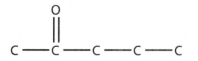

Test Yourself

Draw the structure of methyl butyl ketone.

Answer

The combination of a carbonyl functional group and an OH group makes the **carboxyl group**.

> **carboxyl group**
>
> A functional group composed of a carbonyl group and an OH group.

Molecules with a carboxyl group are called **carboxylic acids**. As with aldehydes, the functional group in carboxylic acids is at the end of a carbon chain. Also as with aldehydes, the C atom in the functional group is counted as one of the C atoms that defines the parent hydrocarbon name. To name carboxylic acids, the parent name of the hydrocarbon is used, but the suffix -*oic acid* is added:

> **carboxylic acid**
>
> A molecule with a carboxyl group.

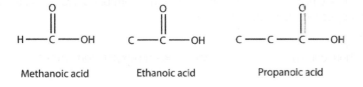

Methanoic acid   Ethanoic acid   Propanoic acid

Methanoic acid and ethanoic acid are also called formic acid and acetic acid, respectively. Formic acid is the compound that makes certain ant bites sting, while acetic acid is the active substance in vinegar.

How acidic are carboxylic acids? It turns out that they are not very acidic. No carboxylic acid is on the list of strong acids (Table 15.2). (For more information about strong acids, see Chapter 15 Section 5.) This means that all carboxylic acids are weak acids. A 1 M solution of formic acid is only about 1.3% dissociated into H^+ ions and formate ions, while a similar solution of acetic acid is ionized by about only 0.4%. Some carboxylic acids are stronger—for example, trichloroacetic acid is about 45% dissociated in aqueous solution. But no carboxylic acid approaches the 100% dissociation amount required by the definition of a strong acid.

As their name suggests, however, carboxylic acids do act like acids in the presence of bases. The H atom in the carboxyl group comes off as the H^+ ion, leaving a **carboxylate** anion:

> **carboxylate**
>
> A negatively charged ion derived from a carboxylic acid.

Carboxylate ion

Here, the letter R represents any organic group (methyl, ethyl, etc.). Carboxylate ions are named from the acid name: the -*oic acid* is replaced with -*oate* to name the ion.

Example 10

Complete the chemical reaction. Can you name the carboxylate ion formed?

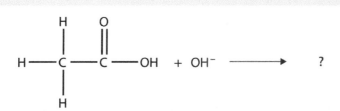

Solution

The OH⁻ ion removes the H atom that is part of the carboxyl group:

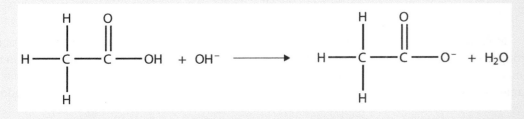

The carboxylate ion, which has the condensed structural formula $CH_3CO_2^-$, is the ethanoate ion, but it is commonly called the acetate ion.

Test Yourself

Complete the chemical reaction. Can you name the carboxylate ion formed?

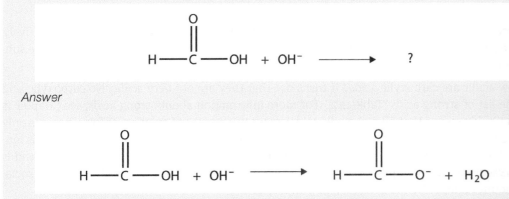

Answer

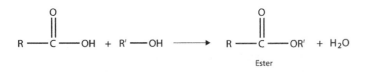

The anion is the methanoate ion, which is commonly called the formate ion.

ester

A functional group made by combining a carboxylic acid with an alcohol.

One reaction to consider is that of a carboxylic acid and an alcohol. When combined under the proper conditions, a water molecule will be removed, and the remaining pieces will combine to form a new functional group—the **ester** functional group:

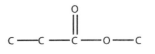

Note how the acid molecule contributes one alkyl side (represented by R), while the alcohol contributes the other side (represented by R′). Esters are named using the alkyl group name from the alcohol plus the carboxylate name from the acid—for example, the molecule is called methyl propanoate.

Chemistry Is Everywhere: Esters, Fragrances, and Flavorings

Esters are very interesting compounds, in part because many have very pleasant odors and flavors. (Remember, never taste anything in the chemistry lab!) Many esters occur naturally and contribute to the odor of flowers and the taste of fruits. Other esters are synthesized industrially and are added to food products to improve their smell or taste; it is likely that if you eat a product whose ingredients include artificial flavorings, those flavorings are esters. Here are some esters and their odors/flavors:

Ester	Tastes/Smells Like	Ester	Tastes/Smells Like
allyl hexanoate	pineapple	isobutyl formate	raspberry
benzyl acetate	pear	isobutyl acetate	pear
butyl butanoate	pineapple	methyl phenylacetate	honey
ethyl butanoate	banana	nonyl caprylate	orange
ethyl hexanoate	pineapple	pentyl acetate	apple
ethyl heptanoate	apricot	propyl ethanoate	pear
ethyl pentanoate	apple	propyl isobutyrate	rum

Finally, the **ether** functional group is an O atom that is bonded to two organic groups:

$$R—O—R'$$

The two R groups may be the same or different. Naming ethers is like the alternate way of naming ketones. In this case, the R groups are named sequentially, and the word *ether* is appended. The molecule

$$CH_3OCH_3$$

is dimethyl ether, while the molecule

$$CH_3OCH_2CH_3$$

is methyl ethyl ether. Diethyl ether, another ether, was once used as an anesthetic, but its flammability and toxicity caused it to fall out of favor. Smaller ether molecules that are liquids at room temperature are common solvents for organic chemical reactions.

ether

A functional group that has an O atom attached to two organic groups.

Key Takeaway

- Aldehydes, ketones, carboxylic acids, esters, and ethers have oxygen-containing functional groups.

Exercises

1. Name a similarity between the functional groups found in aldehydes and ketones. Can you name a difference between them?
2. Explain how a carboxylic acid is used to make an ester.

3. Name each molecule.

   a.

   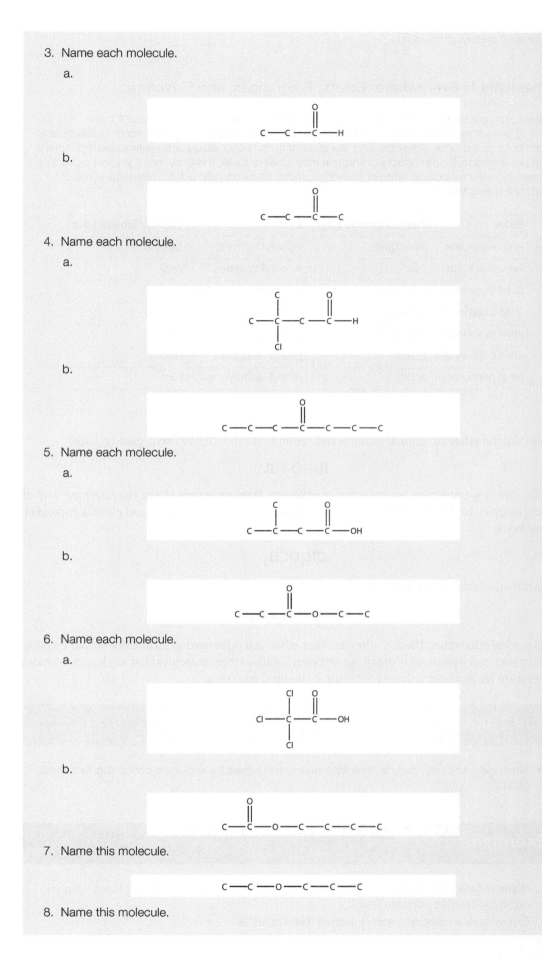

   b.

4. Name each molecule.

   a.

   b.

5. Name each molecule.

   a.

   b.

6. Name each molecule.

   a.

   b.

7. Name this molecule.

8. Name this molecule.

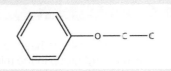

9. Give an alternate but acceptable name to the molecule in Exercise 3b.

10. Give an alternate but acceptable name to the molecule in Exercise 4b.

11. Complete this chemical reaction.

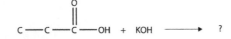

12. Complete this chemical reaction.

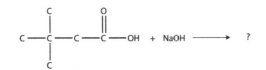

13. The drug known as aspirin has this molecular structure:

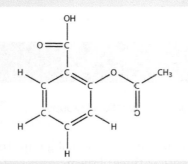

    Identify the functional group(s) in this molecule.

14. The drug known as naproxen sodium is the sodium salt of this molecule:

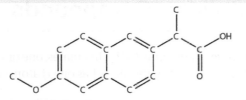

    (The extra H atoms are omitted for clarity.) Identify the functional group(s) in this molecule.

15. Identify the ester made by reacting these molecules.

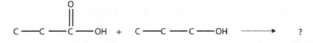

16. Identify the ester made by reacting these molecules.

Answers

1. They both have a carbonyl group, but an aldehyde has the carbonyl group at the end of a carbon chain, and a ketone has the carbonyl group in the middle.
3. a. propanal
   b. 2-butanone
5. a. 3-methylbutanoic acid
   b. ethyl propionate
7. ethyl propyl ether
9. methyl ethyl ketone
11. $H_2O + KCH_3CH_2CO_2$
13. acid, ester, and aromatic (benzene ring)
15. propyl propionate

17.5 Other Functional Groups

Learning Objective

1. Identify the amine, amide, and thiol functional groups.

There are some common—and important—functional groups that contain elements other than oxygen. In this section, we will consider three of them.

Nitrogen-Containing Compounds

amine

An organic derivative of ammonia.

An **amine** is an organic derivative of ammonia (NH_3). In amines, one or more of the H atoms in NH_3 is substituted with an organic group. A *primary* amine has one H atom substituted with an R group:

$$CH_3 \!-\! NH_2$$

Methylamine

A *secondary* amine has two H atoms substituted with R groups:

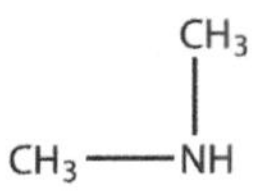

$$CH_3 \!-\! \underset{\displaystyle \overset{|}{NH}}{} \quad \overset{CH_3}{|}$$

Dimethylamine

A *tertiary* amine has all three H atoms substituted with R group:

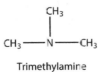

Trimethylamine

Naming simple amines is straightforward: name the R groups as substituents and then add the suffix -*amine*, using numerical suffixes on the substituent names as necessary. This amine

is diethylamine (the H atoms on the C atoms are omitted for clarity), while this amine

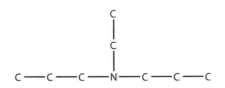

is ethyldipropylamine.

Example 11

Name this amine.

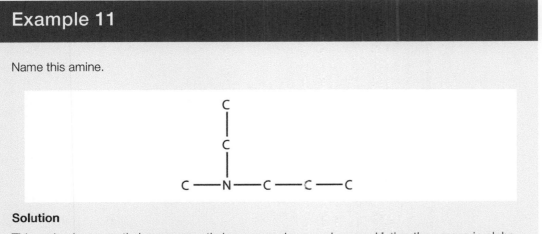

Solution

This amine has a methyl group, an ethyl group, and a propyl group. Listing the names in alphabetical order, this amine is ethylmethylpropylamine.

Test Yourself

Name this amine.

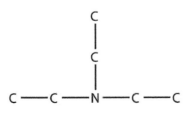

Answer

triethylamine

As with NH_3, the N atom in amines can accept a proton onto the lone electron pair on the N atom. That is, amines act as Brønsted-Lowry bases (i.e., proton acceptors):

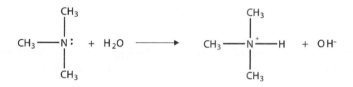

(For more information on Brønsted-Lowry bases, see Chapter 15 Section 3.) The amine becomes an ion, the organic counterpart of the ammonium (NH_4^+) ion.

Because no amine is presented in Table 15.2, all amines are weak bases. The weakness of amines is about as the same as that for carboxylic acids. N-containing organic compounds are very common in nature, and they all act as weak bases. Some of these compounds have rather complicated structures. Figure 17.4 shows some N-containing substances that you may recognize.

FIGURE 17.4 Some Naturally Occurring N-Containing Compounds

Nitrogen-containing compounds occur frequently in nature. Here are some that you might encounter in the course of your everyday life.

Compound	Structure	Atoms not shown are assumed to be H atoms, which are omitted for clarity
Caffeine (stimulant found in teas and coffees)		
Nicotine (addictive compound found in tobacco)		
Morphine (painkiller)		
Monosodium glutamate (food additive and flavor enhancer)		
Quinine (antimalaria compound found in the bark of the cinchona tree)		

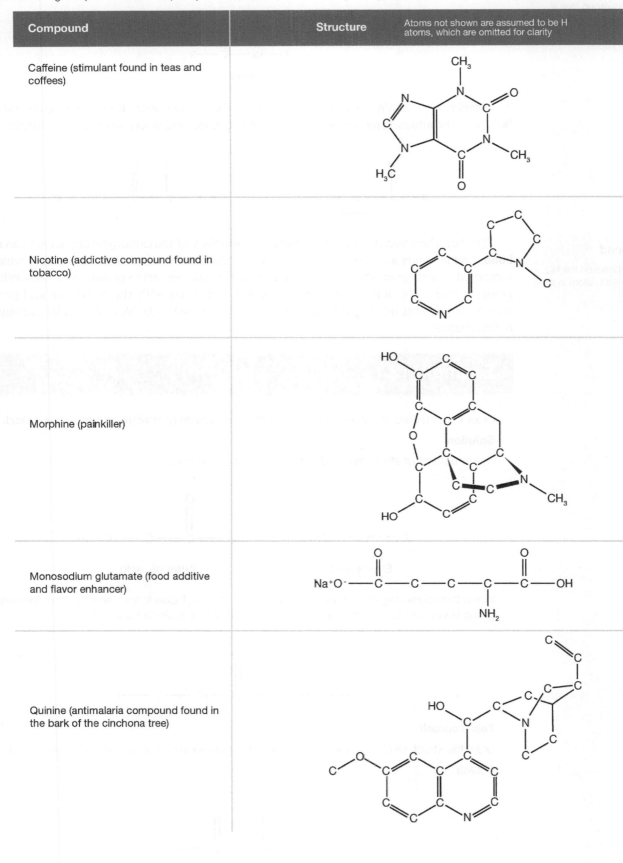

amide

A functional group that is the combination of the amine and carbonyl functional groups.

An **amide** functional group is a combination of an amine group and a carbonyl group:

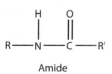

Amide

Amides are actually formed by bringing together an amine-containing molecule and a carboxylic acid-containing molecule. A molecule of H_2O is lost, much like when an ester forms:

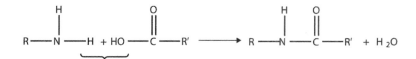

amide bond

The bond between the N atom and the C atom in an amide.

The bond between the N of the amine group and the C of the carbonyl group is called an **amide bond**. Amide bonds are particularly important in biological molecules called proteins, which are composed of strings of amino acids—molecules that have an amine group and a carboxylic acid group in them. The amine group on one amino acid reacts with the carboxylic acid group of another amino acid, making a chain held together by amide bonds. We will consider proteins later in this chapter.

Example 12

Draw the structure of the amide formed by the combination of ethylamine and butanoic acid.

Solution

The structures of ethylamine and butanoic acid are as follows:

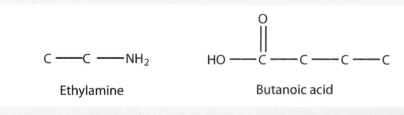

When they come together to make an amide, an H_2O molecule is lost, and the N of the amine group bonds to the C of the carboxyl group. The resulting molecule is as follows:

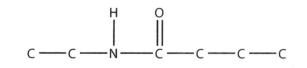

Test Yourself

Draw the structure of the amide formed by the combination of methylamine and formic acid.

Answer

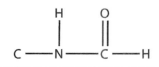

Sulfur-Containing Compounds

Sulfur is below oxygen on the periodic table, and it occasionally shows some similar chemistry. One similarity is that an S atom can take the place of an O atom in an alcohol, to make a molecule that looks like this:

$$R–SH$$

The sulfur analog of an alcohol is called a **thiol**. The formal way of naming a thiol is similar to that of alcohols, except that instead of using the suffix -ol, you use -thiol as the suffix. The following illustrates thiol nomenclature:

$$CH_3—SH \qquad C_2H_5—SH \qquad C_3H_7—SH$$

Methanethiol   Ethanethiol   Propanethiol

An older system uses the word *mercaptan* in naming simple thiols, much like the word *alcohol* is used with small alcohols. These thiols can also be named like this:

$$CH_3—SH \qquad C_2H_5—SH \qquad C_3H_7—SH$$

Methyl mercaptan   Ethyl mercaptan   Propyl mercaptan

Many thiols have strong, objectionable odors; indeed, the spray from skunks is composed of thiols and is detectable by the human nose at concentrations less than 10 ppb. Because natural gas is odorless, thiols are intentionally added to natural gas—at very low levels, of course—so that gas leaks can be more easily detected. Not all thiols have objectionable odors; this thiol is responsible for the odor of grapefruit:

One amino acid that is a thiol is cysteine:

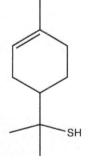

Cysteine plays an important role in protein structure. If two cysteine amino acids in a protein chain approach each other, they can be oxidized, and a S–S bond (also known as a *disulfide bond*) is formed:

$$R-SH + HS-R \rightarrow R-S-S-R$$

where the R group is the rest of the cysteine molecule. The disulfide bond is strong enough to fix the position of the two cysteine groups, thus imposing a structure on the protein. Hair is composed of about 5% cysteine, and the breaking and remaking of disulfide bonds between cysteine units is the primary mechanism behind straightening and curling hair (hair "perms").

Food and Drink App: Amino Acids—Essential and Otherwise

The text mentioned cysteine, an amino acid. Amino acids are the fundamental building blocks of proteins, a major biological component. Proteins are a necessary part of the diet; meat, eggs, and certain vegetables such as beans and soy are good sources of protein and amino acids.

All life on Earth—from the lowliest single-celled organism to humans to blue whales—relies on proteins for life, so all life on Earth is dependent on amino acids. The human body contains 20 different amino acids (curiously, other organisms may have a different number of amino acids). However, not all of them must be obtained from the diet. The body can synthesize 12 amino acids. The other 8 *must* be obtained from the diet. These 8 amino acids are called the *essential amino acids*. Daily requirements range from 4 mg per kilogram of body weight for tryptophan to 40 mg per kilogram of body weight for leucine. Infants and children need a greater mass per kg of body weight to support their growing bodies; also, the number of amino acids that are considered essential for infants and children is greater than for adults due to the greater protein synthesis associated with growth.

Because of the existence of essential amino acids, a diet that is properly balanced in protein is necessary. Rice and beans, a very popular food dish in Latin cuisines, actually provides all the essential amino acids in one dish; without one component, the dish would be nutritionally incomplete. Corn (maize) is the most-grown grain crop in the world, but an overreliance on it as a primary food source deprives people of lysine and tryptophan, which are two essential amino acids. (Indeed, it is now widely accepted that the disappearance of certain native American groups was largely due to the overuse of corn as the staple food.) People on restricted diets—whether out of necessity or by choice (e.g., vegetarians)—may be missing the proper amount of an essential amino acid, so it is important to vary the diet when possible to ensure ingestion of a wide range of protein sources.

Key Takeaway

- Other functional groups include amine, amide, and thiol functional groups.

Exercises

1. What are the structure and name of the smallest amine?
2. What are the structure and name of the smallest thiol?
3. Identify each compound as a primary, secondary, or tertiary amine.

   a.

   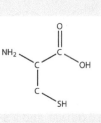

   b.

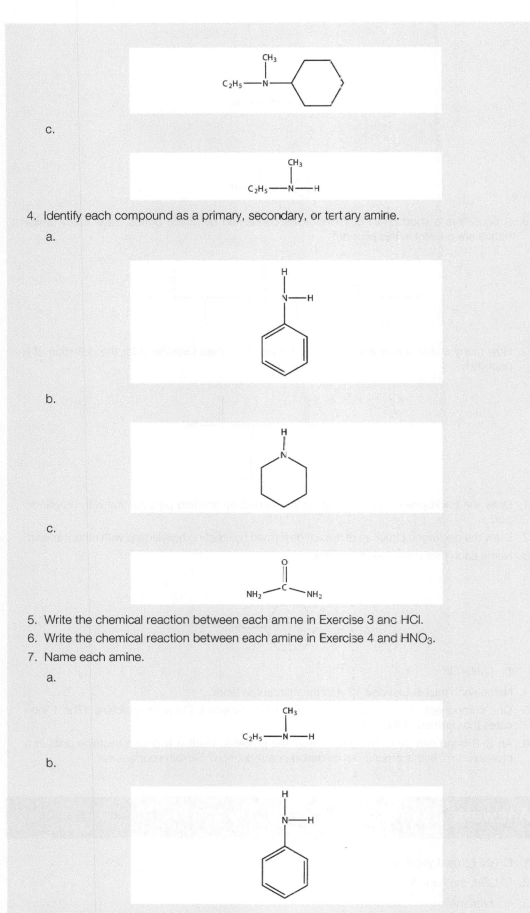

c.

4. Identify each compound as a primary, secondary, or tertiary amine.

   a.

   b.

   c.

5. Write the chemical reaction between each amine in Exercise 3 and HCl.
6. Write the chemical reaction between each amine in Exercise 4 and HNO₃.
7. Name each amine.

   a.

   b.

8. Name each amine.

a.

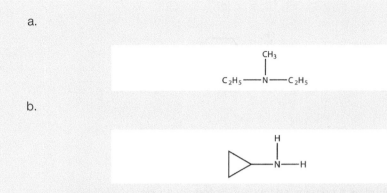

b.

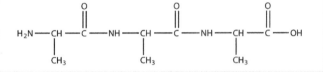

9. A *peptide* is a short chain of amino acids connected by amide bonds. How many amide bonds are present in this peptide?

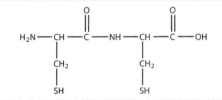

10. How many amide bonds are present in this peptide? (See Exercise 9 for the definition of a peptide.)

11. Draw the backbone structure of the amide formed by reacting propylamine with propanoic acid.

12. Draw the backbone structure of the amide formed by reacting hexylamine with ethanoic acid.

13. Name each thiol using the *-thiol* suffix.

a.

b. $C_4H_9–SH$

14. Name each thiol in Exercise 13 with the mercaptan label.

15. One component of skunk spray is 3-methyl-1-butanethiol. Draw its structure. (The 1 indicates the position of the S atom.)

16. An S–S bond can be fairly easily broken into proteins, yielding two lone cysteine units in a protein chain. Is this process an oxidation or a reduction? Explain your answer.

Answers

1. CH_3NH_2; methylamine
2. CH_3SH; methanethiol
3. a. primary

    b. tertiary

    c. secondary

4. a. primary

    b. secondary

    c. primary

5. a. $C_3H_3CO_2HSHNH_2 + HCl \rightarrow C_3H_3CO_2HSHNH_3Cl$

    b. $(C_6H_{11})(C_2H_5)(CH_3)N + HCl \rightarrow (C_6H_{11})(C_2H_5)(CH_3)NHCl$

    c. $(C_2H_5)(CH_3)NH + HCl \rightarrow (C_2H_5)(CH_3)NH_2Cl$

6. a. $C_6H_5NH_2 + HNO_3 \rightarrow C_6H_5NH_3NO_3$

    b. $C_5H_{10}NH + HNO_3 \rightarrow C_5H_{10}NH_2NO_3$

    c. $(NH_2)_2CO + HNO_3 \rightarrow NH_2CONH_3NO_3$

7. a. ethylmethylamine

    b. phenylamine

8. a. diethylmethylamine

    b. cyclopropylamine

9. two

10. one

11.

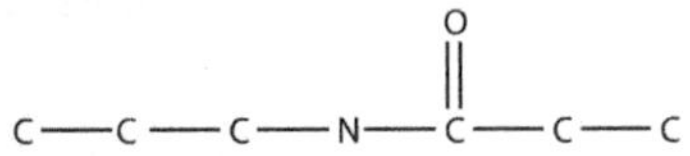

12.

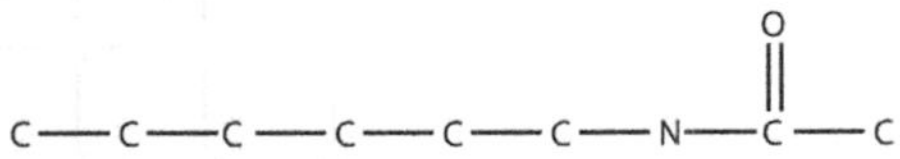

13. a. cyclohexanethiol

    b. butanethiol

14. a. cyclohexyl mercaptan

    b. butyl mercaptan

15.

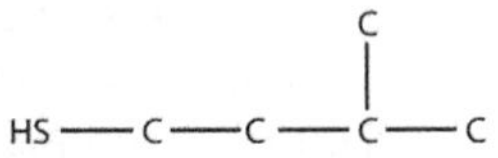

16. reduction because each S atom adds an H atom in the process

17.6 Polymers

Learning Objectives

1. Define the terms *monomer* and *polymer*.

2. Draw the structure of a polymer from its monomer.

Among other applications, organic chemistry has had a huge impact on the development of modern materials called polymers. Many objects in daily life are composed of polymers; curiously, so are several important biological materials.

Consider a molecule with a double bond, such as ethylene:

Imagine the bond between the carbons opening up and attacking another ethylene molecule:

Now imagine further that the second ethylene molecule's double bond opens up and attacks a third ethylene molecule, which also opens up its double bond and attacks a fourth ethylene molecule, and so forth. The end result is long, virtually endless molecule:

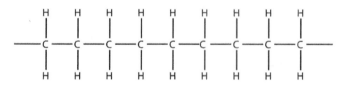

This long, almost nonstop molecule is called a **polymer** (from the Greek meaning "many parts"). The original part—ethylene—is called the **monomer** (meaning "one part"). The process of making a polymer is called **polymerization**. A polymer is an example of a *macromolecule*, the name given to a large molecule.

Simple polymers are named after their monomers; the ethylene polymer is formally called poly(ethylene), although in common use, the names are used without parentheses: polyethylene. Because adding one monomer to another forms this polymer, polyethylene is an example of a type of polymer called *addition polymers*. Figure 17.5 lists some addition polymers and their monomers. One of them, poly(ethylene oxide), results not from the opening of a double bond but the opening of a ring in the monomer; the concept of bonding with other monomers, however, is the same.

polymer

A long molecule made of hundreds or thousands of repeating units.

monomer

The repeated unit of a polymer.

polymerization

The process of making a polymer.

FIGURE 17.5 Some Monomers and Their Addition Polymers

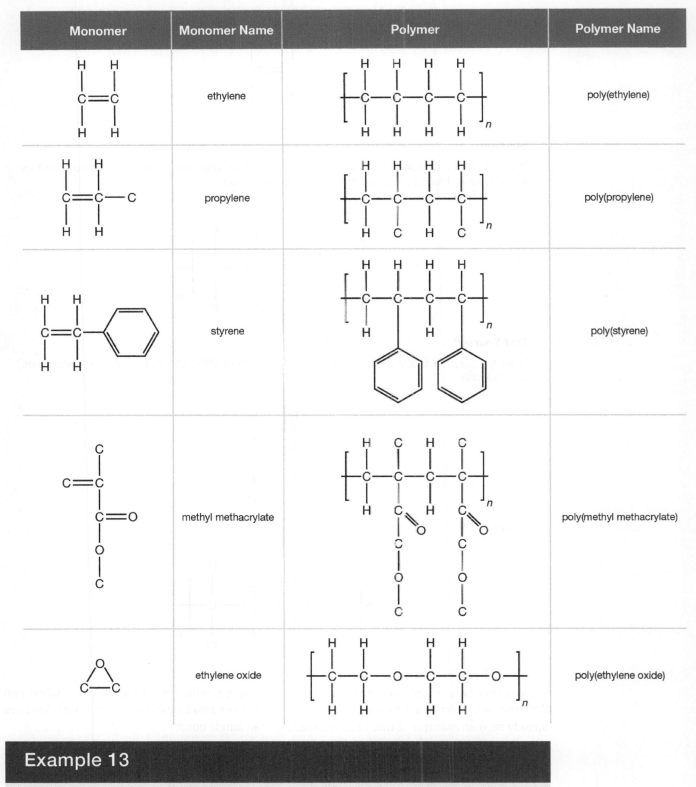

Monomer	Monomer Name	Polymer	Polymer Name
	ethylene		poly(ethylene)
	propylene		poly(propylene)
	styrene		poly(styrene)
	methyl methacrylate		poly(methyl methacrylate)
	ethylene oxide		poly(ethylene oxide)

Example 13

Draw the polymer that results from the polymerization of tetrafluoroethylene.

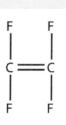

Solution

In the case of this monomer, the double bond opens up and joins to other monomers, just as with ethylene. The polymer that is made has this structure:

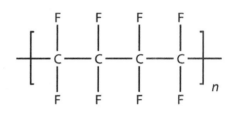

Test Yourself

Draw the polymer that results from the polymerization of chloroethylene, commonly known as vinyl chloride.

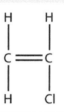

Answer

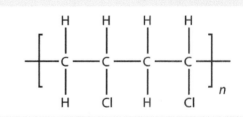

Another type of polymer is the *condensation polymer*, which is a polymer made when two different monomers react together and release some other small molecule as a product. We have already seen an example of this, in the formation of an amide bond:

Here, H_2O is released when the ends of the molecules react to form a polymer.

Related to condensation polymers are the *copolymers*, polymers made from more than one type of monomer. For example, ethylene and propylene can be combined into a polymer that is a mixture of the two monomers. A common form of synthetic rubber called styrene butadiene rubber (SBR) is made from two monomers: styrene and butadiene:

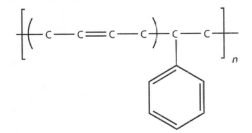

The physical and chemical properties of polymers vary widely, based on their monomers, structures, and additives. Among the other properties that can be modified based on these factors include solubility in H_2O and other solvents, melting point, flammability, color, hardness, transparency, film thickness, wetability, surface friction, moldability, and particle size—the list goes on.

The uses of polymers are almost too numerous to consider. Anything that you might describe as "plastic" is likely a polymer. Polymers are used to make everything from toothbrushes to computer cases to automobile parts. Many epoxy-based adhesives are condensation polymers that adhere strongly to other surfaces. Polyurethane paints and coatings are polymers, as are the polyester fabrics used to make clothing. Nylon, Dacron, and Mylar are polymers (in fact, both Dacron and Mylar are forms of polyethylene terephthalate [PET]). The product known as Saran Wrap was originally constructed from Saran, a name for poly(vinylidene chloride), which was relatively impervious to oxygen and could be used as a barrier to help keep food fresh. (It has since been replaced with polyethylene, which is not as impervious to atmospheric oxygen.) Poly(vinyl chloride) is the third-most produced polymer [after poly(ethylene) and poly(propylene)] and is used to make everything from plastic tubing to automobile engine parts, water pipes to toys, flooring to waterbeds and pools.

All the polymers we have considered so far are based on a backbone of (largely) carbon. There is another class of polymers based on a backbone of Si and O atoms; these polymers are called **silicones**. The Si atoms have organic groups attached to them, so these polymers are still organic. One example of a silicone is as follows:

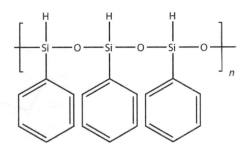

Silicones are used to make oils and lubricants; they are used as sealants for glass objects (such as aquariums) and films for waterproofing objects. Solid silicones are heat resistant and rubbery and are used to make cookware and electrical insulation.

Some very important biological materials are polymers. Of the three major food groups, polymers are represented in two: proteins and carbohydrates. Proteins are polymers of amino acids, which are monomers that have an amine functional group and a carboxylic acid functional group. These two groups react to make a condensation polymer, forming an amide bond:

silicone

A polymer based on a silicon and oxygen backbone.

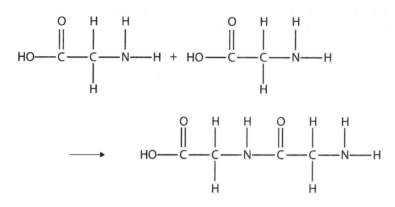

Proteins are formed when hundreds or even thousands of amino acids form amide bonds to make polymers. Proteins play a crucial role in living organisms.

A *carbohydrate* is a compound that has the general formula $C_n(H_2O)_n$. Many carbohydrates are relatively small molecules, such as glucose:

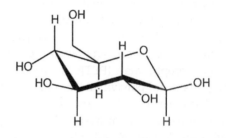

Linking hundreds of glucose molecules together makes a relatively common material known as *starch*:

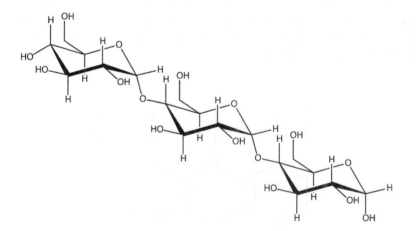

Starch is an important source of energy in the human diet. Note how individual glucose units are joined together. They can also be joined together in another way, like this:

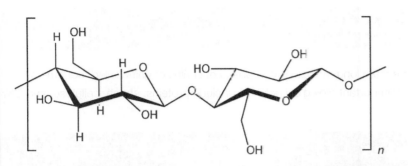

This polymer is known as *cellulose*. Cellulose is a major component in the cell walls of plants. Curiously, despite the similarity in the building blocks, some animals (such as humans) cannot digest cellulose; those animals that can digest cellulose typically rely on symbiotic bacteria in the digestive tract for the actual digestion. Animals do not have the proper enzymes to break apart the glucose units in cellulose, so it passes through the digestive tract and is considered *dietary fiber*.

Deoxyribonucleic acid (DNA) and *ribonucleic acid (RNA)* are also polymers, composed of long, three-part chains consisting of phosphate groups, sugars with 5 C atoms (ribose or deoxyribose), and N-containing rings referred to as bases. Each combination of the three parts is called a nucleotide; DNA and RNA are essentially polymers of nucleotides that have rather complicated but intriguing structures (Figure 17.6). DNA is the fundamental material in chromosomes and is directly responsible for heredity, while RNA is an essential substance in protein synthesis.

FIGURE 17.6 Nucleotides

The DNA in our cells is a polymer of nucleotides, each of which is composed of a phosphate group, a sugar, and a base that contains several nitrogen atoms.

Source: © Thinkstock

Key Takeaways

- Polymers are long molecules composed of chains of units called monomers.
- Several important biological polymers include proteins, starch, cellulose, and DNA.

Exercises

1. Explain the relationship between a monomer and a polymer.
2. Must a monomer have a double bond to make a polymer? Give an example to illustrate your answer.
3. Draw the polymer made from this monomer.

4. Draw the polymer made from this monomer.

5. What is the difference between an addition polymer and a condensation polymer?
6. What is the difference between a condensation polymer and a copolymer?
7. List three properties of polymers that vary widely with composition.
8. List three uses of polymers.
9. Draw the silicone made from this monomer.

10. Draw the silicone made from this monomer.

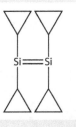

11. Explain how starch is a polymer.
12. What is the difference between starch and cellulose?
13. Explain how protein is a polymer.
14. What are the parts that compose DNA?

Answers

1. A polymer is many monomers bonded together.

2. Double bonds are not necessary to make a polymer. Condensation polymers are made from monomers that do not have double bonds.

3.

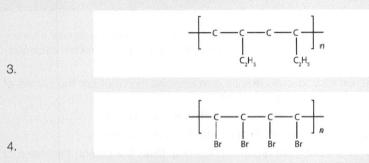

4.

5. In an addition polymer, no small molecule is given off as a product, whereas in a condensation polymer, small parts of each monomer come off as a small molecule.

6. A copolymer is usually an addition polymer made from two different monomers, whereas a condensation polymer may have a single monomer or more than one but still gives off a small molecule when the monomers react.

7. solubility in H_2O and other solvents, melting point, flammability, color, hardness, transparency, film thickness, wetability, surface friction, moldability, and particle size (answers will vary)

8. plastics, films, rubber, coatings, oils, insulation, and sealants (answers will vary)

9.

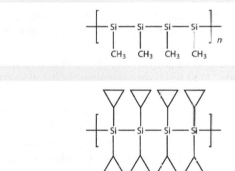

10.

11. Starch is composed of many glucose monomer units.

12. The glucose units are bonded in a different orientation so that starch and cellulose have different chemical and physical properties.

13. Proteins are polymers of amino acids, which act as the monomers.

14. DNA is composed of a sugar, a phosphate group, and an N-containing base.

17.7 End-of-Chapter Material

Additional Exercises

1. Cycloalkanes are named based on the number of C atoms in them, just like regular alkanes, but with the prefix *cyclo-* on the name. What are the names of the three smallest cycloalkanes?

2. Cycloalkenes are named similarly to cycloalkanes (see Exercise 1). What are the names of the cycloalkenes with five, six, and seven C atoms?

3. Draw the carbon backbone of all noncyclic alkanes with only four C atoms.

4. Draw the carbon backbone of all noncyclic alkanes with only five C atoms.

5. Cyclic alkanes can also have substituent groups on the ring. Draw the carbon backbone of all cyclic alkanes with only four C atoms.

6. Cyclic alkanes can also have substituent groups on the ring. Draw the carbon backbone of all cyclic alkanes with only five C atoms.

7. Draw and name all possible isomers of pentene.

8. Draw and name all possible normal (that is, straight-chain) isomers of heptyne.

9. Polyunsaturated alkenes have more than one C–C double bond. Draw the carbon backbone of all possible noncyclic polyunsaturated alkenes with four C atoms and two double bonds. What are the complete molecular formulas for each possible molecule?

10. Draw the carbon backbone of all possible five-carbon cyclic alkenes with two double bonds, assuming no substituents on the ring.

11. If a hydrocarbon is combined with enough halogen, all the H atoms will eventually be substituted with that halogen atom. Write the balanced chemical reaction between ethane and excess chlorine.

12. If a hydrocarbon is combined with enough halogen, all the H atoms will eventually be substituted with that halogen atom. Write the balanced chemical reaction between butane and excess bromine.

13. Molecules with multiple double bonds can also participate in addition reactions. Draw the structure of the product when butadiene, $CH_2=CH–CH=CH_2$, reacts with chlorine.

14. Molecules with multiple double bonds can also participate in addition reactions. Draw the structure of the product when allene, $CH_2=C=CH_2$, reacts with bromine.

15. What is the maximum number of methyl groups that can be on a propane backbone before the molecule cannot be named as a propane compound?

16. Explain why cycloethane cannot exist as a real molecule.

17. In the gasoline industry, what is called *isooctane* is actually 2,2,4-trimethylpentane. Draw the structure of isooctane.

18. Isooctane (see Exercise 17) is an isomer of what straight-chain alkane?

19. The actual name for the explosive TNT is 2,4,6-trinitrotoluene. If the structure of TNT is

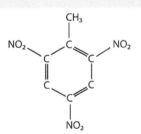

propose the structure of the parent compound toluene.

20. Phenol is hydroxybenzene, the simplest aromatic alcohol. Picric acid is an explosive derivative of phenol whose formal name is 2,4,6-trinitrophenol. With reference to Exercise 19, draw the structure of picric acid.

21. Draw the structures of all possible straight-chain isomers of bromopentane.

22. Draw the structures of all the possible isomers of butanol. Include branched isomers.

23. What is the final product of the *double* elimination of HCl from 1,1-dichloroethane?

24. Draw the structure of the final product of the *double* elimination of 1,3-dibromopropane.

25. Draw the structure and name of the alcohol whose double elimination would yield the same product as in Exercise 23. Name the molecule as a hydroxyl-substituted compound.

26. Draw the structure and name of the alcohol whose double elimination would yield the same product as in Exercise 24. Name the molecule as a hydroxyl-substituted compound.

27. Draw the smallest molecule that can have a separate aldehyde and carboxylic acid group.

28. Name the functional group(s) in urea, a molecule with the following structure:

29. Ethyl acetate is a common ingredient in nail-polish remover because it is a good solvent. Draw the structure of ethyl acetate.

30. A lactone is an ester that has its ester functional group in a ring. Draw the structure of the smallest possible lactone (which is called acetolactone, which might give you a hint about its structure).

31. Draw the structure of diethyl ether, once used as an anesthetic.

32. The smallest cyclic ether is called an epoxide. Draw its structure.

33. The odor of fish is caused by the release of small amine molecules, which vaporize easily and are detected by the nose. Lemon juice contains acids that react with the amines and make them not as easily vaporized, which is one reason why adding lemon juice to seafood is so popular. Write the chemical reaction of HCl with trimethylamine, an amine that is given off by seafood.

34. Putrescine and cadaverine are molecules with two amine groups on the opposite ends of a butane backbone and a pentane backbone, respectively. They are both emitted by rotting corpses. Draw their structures and determine their molecular formulas.

35. With four monomers, draw two possible structures of a copolymer composed of ethylene and propylene.

36. With four monomers, draw two possible structures of a copolymer composed of ethylene and styrene.

37. Draw the silicon-based polymer that can be made from this monomer:

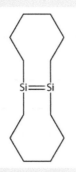

38. One of the ingredients in the original Silly Putty was a silicone polymer with two methyl groups on each Si atom. Draw this silicone. Don't forget to put oxygen atoms between the Si atoms in the polymer backbone.

Answers

1. cyclopropane, cyclobutane, and cyclopentane
2. cyclopentene, cyclohexene, and cycloheptene

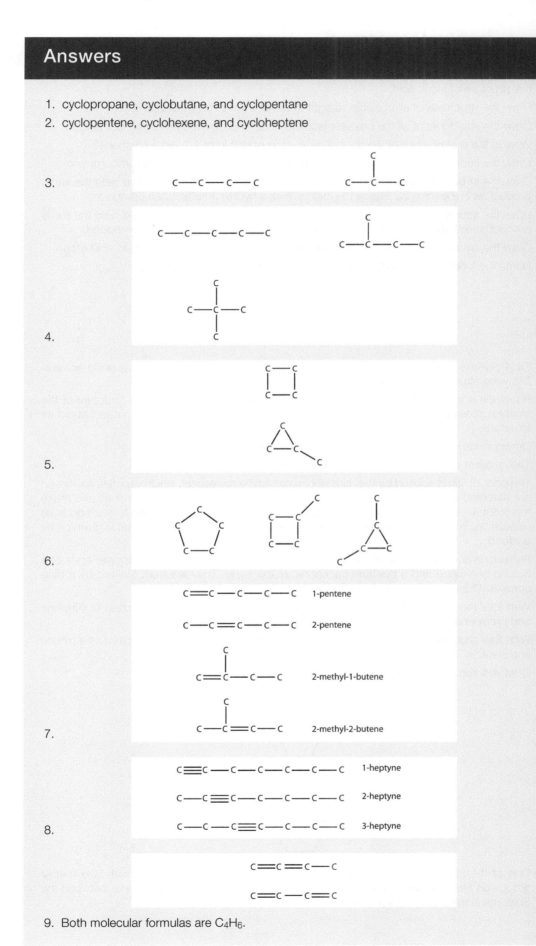

3.

4.

5.

6.

C≡C — C — C — C   1-pentene

C — C≡C — C — C   2-pentene

2-methyl-1-butene

2-methyl-2-butene

7.

C≡C — C — C — C — C — C   1-heptyne

C — C≡C — C — C — C — C   2-heptyne

C — C — C≡C — C — C — C   3-heptyne

8.

9. Both molecular formulas are C_4H_6.

10.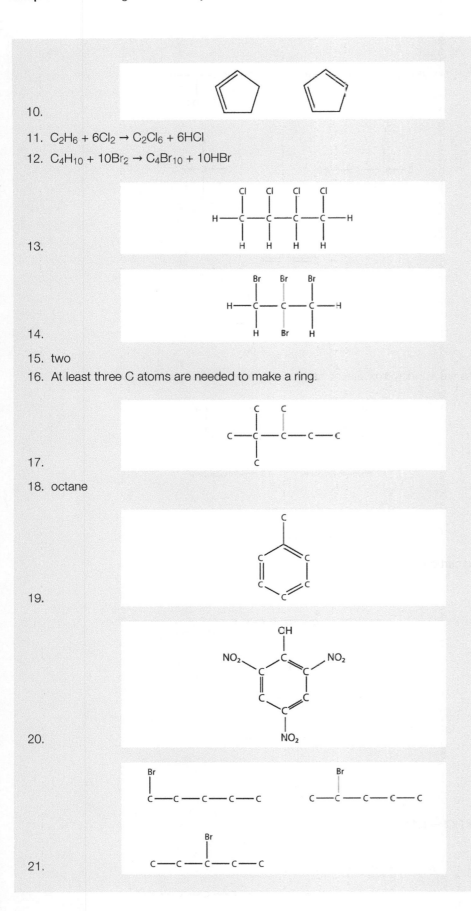

11. $C_2H_6 + 6Cl_2 \rightarrow C_2Cl_6 + 6HCl$

12. $C_4H_{10} + 10Br_2 \rightarrow C_4Br_{10} + 10HBr$

13.

14.

15. two

16. At least three C atoms are needed to make a ring.

17.

18. octane

19.

20.

21.

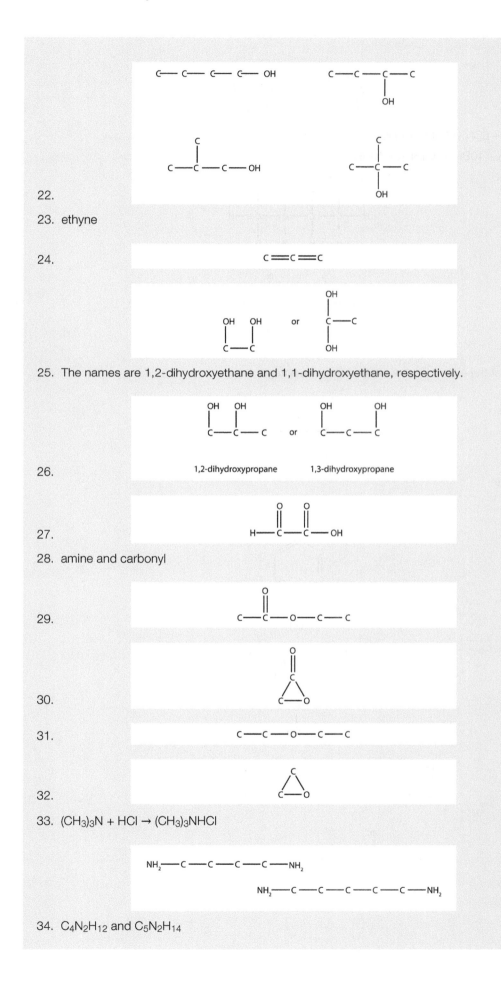

22.

23. ethyne

24.

25. The names are 1,2-dihydroxyethane and 1,1-dihydroxyethane, respectively.

26.

       1,2-dihydroxypropane   1,3-dihydroxypropane

27.

28. amine and carbonyl

29.

30.

31.

32.

33. $(CH_3)_3N + HCl \rightarrow (CH_3)_3NHCl$

34. $C_4N_2H_{12}$ and $C_5N_2H_{14}$

35. (answers will vary)

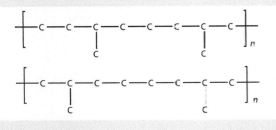

36. (answers will vary)

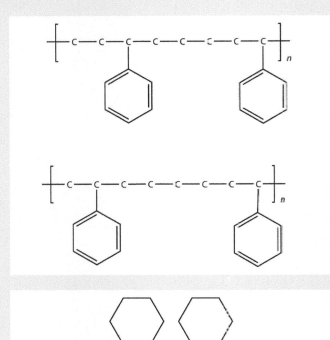

37.

38.

Endnotes

1. There will need to be 24 H atoms to complete the molecule.

APPENDIX A
Periodic Table of the Elements

In this chapter, we present some data on the chemical elements. The periodic table, introduced in Chapter 3, lists all the known chemical elements, arranged by atomic number (that is, the number of protons in the nucleus). The periodic table is arguably the best tool in all of science; no other branch of science can summarize its fundamental constituents in such a concise and useful way. Many of the physical and chemical properties of the elements are either known or understood based on their positions on the periodic table. Periodic tables are available with a variety of chemical and physical properties listed in each element's box. What follows here is a more complex version of the periodic table than what was presented in Chapter 3. The Internet is a great place to find periodic tables that contain additional information.

One item on most periodic tables is the atomic mass of each element. For many applications, only one or two decimal places are necessary for the atomic mass. However, some applications (especially nuclear chemistry; see Chapter 16) require more decimal places. The atomic masses in Table A.1 represent the number of decimal places recognized by the International Union of Pure and Applied Chemistry, the worldwide body that develops standards for chemistry. The atomic masses of some elements are known very precisely, to a large number of decimal places. The atomic masses of other elements, especially radioactive elements, are not known as precisely. Some elements, such as lithium, can have varying atomic masses depending on how their isotopes are isolated.

The web offers many interactive periodic table resources. For example, see http://www.ptable.com.

FIGURE A.1 Periodic Table

IUPAC Periodic Table of the Elements

For notes and updates to this table, see www.iupac.org. This version is dated 1 December 2018.
Copyright © 2018 IUPAC, the International Union of Pure and Applied Chemistry.

INTERNATIONAL UNION OF PURE AND APPLIED CHEMISTRY

United Nations Educational, Scientific and Cultural Organization

2019 IYPT International Year of the Periodic Table of Chemical Elements

TABLE A.1 The Basics of the Elements of the Periodic Table

Name	Atomic Symbol	Atomic Number	Atomic Mass	Footnotes
actinium*	Ac	89		
aluminum	Al	13	26.9815386(8)	
americium*	Am	95		
antimony	Sb	51	121.760(1)	g
argon	Ar	18	39.948(1)	g, r
arsenic	As	33	74.92160(2)	
astatine*	At	85		
barium	Ba	56	137.327(7)	
berkelium*	Bk	97		
beryllium	Be	4	9.012182(3)	
bismuth	Bi	83	208.98040(1)	
bohrium*	Bh	107		
boron	B	5	10.811(7)	g, m, r
bromine	Br	35	79.904(1)	
cadmium	Cd	48	112.411(8)	g
caesium (cesium)	Cs	55	132.9054519(2)	
calcium	Ca	20	40.078(4)	g
californium*	Cf	98		
carbon	C	6	12.0107(8)	g, r
cerium	Ce	58	140.116(1)	g
chlorine	Cl	17	35.453(2)	g, m, r
chromium	Cr	24	51.9961(6)	
cobalt	Co	27	58.933195(5)	
copernicium*	Cn	112		
copper	Cu	29	63.546(3)	r
curium*	Cm	96		
darmstadtium*	Ds	110		
dubnium*	Db	105		
dysprosium	Dy	66	162.500(1)	g

*Element has no stable nuclides. However, three such elements (Th, Pa, and U) have a characteristic terrestrial isotopic composition, and for these an atomic mass is tabulated.

†Commercially available Li materials have atomic weights that range between 6.939 and 6.996; if a more accurate value is required, it must be determined for the specific material.

g Geological specimens are known in which the element has an isotopic composition outside the limits for normal material. The difference between the atomic mass of the element in such specimens and that given in the table may exceed the stated uncertainty.

m Modified isotopic compositions may be found in commercially available material because it has been subjected to an undisclosed or inadvertent isotopic fractionation. Substantial deviations in the atomic mass of the element from that given in the table can occur.

r Range in isotopic composition of normal terrestrial material prevents a more precise $Ar(E)$ being given; the tabulated $Ar(E)$ value and uncertainty should be applicable to normal material.

Name	Atomic Symbol	Atomic Number	Atomic Mass	Footnotes
einsteinium*	Es	99		
erbium	Er	68	167.259(3)	g
europium	Eu	63	151.964(1)	g
fermium*	Fm	100		
fluorine	F	9	18.9984032(5)	
francium*	Fr	87		
gadolinium	Gd	64	157.25(3)	g
gallium	Ga	31	69.723(1)	
germanium	Ge	32	72.64(1)	
gold	Au	79	196.966569(4)	
hafnium	Hf	72	178.49(2)	
hassium*	Hs	108		
helium	He	2	4.002602(2)	g, r
holmium	Ho	67	164.93032(2)	
hydrogen	H	1	1.00794(7)	g, m, r
indium	In	49	114.818(3)	
iodine	I	53	126.90447(3)	
iridium	Ir	77	192.217(3)	
iron	Fe	26	55.845(2)	
krypton	Kr	36	83.798(2)	g, m
lanthanum	La	57	138.90547(7)	g
lawrencium*	Lr	103		
lead	Pb	82	207.2(1)	g, r
lithium	Li	3	[6.941(2)]†	g, m, r
lutetium	Lu	71	174.967(1)	g
magnesium	Mg	12	24.3050(6)	
manganese	Mn	25	54.938045(5)	
meitnerium*	Mt	109		
mendelevium*	Md	101		
mercury	Hg	80	200.59(2)	
molybdenum	Mo	42	95.94(2)	g

*Element has no stable nuclides. However, three such elements (Th, Pa, and U) have a characteristic terrestrial isotopic composition, and for these an atomic mass is tabulated.

†Commercially available Li materials have atomic weights that range between 6.939 and 6.996; if a more accurate value is required, it must be determined for the specific material.

g Geological specimens are known in which the element has an isotopic composition outside the limits for normal material. The difference between the atomic mass of the element in such specimens and that given in the table may exceed the stated uncertainty.

m Modified isotopic compositions may be found in commercially available material because it has been subjected to an undisclosed or inadvertent isotopic fractionation. Substantial deviations in the atomic mass of the element from that given in the table can occur.

r Range in isotopic composition of normal terrestrial material prevents a more precise $Ar(E)$ being given; the tabulated $Ar(E)$ value and uncertainty should be applicable to normal material.

Name	Atomic Symbol	Atomic Number	Atomic Mass	Footnotes
neodymium	Nd	60	144.242(3)	g
neon	Ne	10	20.1797(6)	g, m
neptunium*	Np	93		
nickel	Ni	28	58.6934(2)	
niobium	Nb	41	92.90638(2)	
nitrogen	N	7	14.0067(2)	g, r
nobelium*	No	102		
osmium	Os	76	190.23(3)	g
oxygen	O	8	15.9994(3)	g, r
palladium	Pd	46	106.42(1)	g
phosphorus	P	15	30.973762(2)	
platinum	Pt	78	195.084(9)	
plutonium*	Pu	94		
polonium*	Po	84		
potassium	K	19	39.0983(1)	
praseodymium	Pr	59	140.90765(2)	
promethium*	Pm	61		
protactinium*	Pa	91	231.03588(2)	
radium*	Ra	88		
radon*	Rn	86		
roentgenium*	Rg	111		
rhenium	Re	75	186.207(1)	
rhodium	Rh	45	102.90550(2)	
rubidium	Rb	37	85.4678(3)	g
ruthenium	Ru	44	101.07(2)	g
rutherfordium*	Rf	104		
samarium	Sm	62	150.36(2)	g
scandium	Sc	21	44.955912(6)	
seaborgium*	Sg	106		
selenium	Se	34	78.96(3)	r
silicon	Si	14	28.0855(3)	r

*Element has no stable nuclides. However, three such elements (Th, Pa, and U) have a characteristic terrestrial isotopic composition, and for these an atomic mass is tabulated.

†Commercially available Li materials have atomic weights that range between 6.939 and 6.996; if a more accurate value is required, it must be determined for the specific material.

g Geological specimens are known in which the element has an isotopic composition outside the limits for normal material. The difference between the atomic mass of the element in such specimens and that given in the table may exceed the stated uncertainty.

m Modified isotopic compositions may be found in commercially available material because it has been subjected to an undisclosed or inadvertent isotopic fractionation. Substantial deviations in the atomic mass of the element from that given in the table can occur.

r Range in isotopic composition of normal terrestrial material prevents a more precise $Ar(E)$ being given; the tabulated $Ar(E)$ value and uncertainty should be applicable to normal material.

Name	Atomic Symbol	Atomic Number	Atomic Mass	Footnotes
silver	Ag	47	107.8682(2)	g
sodium	Na	11	22.98976928(2)	
strontium	Sr	38	87.62(1)	g, r
sulfur	S	16	32.065(5)	g, r
tantalum	Ta	73	180.94788(2)	
technetium*	Tc	43		
tellurium	Te	52	127.60(3)	g
terbium	Tb	65	158.92535(2)	
thallium	Tl	81	204.3833(2)	
thorium*	Th	90	232.03806(2)	g
thulium	Tm	69	168.93421(2)	
tin	Sn	50	118.710(7)	g
titanium	Ti	22	47.867(1)	
tungsten	W	74	183.84(1)	
ununhexium*	Uuh	116		
ununoctium*	Uuo	118		
ununpentium*	Uup	115		
ununquadium*	Uuq	114		
ununtrium*	Uut	113		
uranium*	U	92	238.02891(3)	g, m
vanadium	V	23	50.9415(1)	
xenon	Xe	54	131.293(6)	g, m
ytterbium	Yb	70	173.04(3)	g
yttrium	Y	39	88.90585(2)	
zinc	Zn	30	65.409(4)	
zirconium	Zr	40	91.224(2)	g

*Element has no stable nuclides. However, three such elements (Th, Pa, and U) have a characteristic terrestrial isotopic composition, and for these an atomic mass is tabulated.

†Commercially available Li materials have atomic weights that range between 6.939 and 6.996; if a more accurate value is required, it must be determined for the specific material.

g Geological specimens are known in which the element has an isotopic composition outside the limits for normal material. The difference between the atomic mass of the element in such specimens and that given in the table may exceed the stated uncertainty.

m Modified isotopic compositions may be found in commercially available material because it has been subjected to an undisclosed or inadvertent isotopic fractionation. Substantial deviations in the atomic mass of the element from that given in the table can occur.

r Range in isotopic composition of normal terrestrial material prevents a more precise Ar(E) being given; the tabulated Ar(E) value and uncertainty should be applicable to normal material.

Source: Adapted from *Pure and Applied Chemistry* 78, no. 11 (2005): 2051–66. © IUPAC (International Union of Pure and Applied Chemistry).

Index